America in the World includes state-of-the-art essays and historiographical surveys of American foreign relations since 1941 by some of the country's leading diplomatic historians. The essays by Bruce Cumings, Michael Hunt, and Melvyn P. Leffler in Part One offer sweeping overviews of the major trends in the field of diplomatic history. Part Two features essays that survey the literature on U.S. relations with particular regions of the world or on the foreign policies of presidential administrations by Mark A. Stoler, Howard Jones, Randall Woods, J. Samuel Walker, Rosemary Foot, John Ferris, Diane B. Kunz, Mark T. Gilderhus, Douglas Little, Robert J. McMahon, Stephen G. Rabe, Burton I. Kaufman, Gary R. Hess and Robert D. Schulzinger. The result is the most comprehensive assessment of the literature on U.S. foreign policy to be published in nearly twenty years.

America in the World

America in the World

The Historiography of American Foreign Relations since 1941

Edited by

MICHAEL J. HOGAN

The Ohio State University

CAMBRIDGE
UNIVERSITY PRESS

Published by the Press Syndicate of the University of Cambridge
The Pitt Building, Trumpington Street, Cambridge CB2 1RP
40 West 20th Street, New York, NY 10011–4211, USA
10 Stamford Road, Oakleigh, Melbourne 3166, Australia

First published 1995

Printed in the United States of America

Library of Congress Cataloging-in-Publication Data

America in the world : the historiography of American foreign relations since 1941 / edited by Michael J. Hogan.
p. cm.
Includes bibliographical references and index.
ISBN 0–521–49680–2. – ISBN 0–521–49807–4 (pbk.)
1. United States – Foreign relations – 1945–1989 – Historiography.
2. United States – Foreign relations – 1933–1945 – Historiography.
I. Hogan, Michael J., 1943– .
E744.A486 1996
327.73′0072 – dc20 95–23512

A catalog record for this book is available from the British Library.

ISBN 0–521–49680–2 hardback
ISBN 0–521–49807–4 paperback

To My Graduate Students

Contents

Preface *page* xi
The Authors xv

Part One. The State of the Art

1 State of the Art: An Introduction 3
Michael J. Hogan
2 "Revising Postrevisionism," Or, The Poverty of Theory in Diplomatic History 20
Bruce Cumings
3 New Approaches, Old Interpretations, and Prospective Reconfigurations 63
Melvyn P. Leffler
4 The Long Crisis in U.S. Diplomatic History: Coming to Closure 93
Michael H. Hunt
5 Commentaries 127
Bruce Cumings, Melvyn P. Leffler, Michael H. Hunt

Part Two. The Historiography of American Foreign Relations since 1941

6 The Historiography of American Foreign Relations: An Introduction 159
Michael J. Hogan

7 A Half-Century of Conflict: Interpretations of U.S. World War II Diplomacy 166
Mark A. Stoler

8 The Decision to Use the Bomb: A Historiographical Update 206
J. Samuel Walker

9 Origins of the Cold War in Europe and the Near East: Recent Historiography and the National Security Imperative 234
Howard Jones and Randall B. Woods

10 Making Known the Unknown War: Policy Analysis of the Korean Conflict since the Early 1980s 270
Rosemary Foot

11 Eisenhower Revisionism: The Scholarly Debate 300
Stephen G. Rabe

12 John F. Kennedy as World Leader: A Perspective on the Literature 326
Burton I. Kaufman

13 The Unending Debate: Historians and the Vietnam War 358
Gary R. Hess

14 Complaints, Self-Justifications, and Analysis: The Historiography of American Foreign Relations since 1969 395
Robert D. Schulzinger

15 An Emerging Synthesis? U.S.–Latin American Relations since the Second World War 424
Mark T. Gilderhus

16 Gideon's Band: America and the Middle East since 1945 462
Douglas Little

17 The Cold War in Asia: The Elusive Synthesis 501
Robert J. McMahon

18 The Power of Money: The Historiography of American Economic Diplomacy 536
Diane B. Kunz

19 Coming in from the Cold War: The Historiography of American Intelligence, 1945–1990 562
John Ferris

Index 599

Preface

This volume is intended to complement *Explaining the History of American Foreign Relations*, another book of essays on diplomatic history that I coedited with Thomas G. Paterson in 1991. The essays in that book dealt with some of the new conceptual approaches to the study of foreign relations; these essays provide an overview of the recent literature in that field. Most of them first appeared in the journal *Diplomatic History*. They grew out of the journal's efforts to keep its readers abreast of the newest literature and to assess the state of the field – both missions appropriate to a journal of record. Because readers responded favorably to these efforts, it made sense to update the essays and bring them together in a single volume for scholars who specialize in diplomatic history and related fields, and especially for graduate students who are seeking a basic mastery of the most recent literature.

In the preface to *Explaining the History of American Foreign Relations*, Paterson and I struck an optimistic note. We were excited by the way many diplomatic historians were experimenting with new conceptual approaches and by the cross-fertilization that was going on with other fields. The results revealed a new vitality in a field of history that has been wrenched by numerous controversies and repeated criticism. The essays in this volume capture some of that vitality as well. To be sure, there is much room for criticism, as my own contributions suggest. To a large extent the field is locked in a defensive posture, and approaches to the study of foreign relations are still less varied and innovative than I would like. Nevertheless, even traditional diplomatic history has reached new heights of excellence, and fresh approaches are making important inroads. Michael H. Hunt may be too optimistic in assuming that the "long crisis" in diplomatic history is over, but he is surely correct in concluding that diplomatic historians are writing with more confidence than was the case just a few years ago.

This book is divided into two sections. Part One includes essays by Bruce Cumings, Melvyn P. Leffler, and Michael Hunt that attempt to make a large statement about the state of the field as a whole. Because the essays are often controversial, I asked each of the authors to provide a brief commentary on the contributions of the other two. I also gave the authors an opportunity to react to my essay introducing their contributions, as that essay spells out some of my own views on their work. I think readers will find this first section of the book lively and provocative reading.

Part Two contains a number of focused historiographical essays, one of which, by Diane B. Kunz, appears here for the first time. These essays survey recent literature on the history of American foreign relations since the start of the Second World War, a period that has preoccupied diplomatic historians, almost to the exclusion of other eras. Each of the authors was asked to address the literature on a particular topic or presidential administration that has appeared since 1981, when Gerald K. Haines and J. Samuel Walker published what was until now the most recent collection of historiographical articles.[1] The essays do not present a unified theme or approach, but the combined result is a generally comprehensive survey of the best recent literature in the field.

I am indebted to many friends and colleagues who helped in the preparation of this volume. The first debt is to the authors whose work appears in these pages. They agreed to the publication or republication of their essays. Given the inevitable constraints of a publication schedule and the ongoing appearance of new literature, they did the best they could to revise and update

1 Gerald K. Haines and J. Samuel Walker, eds., *American Foreign Relations: A Historiographical Review* (Westport, 1981).

their contributions. Historiographical essays are very difficult to write. For the authors the reward is surely to be found in the great utility of such essays to colleagues who rely on them to stay abreast of the newest works. I am particularly grateful to the contributors for waiving their claim to the usual republication fees. Instead, those fees will be contributed as royalties from the sale of this book to the Armin Rappaport Fund of the Society for Historians of American Foreign Relations. Tom Paterson and I established that fund several years ago in support of the society's journal, *Diplomatic History*.

I am also indebted to The Ohio State University for its ongoing support of my work as editor of *Diplomatic History*, and to Frank Smith of Cambridge University Press for his faith in this enterprise. Thanks go as well to Mary Ann Heiss, the journal's associate editor, for copyediting the essays in this volume, and to Amy Staples and Bruce Karhoff, the assistant editors, for helping me prepare the volume for publication. In addition, I am deeply grateful to all of the graduate students who have served the journal as assistant editors and editorial assistants over the past nine years: Ann Heiss, Kurt Schultz, Toby Rosenthal, Paul Wittekind, Darryl Fox, Jozef Ostyn, Paul Pierpaoli, Amy Staples, and Bruce Karhoff. Finally, I owe a very special thanks to the students in History 770, my graduate seminar, who shared with me their reaction to all of the essays in this volume, my own included.

When I was a junior in college I read Howard K. Beale's wonderful book, *Theodore Roosevelt and the Rise of America to World Power*. Still interesting and eminently readable, Beale's book was one of those that led me to graduate school in history at the University of Iowa. There I studied with Ellis W. Hawley, who, as it turned out, had dedicated his first book to Howard K. Beale, his mentor in graduate school at the University of Wisconsin. My other mentor at Iowa was Lawrence E. Gelfand, whose own adviser at the University of Washington had been W. Stull Holt. Holt trained several excellent students who went on to become prominent diplomatic historians. Led by Larry Gelfand, they later remembered their mentor by establishing the Holt Dissertation Fellowship of the Society for Historians of American Foreign Relations. Still later I would serve on that committee, and some of my own students would benefit from a Holt Fellowship. So it goes, from one generation to the next, for those of us who have been fortunate to have good mentors and to mentor good students.

This book is dedicated to the graduate students with whom I have worked in seminar and on the journal *Diplomatic History* over many years. They have been the best of students, and the best of teachers. I am proud to know them, and forever in their debt.

Columbus, Ohio MJH
March 1995

The Authors

BRUCE CUMINGS, professor of history at Northwestern University, is the author of a prize-winning, two-volume study entitled *The Origins of the Korean War* (1981 and 1990). The first volume won the John K. Fairbank Prize of the American Historical Association and the Harry S. Truman Book Award. The second received the Quincy Wright Book Prize of the American Studies Association. His most recent book is *War and Television* (1992).

JOHN FERRIS is the author of *Men, Money, and Diplomacy: The Evolution of British Strategic Policy, 1919–1926* (1988) and the editor of *The British Army and Signals Intelligence during the First World War* (1992). He has published many articles on intelligence, especially signals intelligence, and on British strategic policy during the nineteenth and twentieth centuries. He is an associate professor in the Department of History at the University of Calgary.

ROSEMARY FOOT is senior research fellow in international relations and a fellow of St. Antony's College, Oxford. Her publications on the Korean War include *The Wrong War* (1985) and *A Substitute for Victory* (1990).

MARK T. GILDERHUS is professor of history at Colorado State University. His publications include *Diplomacy and Revolution: The United States and Mexico under Wilson and Carranza* (1977); *Pan American Visions: Woodrow Wilson in the Western Hemisphere* (1986); and *History and Historians: A Historiographical Introduction* (2d ed., 1992).

GARY R. HESS is Distinguished Research Professor at Bowling Green State University and a past president of SHAFR. His research has focused on U.S. policy in South and Southeast Asia. His most recent book is *Vietnam and the United States: Origins and Legacy of War* (1990).

MICHAEL J. HOGAN is professor of history at The Ohio State University and editor of *Diplomatic History*. He is the author of *Informal Entente: The Private Structure of Cooperation in Anglo-American Economic Diplomacy, 1918–1928* (1977) and *The Marshall Plan: America, Britain, and the Reconstruction of Western Europe, 1947–1952* (1987). He is the recipient of numerous prizes, including the Quincy Wright Book Prize of the American Studies Association, the George Louis Beer Prize of the American Historical Association and SHAFR's Stuart L. Bernath Prize.

MICHAEL H. HUNT, professor of history at the University of North Carolina at Chapel Hill, is a past president of SHAFR. His publications include *Ideology and U.S. Foreign Policy* (1987) as well as studies of Sino-American relations recognized by three Stuart L. Bernath awards. His most recent book, *The Genesis of Chinese Communist Foreign Policy*, was published this year by Columbia University Press.

HOWARD JONES is University Research Professor of History at the University of Alabama and the author of several books, including *The Course of American Diplomacy* (1985, 1988); *"A New Kind of War": America's Global Strategy and the Truman Doctrine in Greece* (1989); *The Dawning of the Cold War* (with Randall Bennett Woods) (1991); and *Union in Peril: The Crisis over British Intervention in the Civil War* (1992).

BURTON I. KAUFMAN is professor of history and department head at Virginia Polytechnic Institute and State University (Virginia Tech). His books include *Trade and Aid: Eisenhower's Foreign Economic Policy, 1953–1961* (1982); *The Korean War: Crisis, Credibility, and Command* (1986); and, most recently, *The Presidency of James Earl Carter, Jr.* (1993).

DIANE B. KUNZ is associate professor of history at Yale University. She is the author of *The Battle for Britain's Gold Standard in 1931* (1987) and *The Economic Diplomacy of the Suez Crisis* (1991). A former corporate lawyer, she is at work on a history of American economic diplomacy during the Cold War.

MELVYN P. LEFFLER is Edward R. Stetinnius Professor of American

History at the University of Virginia. He has written on U.S.-European relations in the 1920s and 1930s and on U.S. national security policy after World War II. His most recent book is *The Specter of Communism: The United States and the Origins of the Cold War, 1917–1953* (1994).

DOUGLAS LITTLE is professor of history at Clark University. His essays on U.S. policy toward the Middle East have appeared in the *Journal of American History*, the *Middle East Journal*, and the *International Journal of Middle East Studies*.

ROBERT J. MCMAHON is professor of history at the University of Florida. The author most recently of *The Cold War on the Periphery: The United States, India, and Pakistan* (1994), he is currently writing a book on American relations with Southeast Asia since World War II.

STEPHEN G. RABE is professor of history at the University of Texas at Dallas. He recently edited, with Thomas G. Paterson, *Imperial Surge: The United States Abroad, The 1890s–Early 1900s* (1992).

ROBERT D. SCHULZINGER is professor of history at the University of Colorado at Boulder, where he has taught since 1977. He is the author of numerous books, including *American Diplomacy in the Twentieth Century* (1994) and *Henry Kissinger: Doctor of Diplomacy* (1989).

MARK A. STOLER is professor of history at the University of Vermont. His publications include *The Politics of the Second Front: American Military Planning and Diplomacy in Coalition Warfare, 1941–1943* (1977); *George C. Marshall: Soldier-Statesman of the American Century* (1989); and numerous articles on World War II strategy and diplomacy.

J. SAMUEL WALKER is historian of the U.S. Nuclear Regulatory Commission, where his job is to write a scholarly history of nuclear power (but not nuclear weapons). His most recent book is *Containing the Atom: Nuclear Regulation in a Changing Environment, 1963–1971* (1992).

RANDALL B. WOODS is John A. Cooper, Sr., Professor of Diplomatic History at the University of Arkansas. His books include *The Roosevelt Foreign Policy Establishment and the Good Neighbor: The United States and Argentina, 1941–1945* (1979); *The Dawning of the Cold War* (with Howard Jones) (1991); and *J. William Fulbright: A Biography* (1993).

Part One

The State of the Art

1

State of the Art: An Introduction

MICHAEL J. HOGAN

The last half-dozen years have seen the publication of several major essays on the state of American diplomatic history. These include widely read articles by John Lewis Gaddis, Bruce Cumings, Melvyn P. Leffler, and Michael H. Hunt. Gaddis is a leading post-revisionist scholar in the field and has a large following among political scientists who specialize in international relations. Cumings blends the assets of an East Asian specialist with insights into American politics and foreign policy. Leffler is associated with those historians who focus on American national security and geostrategy. Hunt is an area specialist whose work has dealt with Sino-American relations as well as the role of ideology in American foreign policy.

This introduction reviews the state of diplomatic history by evaluating what these four historians have said on the same subject. Three of them, Cumings, Leffler, and Hunt, outline their own thinking in the essays that follow and have contributed commentaries that critique each other's work and react to the views expressed in this introduction. The fourth, John Lewis Gaddis, spelled out his thinking in a controversial address to the Society for Historians of American Foreign Relations. His views are evaluated below and are also taken up in the essay by Cumings and in the commentaries by the three contributors to this section of the volume. All of these scholars have different agendas. Each assesses the field, or at least some of the key works and major schools of thought, and each urges us to take diplomatic history in a certain direction. My goal is to summarize, sometimes critically, what these scholars tell us, not only about their own approaches but also about the future of diplomatic history. What do they have to say about the state of the art as we near the end of what Henry Luce called "The American Century," and what advice do they have for a new generation of historians who will be writing in the post–Cold War era?

John Lewis Gaddis: The Return of Samuel Flagg Bemis

John Lewis Gaddis has sought on several occasions to set the agenda for diplomatic history, most recently in his 1992 presidential address to the Society for Historians of American Foreign Relations.[1] That speech recalled Samuel Flagg Bemis's provocative presidential address to the American Historical Association in 1961. In that address, Bemis lectured his audience on "American Foreign Policy and the Blessings of Liberty." These blessings were the fundamental rights and freedoms "for which the United States has stood throughout its history," not only at home but in the world at large. Bemis noted how "changes in the balance of power" over time had "affected the configuration, number, identity, and policy of nations," much like "movements of the earth's land masses" had "wrought compelling changes in the number and configuration of the continents." Throughout these "shifting configurations," however, the United States had been steadfast in the defense of liberty.[2]

Gaddis used similar geological metaphors to make many of the same points in his own presidential address. Where Bemis talked about "great geological shift[s]," Gaddis spoke of "'fault lines' along which tectonic forces intersect." Where Bemis was critical of the "academic world," especially "social studies," Gaddis was critical of most diplomatic historians, especially William Appleman Williams. Bemis thought that social studies had tended toward "too much self-criticism," which he said was "weakening to a people" and obscured "our national purpose." Gaddis leveled a

1 John Lewis Gaddis, "The Tragedy of Cold War History," *Diplomatic History* 17 (Winter 1993): 1–16.
2 Samuel Flagg Bemis, "American Foreign Policy and the Blessings of Liberty," *American Historical Review* 67 (January 1962): 291–305. Quotes on pp. 292–93.

similar criticism at Williams and the revisionist historians who followed his lead. "The historian of the future," Bemis wrote at the height of the Cold War, "will have to decide, in taking the historical measure of American foreign policy, whether the people in this government of the people, by the people, and for the people" had not only the power but also "the social discipline, the spirit of sacrifice, the nerve and the courage to guard for themselves and their posterity the Blessings of Liberty." Gaddis took up this task in his presidential address, delivered thirty-one years to the day after Bemis spoke, and came to the conclusion that American leaders in the Cold War had been faithful to their "ancient heritage." They had preserved the Blessings of Liberty.[3]

Although Gaddis's essay had a historiographical purpose, it was also the statement of a scholar who identified with American foreign policy, as is apparent in his use of the pronouns "we" and "our" to describe that policy, much as Bemis did in his presidential address. To be sure, Gaddis had some critical things to say about U.S. diplomacy over the last half-century, but these criticisms paled in comparison to his ultimate vindication of American policy. U.S. "hubris and arrogance" seemed to be limited to part of "the 1960s and early 1970s," no doubt a reference to American policy in Vietnam, while U.S. mistakes could seemingly be explained as the unfortunate by-products of an American effort to defend the free world against Soviet imperialism. "Whatever could have justified the massive expenditures on armaments, the violations of human rights abroad and civil liberties at home, the neglect of domestic priorities, the threats to blow up the world – whatever could have excused all the deplorable things the United States did during the Cold War," Gaddis asked rhetorically, "if no genuine threat ever existed?" His answer: A genuine threat did exist and was so great, so sinister, as to "excuse all the deplorable things the United States did."

Gaddis's answer illuminated the interpretive point of view that informed his essay and the historiographical roadmap he recommended for the field. As in the past, he was reacting to Williams's famous book, *The Tragedy of American Diplomacy*. The purpose

3 Bemis, "American Foreign Policy," 293, 304–5; Gaddis, "Tragedy," 16.

of his presidential address was to ask if that book held up when placed in an international context. To be sure, Gaddis was not concerned with the international setting broadly defined. He did not analyze how the Germans viewed the Cold War, or the British, or the countries of the developing world. Nor did he view the Cold War through the eyes of working people, women, or minorities, who exist only in the background of his address as the hapless victims of Soviet diplomacy. Instead, Gaddis was interested in the global view of American elites and, secondarily, their counterparts in the Soviet Union.

So far as the Americans were concerned, Gaddis conceded, almost as an aside, that they were interested in "material advantage." They expected to "lead the new world order" and to "dominate the international scene," although their true purpose, Gaddis went on to argue, was fundamentally altruistic. American leaders did not seek "domination," after all, but a great-power concert based on what Bemis had called the "Blessings of Liberty," on what Gaddis called the principles of "consent" and "*common* security." Gaddis moved from that conclusion to the argument that America's "empire by invitation" ran up against the iron-curtain colonialism promoted by Soviet Premier Josef Stalin, whose paranoid and sadistic style Gaddis illustrated with a series of familiar vignettes. In short, the Cold War was all about two different kinds of empire: America's "open and relaxed form of hegemony" and the Soviet Union's closed and repressive imperialism.[4]

Gaddis admitted that his presidential address revived many of the old questions about the origins of the Cold War, but he saw this as necessary in order to set the record straight. He argued that the suffering inflicted by the Soviet empire was a tragedy far greater than the one identified by Williams, which had already received more attention than Gaddis thought it deserved. Some will hear echoes in this argument of Bemis castigating Charles A. Beard and other historians, whose critical "tone," Bemis said, was part of a "national neurosis" that obscured America's benevolent

4 Gaddis, "Tragedy," 3–4. The phrase "empire by invitation" was coined by Geir Lundestad. See Lundestad, "Empire by Invitation? The United States and Western Europe, 1945–1952," *Journal of Peace Research* 23 (September 1986): 263–77.

"purpose" in the world. Diplomatic historians, Gaddis complained in a similar vein, had been "preoccupied" with "the 'first' world," by which he meant the Western world, notably the United States. They had tried to include the third world as well, where the emphasis was on the "intrusive impact" of American diplomacy, but had slighted the Communist world, the so-called second world, where Stalin and his "clones" had inflicted a tragedy of unparalleled proportions. Gaddis urged historians to focus on this tragedy, rather than on U.S. mistakes that tended to detract from the heroic nature of the American struggle against communism.[5]

Nor did Gaddis want diplomatic historians to fall into the trap of believing that it was ever possible to negotiate successfully with the Soviets or to hammer out reasonable compromises. This was evident in his unfortunate reference to the "'Rodney King' question." "The most persistent issue historians of the Cold War's origins have had to wrestle with," Gaddis argued in his presidential address, "is a variation on what we would today call the 'Rodney King' question: 'Couldn't we all have gotten along if we had really tried?'" According to Gaddis, diplomatic historians had "answered that question long ago with respect to another great twentieth-century dictator, Adolf Hitler." He compared Stalin to Hitler and found little reason to believe that "we" could ever have coexisted with such an "evil" force. Posing the Rodney King question, in other words, led Gaddis inexorably to the conclusion that there was nothing the United States could have done to alter Soviet diplomacy or lessen the severity of the Cold War. That line of argument recalled Bemis's reference to the Soviet Union as a "malignant antagonist," his conviction that no "middle way" existed between the "extremes" of accepting Communist "slavery" and defending liberty, and even his references to "Anglo-American freedoms" and "the risen tide of color." This last comparison is what makes the Rodney King analogy so unfortunate. Although Gaddis surely did not intend this interpretation, some critics are bound to note how the analogy leads implicitly to the conclusion that whites and blacks are also incapable of getting along, as were the United States and the Soviet Union.[6]

5 Bemis, "American Foreign Policy," 304; Gaddis, "Tragedy," 7, 11.
6 Gaddis, "Tragedy," 9; Bemis, "American Foreign Policy," 305, 298, 301.

Many diplomatic historians are likely to question the utility of Gaddis's assumption, buried in his presidential address, that Marxist-Leninist regimes were worse than the dictatorships sometimes supported by the United States. Others will reject his vague, cyclical theory of causation, whereby the United States becomes the historical agent of a liberating, bourgeois capitalism. According to this theory, briefly summarized in the same address, the hardships of industrialization and urbanization initially called into question the credibility of bourgeois capitalism and set the stage for Communist authoritarianism. Communism was undermined in turn, however, by postindustrial forces that permitted a resurgence of democratic capitalism in the second half of the twentieth century. This line of argument links Gaddis and his brand of postrevisionism back to Walt W. Rostow and other advocates of modernization theory, which has been in disrepute for some time now, in part because of its profoundly conservative implications.

Gaddis argued in his presidential address that Williams and other revisionists constituted a new orthodoxy in the field of diplomatic history, although that argument will not be taken seriously by most scholars. After all, New Left revisionists never made up a majority of diplomatic historians, and few would put themselves in that category today. Gaddis's assertion to the contrary seems to suggest that he sees himself as an outsider to the field, not because diplomatic history is dominated by revisionists but because so few diplomatic historians share his historiographical priorities or the moral point of view that infused his presidential address. Certain that new Soviet archives will prove his viewpoint, Gaddis urged diplomatic historians to seize the opportunity created by the end of the Cold War to recast that conflict as a morality play in which the tragic aspects of American diplomacy appear "more to fade out than to stand out." Other diplomatic historians may be reluctant to slight the "deplorable" in U.S. diplomacy or to bring the field back to the same questions that have largely preoccupied it since 1945. On the contrary, younger historians may wish to move beyond the Cold War, to write international history as if it were more than a history of Soviet-American relations, and to explore such new areas of inquiry as state making, nationalism, culture, gender, ethnicity, and religion.[7]

Bruce Cumings: A Williams for the World System

Bruce Cumings is among those historians who have been trying to point the field in a different direction from the one that Gaddis has in mind. In his article "'Revising Postrevisionism,'" which is reprinted in the following pages, Cumings took issue with the strong criticism that Gaddis has leveled over the years against revisionism, corporatism, world-systems theory, and other departures from postrevisionism. In doing so he was joining in a debate already begun with a few brief paragraphs in an essay I had published in the June 1993 issue of *Reviews in American History*.[8] The result was the noisiest controversy to hit the field in decades. The whole affair broke into the open with a long story in the *Chronicle of Higher Education*.[9] Then came a debate between Gaddis and Cumings at the summer 1994 meeting of the Society for Historians of American Foreign Relations, which was followed in turn by an exchange of letters between Cumings and Arthur Schlesinger, Jr., in the society's *Newsletter*.[10]

7 Gaddis, "Tragedy," 15.

8 Michael J. Hogan, "The Vice Men of Foreign Policy," *Reviews in American History* 21 (June 1993): 320–28.

9 Karen J. Winkler, "Scholars Refight the Cold War," *Chronicle of Higher Education*, 2 March 1994, A8ff.

10 The Schlesinger-Cumings exchange captured the bitter flavor of the controversy. In his article, Cumings had charged orthodox historians with trying to discredit William Appleman Williams by calling him a Communist. He attacked Schlesinger, in particular, for calling Williams "a pro-Communist scholar." Schlesinger counterattacked in the SHAFR *Newsletter*: "If Cumings cannot see any difference between membership in the Communist Party and scholarship that absolves the Soviet Union and Stalin and places the blame for the Cold War on the United States and capitalism, he ought to abandon the historical trade. We all used to complain when Joe McCarthy refused to make precisely this distinction. It is no more defensible when Cumings rejects the distinction today." Cumings, however, saw no merit in the distinction that Schlesinger was drawing. Schlesinger had come "as close to calling Williams a Communist as one can without getting hauled into court," said Cumings, who stuck by his charge that orthodox gate keepers like Schlesinger had relied on "euphemisms" like "leftists" to "stigmatize alternative scholarship." Cumings also concluded that it was Schlesinger, not he, who was guilty of "academic McCarthyism." See Schlesinger letter to the editor, 25 January 1994, SHAFR *Newsletter* (June 1994): 44–45; and Cumings letter to the editor, 3 November 1994, ibid. (March 1995): 52–53.

In "'Revising Postrevisionism,'" Cumings starts by assessing some of the leading trends and key works in the field and ends with his own recommendations about where the field should go in the future. Like Michael Hunt, Cumings sees postrevisionism as the dominant paradigm in diplomatic history, despite Gaddis's claim to the contrary, and is harshly critical of this development. He agrees with Warren F. Kimball's conclusion that postrevisionism amounts to "orthodoxy plus archives," although it might be more accurate to argue that Gaddis's recent work, including his presidential address, moves toward orthodoxy at the expense of his earlier efforts to build a case for the Cold War as a shared Soviet and American responsibility.[11]

According to Cumings, moreover, postrevisionism is informed by a point of view that is essentially moral rather than historical. That view is evident in Gaddis's presidential address, not to mention his recent comments on the end of the Cold War, in which he frames that contest as a battle between good and evil.[12] Cumings also accuses Gaddis of treating the historiography of the Cold War in a similar fashion: Historians who share his views are good, while those who differ are bad. They are "bad" in the moral sense, at least by implication, but also because their work is not objective, not grounded in the newest documents, and not historical. It is this line of argument that provokes the sharpest attack from Cumings.

Cumings also criticizes the field's general reluctance to apply theory to the study of American foreign relations. He places some of the blame for this trend on the "gate keepers" of the field, such as Gaddis and Leffler. Although Gaddis once celebrated the value of "lumping,"[13] which involves theorizing, he and Leffler

11 Warren F. Kimball, "Response to John Lewis Gaddis, 'The Emerging Post-Revisionist Synthesis on the Origins of the Cold War,'" *Diplomatic History* 7 (Summer 1983): 198–200. Quote on p. 198. For Gaddis's earlier work that made a case for shared responsibility see *The United States and the Origins of the Cold War, 1941–1947* (New York, 1972).

12 John Lewis Gaddis, "The Cold War, the Long Peace, and the Future," in *The End of the Cold War: Its Meaning and Implications*, ed. Michael J. Hogan (New York, 1992), 21–38.

13 John Lewis Gaddis, *Strategies of Containment: A Critical Appraisal of Postwar American National Security Policy* (New York, 1982), vii; idem, "The Corporatist Synthesis: A Skeptical View," *Diplomatic History* 10 (Fall 1986): 357–62.

are now the sultans of synthesis, according to Cumings. They approach history writing as one approaches a cafeteria line, taking something here and something there until the plate is full. For Gaddis, in particular, truly theoretical approaches to history are essentially reductionist, a criticism he has leveled at revisionism, dependency theory, corporatism, world-systems theory, postmodernism, and analyses that emphasize cultural categories, such as race and gender. The list of historians that Gaddis attacks includes almost every scholar of standing in the field, all denounced, Cumings implies, not because they are reductionists but because their historical theories are left of center and therefore deflect attention from the issues of right and wrong, as Gaddis defines them.

Cumings, on the other hand, champions theory. Although he casts a critical eye on other historians, including Leffler and Hunt, his criticism does not conceal the respect he has for their work, in part, I suspect, because they are less hostile toward theory than Gaddis or more critical in their point of view. Hunt, in fact, is a substantial theorist in his own right, while Leffler borrows insights from theoretically minded historians to frame a powerful critique of American diplomacy in the early Cold War. On the other hand, neither Hunt nor Leffler would subscribe to the theories of Immanuel Wallerstein that inform Cumings's work, including his essay in this book and the second volume of his history of the origins of the Korean War.[14]

Cumings concludes his essay with praise for Thomas J. McCormick's world-systems analysis of the Cold War and with the implicit suggestion that world-systems theory is the best path for diplomatic historians to take in the future.[15] It "leaves Williams intact," he says, while updating his approach. Cumings believes

14 Bruce Cumings, *The Origins of the Korean War*, vol. 2, *The Roaring of the Cataract, 1947–1950* (Princeton, 1990). Wallerstein's important works include *The Modern World-System: Capitalist Agriculture and the Origins of the European World-Economy in the Sixteenth Century* (New York, 1974); *The Modern World-System II: Mercantilism and the Consolidation of the European World-Economy, 1600–1750* (New York, 1980); *The Modern World-System III: The Second Era of Great Expansion of the Capitalist World-Economy, 1730–1840s* (San Diego, 1989); and *Geopolitics and Geoculture: Essays on the Changing World-System* (New York, 1991).

15 Thomas J. McCormick, *America's Half-Century: United States Foreign Policy in the Cold War* (Baltimore, 1989).

that this approach is capable of marrying the insights of area specialists to those of Americanists while simultaneously linking American policy abroad to changes in the political economy at home. Others are less enthusiastic. To Gaddis, world-systems theory is reductionist. To Leffler as well, no single theory, including world-systems theory, can comprehend or explain the many dimensions of American foreign policy. To Hunt, world-systems theory shares the same flaws as dependency theory and revisionism: It is one-dimensional, marginalizes noneconomic concerns, and is poorly grounded in business and economic history. According to still other critics, Wallerstein's theory is ideologically biased; it highlights the faults of capitalist countries while downplaying those of Communist countries. It also assumes that social change is driven almost wholly by external forces, and it lumps societies together in a way that slights the role of personality, class structures, and cultural tradition.[16]

Melvyn P. Leffler: The Half-Opened Door

Recent SHAFR presidential addresses have had a defensive tone. Gaddis's address falls into that category, as do portions of Warren Kimball's address of January 1994, which laments how diplomatic history has become marginalized in the age of postmodernism.[17] Leffler's 1995 presidential address, republished below, sounds a similar note. He, too, laments the turn toward postmodernism and joins a long list of historians calling for a revival of interest in politics, diplomacy, and the state. To his credit, Leffler, unlike many conservatives, urges diplomatic historians to explore the "hottest" new approaches and topics, such as gender, race, culture, and discourse. Nevertheless, the language of his address suggests that these approaches and topics must remain on the periphery of the field. They must be adapted, he says at one

16 For convenient summaries and friendly criticisms of Wallerstein's work see Daniel Chirot and Charles Ragan, "The World System of Immanuel Wallerstein: Sociology and Politics as History," in *Vision and Method in Historical Sociology*, ed. Theda Skocpol (Cambridge, England, 1979), 276–312; and Chirot and Thomas D. Hall, "World Systems Theory," *Annual Review of Sociology* 8 (1982): 81–106.

17 Warren F. Kimball, "Thirty Years After, or the Two Musketeers," *Diplomatic History* 18 (Spring 1994): 161–76.

point, to "the most salient issues within our own specialty." As cultural and social historians begin to write the history of the postwar era, Leffler imagines at another point, they will become "more familiar with the work many of us have been doing." They will "reorient their attention to the state and toward power, toward politics and policy" and will enter "a more constructive dialogue with us rather than ignoring us."

The concept of causation is at the heart of Leffler's argument with postmodernist historiography. Postmodernism, he insists, either deflects our attention from issues of causation and agency to issues of culture and discourse or ignores the hierarchy of causal factors that have been identified by historians, like himself, who work in "the older categories of analysis." Discourse theory can certainly help historians appreciate the linkages between discursive strategies, the construction of truth or knowledge, and the institutions of authority. But Leffler rebels at the possibility that such an approach might deny moral authority to the historian. Michel Foucault and other postmodernists, he complains, "deny our ability to represent reality in any objectively true fashion." That remark establishes a link between Leffler's view of history and that of Gaddis. Both seek to discover reality in an "objectively true fashion," which is supposedly not possible for those using postmodernist strategies or, for that matter, revisionist, corporatist, or world-system theories.

If Gaddis finds the high ground in new archival evidence, Leffler finds it in a hierarchy of causation that puts geopolitics at the top, and that associates geopolitics, rather than race, gender, or other cultural categories, with the most fundamental truths about American diplomacy.[18] In this sense, Leffler is determined to engage other historians from a position of strength and on terms of his own choosing. He seems to be saying that diplomatic historians have been doing the right thing all along, or at least those diplomatic historians who focus on policymaking elites, on state-to-

18 In his book, *A Preponderance of Power: National Security, the Truman Administration, and the Cold War* (Stanford, 1992), Leffler's definition of geopolitics slides off into geostrategy. In his presidential address, on the other hand, the term is sometimes used to embrace issues of political economy and the connection among strategy, economics, and state power.

state relations, and on national power. The burden is on other historians to address the issues and approaches that have always been central to the study of diplomacy. Only at that point will "constructive dialogue" be possible.

Leffler also shares Gaddis's reservations about theory. He seems to give ground to Cumings's complaint that his work reflects the "poverty of theory" in the field of diplomatic history, but he turns what Cumings sees as a shortcoming into an asset. Like Gaddis, he appears to consider a theoretically informed history reductionist. "Reality," as he puts it, "is too complex to be captured by a single theory." Like Gaddis, Leffler prefers an "eclectic brew" to straight whiskey. He decries the proliferation of theories in the field and says the real challenge is to synthesize the theories now at hand. In effect, Leffler cites his own work as an example of the gains to be made by borrowing insights from a variety of conceptual approaches, including revisionism, corporatism, and world-systems theory. But he is not talking about the kind of synthesis that we see in works such as Robert Wiebe's *The Search for Order*, where the whole is greater than the sum of its parts – in effect, a new historical theory.[19] He is talking about putting theories of causation together in a way that permits each one to occupy a separate place in a hierarchy of causation – a hierarchy, as noted earlier, that places geopolitical considerations above those identified by revisionists, corporatists, world-systems theorists, cultural historians, and postmodernists.

The hierarchy that Leffler has identified puts him in the post-revisionist camp, as it does Gaddis. In their work, strategy is privileged over issues of class, industrial structure, or geoeconomic systems; their brand of diplomatic history is privileged over studies that might emphasize the role of gender, race, culture, religion, or discourse in foreign affairs; and synthesis is privileged over the theoretical devices that allow historians to get at such topics. Much of Leffler's presidential address is devoted to a critique of recent histories that explore issues of culture or that use corporatist or world-system paradigms. Works by Akira Iriye, John W. Dower, Thomas A. Ferguson, Cumings, and others are tested and found

19 Robert Wiebe, *The Search for Order, 1877–1920* (New York, 1967).

wanting. It is possible to dispute Leffler's criticisms, of course, although he is probably correct in implying that these heavily theorized works are more on the margin of the field than in the mainstream, which is crowded instead with the kind of geostrategic studies that Leffler champions.

In the end, however, Leffler's position has problems of its own, particularly because his analysis of geostrategy is essentially an analysis of perceptions, not some objective and knowable reality. In that sense, it is chess without the chess board. The emphasis on the geostrategic setting of American policy, instead of the domestic context, is what makes this brand of diplomatic history less interesting to historians of American society, culture, politics, and economy. At the same time, the emphasis on American perceptions leaves Leffler vulnerable to international historians and area specialists, whose biarchival or multiarchival research and area training enable them to put American foreign policy in a global, regional, or bilateral context and to test American perceptions against reality as revealed in the records of other countries. It also leaves Leffler vulnerable to students of culture and discourse, who must wonder why it is important to emphasize something as ethereal as perception but not the culture from which perception springs or the discourse that mediates betwen perception and reality. Finally, those who study foreign relations, rather than diplomacy per se, are bound to ask why state-to-state relations are more important, objectively speaking, than the international women's movement or the international labor movement, to give two examples; why state power is more worthy of analysis than power relations between ethnic groups, social classes, functional groups, genders, or races; or why the perceptions of policymakers are worth more attention than the perceptions of business leaders, trade unionists, environmentalists, the membership of the NAACP, or non-elites in general.

Michael Hunt: A Mansion of Many Rooms

Michael Hunt has a relatively optimistic view of the field and its future. He deplores the "babble of labels" in diplomatic history, as does Bruce Cumings in his essay. He is both impressed and fatigued by the "sustained exercise in self-reflection and self-criticism" that has marked the field over the last couple of decades. He knows that the field has come under strong attack from without, as well as from within, and seems to agree with those diplomatic historians, like Melvyn Leffler, who call for a moratorium on theorizing. But Hunt is more confident than the other three authors that the "long crisis" in diplomatic history is coming to an end. Diplomatic historians, he says, are writing with new verve and "fresh confidence."

Hunt tries to rise above the babble of labels by aggregating rather than disaggregating the various approaches to diplomatic history. In this sense, his essay is an excellent primer, especially useful to those who are new to the field. Hunt breaks the field into three broad groups, each of which is marked by the questions it asks and by the methodological and theoretical tools it brings to bear. The dominant group encompasses the realist writers of the 1950s, as well as the postrevisionists of today. The historians in this group celebrate archival research and concentrate on policymaking within the American state, particularly on the exercise of national power by the policymaking elite. They are less concerned with economic power, or cultural forces, than with military power, and they think in familiar geostrategic categories, such as "the balance of power," "vital interests," and "national security."

The second group includes progressive historians like Charles Beard and revisionist historians like William Appleman Williams, as well as corporatist, dependency, and world-systems theorists. These historians are concerned with the connections between American foreign policy and the "domestic sphere." For the most part, this concern has taken the form of questions regarding the ways in which economic systems and political structures influence American diplomacy, although the approach itself is open to other, wider connections. In his work, for example, Bruce Cumings sheds light on the connection between the American and the global spheres, and between the American system and the domestic systems of other countries – usually those on the receiving end of American imperialism. Other connections might include those between economic and cultural forces, or between ideology, discourse, and state making in American foreign policy. Although Hunt suggests that the state will always remain central to the study of foreign policy, he seems to credit this second group of progressive historians with much of what is interesting and innovative in the field.

The third group of historians includes those who connect American diplomacy, not to domestic systems necessarily, but to the international environment. These international historians tell their story from the point of view of two or more countries, the United States included, and use the sources of those countries. They are often trained as area specialists, as well as Americanists. For the most part, their approach remains state-centered, which Hunt regrets, but it is open to those who are concerned with the relationship between national cultures, with geoeconomic developments, with the emergence of international organizations, and even with dependency relationships and the modern world system. Himself an international historian of the first order, Hunt is willing to admit that international history is less an analytical design than a methodology that can be used by most of the historians in the other two groups. His own bias seems to lie in combining international history with the new work on state making, ideology, and culture.

Hunt draws out the negatives of the three groups. The first group suffers from a national, gender, and class bias and employs often ahistorical interpretive schemes; the second would benefit from neo-Marxist theory and from the anthropological concept of culture; and the third is too state-centered in its approach. But what sets Hunt's essay apart is its optimism and plea for tolerance. He believes that the questions posed by each group are important and equally relevant to the field. Each group occupies one of the rooms that together make up the large mansion of diplomatic history. Ultimately, the difference in the questions asked by each group determines the analytical tools and interpretive positions that they will utilize.

Hunt is surely correct in his conclusion. For several years now, diplomatic historians have searched for an umbrella concept, an idea big enough to embrace, or rather subsume, all of the different questions they ask. Some diplomatic historians, myself included, have claimed at one time or another to have found the magical concept. Several years ago, Thomas G. Paterson and I edited a collection of essays on the leading paradigms in the field.[20] The authors of almost all of those essays, mine among them, saw their paradigms as the be-all-and-end-all in diplomatic history. We were wrong. As Hunt argues, there are different paradigms for different sets of questions, all of which are germane to the field.

Conclusion: An Open Door for Diplomatic History

The preceding discussion suggests my own reservations about the work of some of the most prominent diplomatic historians. Nevertheless, it is easy to see why this work has carried the field to new heights. John Gaddis remains the best essayist in the field and one of its leading synthesizers. He and Michael Hunt are among the very few diplomatic historians who seem to be as skilled at the long synthesis as they are at the focused monograph. Hunt's monographic work deserves the accolades it has received, while his provocative recent book, *Ideology and U.S. Foreign Policy*, marks him as one of the most innovative thinkers in the field. The sheer size and sweep of a book like Melvyn Leffler's *A Preponderance of Power* commands respect, as do the depth of its research and the rigor of its argument. Much the same can be said of a very different book by Bruce Cumings, *The Origins of the Korean War*, vol. 2, *The Roaring of the Cataract*, which is notable as well for its dazzling prose, provocative speculation, and fundamental honesty.[21]

Does the high quality of the work produced by these scholars mean that diplomatic history is in good shape? Not necessarily, although the answer surely depends on your perspective. The bitter exchange between Gaddis and Cumings suggests that diplomatic historians remain deeply divided over key issues and questions, notably the origins of the Cold War and how that epic

20 Michael J. Hogan and Thomas G. Paterson, eds., *Explaining the History of American Foreign Relations* (New York, 1991).

21 Michael H. Hunt, *Ideology and U.S. Foreign Policy* (New Haven, 1987). For full citations to Leffler's and Cumings's books see footnotes 18 and 14.

struggle should be approached. These divisions are not likely to dissipate, nor are traditional diplomatic historians likely to welcome new approaches and topics on terms that invite them into the field. This, it seems to me, is the most serious issue facing diplomatic historians today. Proud of our work and convinced of our field's intrinsic value, we are naturally upset by the tendency of other historians to belittle our accomplishments and inclined to take a defensive posture. But such a response is unlikely to improve our situation. We would be better off to follow Hunt's advice, open our minds to new ideas and approaches, and benefit from the productive cross-fertilization that results. By remaining open to new methodologies and new theories, we will allow members of our field to pose new questions about the past. It is ultimately the questions we ask that determine the histories we write, and by asking new and innovative questions we will only strengthen the field. At a time when diplomatic history is beleaguered, circling our wagons will make things worse, while an open door policy offers hope, perhaps the only hope, for the field's improvement.

2

"Revising Postrevisionism," Or, The Poverty of Theory in Diplomatic History

BRUCE CUMINGS

In spite of the title, this is not another essay about how badly read and provincial are American diplomatic historians; in fact, my temperature reading indicates a lot of good and interesting work out there. The title would have been unwieldy had I made my intent perfectly clear: This is an essay about how badly read and provincial are the keepers of the field – those who clean out the barnyard, get the cattle back into their cubbyholes, rake out the old, rake in the new, plant shoots, root out weeds, forecast crises and watersheds, sow discord, reap textbooks, pocket the rutabaga, and scold the rest of us for our lack of theory. My focus is on what is sometimes called "postrevisionism," an odd season coming after the shimmering summer of orthodoxy and the dusky winter of heterodoxy.

Rather than recite the Farmer's Almanac of postrevisionism, however, after some initial observations I will focus on one textbook, on the work of one self-described postrevisionist and one postrevisionist in spite of himself, and finally, on a postrevisionism that I can recommend highly – even if it is not our solution, but still part of the problem. I offer my critique in the spirit of Carl Becker's radical idea that a professor's purpose is "to think otherwise."[1]

I would like to thank Warren Kimball, James Kurth, Walter LaFeber, Marilyn Young, and the editors of *Diplomatic History* for their helpful comments on this essay, and Melvyn Leffler for an enthusiastic dissent.

1 Quoted in Walter LaFeber, "Fred Harvey Harrington," *Diplomatic History* 9 (Fall 1985): 313.

Orthodoxy and Revision: Perfect, Imperfect, or Pluperfect?

The most elemental act of "theory" is to name things: "x is y" might be the simplest summary of Heidegger's theme in *What is Called Thinking*. Without comparing this to that, we cannot think. Without naming or "calling" we cannot think – "thinking *qua* thinking, is essentially a call," Heidegger wrote.[2] But there are better and worse names, better and worse calls, as the ancient Chinese philosophers knew. So we need another fillip to our "thinking": the rectification of names, another term for classification, or even dialogue and debate. And finally there is the problem Nietzsche posed, and that also became Heidegger's concern: "What things are called is incomparably more important than what they are."[3]

With this paragraph, we crank open a can of worms, true, but we retrieve it from a darkened pantry that the literature in question rarely if ever opened. The literature is suffused with "naming" and "calling" to be sure (a "Babel of labels," as we will see), but it barely gets us to the second level of rectification and debate. Furthermore, the names can barely stand the light of day.

The formulation that wishes to reign can be put simply: There is the orthodox literature on the Cold War, which was followed by the revisionist literature, which was then followed by the postrevisionist literature. What is called orthodoxy is usually assumed (something no self-respecting Chinese scholar would ever have done), but we recognize it in its solidity, its respectability, its immanent power. Revisionism then appears like a bucking bronco needing a saddle: unconfined, not reputable (if not disreputable), of fleeting influence. Postrevisionism is the wagon claiming to tether these two horses, taking energy from both. If this were "thesis: antithesis: synthesis," it might work. But it turns out that we do not know the thesis (what is the orthodox view?), the antithesis is badly understood, and the synthesis struts forth as a

2 Martin Heidegger, *What is Called Thinking?* trans. J. Glenn Gray (New York, 1968), 161.
3 Friedrich Nietzsche, *The Gay Science*, trans. Walter Kaufmann (New York, 1974), 121.

Whig attempt on a Chinese menu (to mix several metaphors), choosing one from Column A and one from Column B only to produce a dish that resuscitates "orthodoxy" for a new generation.

The proof of this pudding will come later. For now let us return to the phrase, "what things are called is incomparably more important than what they are." *What they are* is a phrase expressing the historian's *point d'honneur*: objectivity. The past "as it really was," the historian as the objective recorder of primary sources, history not as *a* pursuit of truth but as *the* pursuit of truth. Rankean method, which still holds sway in many history departments (albeit with a strong admixture of Anglo-Saxon positivism),[4] assumed that the historian could be trained to the objective standard of a camera lens, achieving results identical to the popular notion of the innocent eye of the camera: the historian's "eye" is merely there to record "the facts." The historian then performs the linguistic magician's trick of letting them "speak for themselves."

So, *what things are called* cannot be more important than what they *are*; to suggest so leads straight to a hell of nihilism and irrationality.[5] Is this Nietzsche's position?

It is not. He did not, of course, believe in positivist objectivity. He found in it an "unscrupulous benevolence": "The objective man is indeed a mirror," he wrote, "accustomed to submitting before whatever wants to be known."[6] But neither is this rejection of objectivity an act of nihilism and irrationality. The act of naming is, to paraphrase Heidegger, a "call" for the memory, a procedure

4 Peter Novick has an excellent passage on how Ranke was misinterpreted in England and America in *That Noble Dream: The "Objectivity Question" and the American Historical Profession* (New York, 1988), 25–31.

5 Novick has many examples of this assumption in practice among historians, particularly those who see themselves as guardians of the discipline. See *Noble Dream*, 606–9.

6 The full passage, beautiful and pregnant with meaning, reads as follows:

> [The objective man] is accustomed to submitting before whatever wants to be known, without any other pleasure than that found in knowing and "mirroring"; he waits until something comes, and then spreads himself out tenderly lest light footsteps and the quick passage of spiritlike beings should be lost on his plane and skin. Whatever still remains in him of a "person" strikes him as accidental, often arbitrary, still more often disturbing: to such an extent has he become a passageway and reflection of strange forms and events even to himself.

Nietzsche, *Beyond Good and Evil: Prelude to a Philosophy of the Future*, trans. Walter Kaufmann (New York, 1966), 126–27.

of memory.[7] Historians are the custodians of memory, true, but Nietzsche has a different point. He takes us back to the barnyard.

Memory is precisely what distinguishes human beings from animals: "Consider the cattle," Nietzsche begins – they graze, munch grass, ingest and digest, buck snort into the ozone layer, and leap about with no sign of pleasure or melancholy. "This is a hard sight for man to see. . . . He cannot help envying them their happiness." The human wonders why the cow does not speak to him of his happiness (or not); the cow "would like to answer, and say: 'The reason is I always forget what I was going to say' – but then he forgot this answer too."[8]

Humans are not like that: Man "clings relentlessly to the past: however far and fast he may run, this chain runs with him." And this is "a matter for wonder": "A moment, now here and then gone, nothing before it came, again nothing after it has gone, nonetheless returns as a ghost and disturbs the peace of a later moment. A leaf flutters from the scroll of time, floats away – and suddenly floats back again and falls into a man's lap. Then the man says 'I remember' and envies the animal."[9]

The barnyard animal, Nietzsche says, "lives *unhistorically*," like the child playing "in blissful blindness between the hedges of past and future." But unlike the cow, the child's play will be disturbed: "Then it will learn to understand the phrase 'it was': that password which gives conflict, suffering, and satiety access to man . . . *an imperfect tense that can never become a perfect one.*"[10]

What things are called is how memory establishes its categories: Herbert Feis and Arthur Schlesinger, Jr., occupy a place in diplomatic history's mind as orthodox historians of the Cold War. William Appleman Williams locates in the memory as a "revisionist." But what does it mean, this term "revisionist"? Does

7 "What is it that is named with the words 'think,' 'thinking,' 'thought'? Toward what sphere of the spoken word do they direct us? A thought – where is it, where does it go? Thought is in need of memory, the gathering of thought." Heidegger, *What is Called Thinking?* 138.

8 "On the Uses and Disadvantages of History for Life," in Nietzsche, *Untimely Meditations*, trans. R. J. Hollingdale, intro J. P. Stern (New York, 1983), 60–61.

9 Ibid., 61. This passage had influence on thinkers as dissimilar as Freud and Walter Benjamin.

10 Ibid. (emphasis added).

it mean he revised earlier views? Or does it function semiotically for something else?

The orthodox school supplied an early and pithy answer: Williams is a Communist. Not a revisionist, not a neo-Marxist, but a Communist. In a letter to the executive secretary of the American Historical Association in 1954 (the apogee of McCarthyism), Schlesinger termed Williams a "pro-Communist scholar." The archly orthodox Feis, usually one to mince words, was not so inclined when referring to Cold War revisionists: He castigated the editor of the *New York Times Book Review* in 1971 for having the temerity to substitute "Marxian" for "Communist" in a letter he wrote to the *Review*: "I meant Communist, not merely Marxian. . . . Most of the writings and analyses of the historians of the New Left seemed to me poor imitations of Communist official doctrine."[11] Indeed, what things are called seems to be more important than what they are.

Unconvinced? Then identify the author of these words: "The intense quest for exports . . . was inadvisable and always an impending source of conflict. . . . [I deplore] the fanaticism with which from the time of Secretary Hull, Will Clayton and Dean Acheson the American Government had made itself the exponent of trade expansion." This person went on to say that Stalin had not, in fact, supported the Greek guerrillas and that the invitation to the Soviets to join the Marshall Plan was just for show, framed precisely to elicit rejection. Is it Beard? Probably not, considering that he died in 1947. Williams? His ideas, but not his language. Gabriel Kolko or Harry Elmer Barnes? Too mild. It is Feis in a letter mailed to Schlesinger within a month of the letter to the *Times Book Review*.[12]

No innocent bystander, no one uninvolved in our peculiarly American debates, would believe that truth, rather than naming,

11 Novick, *Noble Dream*, 450. Schlesinger's letter to Boyd Shafer was dated 1 July 1954; Feis's to John Leonard, 15 April 1971. "Pro-Communist scholar" is an interesting McCarthyite wrinkle: pro-Communist, yes, but also a scholar. It reminds me of Donald Zagoria's reference to me as a "leftist scholar" when my first book was blurbed in *Foreign Affairs* in 1982. To academics, this would make a difference, just as it would in a courtroom. But to students? For them, Schlesinger had called Williams a Communist, Zagoria had called Cumings a leftist.

12 Feis to Schlesinger, 7 May 1971, cited in ibid., 449.

labeling, and stigmatizing, is at stake here: a hermeneutics of censure and exclusion. One observant foreigner, Mary Kaldor, dissects our Cold War debates with a few flourishes of her scalpel, coming to the conclusion that the real issue seems to be who started the Cold War, and little more than that – a question she rightly sees as moral or political, not historical.[13]

There is a historical method that can account for this American dissensus, however, and lead us to truth. It is Nietzsche's – made popular by Foucault as *genealogy*. "What then is truth?" Nietzsche asked in 1873: "A mobile army of metaphors, metonyms, anthropomorphisms, a sum, in short, of human relationships which . . . come to be thought of, after long usage by a people, as fixed, binding, and canonical. Truths are illusions which we have forgotten are illusions." Or as Alasdaire MacIntyre puts Nietzsche's broader point, truth is "an unrecognized motivation serving an unacknowledged purpose."[14]

There is not truth, but many claims to truth: To do history is to grasp the origins of a particular truth-claim. This is what Nietzsche did brilliantly in *The Genealogy of Morals*, thus to reconstruct the genealogy of Judeo-Christian morality. This is a better way of thinking about the *descent* of Cold War debate from 1945 to the present – it "explains more of the variance," to use the language of a political scientist.[15]

Nietzsche wrote that words like "meaning" and "purpose" are only signs that some master has imposed upon history, an assessment: What we know as history is always "a fresh interpretation . . . through which any previous 'meaning' and 'purpose' are necessarily obscured and even obliterated." History is thus "a

13 Kaldor, *The Imaginary Conflict* (New York, 1990), 35–48. For a broader inquiry into the provincialism of American diplomatic history that in the text, but especially in the footnotes, also gives a good sense of the vibrance of international history that I mentioned at the start of this essay see Christopher Thorne, *Border Crossings: Studies in International History* (New York, 1988).

14 Alasdair MacIntyre, *Three Rival Versions of Moral Enquiry: Encyclopaedia, Genealogy, and Tradition* (Notre Dame, 1990), 35.

15 Several of my friends who like to read Marx have chided me for my interest in Nietzsche. They would do well to ponder Adorno's statement that *The Genealogy of Morals* is far better Marxism than the texts in the *ABCs of Communism* genre, or Benjamin's forays into dialectical materialism. See Theodor Adorno to Walter Benjamin, 10 November 1938, in Adorno et al., *Aesthetics and Politics* (London, 1977), 132.

continuous sign-chain of ever new interpretations" (incessant "revisionism" in our terms), expressing a genealogy of moral valence.[16]

Foucault took this argument up in a famous essay, "Nietzsche, Genealogy, History." Genealogy "opposes itself to the search for 'origins'"; for historians, origins means "that which was already there," as if it does not require a human being to determine "what was there," but can simply be "found." Instead, history "is the concrete body of a development, with its moments of intensity, its lapses, its extended periods of feverish agitation, its fainting spells; and only a metaphysician would seek its soul in the distant ideality of the origin."[17]

If there is truth in history, it does not reside in the shifting debates of historians, or in what statesmen say about their policies, or in what historians find in primary documents observed "pristine" in the archives, in the positivist sense that a transparent weathervane registers these documents correctly, without necessary recourse to a frame of reference, a set of assumptions, a theory. History with a capital H is not truth but a descent through various interpretations.

If we accept Foucault's arguments about "discourse," perhaps truth must be reconnoitered in some "prediscursive" structure, something prior to language and interpretation. What Foucault meant by the "prediscursive" is subject to sharp debate, but my sense of his and Nietzsche's thought is that they would see something like "class struggle" as discursive, something like a steel mill or an oil field, or perhaps a world market economy, as prediscursive.[18] If this is the case, the oil field remains uncomprehended

16 Nietzsche, *On the Genealogy of Morals*, ed. and trans. Walter Kaufmann (New York, 1969), 15–23, 77–78.

17 "Nietzsche, Genealogy, History," in Michel Foucault, *Language, Counter-Memory, Practice: Selected Essays and Interviews*, trans. Donald F. Bouchard and Sherry Simon (Ithaca, 1977).

18 MacIntyre argues that Foucault consistently denied any "fundamental sets or structures" that create explanation or understanding (*Rival Versions*, p. 52), whereas Gary Gutting says Foucault never was explicit (see his *Michel Foucault's Archaeology of Scientific Reason* [New York, 1989]). Gutting notes that *L'Archeologie du Savoir* provided "no serious discussion of the nature of the nondiscursive factors and of the influence they exert"; "there is no elucidation of the fundamental nature and ultimate significance of the link between the discursive and the nondiscursive" (p. 259). Unless a remove into Berkeleyean phenomenalism is proposed, I think the

without knowledge of what it is good for, without a conception of oil's relationship to something else: oil's value, perhaps, or a variant of the same thing, its uses for an industrial machine.

In this sense, the House of Saud, without a divining rod or a clue, ensconced itself on top of the prediscursive: the largest oil pools in the world. During World War II, the mammoth dimensions of the prediscursive disclosed themselves or, more properly, were discovered by people with the proper divining rods – but to do that you needed a theory (although not much of one).[19] Whereupon the House of Saud entered the industrial discursive . . . and Washington came to "a wholesale redefinition of the importance of the Middle East."[20]

Let us return to MacIntyre's rendering of Nietzsche's method of discovering truth through genealogy: Truth is "an unrecognized motivation serving an unacknowledged purpose." A Freudian idea perhaps, but also an Achesonian idea, a "Wise Men" idea. I was struck in Acheson's finely crafted memoirs to see him refer to the stillness that fell upon U.S.-Japanese relations in the days before Pearl Harbor by reference to "the apprehension of imponderables." As I wrote in my recent book,[21] he appeared to say that through his actions and those of others in the Roosevelt

industrial installations of the past two hundred years, if not necessarily their relationships, represent a "fundamental set or structure" that cannot be deconstructed, that can be apprehended by human senses like eyesight, and that do create relationships that require explanation and understanding, i.e., humans trying to comprehend their meaning (for example, they generate interests). Nietzsche rarely comments on this problem, because he was mostly concerned with moral and philosophical discourse, but occasionally he condemned the "money economy" of his time and clearly recognized an entity called the state.

19 Daniel Yergin, *The Prize: The Epic Quest for Oil, Money, and Power* (New York, 1991), 439–43. J. Paul Getty reached the pinnacle of billionaire status (enabling him to increase his contributions to the Democratic party, if not to enjoy better restaurants because "he made it a point to chew each mouthful of food thirty-three times") by virtue of paying a young geologist named Paul Walton to fly over the Saudi desert in a DC-3. Walton noticed a saucer-shaped mound pushing up the sand and thought that might be a good place to drill a hole. Thus was brought in an oil field described by *Fortune* as "somewhere between colossal and history-making."

20 Ibid., 395. Rather like the famous territorial division between Churchill and Stalin, in 1944 Roosevelt drew "a rough sketch" of the Middle East for British ambassador Lord Halifax: "Persian oil," he told the ambassador, "is yours. We share the oil of Iraq and Kuwait. As for Saudi Arabian oil, it is ours." (Ibid., 401.)

21 Bruce Cumings, *The Origins of the Korean War*, vol. 2, *The Roaring of the Cataract, 1947–1950* (Princeton, 1990), 408–38.

administration, a field of choice had corralled the Japanese, and that the only thing to do was wait and see which choice they made (attack – and lose; submit – and lose). Acheson went to chop trees in Archibald MacLeish's field on that Sunday morning, and before he was done chopping he got his answer – the one he appeared to want . . . a motivation unrecognized *by others* serving an unacknowledged purpose *of Acheson's.*

In Kai Bird's new book on John J. McCloy, we find this same seemingly indeterminate phrase reappearing, this time via Felix Frankfurter – who credited Bismarck with putting "'imponderables' into the vocabulary of affairs." McCloy also liked to use the term.[22] Then again, it might simply be that men like McCloy and Robert Lovett reserved their real thoughts (ponderables?) for people like Russell Leffingwell, chairman of the House of Morgan, when they were not sharing them with the Rockefellers.[23]

There seems to be something in the prediscursive that the Wise Men did not want to talk about with the rest of us, however, but merely wanted to "represent." Maybe oil is the answer, here, too. "Who says national security says Western Europe and oil" might be the simplest formulation of McCloy's 1940s viewpoint. Two weeks after Pearl Harbor he "startled" Henry Stimson by backing a campaign against Hitler in North Africa – "it must constantly be borne in mind that the greatest oil deposits in the world are in this area," he wrote.[24]

22 Kai Bird, *The Chairman: John J. McCloy, the Making of the American Establishment* (New York, 1992), 154.

23 In 1947, McCloy and Leffingwell had long discussions on the World Bank, reflecting back on the errors of the 1920s; in the same year, Leffingwell warned Lovett – his "Locust Valley neighbor" – that Europe was "drifting toward catastrophe" unless the United States provided loans and grants "on a great scale." He then tutored Lovett on how to keep the Russians out of the Marshall Plan, without seeming to do so. See their discussions in Ron Chernow, *The House of Morgan: An American Banking Dynasty and the Rise of Modern Finance* (New York, 1990), 486–89. At an early meeting of the World Bank, with McCloy in charge, the British Director Sir James Grigg remarked, "here goes a meeting of the Chase Bank," whereupon McCloy set about organizing bank affairs in a house Nelson Rockefeller lent him on Georgetown's Foxhall Road. Bird, *The Chairman*, 289; see also p. 387 for McCloy as "a Rockefeller man." When Eisenhower suggested that McCloy be named high commissioner of Germany, Robert Morgenthau told Harry Hopkins "McCloy isn't the man to go. . . . After all, his clients are people like General Electric, Westinghouse, General Motors" – in other words, the high-technology, labor-accommodating multinational firms Tom Ferguson writes about. (Bird, *The Chairman*, 225.)

24 Bird, *The Chairman*, 143, 178.

In early 1947, petroleum policy in the State Department was in Paul Nitze's hands, supervised by Dean Acheson (no doubt it is mere coincidence that these names keep popping up). The issue was how to erase the famous "Red Line" that Calouste Gulbenkian had drawn on the map in 1928, how now to divide Persian Gulf oil between American, British, and French companies, and even more, how to divvy up Saudi Arabia's vast new discoveries among American companies and find distributors capable of absorbing the tidal wave of oil about to slosh onto the world market, without destroying the world oil regime. The answer? Form a cartel with Socony, Socal, Standard of New Jersey, and Texaco and sell the oil to Western Europe and Japan – just then being reconstituted industrially by the United States. The four companies signed the historic agreement on 12 March 1947, which just happened to be the day that Truman spoke to a joint session of Congress about the defense of Greece and Turkey.[25]

Now loping into the field comes William S. Borden, to show how Japan and Germany were posted as industrial workshops in the late 1940s, linked to regional spheres of economic influence, and fueled by cheap oil from the Middle East – something he calls "capitalist-bloc multilateralism" (not a bad name, that). Industrial revival would create markets for American goods, particularly if cheap energy kept the costs of production down. (Getting Europe and Japan off coal and onto oil would also weaken the power of left-wing miners' unions.) All this, of course, meant restoring colonial relationships "to the south," now viewed as "natural economies" functioning according to the doctrine of comparative advantage, no longer exclusive to the colonizers but "open" to American influence. The "reverse course" in Japan was thus not a product of the Cold War so much as a rearrangement of the world economy. (Alfred Chandler was once asked how Japan and West Germany "did it": "improved institutional

25 Yergin, *The Prize*, 413–16. There was the irksome problem of antitrust, because three of the four firms were fashioned out of John D. Rockefeller's Standard Oil. But Truman's attorney general did not think that was a problem and okayed the agreement. This was followed in September 1947 by huge deals involving Anglo-Iranian, Gulf, and Shell, and thus "the mechanisms, capital and marketing systems were in place to move vast quantities of Middle Eastern oil into the European market" and to move Europe off coal and onto oil. (Ibid., 422–24.)

arrangements and cheap oil" was his answer.) None of it really got working smoothly, however, until the Korean War came along, solving (with its military procurements and the pump-priming of NSC-68-style military Keynesianism) the "dollar gap" problem.[26]

With Borden's fine book, we move forward to the apprehension of ponderables, to motivations recognized and serving acknowledged purposes: that is, the truth of the early Cold War period. And lo and behold, the declassified discursive finds the orthodox Kennan fretting about how Japan might "reopen some sort of Empire toward the South."[27]

In my recent book, I sought, in the most careful language I could muster, to suggest that Acheson's thinking about the unmentionable, signified by "the apprehension of imponderables," might also have had something to do with his famed "Press Club speech" in January 1950. The general reaction has been this: "you must subscribe to a conspiracy theory." "Conspiracy theory" in the American context, as we will see, connotes atheory, the capitalist clique/plot as the only way of thinking about the generalized interest that Acheson and McCloy represented (and *said* they represented, not to mention being *paid* to represent).

With this discussion as preface, we now seek to demonstrate our points from the literature of orthodoxy and revisionism.

History in the Pluperfect[28] Tense: Who Will Educate the Educators?

I now wish to lasso three representative examples of naming, cubbyholing, and theorizing from the field of American diplomatic history. The first is a representative textbook; the second, the work of arch-postrevisionist John Lewis Gaddis; and the third, arch-cubbyholer and devotee of theory, Michael H. Hunt.

We begin with Jerald A. Combs's *American Diplomatic History*,[29] a taxonomic effort useful for my task on three counts: (1)

26 William S. Borden, *The Pacific Alliance: United States Foreign Economic Policy and Japanese Trade Recovery, 1947–54* (Madison, 1984), 1–17.
27 Cumings, *Origins*, 2:57.
28 As in Eisenhower's rumored comment, "Why in pluperfect hell do we have to worry so much about that little teat of a country [Korea]?"
29 University of California Press, 1983.

Professor Combs assumes that we all know what we mean when we say "orthodox" and "revisionist"; (2) he recapitulates Schlesinger's and Feis's concerns with "naming"; and (3) Michael Hunt's backcover endorsement enthusiastically calls it "detailed, scrupulous, fair-minded." (The reader should keep in mind that this is a textbook, designed to introduce students to the field, and that therefore many of my criticisms of Dr. Combs are better directed at the field he tills.)

Although "orthodoxy" is never quite specified, we deduce from chapter fourteen ("The Cold War") that it is solid and mainstream and that the correct position was first inscribed by George Kennan, Louis Halle, Hans Morgenthau, Samuel Flagg Bemis, Winston Churchill, Robert Murphy, and Herbert Feis. Only one of these names a historian (Bemis). Revisionism's meaning is also assumed. It first sallies forth with the Wilsonian D. F. Fleming, thence with "neo-Marxist" William Appleman Williams and his prominent students (Thomas J. McCormick, Walter LaFeber, Lloyd Gardner – p. 256), and finally with "hard-line economic determinist" Gabriel Kolko (p. 314). Kolko's appearance begets adjectival distinction, and we now learn of "moderate" and "radical" revisionists.[30]

Williams and his group appear at first to belong to the "moderate" camp. We learn (and they learn) that "their critique was based on Lenin's theory that imperialism was an inevitable consequence of capitalism." Still, according to Combs, they do not treat American policy as "a vicious plot by an evil capitalist clique but as a product of general American ideology" (p. 257). Unpacking this particular rectification of names is taxing, but it appears to mean this: (1) "radical" revisionists treat American policy as a vicious plot by evil capitalist cliques; and (2) "moderate" revisionists, to the contrary, follow in the van of Vladimir Ilyich who – based on the above evidence – thought imperialism was an inevitable consequence of capitalism, that is, a product of general American ideology. Or perhaps it means that by focusing on "ideology," the "moderates" avoid the pitfall of conjuring evil

30 Sometimes the distinction is worthy of a contortionist, as in Combs's judgment on Barton Bernstein: "radical revisionist . . . somewhat harsher in tone than Ronald Steel, a moderate revisionist" (p. 333n).

capitalist clique plots (which the "radicals" do not). But then further on Combs speaks of "Kolko and other socialists of strong economic determinist leanings like the William Appleman Williams group" (p. 315); on the same page LaFeber is specifically included in the "radical revisionist" category for making the (empirical) observation that it was Roosevelt rather than Truman who accepted French reoccupation of Indochina. As we turn the page, the now-seamless unanimity of the revisionists is illustrated with a quote from Noam Chomsky. The first nonhistorian to intrude the revisionist circle in Combs's account, Chomsky is chided for asking how historians could "regard America's leaders as merely mistaken, 'noble and virtuous, bewildered and victimized but not responsible, never responsible.'"

At the end of this same paragraph, however, Combs quite inadvertently says what he really thinks: that during the Vietnam years, "the revisionist view had acquired respectability, and historians found themselves compelled to deal with it in earnest." Later on (p. 333) he makes the same point: "The revisionist voice was never more than a minority voice in the historical community [*sic*], but . . . it could be ignored no longer by the leading diplomatic historians as it had been in the previous era."

That is, there are revisionists, and then there are historians. We found but one academic historian in the orthodox column and only one nonhistorian in the revisionist, but nonetheless there are people – "leading historians" would be a good guess – who decide what to ignore and what not to, what to respect and what not to. By a rhetorical inversion, made no less impressive to eager students by Combs's unconscious sleight of hand, the orthodox (non-)historian now strides forth as solid, respectable, and powerful; the revisionist (historian) as wild (Leninist when not "vehement and relentless in [his] Marxism" like Kolko – p. 327), not reputable (the revisionist is not really a historian), and of fleeting influence (destined to be ignored in any but an unusual era like Vietnam). Postrevisionism is barely a murmur in Combs's account, but encomiums to John Lewis Gaddis close chapter nineteen: He (together with Alonzo Hamby) did not do much to alter "the overall perspective" of a Kennan or a Lippmann, to be sure; instead, in Combs's view, "they simply elaborated upon it and *placed it more accurately in historical context*" (my emphasis).

To summarize Professor Combs's rectification of names: American officials are the authors of the orthodox historical position. Revisionists are people who reject this position, drawing on Marx and Lenin. Historians are the people who ignore the revisionists while elaborating upon and placing in historical perspective the orthodox view.

If this procedure exemplifies the thinking in a cubbyholing "book on the field," it also serves as an unwritten rule of politics and discourse in academe. The truth of the matter is – and I do not say this to single out Professor Combs, but to single out the profession – that all these labels (radical, revisionist, determinist, not to mention neo-Marxist or Leninist) signify not an intellectual approach to the subject, but a politics of censure. They signify not thinking, but fear. They signify exclusion.

In Heidegger's terms, these names "call" people for our memory, where they reside in a category called stigma. They connote Peter Novick's observation: "By aggregating a carefully selected list of writers – including the most vulnerable, and omitting the most circumspect, all Cold War revisionists could be tarred . . . and made collectively responsible" for the work of all those so designated.[31] They signify Chomsky's original, devastating insight in his famous article in 1966,[32] that most scholars do not wish to speak truth to power, they do not wish to hold our public servants responsible for their acts, but busy themselves instead in apologetics, in succoring the powerful and ignoring or blaming the victims. They tell us, in short, what a blight on the mind was the Cold War struggle.

For this essay I reread Lloyd Gardner's *Architects of Illusion*, to see if I still thought it was the fine book I did when I first read it in 1970. I noticed some scribbling in the margins by a young graduate student who wondered if Gardner had really read Kolko. Other than that, I would not change a word in the light of more than two decades passing, and I doubt that Lloyd would either.

31 Novick, *Noble Dream*, 450–51. That is, LaFeber's finely crafted history is no different than the rantings and near-plagiarism (apparent if you first read D. F. Fleming and I. F. Stone and then read him) of David Horowitz in *The Free World Colossus: A Critique of American Foreign Policy in the Cold War* (New York, 1965).

32 "The Responsibility of the Intellectuals," *New York Review of Books*, December 1966, reprinted in Chomsky, *American Power and the New Mandarins* (New York, 1967).

Disciple of the "Leninist" Williams that he was, Gardner cited Vladimir Ilyich exactly twice: first to show Lenin's affinity with William Bullitt's views on Germany; second to show his affinity with Listian political economy – according to Lord Keynes. Gardner's brilliant chapter on Kennan led me to reflect on what a masterful name George Frost brought to his doctrine: containment! Imagine, for an America to march outward and inherit Britain's role, and you mark it up for the *defense*. Imagine, a doctrine defining hegemony by what it *opposes*, obviating the necessity to explain to the American people what it is, and what its consequences will be for them.

Here is what Gardner says about the "orthodox" Cold War histories (p. 301): "Early books on the origins of the Cold War were little more than annotated collective memoirs of Americans who participated in that transition period. The historian's facts and conclusions had already been chosen for him before he began." What was the Cold War about, according to Gardner? When all was said and done, Eugene Meyer, head of the World Bank in 1947, got it right (p. 318): Meyer had "one conception," "the idea of America's having succeeded to the world power which was once Britain's."

John Lewis Gaddis as Educator

We begin with my well-thumbed and annotated copy of John Gaddis's first book.[33] I see by the furious marginal scribblings that I could write fifty pages on his first chapter. So let me be brief: By 1972, that is, two decades ago, Gaddis's postrevisionism was already well advanced, even if not yet named. The orthodox school no longer reigned: Schlesinger appears only in the bibliography, Feis comes in for mild criticism (p. 266n), Kennan comes in for long discussion and nuanced appreciation, but not without some demurrals (for example, p. 323). Orthodoxy is not questioned, it merely disappears; Gaddis has no sustained account of how his work differs from the old school.

33 John Lewis Gaddis, *The United States and the Origins of the Cold War, 1941–1947* (New York, 1972).

We do come to know that he differs from revisionists, however. Such people, we learn on the second page of the preface, have "performed a needed service," but alas, "their focus has been too narrow." Gaddis, to the contrary, has "tried to convey the full diversity" of the many other forces that helped determine American policy.

Kolko gets his dismissal in a footnote (pp. 50–51): He was wrong about the United States "deliberately set[ting] out to counteract" the Left on a world scale (in fact, when American authorities disarmed local resistance groups, according to Gaddis, they did so to secure communications and restore civilian governments); Kolko also "focuses too narrowly on economic factors." The conclusion has a somewhat longer discussion (pp. 357–58), emphasizing again the narrowness of an economic focus, the assumption (just like Combs) that a host of disparate revisionists subscribe to "the basic elements of the Williams thesis" (Barton Bernstein, Gardner, Kolko, LaFeber, Gar Alperovitz, David Horowitz). All neglect "the profound impact of the domestic political system on the conduct of American foreign policy." Yet Gaddis's book mostly lacks the evidence to make this last point, his central one: an unsystematic, nearly random survey of articles in the popular press, sermons by Fulton J. Sheen, speeches in the *Congressional Record*, etc., is no way to judge how "profound" was the impact of domestic politics.

Shortly we get this sentence: "One might, of course, argue that the political system reflected the economic substructure, and that American officials were unwitting tools of capitalism, but it is difficult to justify this assumption [*sic*] without resorting to the highly questionable techniques of economic determinism." Lest anyone fail to get the point, the next sentence begins, "At times, it seems as if revisionists do employ this approach."

Translated: Some people argue that the American political system reflected the economic substructure. What that means is that American officials were unwitting tools of capitalism. It is difficult to justify this assumption. (Untranslatable: justify Gaddis's attributed assumption? Which one? Or does he mean prove or disprove the relationships just posited?) To justify that highly questionable assumption you need to resort to the highly questionable "techniques" (methods, presumably) of "economic determinism" (not explained; it is assumed we all know what that is).

If my angst shows through, perhaps it is because we assign these books to young students. And here is the logic a student would pick up: Revisionists are people who focus narrowly on economics and believe in the capitalist clique/plot theory, which can only be justified by the highly questionable methods of the capitalist clique/plot methodology. And with that, you can dismiss a book like *The Politics of War* – which has at least one substantive (and often empirical or evidential) alternative judgment per page to Gaddis's book.

Rather than structure a debate (in which case a fair presentation of your opponent's ideas is obligatory) or try to refute the revisionist account with evidence (in which case Kolko merits a chapter, not a footnote), Gaddis's treatment is purely discursive, designed rhetorically to malign the enemy, close off debate, warn readers away, and, perhaps most important in 1972, return a generation of young people to the fold.

Having said all that, Gaddis's first book was a useful, thoughtful contribution to the debate on the Cold War, one that I always suggest to students. It just is not as good as Kolko's, which still stands today as the best single account of the origins of the Cold War.[34]

By 1983, "postrevisionism" had pushed up roots as such, with Gaddis's influential article – although, as he acknowledges, he did not invent the term.[35] It would be a fruitless exercise for me to indicate my points of disagreement with this text, because Lloyd Gardner and Warren Kimball did that so well at the

34 Gabriel Kolko, *The Politics of War: The World and United States Foreign Policy, 1943–1945* (New York, 1968). Merely to read Kolko's nine-page introduction is to behold a superior historian, whose views could only be reduced to "economic determinism" with great violence to his argument – one I fully share – that knowing the Cold War begins with "the history of the great shifting and reintegration of the world political system that occurred between 1943 and 1949."

35 John Lewis Gaddis, "The Emerging Post-Revisionist Synthesis on the Origins of the Cold War," *Diplomatic History* 7 (Summer 1983): 171–90. Gaddis says J. Samuel Walker first coined the term. Meanwhile, I do not know whether to put a pluperfect hyphen in the middle or not: Gaddis's title is "Post-Revisionist," but in the text it is "postrevisionist."

time.[36] But I would remind readers of Kimball's conclusion: Post-revisionism is "orthodoxy plus archives." It is also revisionism minus archives.

For much of the article, Gaddis cites recent work presumably proving this and disproving that about the origins of the Cold War, while calling for more "sophisticated" analysis of imperialism (for example, the work of Wolfgang Mommsen), and better understanding of the balance of power, the role of bureaucracies, internal "determinants" of foreign policy, comparative history, and "the impact of United States policies on foreign societies."[37] Gaddis seems to have grown more sophisticated himself by this time, writing freely of "the American empire."

In fact, the hermeneutics of censure and exclusion had not changed, and Gaddis's reading of the revisionists had become worse, more malevolent – akin to the Schlesinger and Feis position (these are Communists). The synonym for revisionists used throughout the text is "New Left." It was not only Combs in 1983 but also Gaddis in 1983 who lumped Williams together with other revisionists as those utilizing "the classical [*sic*] Leninist model of imperialism" (p. 172; see also pp. 175, 183).[38] While granting that revisionists were never monolithic, Gaddis proceeded to make them sound very much so, once again rounding up the usual suspects: Alperovitz, Bernstein, Gardner, LaFeber, Kolko, Williams (p. 173n). But as with Combs, Kolko begat distinction: "militantly revisionist" (p. 181n). The revisionist theory, according to Gaddis, had to do with an American "crisis of capitalism" necessitating exports and foreign markets, an "internally motivated drive for empire."[39] And, of course, the clique/plot soon trots along: Americans, the revisionists say, were "tricked by

36 "Responses to John Lewis Gaddis," ibid., 191–93, 198–200. Gardner placed before readers Robert A. Divine's masterful portrait of "the internationalists" (from his *Second Chance: The Triumph of Internationalism in America during World War II*), which ought to be read over and over to Gaddis, Leffler, and anyone else who thinks "national security" came before world economy.

37 Here (p. 187n) is where I come in for honorable mention, for having made "a start" in that direction with my first book, *The Origins of the Korean War*, vol. 1, *Liberation and the Emergence of Separate Regimes* (Princeton, 1981).

38 I do not know which would upset Bill Williams more – to be called New Left or Leninist. Probably the former.

39 Whereas, as we have just seen (footnote 34), Kolko located the crisis in the world system.

cynical but skillful leaders into supporting this policy of imperialism" (p. 173).

By the end of the article (p. 189) we learn that revisionists were tempted by the siren song of turning "history into an instrument of politics" and genuflected "as if by reflex, to the changing ideological fashions of the day." But now, Gaddis wrote, it was time to remember the impact historians have on society generally, thereby imposing "an obligation to get our history as straight as we can at the beginning." This was now being done by people who "put childish things away," by mature historians who had marched into the archives. Translation: Revisionists did not do history and do not use archives.[40]

Somehow the image of Bill Williams trimming his coat to the "ideological fashions of the day" in the late 1950s is almost as funny as the idea that Cold War historians ought to have gotten their history as straight as they could "at the beginning" – presumably 1947, when Beard scolded Truman for his new doctrine and Schlesinger fashioned "the vital center" while judging James Burnham's new book (calling for a unilateral American global empire) to be brilliant and perceptive. I prefer this formulation, recalling Gardner's reference to Eugene Meyer: "The beginning is, rather, the veil that conceals the origin."[41]

Postrevisionism has the same hermeneutics as the orthodox school: Schlesinger and Feis and Gaddis agree on what to call the revisionists. But perhaps they disagree on what constitutes orthodoxy. For Schlesinger, orthodoxy meant adherence to the position that the Cold War (for Americans) was "the brave and essential response of free men to Communist aggression." The minute he says it, of course, we recognize it as unhistorical: not a statement of fact, nor an idea, but a moral position that can function from 1776 to the Gulf War. It was "brave." These were

40 This judgment is also reflected in Gaddis's statement that "revisionism in one form or another will always be with us, and that is no bad thing, because the writing of history would be much less interesting without it." See Gaddis, "Emerging Post-Revisionist Synthesis," 189. Coming right after the sentence about revisionists turning history into an instrument of politics, the connotation is the same as Combs's: Historians do history, revisionists do something else; sometimes the revisionists cannot be ignored, most of the time they can.

41 Heidegger, *What is Called Thinking?* 152.

"free men." Passive and inert, they responded to "aggression," modified and made more threatening by the adjective "Communist." ("Essential" can have at least two meanings in this context, so I leave it uninterpreted.)[42] By the late 1960s, "Communist aggression" had become, at least for a younger generation, a signifier for Dean Rusk lying about Vietnam. And by 1983, *a fortiori*, no ambitious historian-of-the-field seeking consensus would be caught dead saying something quite so revealing.

So: an agreement on names, on "what things are called," but not on substance now characterized orthodoxy and postrevisionism. Why? Is it a matter of new primary materials, yielding new knowledge? Perhaps – but if so, that would explain 1983, but not 1993, when diplomatic historians tack to a zeitgeist now willing, in the face of the collapse of Western communism, to read the historical judgment of 1989–1993 back into the origins of the Cold War, thereby dusting off Schlesinger's position for a new generation.

It might be a matter of theory, in that Feis, Schlesinger, and Gaddis truly must have no idea what the multivariate school they call revisionism is talking about; to give a student *The Tragedy of American Diplomacy* and get back the notion that Williams uses Lenin's theories, or is a Communist, would merit an *F*. Perhaps for Feis at least, any theory linking American expansion to economic motivation sent him scurrying to the shelf where he kept Stalin's speeches (unless he was castigating Cordell Hull privately to Schlesinger). But even so, the grade is *F*; this is not theoretical debate so much as theory confronting a *tabula rasa*, theory against atheory, the failure of orthodoxy and postrevisionism to grasp theory (let alone present one themselves). Nor can the disagreement on substance be a matter of truth, that what was "true" in 1955 became "false" in 1967, partially true in 1983, and fully true in 1989. Merely to formulate this sequence is to conjure with "relativism," another bogeyman for historians.

42 As Novick notes, Schlesinger characterized this as the orthodox view, while allowing that he did not see the Cold War as "a 'pure' case of Russian aggression and American response" in his influential 1967 article. *Noble Dream*, 448. For the article see Arthur Schlesinger, Jr., "Origins of the Cold War," *Foreign Affairs* 46 (October 1967): 22–52. Today it reads like a pure exercise in discursive politics.

For the orthodox school, then, there must have been truth followed by the interruption of passion, whereupon truth outed again: precisely what Allan Bloom manifestly thought, for example, in his best-selling book where everything connoted by "the 60s" functions as foolish passion, when it is not original sin.[43] It is also what Gaddis thinks: Put your childish things away.

Gaddis found another "synthesis" in 1986, with a new name: "corporatism." Again, I cannot offer a better defense of corporatism than its advocates have done.[44] I merely want to replay one part of one paragraph (Gaddis, p. 358):

> At this point, I must confess to a certain perplexity as to just what corporatism is. . . . It is clearly not the Marxist-Leninist view of capitalism, because in the corporatist scheme of things the state is not solely the puppet of economic interests, but exerts some degree of control over them. At the same time, though, neither is corporatism a system of absolute state control, as is found in the Soviet Union today. . . . Corporatism does not connote simply the interest of the business community, because it includes as well the concerns of labor and agriculture.

In 1986 the literature on the relative autonomy of the capitalist state was all the rage, Thomas Ferguson had spelled out his theory on which industrial firms accommodated labor and which did not, and students of communism were beginning to understand the imbedded character of socialist states (for example China's "iron rice bowl"). If we cannot expect Gaddis to have read that literature, let alone Marx or Lenin on the state (grotesquely caricatured here), we might expect him to have read Beard, who, in *The Open Door at Home*, understood that American capitalism had not one but two broad tendencies (which he grouped under the industrial and the agrarian "theses"), each having a differential relationship to the state. Gaddis's perplexity, though, is surely American: If you look up "corporatism" in the *Encyclopedia of the Social Sciences*, you will find this: "See fascism." This perplexity did not keep Gaddis from finding a new wagon

43 Allan David Bloom, *The Closing of the American Mind* (New York, 1987) builds toward the penultimate chapter, "The Sixties," where the world-historical event of his (and presumably) our life takes place, in isolated, weatherbeaten Ithaca, New York.

44 See Gaddis, "The Corporatist Synthesis: A Skeptical View," and Michael J. Hogan, "Corporatism: A Positive Appraisal," *Diplomatic History* 10 (Fall 1986): 357–72.

with which to tether two broncos (revisionism and corporatism): "reductionism."

We find this term in Gaddis's next attempt to till the field, his 1990 critique of the "parochialism," "American exceptionalism," and "systematic innocence" of American historians who try to understand foreign relations.[45] "Our generalizations have not been as sophisticated as they might have been," he says, and then leaps to the attack against – are you ready? – Bill Williams! As if animated by some hidden reflex (to use his metaphor), Gaddis begins just as he did two decades earlier, just as he did a decade earlier: hiving off after the revisionists, now lumped under a new rubric: "reductionists." Williams, Gardner, LaFeber, McCormick – the whole gang tried to explain American behavior "almost exclusively in economic terms" (p. 407). If these horses were not in the barnyard Gaddis would have to buy them at auction, so intent is he on flogging them yet again (which is not to suggest they are in any sense "dead," quite the contrary). Is it possible that the entire field of diplomatic history would have nothing to talk about if Bill Williams had stayed in the United States Navy?

True to hermeneutic form, Kolko also gets his licks, disguised as praise: He had the "strength" to provide "an explicit methodological justification for reductionism" (p. 409). When I looked up the reference in *Politics of War* I could not imagine what Gaddis referred to, but then I understood that his comment was mimetic of the earlier claim that those who theorize the capitalist clique/plot use capitalist clique/plot methods.

There are new books, however, that "go beyond the reductionism of Williams and the corporatists" (the new conflation). Michael Hunt's *Ideology and U.S. Foreign Policy* is Gaddis's example, which we treat below. But alas, Hunt also wanders into reductionist pastures, by putting "race" at the center of the American worldview. (This is the part of his book that I particularly liked.) So, how to get beyond those who think in single categories – "whether economic, corporatist, or racist"?

Gaddis suggests "eclecticism," while noting its demerits (p. 409).

45 John Lewis Gaddis, "New Conceptual Approaches to the Study of American Foreign Relations: Interdisciplinary Perspectives," *Diplomatic History* 14 (Summer 1990): 405–23.

If "ours is, after all, a *social* science," can we not be as content as scientists doing quantum mechanics with "imperfect explanations"? Did Einstein not allow for a four-dimensional universe? Returning us to the corn field, Gaddis then discovers the "cropduster" approach to history, which certainly is not one-dimensional, even if it does get applied "in an indiscriminate way." Here (p. 410) the example is Emily Rosenberg's *Spreading the American Dream*, a good book he says, but weakened by adherence to "what she calls 'liberal-developmentalism,'" arguing that there could be (quoting Rosenberg) "no truly enlightened dissent against the ultimate acceptance of American ways, and this faith bred an intolerance, a narrowness, that was the very opposite of liberality."

True perhaps of the American role in Guatemala or Vietnam, Gaddis allows, but what about South Korea (he also mentions Japan and West Germany)? Here I must pass, if not pass out (history as Foucault's "fainting spell"), because forty years of American-supported state terror in South Korea is not sufficient evidence to make Professor Rosenberg's point. Soon Gaddis is back to flaying Williams (this time as an American exceptionalist) and assaying another brand of reductionism: dependency theory ("dependency theory . . . combine[s] the worst features of the 'reductionist' and 'crop-duster' approaches" – pp. 414–15). The first book illustrating this discussion is LaFeber's *Inevitable Revolutions* – and by now I imagine that LaFeber is ready to strap himself into that cropduster in *North By Northwest* and take a flyer over some Ohio cornfields.[46]

The most recent of Gaddis's essays (at this writing), his 1992 SHAFR Presidential Address,[47] arrived perfectly timed and miraculously appropriate for my conclusions on his work. As if I had scripted the essay, he begins again with Williams (first sentence). Even the title is taken from Williams. And then come the labels. But a dialectical reversal has occurred: Gaddis is the revisionist,

46 There are, let it be said, lots of good suggestions in this essay for what diplomatic historians ought to do to acquire theory: I assign the article to my students and have noticed them taking Gaddis to heart.

47 John Lewis Gaddis, "The Tragedy of Cold War History," *Diplomatic History* 17 (Winter 1993): 1–16.

Williams the champion of orthodoxy. *Tragedy* had now become "the conventional wisdom." The end of the Cold War, however, must cause historians "to jettison . . . orthodoxies, and long-cherished pearls of conventional wisdom" and become instead "post-Cold War revisionists" (p. 2).

The rest of the essay dwells mainly on what a monster Stalin was, how much citizens of the former Soviet Union now agree with Ronald Reagan that theirs was an "evil empire," how all the world's Communist leaders were just like Stalin ("Stalin's clones"), and just like Hitler ("murderous idealists"). Gaddis then executes another reversal, opining that "we have neglected Marx's approach to history."

The essay concludes by suggesting that at the dawn of the Cold War only the United States stood between civilization and mass murder, but that we still fail to see this because "we have allowed Williams's 'tragic' view of American diplomacy to obscure our vision" (p. 15). It is now our "universal frame of reference," our new "orthodoxy" and "conventional wisdom." Gaddis closes with this missive: "We need to regain a clearer sense of what real tragedy, in this less than perfect world, is all about. . . . [This] means, in the most fundamental sense, meeting our obligations as historians, which involve being honest not only about ourselves but about the environment in which we had to live. And it means according equal respect, as I fear we have not yet done, to *all* of the survivors, to *all* of the dead."

Thus, Bill Williams gets flogged whether he is a pro-Communist, a revisionist, a reductionist, an American exceptionalist, the author of the new orthodoxy in diplomatic history, or, by implication, a dishonest historian who ignored the millions who died at the hands of world-historical monsters. And we still wait, through two decades of writing, for John Lewis Gaddis to take one of his arguments seriously and try to refute it.

This latest essay struck me as an exercise in fiction. (No serious person can claim that Williams or his school represent orthodoxy.) It is akin to what I wrote about Schlesinger – we recognize the viewpoint as unhistorical: not a statement of fact, nor an idea, but a moral position, a political point, Gaddis getting his licks in on Williams again.

Of course, Hegel was right: There is a cunning to history, it has its utterly unexpected reversals and inversions. One of them is happening in 1993: We can now see that the end of the Cold War was not the victory of democracy and the market, the death knell of the Beard/Williams critique, the occasion for a definitive reckoning with "tragedy," the finale for monsters profligate in taking lives, or the end of history. It was a return, in the Old Testament sense: to history, to the imperial overstretch Beard warned against, and to ethnic and racial barbarism that was Hitler's distinctive form of evil.

But we can now take stock of Gaddis's critique and, as 1992 presidential candidate Ross Perot liked to say, clean out the barn. We can rectify names. Professor Gaddis is not a postrevisionist. He is an anti-revisionist, every bit as determined as 1950s historians like Schlesinger and Samuel Eliot Morison to plow their furrow and call it "mainstream," and to put Beard out to pasture:[48] It is just that Bill Williams is Gaddis's Beard. But Gaddis is not anti-orthodox.[49] The corpus of his work is entirely bereft of "thinking otherwise" about our leaders and their policies, or speaking truth to power (to cite a realist named Morgenthau). "Postrevisionism" in this case connotes not a synthesis, but a vain attempt at post–Indochina War consensus, marred continuously by the habits of stigma and exclusion. Fortunately it has not worked, and we may say of Williams in the 1990s what Hartz said of Beard in the 1950s, that when all is said and done "Beard somehow stays alive, and the reason for this is that, as in the case of Marx, you merely demonstrate your subservience to a thinker when you spend your time attempting to disprove him."[50]

48 See Novick, *Noble Dream*, 332–48.

49 And getting more orthodox all the time: see chapter two in *The Long Peace: Inquiries into the History of the Cold War* (New York, 1987), and Gaddis's (re-)discovery that the Cold War was about freedom vs. tyranny after all, in *The End of the Cold War: Its Meaning and Implications*, ed. Michael J. Hogan (New York, 1992), 24. The very idea of "a long peace" in the post-1945 period is obscene, given the millions of lives lost in Korea, Vietnam, and elsewhere. But I have criticized this notion in my contribution to the Hogan volume (pp. 87–89), and will say no more here.

50 Louis Hartz, *The Liberal Tradition in America* (New York, 1955), 28.

Michael Hunt as Educator

Professor Hunt is another keeper of the field, and may also be called a postrevisionist even if he does not use the term. His *Ideology and U.S. Foreign Policy*[51] seeks to show how both Kennan (orthodox) and Williams (revisionist) were acts in a long-running American drama. The curtain went up with Thomas Paine and his likes (1776 and all that), and the way Americans think about the world has not changed much since. This is a good and useful book, like Hunt's others.[52] It has an excellent chapter showing how Anglo-Saxon males from Ben Franklin to Dean Acheson discoursed authoritatively on the manifold demerits of every (other) racial and ethnic group and often despised the American mass democracy that they purported to champion.[53]

Hunt is good at revealing the moral side to Kennan's vaunted realpolitik, and the discussion of Williams and his students has better aim than the Combs/Gaddis buckshot. After a reasonable summary of Williams's account of "informal open door imperialism," Hunt says rightly that Williams "also drew, in a free-wheeling way, on Marxist theory" (pp. 9–10) and later notes the many differences among Williams's students (p. 200). Shortly, however, a fly buzzes into the ointment (p. 11):

> Though he claimed that the open-door ideology was the product of objective economic forces, little of *Tragedy* is devoted to demonstrating the link between the requirements of the economy and the concerns of policymakers. Indeed, Williams has on occasion seemingly rejected a clear-cut economic determinism. Ideas, he noted in a 1966 essay, may "originate as instruments of specific interests" only in time to "break their narrow bounds and emerge as broad, inclusive conceptions of the world."

51 Michael H. Hunt, *Ideology and U.S. Foreign Policy* (New Haven, 1987).

52 Michael H. Hunt, *The Making of a Special Relationship: The United States and China to 1914* (New York, 1983), for example, has an excellent account of the "open door constituency."

53 Even Germans and Swedes were too "swarthy" for Franklin – "Palantine boors," he hoped they would go back where they came from. Only Saxons entered his hallowed realm of "not swarthy" (p. 46). As for Acheson, "If you truly had a democracy and did what the people wanted, you'd go wrong every time" (p. 180).

Thus, Hunt finds Williams guilty of an "interpretive ambiguity": "*Tragedy* insists on the centrality of the connection, but... having made his concession [Williams] leaves us wondering how central economic self-interest is." This lapse, Hunt thinks, "deserves attention for the limitations it reveals about any conception of ideology that is tied tightly to economic self-interest." What is the source of Williams's confusion? It is his "excessively narrow conception of ideology colliding with his sensitivity to historical complexity."

Let me summarize Hunt's point: Williams rejected "a clear-cut economic determinism." Williams thereby escapes being hoisted on that petard. But this makes his theory confusing, in Hunt's understanding. Why is that? Because Williams's "excessively narrow conception of ideology" (which Hunt just said he did not have) has bumped into "historical complexity." Hunt goes on in the next paragraph to reject definitions of ideology that are "either dismissive [Kennan] or reductionist [Williams]." In sum: Williams is reductionist whether he is reductionist or not.

Hunt now invokes Clifford Geertz, Gabriel Almond, and Sidney Verba to make perfectly clear things ideological (p. 12). They help us to understand that ideology "is much more than simply a tool wielded in the self-interest of... symbols, values and beliefs." At the heart of their approach is, first, "a refusal to posit a single, simple reason for the origins and persistence of a particular ideology," for example, "the existence of a 'base' that determines the 'superstructure.'" Again, an inquiring student would conclude that with Williams you really get, when all is said and done, the capitalist clique/plot. Hunt, however, associates his own definition of ideology with Geertz and "culture."

Terry Eagleton's recent study entitled *Ideology* lists sixteen different meanings of this term in circulation at the moment and suggests that ideology is like halitosis: It is "what the other person has."[54] The notion that Marxist ideology is narrow, determinist, rigid, and susceptible to the capitalist clique/plot tendency, Eagleton argues (p. 4), "was elevated in the post-war period from a piece of popular wisdom to an elaborate [American] sociological

54 Terry Eagleton, *Ideology: An Introduction* (London, 1991), 1–2.

theory." (Eagleton's catalog of the myriad ways in which Marxists use "ideology" might help to educate the educators, if they would consent to read it.) The idea that ideology equals culture, he writes, is "the most general of all meanings of ideology," "unworkably broad and suspiciously silent on the question of political conflict" (p. 28). He locates Geertz's conception[55] not in Parsonian structural/functionalism as Hunt does, but in Hegel's lineage, kin to Althusser's structuralism (p. 151).

Perhaps of most interest for the orthodox/revisionist/postrevisionist discourse is Eagleton's observation that "exactly the same piece of language may be ideological in one context and not in another" (p. 9). When Hunt discusses Williams, he seeks to be fair and merely indicates his own misunderstanding. When we turn the page and arrive at Geertz, his implicit comparisons with Williams are purely ideological (in Eagleton's sense), and fully consonant with early postwar structural/functionalism – which postulated that the Soviets were "in the grip of ideology while the United States sees things as they really are."[56] Thus, although Hunt's brand of postrevisionism is far more nuanced and critical of American diplomacy than Gaddis's, conceptually and genealogically he ends up where Gaddis does: Mainstream historians do history, and revisionists do something else. Curiously, Louis Hartz nowhere intrudes Hunt's book. Yet Hartz's class analysis (no feudalism = no socialism, a nation born free in an unfree world) predicts America's inability to understand social revolutions, the subject of Hunt's chapter four. Instead, Hunt recommends Packenham's *Liberal America and the Third World* (pp. 2, 211), a Hartzian derivative distinctly inferior to the original. In his concluding chapter, Hunt begins with a quote from Marx ("men make their own history, but . . . they do not make it under circumstances chosen by themselves") and says "we would do well to accept the young Marx's promptings" (p. 171). This is the first time I have seen the young Marx located post-*Manifesto* (1852). But why not take the old Marx, of the *Grundrisse*, on America?

55 Hunt at first cites Geertz's "Thick Description: Toward an Interpretive Theory of Culture" (p. 215) and later (p. 227) the same text Eagleton uses, "Ideology as a Cultural System."

56 Eagleton, *Ideology*, 4.

> . . . a country where bourgeois society did not develop on the foundation of the feudal system, but developed rather from itself; where this society appears not as the surviving result of a centuries-old movement, but rather as the starting-point of a new movement; where the state, in contrast to all earlier national formations, was from the beginning subordinate to bourgeois society, to its production, and never could make the pretence of being an end-in-itself; where, finally, bourgeois society itself, linking up the productive forces of an old world with the enormous natural terrain of a new one, has developed to hitherto unheard-of dimensions . . . and where, finally, even the antitheses of bourgeois society itself appear only as vanishing moments.[57]

Jean Baudrillard's recent book entitled *America* is merely a "postmodern" embroidering of Marx's brilliant theme here, and of Hartz's idea that North America is not "exceptional" so much as fully bourgeois, the most advanced capitalist society, spinning out its telos in a vacuum called North America and in a time called the future. Frederic Jameson is correct to say that in the *Grundrisse* Marx understood the world market as "the ultimate of capitalism,"[58] with the United States occupying that horizon since the mid-nineteenth century (Perry "discovering" Japan in 1853, etc.). Here too, I might add, is an old Marx who does not seem to be speaking of capitalist clique/plots. Nay, he seems to be an American exceptionalist! In any case, he helps us see how classically *American* Hunt's book is.

Hunt is also a determined stable tender and sower of articles (usually in this journal) that seek to fertilize the field. His most recent missive announces the closure of a "long crisis" in diplomatic history, a crisis signified primarily by other historians pointing out the atheoretical, state-centric, archive-dependent, and conservative nature of the field.[59] If the crisis is not fully overcome, diplomatic history nonetheless "has reached a watershed whose significance justifies yet another act of introspection." If we have not perhaps reached a watershed, nonetheless such "stock-

57 Karl Marx, "Bastiat and Carey," in *Grundrisse: Foundations of the Critique of Political Economy*, trans. Martin Nicolaus (New York, 1973), 883–88.

58 Frederic Jameson, *Postmodernism, Or, The Cultural Logic of Late Capitalism* (Durham, 1991), xix.

59 Michael H. Hunt, "The Long Crisis in U.S. Diplomatic History: Coming to Closure," in this volume.

taking" (I like that metaphor) can supply "a clear and accessible picture of the major tendencies and developments" in the field for graduate students now in "training" (pp. 116–17). That is, the educator will now educate.

Although the footnotes indicate attention to social and cultural history, state theory, and the problems of language in the doing of history (Hunt is the one who criticizes the "Babel of labeling" in the field), the major thrust of the article is that the field has "fragmented" into "three fairly distinct yet interdependent realms of inquiry." We are assured that all are of "primary and equal importance." The next paragraph implies that some are more equal than others, however, because the "most imposing domain" remains U.S. foreign policy, and "the leading citizens" (no longer Combs's "leading historians," but close) are "realists." The leading "elder" in the domain? Kennan. This breathtaking departure is then followed by a standard rundown on the assumptions of the realists (pp. 117–18).

The second major fragmentation? You guessed it: well, not revisionists this time, but "progressives" – Beard to Williams to Gardner/LaFeber/McCormick, but a term also roping in the corporatists. Hunt lauds the postwar drivers for restarting the progressive wagontrain and the corporatists for reformulating and extending the progressive position – not without Hunt's sympathy and care for nuance. Nonetheless, the progressives ought to do better at "establishing greater congruence between economic developments and structure on the one hand and elite perspectives and policy on the other," and (like Gaddis) Hunt suggests that they ought to read more "neo-Marxist theory" – the footnote drawing us to Hunt's *Ideology*, work by Emily Rosenberg and Rosemary Foot, and Craig Murphy's Gramscian analysis of American hegemony (only the latter qualifies as remotely neo-Marxist).

What is the third domain that resolved the crisis of diplomatic history? It is not postrevisionism, but "international history" done multiarchivally. Those who have led the way here include trailblazers Archibald Cary Coolidge, Dexter Perkins, and William Langer, followed by John Fairbank and Ernest May. Some might see this flock as suspiciously Cambridge-centric, but in any case the trailblazers for this new third path did most of their multiarchival work in the interwar period, except for May. A major postwar accomplishment, Hunt writes, was the introduction of "area studies." This is something dear to my heart, but it is perhaps the most atheoretical of scholarly fields (by definition), and atheoretical certainly does not mean apolitical: We now have a stunning and disturbing book on area studies at Harvard and its complicity with the CIA and the FBI, focusing on the Russian Research Center, which served as model for other area studies programs.[60] This book will curl the hair of uninitiates and hardly make the case for a nonstate-centric international history.

When all is said and done, the new Harvard international history seems to mean multiarchival diplomatic history. Hunt goes beyond the Langer/Fairbank tradition, however, to suggest that international historians need better conceptualizations of "the notion of an 'American empire'" and recommends that we consult Mommsen's *Theories of Imperialism* for "conceptual orientation." He also argues for including "previously marginalized actors" and "ordinary people" in our work. If the latter is a welcome suggestion (one acted upon by many historians in recent years), Mommsen is no help: Far from conceptualizing American imperialism (on which he has only a handful of pages – and then only to talk about Williams's influence in Germany), he provides a text useful at best for undergraduates. Concerned with making distinctions between this theory and that, from Hobson to W. W. Rostow, Mommsen's book cannot compare to recent texts like Giovanni Arrighi's *Geometry of Imperialism.* The discussion of Marx is weak, "New Left" theories of imperialism are conflated with Maoist theories, and his grasp of Maoism is about as bad as any I have come across.[61]

60 Sigmund Diamond, *Compromised Campus: The Collaboration of Universities with the Intelligence Community, 1945–1955* (New York, 1992). Harvard takes up the first half of the book, whereupon Diamond moves on to Yale.

61 As soon as Mommsen quotes Marx from *The German Ideology* on the ever-widening scope of the world market, Mommsen says Marx "interpreted capitalism as a closed system" (p. 31). Mommsen has recourse to Karl Wittfogel on the superficiality of Maoism as a type of Marxism (p. 58), and then examines Mao's views on imperialism in the most cursory and even silly fashion, citing two 1930s texts and one broadside (not authored by Mao) from the *Beijing Review* circa 1963, ignoring the substantial work on Mao's worldview by John Gittings, Franz Schurmann, Stuart Schram, and many others whose books were available when this passage was written. When Mommsen finally gets to a few comments on Williams, it is to criticize

For someone who recommends area studies approaches, Hunt leaves the issue of language curiously unexamined – and here I mean foreign languages, for how else can one do multiarchival research? He does at one point ask why we need "some half dozen accounts of the origins of United States involvement in Vietnam when we have so little talent within our own ranks devoted to *translating the Vietnamese experience*" (emphasis added). Otherwise, the problem is not discussed – and yet it is crucial to any decent "international history," both as a matter of theory and practice.

If a personal note is not out of bounds in examining Professor Hunt as educator, my *Origins of the Korean War* is the lead example in footnote 32 of . . . of what? "The cultural-systems and social-structure orientations, with their strong anthropological and sociological points of view so appealing to those in Asian studies." This is one stable I never thought I would find myself roped into: I use the word "culture" as infrequently as anyone I know. I do not read many anthropologists, and the main "social-structural" interpretations in my work come from political economists like Barrington Moore, Karl Polanyi, and Charles Beard. But I do read Korean, and early on determined that there was absolutely no legitimate reason for privileging Americans at the expense of Koreans or vice versa: something that diplomatic history as a field in the United States must do as a matter of method, because (except for the European countries, and even here there are many exceptions) most practitioners cannot read the languages of the countries they study in relation to American diplomacy, and all rely mostly on American documentation. The practice of using materials written by the objects of American policy cannot be separated from the theory of not privileging one group of human beings as against another. Finally, note Hunt's words: We need people to *translate* the Vietnamese experience. Translate it into what? English, as a service to diplomatic historians?[62] Into American conceptions of the world?

his theory as narrow, by which he means that Williams locates imperial policy "chiefly in the economic field" (p. 93) – that is, Hunt's much-reiterated point. See Wolfgang J. Mommsen, *Theories of Imperialism*, trans. S. Falla (New York, 1977).

62 Paradoxically, it is unfair to single out Hunt here, even though these are his words, because he is one of the few diplomatic historians who reads Chinese fluently. My comment is apt for the field as a whole, but not at all for him.

The conclusion to Hunt's article, that the theoretical crisis is now "transformed" by the new "three-realm field" cannot be sustained: Michael Hunt is still part of the problem. Hunt's work is also the solution, however, because it is not given to censure and exclusion, is admirably multiarchival and multilingual, and mostly restricts itself to what ought to be our only realm of activity: thought.

History in the Imperfect Tense

We do have a good example of a proper "postrevisionist" text in Melvyn P. Leffler's new book.[63] Showing no concern whatsoever for the debates over orthodoxy and revisionism and not claiming to be postrevisionist, Leffler nonetheless seeks a synthesis that overcomes both, while summing up their insights: a big leap, this attempted *aufhebung*, and I will have some criticism. But few other books so aptly reflect what historians and political scientists have learned about the Cold War in the past quarter-century. *A Preponderance of Power* is testimony to the potential of cumulation as a way to knowledge in diplomatic history, and it is difficult to categorize in our earlier genealogy – although Leffler supports Gaddis's arguments about economics serving national security, not vice versa.[64]

Deeply researched and clearly written, Leffler's account is reasonably free of bias: He takes good work where he finds it. Furthermore, his biases come, as they ought to, from his approach to the subject, his interpretation, his worldview. He is averse to labeling and cubbyholing, just as his own contributions in this book cannot readily be summarized in a pithy phrase.

If we disinter the labels for a moment, the orthodox school will find little comfort in Leffler's account. Comfort comes only with his agreement on American goals in Western Europe and Japan, and with his somewhat dewy-eyed and distinctly time-bound conclusion.[65] Otherwise, he argues, Truman administration offi-

63 Melvyn P. Leffler, *A Preponderance of Power: National Security, the Truman Administration, and the Cold War* (Stanford, 1992).

64 See Gaddis, "Emerging Post-Revisionist Synthesis," 173–75, for comparison.

65 That is, it could only have been written in the immediate aftermath of the events of 1989 and 1990, before the Gulf War, Yugoslavia, and the mounting evidence that the United States wants to continue the military-industrial complex that sustained

cials consistently distorted Soviet behavior, refused to negotiate, ignored Stalin's conservatism, and deployed an inflated Soviet threat for its uses in getting the other things they wanted (just as Mary Kaldor has argued, although he does not cite her work).[66] Soviet actions, he concludes, were "contradictory," "reactive," "defensive," and "cautious" (except in the 1948 Berlin crisis); their capabilities were "limited" and the United States always knew that – as was reflected in continuous judgments from 1945 through 1952 that the USSR was not ready for war. Truman's policies ranged from the wise and prudent to the regrettable in the First World, and to the foolish and disastrous in the Third World – where Truman and his advisers misconstrued anticolonial movements as Soviet tools, leading to the interventions in Korea and Vietnam and to odious associations with one dictator after another.

Revisionists will be happy with many of Leffler's substantive points, besides those above: that containment arrived early, "before Kennan," and that officials quickly extended it to global dimensions; that the United States sought to reform rather than demolish European colonialism, and that it utterly misconstrued revolutionary nationalism; that the United States tolerated any sort of fascist collaborator or reactionary dictator as long as he was reliably anti-Communist; and that the road to Korea and Vietnam was paved with bad intentions to revive Japan's economic relationship with its Asian periphery.

Democracy and the American public play barely any role in Truman administration deliberations; this structured absence in Leffler's book will stun many readers – if not revisionists – the moment they think about it. The Truman Doctrine, the Marshall Plan, NATO, Korea – all these decisions went forward with remarkable ease, with domestic opposition almost always exaggerated

containment – but directed this time against Third World "renegades" and, implicitly, Germany and Japan. The conclusion also strikes one as perhaps written for another book – for example, in the "Wise Men" section (pp. 499–502), where Leffler sums up what he takes to be wise policy: "Truman administration officials grasped the nature of the Soviet threat," had "a shrewd understanding of Soviet weaknesses," etc., which directly contradicts much of what he said earlier.

66 See in particular Leffler's excellent account of the famed Clifford-Elsey report of 1946 – "a totally misleading rendition of Soviet capabilities," combined with "incredibly disingenuous" judgments about Soviet perceptions (pp. 130–38).

in the literature (according to Leffler). "Postrevisionism" à la John Gaddis is evident throughout the account, but Gaddis also comes in for significant criticism (mostly in the footnotes).

Revisionists are honored in a time-lapse breach, however. Much of Leffler's evidence comes from historians who have toiled in the archives on one regional conflict or another and who published in the 1970s and 1980s; the central figures who created what is called "revisionism" and whose ideas stimulated much of this research are mostly absent. Fleming, Williams, Gardner, LaFeber, and Kolko are not in the index; Kolko and Gardner are in the bibliography but Fleming and Williams are not, and from LaFeber we find but two articles. While synthesizing the empirical insights of a generation of younger historians, Leffler whites out the conceptions that lay behind them, the theoretical searchlights that enabled them to discover and interpret the documents they found in the archives. This turns out to be a significant absence, going to the heart of why *A Preponderance of Power* is not yet our solution, but also remains part of the problem.[67] However learned Leffler is in the newer literature – and he is very much so, an excellent reader – he is atheoretical and depends on discursive techniques to advance his argument. He is also ahistorical, in the specific sense that he has taken a slice of time, called it the origins of the Cold War, and thus isolated it from what went before and came after.[68]

What is his argument? That Truman's policymakers sought a "preponderance of power" in the postwar world, driven by geostrategic conceptions of the relationship of national power to "control of resources, industrial infrastructure, and overseas bases" (p. 12). These conceptions were deeply influenced by fears and

67 Professor Leffler, in his critique of this essay (Melvyn Leffler to Bruce Cumings, 6 August 1992), found it preposterous that I would accuse him of ignoring Williams, Kolko, and the others, because their work has informed his throughout his career. His earlier work certainly shows their influence, but in *Preponderance* he fails to point out that they etched the agenda for the more recent Cold War history that he frequently cites. Furthermore, the basic thrust of *Preponderance* is to grant that they were right on a number of crucial issues, while denying that they were right about the basic motivations of American foreign policy.

68 Dr. Leffler also complained mightily in his letter to me about this criticism, as perhaps any historian would. He argued that given his earlier work on the interwar years, it was a cheap shot. That he is a fine historian who knows the interwar period is beyond doubt, but that does not relieve *Preponderance* of my criticism.

uncertainties about the postwar world, leading to prudent action here, foolish action there. "Economic interests often reinforced geostrategic imperatives and ideological predilections," he writes in a key passage (pp. 14–15), but were still subordinate to "concerns about correlations of power . . . [that] far exceeded" worries about "the well-being of the American economy." Nor were "organizational imperatives" the mainspring of national security policies; they merely "buttressed" them. Partisan politics reinforced rather than divided Washington (liberal anticommunism was just as "fierce" as the conservative variety, if more discriminating), and the public was "malleable."

So, there we have it – a concise statement farming out other interpretations: It was not economics, it was not ideology, it was not bureaucracy, it was not democracy or partisan conflict that shaped Truman's policies. All these things were present, but geostrategic imperatives and inchoate fears were more important. The narrative structure reinforces these ideas with frequent constructions of apprehension, frustration, anxiety, fear, alarm, fright, dread, and horror. The theme is reified throughout the text, making the reader think that Acheson was just as apprehensive about Europe's survival in 1952 as Kennan was in 1945.

I have sought to articulate my position on these questions in my recent book, but suffice it to say that I would exactly reverse the sequence: "Geostrategic imperatives and ideological predilections often reinforced economic interests." It is as simple as Acheson saying "defense perimeter" in public and "great crescent" in private, as complex as "economic interest" being irreducible to "the well-being of the American economy" or the percentage of exports in U.S. production (Leffler, pp. 160–61, 316–17). That may have been true of early and vulgar revisionist accounts, but the sophisticated work is about world economy, not the American economy. Was the health of the world economy less important to Acheson, Lovett, and McCloy than geostrategy and their fears about the Soviets? I do not see how they can be read this way.

Leffler is not sure either. Although his theme is firm at beginning and end, many readers will find parts of his account indistinguishable from those that place world economy first (for example the discussion of an open world and loans to Britain – pp. 61–62). An early restatement of his theme inadvertently elides the economic ("Fear and power – not unrelenting Soviet pressure, not humanitarian impulses, not domestic political considerations, not British influence – were the key factors shaping American policies toward the Kremlin" – p. 51). Take this causal statement, about Russia's place in the postwar world economy: "Fear inspired American officials to prod the Kremlin to accept an open sphere" (p. 54). Why fear and not access to Eastern markets or opposition to state-controlled economies or a desire to link semi-peripheral Eastern Europe with industrial Western Europe (all of which are mentioned in the text)?

Whether geostrategy or world economy was more important can also be posed as whether Kennan or Acheson was more important. Leffler's conception is very close to Kennan's: Advanced industrial structure is central to war-making power, and war-making power is the source of realpolitik conflict, which can only be resolved through strategies seeking a balance of power. But, as I have argued, Kennan never understood his boss, who had a Wall Street internationalist's conception of what made the world go 'round – money, investment, a hidden hegemonic hand.

For Acheson, the leitmotif of the 1940s was the long cycle of British decline and American advance, with "the fifteen weeks" in 1947 marking not the defense of free peoples against Soviet aggression so much as the final passage of the baton from London to Washington. Korea – to take something close to my heart – was, for Acheson, not Kennan's suppurating black hole, but something useful to Japanese industrial revival, a twinkling star in a "great crescent" linking Tokyo with Alexandria. The Korean War was not North Korea's response to the great crescent, but something useful for NSC-68 and military Keynesianism, the pump Acheson found in 1950 that finally primed not the American economy, but the allied economies – and thus the world economy. The Vietnam War was important to shore up the periphery throughout the world, but not more important than the run on the dollar in 1968: So, Acheson decided, the war ought to be shut down.

Kennan the realist was to Acheson, what Henry Kissinger the

realist was to Nelson Rockefeller and then Richard Nixon, what Zbigniew Brzezinski was to David Rockefeller and then Jimmy Carter: realpolitik engineer for an architecture never fully articulated. So was the elected president: As Leffler notes, Acheson "almost never discussed fundamental objectives with the President." Not for Harry Truman, the apprehension of imponderables.

Acheson had an easy and hearty contempt for definitions of security policy that ignored world economy, most of which came from an American military that, in the early postwar period, destroyed several forests to produce the endless reams of strategic surveys, requirements estimates, redefinitions of vital interests, position papers, departmental and interdepartmental committee reports, etc., that now clutter the archives and that seem to have elicited inordinate attention from Mel Leffler. Acheson's papers are a clear, polished lens that illumines the postwar world; Kennan's papers give you that world through a glass darkly; the Pentagon still has not come to a conclusion on its nature.

The competing doctrines of the Cold War period are just so much cut forest, unless they are linked to constituencies within and without the state: Constituencies generate doctrines, and doctrines generate constituencies (this was Franz Schurmann's insight). Rollback was the strategy generated by a dying isolationism and an always-strong American unilateralism and nationalism. NSC-68 was about military Keynesianism, it was about generating constituencies that came to make up the national security state, the required "system maintenance" (to speak structural-functionally) for the extraordinary and unprecedented commitments that the Truman administration had taken upon itself. NSC-68 was about the end of the atomic monopoly, it was about the absence of bipartisanship in the wake of the victory of the Chinese revolution, it was about how to jumpstart the advanced economies, it embodied the year-long debate in Washington over containment and rollback, and finally, it was about fear. (It was not about geostrategy, for there was none worthy of the name in that overblown document.)

Leffler's lack of concern for hegemonic advance and decline is part of the ahistoricity of his text. It is the same with his argument about the Marshall Plan. Whereas Michael J. Hogan makes

World War II into an ellipsis, an interruption in the continuity of corporate capitalist innovation since Hoover in the 1920s, the word capitalism barely intrudes Leffler's text – let alone different ways to organize it. In his implicit refutation of Hogan (pp. 160–61), he says that the "economic motivations behind the Marshall Plan were secondary" but "not unimportant." Economic motivation, however, is reduced to whether the U.S. economy had to export to ensure prosperity. Missed is the substance of the corporatist thesis: for Ferguson, the political coalition at the top of high-technology and labor-accommodating multinational firms that made the second New Deal and took the world as its oyster; for Hogan, the new, organized capitalism of technocratic instrumentality, transnational coordination, bureaucratic planning, associative politics, and state regulation that straddled both sides of World War II.

Leffler gives us the world according to Truman's advisers, without the theoretical underpinning and with, in my view, almost no sense of the obstacles that they faced at home – remnant isolationism, a restive right wing, strong and recalcitrant labor, Republicans out of power for a generation, the nationalism of firms producing for the American market, conflicting strategies for dealing with communism at home and abroad, expansionist Asia-firstism with its deep roots in the body politic, Eastern Establishment internationalism with its correspondingly shallow political roots. There is little politics in the book: Truman's advisers generally get their way. As for the obstacles they faced abroad, it is difficult to figure them out if you visit no foreign archives.[69] Thus, we get little sense of the true dimensions of the crisis that gripped Washington beginning in 1949 and that I have written much about elsewhere. The result is a book that does not tell us much that specialists on the Cold War did not already know, while frequently reinterpreting many disputes in the literature in a manner far more conservative, I think, than was Leffler's original intent.[70]

Tom McCormick did not go into the archives to figure out this

69 I am indebted to Walter LaFeber for pointing out to me that Leffler used not one foreign archive or manuscript source.

70 I am indebted to Michael Hogan for a discussion on this point.

period, but he did some reading through the lenses of world-system theory. He came out with a better rendering of the 1949–50 crisis than we find in Leffler, one that interrogates the idea that evidence is only found in the archives. But let us stop here with Mel Leffler's book, and then go on with McCormick. *Preponderance of Power* is a very good book. It is immensely informative. It is a postrevisionist success. It is worthy of a much longer appreciation and critique than I can bring to bear here. I fling no Montana frisbees. It needed more theory.

It seems to me that the end of the Cold War in Europe demolishes a number of academic theories: most of all the theory of totalitarianism, certainly game theory as applied to international relations, even the sanctified realpolitik doctrine of rationally known national interest, which utterly fails to explain Gorbachev turning a global superpower into a regional basket case – perhaps our most extraordinary example of a world ending not with a bang but a whimper. But the demise of the Cold War leaves world-system theory reasonably intact, I think, and therefore – Gaddis notwithstanding – leaves Williams intact.[71] Indeed, Immanuel Wallerstein predicted the crisis of "actually existing" socialism and its future dependency on Western Europe at least as far back as 1984 – it was the wrong system, in the wrong place, at the wrong time.[72]

To return to the origins of the Cold War and McCormick, however, if 1947 was the critical watershed year, then all the West had to do was hold Kennan's containment lines long enough (until the 1980s let us say), whereupon the other side would collapse and the United States and its allies would win. But 1947 was only the end of the beginning. Containment was unstable, both in the world and at home (in the United States). The period 1947–1950 was the determining "crisis of the new order" (McCormick's words),[73] because vast reaches of the globe were in

71 Williams was, of course, not a formal "world-system" theorist, but every chapter of *Tragedy* has some grist for the world-system mill.

72 I refer to his formal remarks at a panel at the Annual Meeting of the American Political Science Association, Washington, 1984; Tom Ferguson and I shared the platform with him.

73 Thomas J. McCormick, *America's Half-Century: United States Foreign Policy in the Cold War* (Baltimore, 1989), 72–98.

the turmoil of decolonization, the core industrial economies needed primary resources, and therefore the passive/active dialectic of containment and rollback in Soviet-American competition had to be extended to the Third World. Here the much-maligned Mao (I refer to his 1947 ideas on bloc conflict in the "intermediate zone") was a superior theorist to Kennan or Acheson or Stalin, all of whom expressed disdain for and caution about Third World entanglement (but only Kennan escaped it, by hiving off to Princeton in 1950).

The years 1947–1950 were also the determining period for the American home front. The turn to the periphery necessitated permanent empire, what Harry Elmer Barnes called "perpetual war for perpetual peace," what Charles Beard in 1947 called "an unlimited program of underwriting, by money and military 'advice,' poverty-stricken, feeble and instable [*sic*] governments around the edges of the gigantic and aggressive Slavic Empire" – whereby, in the process, "the domestic affairs of the American people became appendages to an aleatory expedition in the management of the world." Beard counseled "a prudent recognition and calculation of the limits on power," lest the United States suffer "a terrible defeat in a war" – like the "wrecks of overextended empires scattered through the centuries."[74] (Presumably that has nothing to say to us in 1993.)

NSC-68 and the Korean War exemplified the new strategy and the First-Third World struggle reinterpreted as East-West crisis that made the strategy appear correct and that got Congress and the American people to hold still for Beard's "expedition." Thus arose the national security state and the military-industrial complex at home and a far-flung imperial structure abroad.

I would also assert that the crisis of 1949–50 can make sense of some mysteries that have long gripped the field of American history: orientations toward the Old World and the New, New England versus the frontier, "Europe-first" versus "Asia-first," and that subject no historian of the United States seems ever to tire of discussing, "exceptionalism." A recent issue of the *American*

74 Charles Austin Beard, *Roosevelt and the Coming of the War* (New York, 1947) 580, 592–93, 597.

Historical Review carries a lead article in which Ian Tyrrel argues that a transnational or world-system perspective can help American historians overcome their addiction to exceptionalism, and a commentary in which Michael McGerr responds that Tyrrel got it all wrong.[75] I found it rather amazing that the *AHR* should find this debate worthy of prominent feature, because the "new transnational history," as it is called, has been "new" since at least 1974, when Wallerstein and Schurmann published their books: And if I may say so, Tyrrel's discussion of both the "new history" and American exceptionalism seemed to me quite pedestrian.

Tyrrel nonetheless has a point, and the way I would put it is that a world economy perspective can do for American history what the study of America's role in the world did for Bill Williams: "Williams discovering America, almost like Columbus," in Warren Susman's brilliant observation.[76] Williams reading America from the outside in, to put it another way. But to see Louis Hartz as the grand American exceptionalist, as Tyrrel and others do, is to get things exactly backwards: Hartz was a *European* exceptionalist, that is, a devotee of what Allan Bloom and others have exalted as "The West" who just happened to grow up in Omaha. He spent his life trying but failing to find Europe's replication in America – could not even find it in Harvard yard (in spite of the brilliance of its international historians), and ended up roaming the British museum.

Louis Hartz had the idea, in other words, that the New World was not Europe: To him the United States was a fragment and an implant that had only a partial understanding of the European project; likewise, the states of South America were a new amalgam of Iberian and indigenous influences. A Lockean liberalism never fully known, understood, or realized – now there is an idea that can help us explain the genealogy of American diplomatic history: its atheoretical character, its lack of intellectualism, its unconscious affinity for state interpretations, its peculiarly American

75 Ian Tyrrel, "American Exceptionalism in an Age of International History," and Michael McGerr, "The Price of the 'New Transnational History,'" *American Historical Review* 96 (October 1991): 1031–55, 1056–67.

76 Warren Susman, "The Smoking Room School of History," in *History and the New Left: Madison, Wisconsin, 1950–1970*, ed. Paul Buhle (Philadelphia, 1990), 44.

lack of connectedness to what European intellectuals think about. It is also typically American in being ahistorical: not about America, of course, but about America in the world, and the world in America. Nietzsche, just after talking about the cattle,[77] linked ahistoricity to a childlike state, to the "plastic power" of people, to human creativity, to the very capacity of those unencumbered by the past *to act*, in a passage full of meaning for this unhistorical nation we live in. But that is where I started, in the barnyard.

My purpose in this essay was not to revisit the shootout at the OK Corral, but to rustle up the sagebrush and stir up the chickencoop. In fact, I do not believe in revisionism, let alone postrevisionism, let alone antirevisionism masquerading as post-revisionism. Michael Hunt is right: This is a Babel of labels. These terms merely give us the genealogy, the descent, and the moral and political valence of Cold War scholarship.

History is not a narrative of the *it was* – "what actually happened"; nor is it a Jack Webb quest after "the facts" – which never speak for themselves; it is a discipline dedicated to the eternal recurrence of revision: arguments, debates, and controversies about "what exactly did happen, why it happened, and what would be an adequate account of its significance."[78] If diplomatic history was the most conservative tendency in the history profession before the Vietnam debates, its subject – America's role in a non-American world – remains the most vulnerable to conflating objective truth with patriotic homily. Of all branches of history it is closest to the state, particularly in a state/empire. Therefore, the diplomatic historian's code ought always to be this: "The state never has any use for truth as such, but only for truth which is useful to it."[79] That code implies a commitment "to think otherwise," while living in the imperfect tense of history.

77 Nietzsche, *Untimely Meditations*, 62–63.

78 Ian Jarvie, quoted in Robert A. Rosenstone, "History in Images/History in Words: Reflections on the Possibility of Really Putting History onto Film," *American Historical Review* 93 (December 1988): 1176.

79 Nietzsche continues, "more precisely for anything whatever useful to it whether it be truth, half-truth, or error." See "Schopenhauer as Educator," in *Untimely Meditations*, 190.

3

New Approaches, Old Interpretations, and Prospective Reconfigurations

MELVYN P. LEFFLER

Read almost any assessment of the state of academic history and the diagnosis appears grim. Historians have been writing more specialized and sophisticated accounts of ordinary people, social groups, local communities, and diplomatic events than ever before, but hardly anyone is interested in them. Whereas history was once the common coin of intellectual and political discourse, Thomas Bender notes, "today's journalists, writers, and intellectuals, to say nothing of political leaders, seem little inclined to attend to the work of our profession."[1]

Since Bender wrote those words, the situation has worsened. The debates over multiculturalism and political correctness augment public skepticism and divide our own ranks. Postmodernist writers and the practitioners of cultural studies question our capacity for objectivity, rejoice in deconstruction, and celebrate fragmentation. Rather than finding inspiration for an "empirical" or "scientific" history espoused by Leopold von Ranke or Karl Marx, they look to Jacques Derrida and Michel Foucault. They are concerned with discourses rather than subjects, structures rather than actions, process rather than agency, the construction of meaning rather than the definition of experience. "History," write Joyce Appleby, Lynn Hunt, and Margaret Jacob, "has been shaken right down to its scientific and cultural foundations at the

This is an expanded version of my SHAFR presidential address delivered at the convention of the American Historical Association in Chicago on 7 January 1995. I want to thank Peter Onuf, Bill Walker, Marvin Zahniser, and Phyllis K. Leffler for their constructive criticisms of a previous draft of this paper.

1 Thomas Bender, "Wholes and Parts: The Need for Synthesis in American History," *Journal of American History* 73 (June 1986): 120.

very time that those foundations themselves are being contested."[2] But a reaction is also visible. Some historians lament the descent into discourse; others decry the sentimentalism of culture.[3] Almost every subdiscipline bemoans its marginality. In her recent presidential address to the American Historical Association, Louise Tilly calls upon social historians to focus on "connections between structure and action, individuals and processes, the past and the present, and settings distant in space."[4] Discussing "The Future of American History," John Higham emphasizes that "the problem of connecting subnational particulars with supranational patterns" has become perhaps the major issue for American historians. And to solve this problem and write a compelling synthesis of American history, Higham continues, it is necessary "to deal with centers as well as margins and peripheries."[5]

The plea for synthesis echoes through the profession, and it takes interesting forms. William Leuchtenburg calls for a reinvigoration of the study of politics and public policy; Peter Stearns urges an integration of social history and international relations; Thomas Bender pleads for an analysis of public culture, meaning "the interplay of various groups . . . and the larger, heterogeneous, and contested political and cultural realm of the nation"; Theda Skocpol tells us to bring the state back in; Melvyn Dubofsky admonishes that we focus on the role of government as well as on relationships of power in the political economy; John Higham beckons for the reconstruction of a genuine national history, "a history of the connections through which state and society have defined one another and dealt with change"; and Carl Degler encourages systematic comparisons with other countries.[6]

2 Joyce Appleby, Lynn Hunt, and Margaret Jacob, *Telling the Truth About History* (New York, 1994), 1. See also Lynn Hunt, ed., *The New Cultural History* (Berkeley, 1989); and John E. Toews, "Intellectual History after the Linguistic Turn," *American Historical Review* 92 (October 1987): 879–907.

3 Bryan D. Palmer, *Descent into Discourse: The Reification of Language and the Writing of Social History* (Philadelphia, 1990); Lawrence T. McDonnell, "'You are too Sentimental': Problems and Suggestions for a New Labor History," *Journal of Social History* 17 (Summer 1984): 629–54.

4 Louise A. Tilly, "Connections," *American Historical Review* 99 (February 1994): 1.

5 John Higham, "The Future of American History," *Journal of American History* 80 (March 1994): 1290, 1305.

6 William E. Leuchtenburg, "The Pertinence of Political History: Reflections on the Significance of the State in America," *Journal of American History* 73 (December 1986): 585–600; Peter Stearns, "Social History and History: A Progress Report,"

If diplomatic historians listen closely we should hear that we are being summoned to play a central role in the future writing of American history. We should realize that we are uniquely positioned to deal with many of the issues that other historians deem central to an understanding of the American experience. We deal with power, politics, and the state.[7] We deal with social groupings within the national polity and with the beliefs and sentiments of ethnic minorities.[8] We deal with myths, symbols, images, and the formation of collective identity.[9] We deal with

Journal of Social History 19 (1985): 330–32; Bender, "Wholes and Parts," 132; Peter B. Evans, Dietrich Rueschmeyer, and Theda Skocpol, eds., *Bringing the State Back In* (New York, 1985); Melvyn Dubofsky, *The State and Labor in Modern America* (Chapel Hill, 1994); Higham, "Future of American History," 1304; Carl Degler, "In Pursuit of an American History," *American Historical Review* 92 (February 1987): 1–12.

7 See, for example, some of the important literature on the formation of early American foreign policy: Samuel Flagg Bemis, *The Diplomacy of the American Revolution* (Bloomington, 1937); Frederick W. Marks III, *Independence on Trial: Foreign Affairs and the Making of the Constitution* (Baton Rouge, 1973); Alexander DeConde, *Entangling Alliance: Politics and Diplomacy under George Washington* (Durham, 1958); Paul A. Varg, *Foreign Policies of the Founding Fathers* (East Lansing, 1963); and J. C. A. Stagg, *Mr. Madison's War: Politics, Diplomacy, and Warfare in the Early American Republic, 1783–1830* (Princeton, 1983).

8 The "Wisconsin School" has provided much information on the attitudes of business, farm, labor, and other social organizations. See, for example, Thomas J. McCormick, *China Market: America's Quest for Informal Empire, 1893–1901* (Chicago, 1967); Lloyd Gardner, *Economic Aspects of New Deal Diplomacy* (Madison, 1964); Walter LaFeber, *The Cambridge History of American Foreign Relations*, vol. 2, *The American Search for Opportunity, 1865–1913* (New York, 1993); and Patrick J. Hearden, *Independence and Empire: The New South's Cotton Mill Campaign, 1865–1901* (Dekalb, IL, 1982). For similar work outside of the Wisconsin School see, for example, Joan Hoff Wilson, *American Business and Foreign Policy, 1920–1933* (Lexington, KY, 1971); and William H. Becker, *The Dynamics of Business-Government Relations: Industry and Exports, 1893–1921* (Chicago, 1982). For ethnicity see, for example, Morrell Heald and Lawrence S. Kaplan, eds., *Culture and Diplomacy: The American Experience* (Westport, 1970); Louis L. Gerson, *The Hyphenate in Recent American Politics and Diplomacy* (Lawrence, 1964); Edward Cuddy, *Irish-American and National Isolationism, 1914–1920* (New York, 1976); Wilson D. Miscamble, "Catholics and American Foreign Policy from McKinley to McCarthy: A Historiographical Survey," *Diplomatic History* 4 (Summer 1980): 223–40; John B. Snetsinger, *Truman, the Jewish Vote, and the Creation of Israel* (Stanford, 1974); and Lorraine Lees, "National Security and Ethnicity," *Diplomatic History* 11 (Spring 1987): 113–25.

9 See, for example, Albert K. Weinberg, *Manifest Destiny: A Study of Nationalist Expansionism in American History* (Baltimore, 1935); Frederick Merk, with Lois Bannister Merk, *Manifest Destiny and Mission in American History: A Reinterpretation* (New York, 1963); Akira Iriye, *Across the Pacific: An Inner History of American-East Asian Relations* (New York, 1967); Harold R. Isaacs, *Images of Asia: American Views of China and India* (New York, 1972); Marilyn B. Young, *The Rhetoric of Empire: American China Policy, 1895–1901* (Cambridge, MA, 1968); Robert Rydell, *All the World's A Fair: Visions of Empire at American International Expositions, 1876–1916* (Chicago, 1984); and Walter L. Hixson, "'Red Storm Rising': Tom Clancy Novels and the Cult of National Security," *Diplomatic History* 17 (Fall 1993): 599–614.

the transnational influence of multinational corporations, labor unions, and philanthropic organizations.[10] We deal with the transmission abroad of our consumer culture and our ideas of personal freedom and a private market economy.[11]

Others think of us as on the periphery, but we should not marginalize ourselves. We need to think more self-consciously about how to connect with the larger enterprise of writing American history. I think we can make these connections rather easily because historians of international relations do take power and the state seriously,[12] because we do study the interrelationships between society, political economy, and national policy,[13] because we do grapple with ideas, ideology, and national identity,[14] because

10 David Painter, *Oil and the American Century: The Political Economy of U.S. Foreign Oil Policy, 1941–1954* (Baltimore, 1986); Elizabeth A. Cobbs, *The Rich Neighbor Policy: Rockefeller and Kaiser in Brazil* (New Haven, 1992); Gregg Andrews, *Shoulder to Shoulder? The American Federation of Labor, the United States, and the Mexican Revolution, 1910–1924* (Berkeley, 1991); Ronald L. Filippelli, *American Labor and Postwar Italy, 1943–1953: A Study of Cold War Politics* (Stanford, 1989); Paul A. Varg, *Missionaries, Chinese, and Diplomats: The American Protestant Missionary Movement in China, 1890–1952* (Princeton, 1958); Warren Cohen, *The Chinese Connection: Roger S. Greene, Thomas W. Lamont, George E. Sokolsky, and American-East Asian Relations* (New York, 1978); Patricia Hill, *The World Their Household: The American Women's Foreign Mission Movment and Cultural Transformation, 1870–1920* (Ann Arbor, 1985).

11 See, for example, Emily S. Rosenberg, *Spreading the American Dream: American Economic and Cultural Expansionism, 1898–1945* (New York, 1982); Frank Costigliola, *Awkward Dominion: American Political, Economic, and Cultural Relations with Europe, 1919–1933* (Ithaca, 1984), esp. 140–84; Ralph Willett, *The Americanization of Germany, 1945–1949* (London, 1989); Richard Kuisel, *Seducing the French: The Dilemma of Americanization* (Berkeley, 1993); and Reinhold Wagnleitner, "The Irony of American Culture Abroad: Austria and the Cold War," in *Recasting America: Culture and Politics in the Age of Cold War*, ed. Lary May (Chicago, 1989), 285–301.

12 For different perspectives see, for example, Norman Graebner, *Foundations of American Foreign Policy: A Realist Appraisal from Franklin to McKinley* (Wilmington, DE, 1985); and Gabriel and Joyce Kolko, *The Limits of Power: The World and United States Foreign Policy, 1945–1954* (New York, 1972).

13 See, for example, Gabriel Kolko, *The Roots of American Foreign Policy: An Analysis of Power and Purpose* (Boston, 1969); Michael J. Hogan, *The Marshall Plan: America, Britain, and the Reconstruction of Western Europe, 1947–1952* (New York, 1987); and Bruce Cumings, *The Origins of the Korean War*, vol. 2, *The Roaring of the Cataract, 1947–1950* (Princeton, 1990).

14 See, for example, Felix Gilbert, *To the Farewell Address: Ideas of Early American Foreign Policy* (Princeton, 1961); James H. Hutson, "Intellectual Foundations of Early American Diplomacy," *Diplomatic History* 1 (Winter 1977): 1–19; Michael H. Hunt, *Ideology and U.S. Foreign Policy* (New Haven, 1987); Frank Ninkovich, *The Diplomacy of Ideas: U.S. Foreign and Cultural Relations, 1938–1950* (New York, 1981); and Robert Dallek, *The American Style of Foreign Policy* (New York, 1983).

we do focus on rhetoric, politics, and political mobilization,[15] because we are concerned with comparative and transnational history,[16] and because we can shed light on the issue of American exceptionalism.[17]

In the long run we will connect most effectively with other American historians by excelling at the enterprises we have been engaged in: studying the formulation of national policy; examining the interconnections between state and society; dissecting the composition and exercise of power at home and abroad; analyzing the links between process and events; illuminating the construction of identity and the role of ideology; elucidating the interactions of our government, society, economy, and culture with those abroad; and illustrating the dynamic interdependence between developments in the domestic arena and changes in the international system.[18]

Our field has the potential to make significant contributions to the larger enterprise of American history. We will do so if we can overcome our own tendencies to fragment into topical subspecialties and warring schools of interpretation. We need to write more

15 See, for example, Roger H. Brown, *The Republic in Peril: 1812* (New York, 1964); Ernest R. May, *American Imperialism: A Speculative Essay* (New York, 1968); idem, *The Making of the Monroe Doctrine* (Cambridge, MA, 1975); Arno J. Mayer, *Political Origins of the New Diplomacy, 1917–18* (New Haven, 1959); and Richard M. Freeland, *The Truman Doctrine and the Origins of McCarthyism: Foreign Policy, Domestic Politics, and Internal Security, 1946–1948* (New York, 1985).

16 See, for example, Jonathan R. Dull, *A Diplomatic History of the American Revolution* (New Haven, 1985); Michael H. Hunt, *Frontier Defense and the Open Door: Manchuria in Chinese-American Relations, 1895–1911* (New Haven, 1973); Akira Iriye, *After Imperialism: The Search for a New Order in the Far East, 1921–1931* (Cambridge, MA, 1965); Arno J. Mayer, *Politics and Diplomacy of Peacemaking: Containment and Counterrevolution at Versailles, 1918–1919* (New York, 1967); Stephen A. Schuker, *The End of French Predominance in Europe: The Financial Crisis of 1924 and the Adoption of the Dawes Plan* (Chapel Hill, 1976); Christopher Thorne, *The Limits of Foreign Policy: The West, the League, and the Far Eastern Crisis of 1931–1933* (New York, 1972); Odd Arne Westad, *Cold War & Revolution: Soviet-American Rivalry and the Origins of the Chinese Civil War* (New York, 1993); and Thomas D. Schoonover, *The United States in Central America, 1860–1911: Episodes of Social Imperialism and Imperial Rivalry in the World System* (Durham, 1991).

17 See, for example, Christopher Thorne, *Border Crossings: Studies in International History* (Oxford, 1988); and Geir Lundestad, "Moralism, Presentism, Exceptionalism, Provincialism, and Other Extravagances in American Writings on the Early Cold War Years," *Diplomatic History* 13 (Fall 1989): 527–46.

18 For a first-rate assessment of the evolution and progress of the field see Michael H. Hunt, "The Long Crisis in U.S. Diplomatic History: Coming to Closure" in this volume.

monographs and more syntheses that transcend our traditional categories of analysis. We need to sharpen and reconfigure our older interpretations and at the same time assimilate the new approaches.

We will be able to do these things more effectively if we pay attention to what is going on elsewhere in the profession as well as in our own field. The "hottest" approaches and topics right now relate to gender, culture, and language. We need to ponder these approaches, examine their utility, and adapt them, where they prove useful, to the most salient issues within our own specialty.

By effectively integrating and reconfiguring our own field, we will be able to speak with more authority to our colleagues in other subdisciplines. For a generation they have ignored us because we have been dealing with the state and national policy while the state has been reviled for its failures abroad as well as at home. "Restless students and young intellectuals," John Higham recently commented, "turned against all large, impersonal structures of authority, bringing scorn for the groups that maintain such structures and disbelief in their principles." Correspondingly, there was a glorification of the resilience of small or submerged communities.[19] While most of us labored on the post–World War II era, the most exciting work in American history dealt with the society and economy of colonial towns, the ideology of the American Revolution, the political realignments of the nineteenth and early twentieth centuries, the life of ethnic and immigrant communities, the resistance of workers on the shop floor, the ubiquitous force of a consumer culture, and the struggle of African Americans to find a voice in freedom as well as in slavery. In the future, however, as historians of culture and society turn to more contemporary history and as they reorient their attention to the state and toward power, toward politics and policy, they will become more familiar with the work many of us have been doing, with the research strategies we have been following, and with the interpretive issues we have not quite solved.

The end of the Cold War will accelerate this trend. While many of us often were scorned for studying an ongoing process,

19 Higham, "Future of American History," 1298.

for analyzing the actions of great white men, and for becoming either their apologists or their critics, the centrality of the Cold War for the history of humanity and ecology in the second half of the twentieth century cannot be disputed. In our own country, historians of culture, gender, and race relations increasingly refer to the culture of the national security state as an indispensable frame of reference for illuminating their subjects. Some of the most popular literature in gender history, for example, links the sexism and homophobia of the 1950s to the Cold War hysteria generated by the Soviet-American confrontation and the specter of nuclear war. The containment of the Kremlin, writes Elaine Tyler May, was accompanied by the containment of women in the home. And Geoffrey Smith shows that the struggle against Communists also pitted the government against gays, narrowing the range of options available to many people living non-conventional lifestyles.[20] Although such works vividly illustrate the interlocking ties of foreign policy and national security with culture and society, they are much better at demonstrating parallel developments than at elucidating causal relationships. If anything, they suggest that foreign policy exerted more importance in shaping the society and culture of the 1950s than vice versa. And if this is the case, domestic historians will need increasingly to grapple with the sources of the Cold War itself, thereby entering a more constructive dialogue with us rather than ignoring us.

I do not think a particular theory will overcome problems of fragmentation in our own field or provide the types of syntheses I am looking for. In his provocative article "'Revising Postrevisionism,'" reprinted here, Bruce Cumings lumps together a number of historians, labels us postrevisionists, and attacks us for our disregard of theory. To my mind, the criticism is rather startling in its generality because it is used to vilify the work of John Lewis Gaddis, with whom I still believe I have considerable differences, but whose attention to theory I greatly admire and whose contributions in this regard I am not alone in considering

20 Elaine Tyler May, *Homeward Bound: American Families in the Cold War Era* (New York, 1988); Geoffrey S. Smith, "National Security and Personal Isolation: Sex, Gender, and Disease in the Cold-War United States," *International History Review* 14 (May 1992): 221–40.

pathbreaking.[21] The truth of the matter is that Cumings's objection lies not in Gaddis's disregard of theory, but in his inattention to a particular theory, namely world-systems theory. But what is most interesting about some of Gaddis's theoretical work is precisely his demonstration of the shortcomings of many theories of international relations, their inability to predict the very phenomena that they purport to predict. Theories, he insists, need to be combined to account for the complexity of events.[22] Indeed, the complexity of human experience is what students in all the human sciences are increasingly aware of, daunted by, and, in some instances, seeking to escape.

Although I believe that no single theory can explain the dynamics of American foreign relations, I am more and more impressed by the utility of theory. For me, different theories outline hypothetical relationships that need to be explored; they illuminate prospective causal relationships and interactions that I might not have thought about. They serve as frames of reference to think about the evidence that I am perusing. In my study of the Cold War, I applied no single theory. But realist theory made me sensitive to the workings of the international system; world systems helped me comprehend the functioning of the world political economy; theories of bureaucratic politics alerted me to the need to look more closely at the behavior of various departments; cognitive theory enhanced my understanding of threat perception and decision making. This is an eclectic brew, not a recipe for

21 John Lewis Gaddis, "Expanding the Data Base: Historians, Political Scientists, and the Enrichment of Security Studies," *International Security* 12 (Summer 1987): 3–21; idem, "New Conceptual Approaches to the Study of American Foreign Relations: Interdisciplinary Perspectives," *Diplomatic History* 14 (Summer 1990): 403–25; idem, "International Relations Theory and the End of the Cold War," *International Security* 17 (Winter 1992/93): 5–58; for appreciative comments see, for example, Richard H. Immerman, "In Search of History – and Relevancy: Breaking Through the 'Encrustations of Interpretation,'" *Diplomatic History* 12 (Summer 1988): 341–56; Robert J. McMahon, "The Study of American Foreign Relations: National History or International History?" in *Explaining the History of American Foreign Relations*, ed. Michael J. Hogan and Thomas G. Paterson (New York, 1991), 19.

22 Gaddis, "International Relations Theory and the End of the Cold War." For similar disillusionment with certain types of theory see Michael H. Hunt, "Beijing and the Korean Crisis, June 1950–June 1951," *Political Science Quarterly* 107 (Fall 1992): esp. 475–78; and Paul Schroeder, "Historical Reality vs. Neo-Realist Theory," *International Security* 19 (Summer 1994): 108–48. Hunt, too, is ridiculed by Cumings for an allegedly "postrevisionist" inattention to theory.

crafting perfect diplomatic history. But if reality is too complex to be captured by a single theory, different theories may help the historian to make sense of different parts of the phenomenon or event or process under scrutiny.

Of course, this assumes that we should illuminate the complexity of an event, and it is not at all clear to me that we all agree that we should be doing this. Increasingly, we talk of different approaches to writing the history of international relations. Michael J. Hogan and Thomas G. Paterson's popular primer, *Explaining the History of American Foreign Relations*, introduces students to culture, ideology, world systems, public opinion, corporatism, and national security as compartmentalized avenues to analysis rather than as parts of a whole. The essays in their volume vividly "highlight the healthy ferment and rich diversity" in the field.[23] But the challenge, as I see it, is to envision how these approaches can work together to answer the questions we deem most important.

Although some historians believe that the pursuit of synthesis masks a desire to exert hegemonic control over the discipline and constrains creativity,[24] I do not see it this way. By looking at the whole, however we may define it, we multiply the interplay of variables, arouse controversy about their relative importance, invite discussions of causation, and vastly augment the realm for creativity. For diplomatic historians, it means grasping not only the multivariate internal variables but also the external ones, including the matrix of domestic variables in the other countries we are dealing with.

The task is daunting. Writing the best type of diplomatic history would force us to reconsider training for work in our field. It would force our students to become much more adept in foreign languages and in the theories and methodologies of cognate disciplines, including anthropology, political science, economics, and literary and cultural studies. It would force us to publish less and read more. It would force us to rethink the wisdom of tenure

23 Hogan and Paterson, eds., *Explaining the History of American Foreign Relations.* The quotation is on p. 7.

24 Allan Megill, "Fragmentation and the Future of Historiography," *American Historical Review* 96 (June 1991): 693–94; Peter Novick, "My Correct Views on Everything," ibid., 701–3.

systems that demand judgments in the fifth or sixth year of a person's academic career. It would impel the purveyors of more and more specialized journals to close shop or seek articles of wider scope.

The pursuit of synthesis will not lead to consensus; quite the opposite. Controversy over the relative weight we should assign a multiplicity of variables will open new interpretive vistas. To be persuasive we will need to be more rigorous, more complex, more creative.

I also believe that thinking in complex and synthetic terms will encourage us to say things that are important rather than new. There is nothing wrong with asking old questions; indeed, old issues tend to stay with us for a long time because they are the important ones. Traditional questions about the relationships of foreign policies to war and peace, to expansion and imperialism, and to democracy and totalitarianism are important, demand complex syntheses, and ensure continual and ongoing controversy. And what is wrong with this, so long as we keep integrating new theories and analytic categories into the interpretive mix of causative factors?

But the postmodernist emphasis on culture, language, and rhetoric often diverts attention from questions of causation and agency. "Discursive analysis," writes Emily Rosenberg in a rather admiring way, "is not concerned with labeling 'cause' and 'effect' but with highlighting symbolic interrelationships among seemingly unrelated institutions and assumptions in order to understand the boundaries of what constitutes 'knowledge.'"[25] The problem with this viewpoint is that although we might learn that seemingly unconnected phenomena are related in some diffuse ways, we do not necessarily get much insight into how relatively important these relationships are to one another. "By focusing on culture," write Joyce Appleby, Lynn Hunt, and Margaret Jacob in their recent book, *Telling the Truth About History*, "one could challenge the virtual commonsensical assumption that there is a clear hierarchy of explanation in history."[26]

The new stress on culture, gender, and language should be

25 Emily S. Rosenberg, "'Foreign Affairs' after World War II: Connecting Sexual and International Politics," *Diplomatic History* 18 (Winter 1994): 65.
26 Appleby, Hunt, and Jacob, *Telling the Truth About History*, 230.

understood, at least in part, as a repudiation of older categories of analysis that dealt with society, economy, and politics; with class, property, and income; with social structure and human motivation. Derrida and Foucault "deny our ability to represent reality in any objectively true fashion and offer to 'deconstruct'... the notion of the individual as an autonomous self-conscious agent." Text and context get blurred, cause and effect are repudiated, agency is obfuscated.[27] In Clifford Geertz's "thick" description, for example, we get little sense of causation, and in Foucault's preoccupation with discourse and power, we get equally little sense of agency.[28]

Nonetheless, proponents of discourse theory and the new cultural history urge us to use Foucault, for example, to study NSC-68, because doing so would make us realize that "the power to shape the symbolic systems of language and meaning is the power over 'knowledge' and 'reality.'"[29] But these proponents fail to acknowledge that Foucault never was much interested in exploring who, in fact, shaped that power, and for what reasons.[30] So before we become habituated to think that new approaches used in isolation from old categories pose solutions to complex questions, we might do well to ponder the implications of Patricia O'Brien's comment: "Foucault's study of culture is a history with beginnings but no causes. In place of the monocause or the primary cause, Foucault gives us a game without causes."[31]

This talk is not a diatribe against the new; quite the opposite. It is an appeal to use the new in nuanced, thoughtful ways. Rather than broad appeals for the utility of gendered, cultural, linguistic, or ideological approaches, I ask for well-directed analyses showing precisely how these new approaches will reconfigure older controversies, how they will stack up against traditional interpretations (no matter how contested they remain).[32] Otherwise

27 Ibid., 208, 226–27. See also Palmer, *Descent into Discourse.*

28 See the essays by Aletta Biersack on Clifford Geertz and Patricia O'Brien on Foucault in Hunt, ed., *New Cultural History*, esp. 74–82 and 43–46.

29 See Emily Rosenberg's provocative comments in *American Cold War Strategy: Interpreting NSC 68*, ed. Ernest R. May (New York, 1993), 162.

30 Mark Poster, "Foucault and History," *Social Research* 49 (Spring 1982): 116–42.

31 Hunt, ed., *New Cultural History*, 44.

32 For an example that we might like to emulate see William O. Walker III, "Drug Control and the Issue of Culture in American Foreign Relations," *Diplomatic History* 12 (Fall 1988): 365–82.

I fear that they will lead us into a scholastic trap, as Anders Stephanson seems to concede at the conclusion of his very learned commentary on culture and theory: "I must . . . remark that most of what I have called theory here has very little to say about the society, the economy, or the state; nor is it particularly conducive to analyses of such subjects." To do important work in international history, Stephanson notes, "we must widen the horizon beyond the politics of representation toward, for example, the critical traditions within geography, historical sociology, and political economy."[33] If so, why not write about those topics? Why concentrate on gender and culture? The answer, according to Susan Jeffords, is rather simple: "I would argue," she writes in a recent symposium in *Diplomatic History*, "that there has been no period, especially in the determination of U.S. foreign policy, in which gender has not been a factor. On the contrary, in many cases it has been the primary factor for the construction of national meaning."[34] The evidence for this, according to Jeffords, is illustrated in articles like the one by Laura McEnaney in that symposium on "The America First Movement and the Gendered Meanings of Patriotism and Isolationism."

McEnaney's article is an attempt to look into one of the most important periods and portentous debates in the history of American foreign policy. Examining the isolationist movement in the 1930s, she argues that "patriotism and isolationism, America First Style, was fundamentally a defense of the nuclear family structure and the conventional gender roles that made this movement's vision of social and sexual purity possible and sustainable." To women proponents of America First, isolationism was more than a foreign policy decision; it was a "philosophy that defended the rights of families and especially validated the insight and experience of motherhood as a political force for the public good."[35]

I found McEnaney's argument intriguing, so I examined her notes carefully, discovering that the primary source evidence came

33 Anders Stephanson, "Commentary: Considerations on Culture and Theory," *Diplomatic History* 18 (Winter 1994): 119.

34 Susan Jeffords, "Commentary: Culture and National Identity in U.S. Foreign Policy," ibid., 91–92.

35 Laura McEnaney, "He-Men and Christian Mothers: The America First Movement and the Gendered Meanings of Patriotism and Isolationism," ibid., 47–57, quotations on pp. 48 and 53.

mostly from two journals, *Women's Voice* and *The Cross and the Flag*. My library had only the second, and my perusal of the issues from 1942–1946 (note that the first issue was 1942, after the war had already begun) was illuminating. Founded by Gerald L. K. Smith, *The Cross and the Flag* remains a fascinating journal for researchers. It championed a "Christian Nationalism" and was filled with the most vicious invective against Jews, blacks, Communists, socialists, and Roosevelts. In its February 1946 issue, it summed up its principles: safeguarding liberty, free enterprise, and majority rule; fighting communism, bureaucratic fascism, and big government; opposing the United Nations, entangling alliances, and immigrants from abroad.[36]

In short, notwithstanding McEnaney's admirable effort to reexamine the isolationist movement, *The Cross and the Flag* offers only the scantiest evidence that America Firsters were preoccupied with the nuclear family or defending traditional gender roles. To be fair, McEnaney acknowledges in a footnote that "this essay highlights the gender and family politics of America First's campaign, but conservative racial and populist politics were integral elements of the America First agenda."[37] But if *The Cross and the Flag* is representative of the data base, highlighting gender and family politics distorts rather than illuminates the evidence and diverts us from seeing the issues of political economy, ideology, and race that seem to have been at the center of the discourse within the isolationist movement.

Although gendered language may not be a key to understanding the isolationist movement, it may have a greater role to play in analyses of the representation and reception of policy.[38] In an

36 "This is Nationalism: For these Principles We Work, Fight, Pray," *The Cross and the Flag* 4 (February 1946): 708–9. The comments I make above are based on my perusal of the issues from 1942–1946.

37 McEnaney, "He-Men and Christian Mothers," 48.

38 I am indebted to the insightful work of Emily Rosenberg and Frank Costigliola. See, for example, Rosenberg, "Gendered Discourses in Dollar Diplomacy," and Costigliola, "The Nuclear Family: Cold War Gendered Discourse in the Western Alliance," both papers delivered at the Annual Meeting of the Organization of American Historians, 1993. One might argue that gendered analysis of international relations should do more, that is, to explain why women everywhere are treated unequally. See Sarah Brown, "Feminism, International Theory, and International Relations of Gender Inequality," *Millennium: Journal of International Studies* 17 (1988): 461–75. But Brown makes no effort to show that the structure of international relations is, in fact, responsible for the situation she abhors.

engrossing article in the journal *Signs*, Carol Cohn has probed the language of defense officials and demonstrated how it allows them to think about the unthinkable. The language is "abstract, sanitized, and full of euphemisms"; it is sexy and funny; its imagery "domesticates and deflates the forces of mass destruction" and "conflates birth and death." If one does not learn the language, Cohn writes, one is not taken seriously; if one does learn the language, one is often co-opted and changed by the very process of learning.[39]

Yet Cohn rightly suspects that the language does not convey the real reasons for the strategies and policies she detests. The "technocratic discourse functions more as a gloss, as an ideological curtain behind which the actual reasons for these decisions hide." Rather than informing and shaping decisions, "it far more often functions as a legitimation for political outcomes that have occurred for utterly different reasons."[40] Cohn, however, makes no effort to assess the strategic, economic, bureaucratic, geopolitical, technological, and ideological reasons for decision making that one can read about in secondary sources or can discern from the primary sources themselves, including the meetings of the National Security Council and discussions among other top officials.

To level this criticism is not to belittle the interest of Cohn's work but to invite that it be placed in a larger context and its salience discussed. When officials make policy, technocratic discourse does not close off examination and analysis of the geopolitical, strategic, economic, and political factors that shape it. Language does not stand as an insuperable barrier to "truth," either to the makers of policy who are conscious of the many considerations at stake or to the historian who can clearly see the influence of these other forces on policy. Yet Cohn does show how language co-opts, limits, legitimates, and entraps in ways that are important to consider and that are indispensable to a larger synthesis.

The analysis of language and rhetoric alone cannot explain

39 Carol Cohn, "Sex and Death in the Rational World of Defense Intellectuals," *Signs: Journal of Women in Culture and Society* 12 (Summer 1987): 687–718, quotation on p. 715.
40 Ibid., 716.

"reality." In their recent book, *The Cold War as Rhetoric*, Lynn Boyd Hinds and Theodore Otto Windt argue that "political language and arguments . . . create political consciousness, define political settings, create national identity, stimulate people to act, and give sense and purpose to these actions."[41] They show how metaphors, like the metaphor of disease, structure reality, resonate with people, and incline them to accept certain types of policies. But their stress is on text rather than context. They focus scant attention on what motivated officials to utilize anti-Communist rhetoric; instead, their book is devoted to "how" Americans fell prey to a rigid ideology.[42]

They do remind us, however, that the rhetoric that accompanies any event "must be based on values that have come to be regarded as basic beliefs."[43] Basic beliefs link language to culture, making the latter a rich field for study. Nobody in our field has written more thoughtfully about culture and diplomacy than Akira Iriye. Culture, he says, "is the creation and communication of memory, ideology, life styles, scholarly and artistic works, and other symbols." Quoting Paul Ricoeur, Iriye reminds us that a nation's behavior in the international system is affected by the "'layer of images and symbols which make up the basic ideals of a nation.'"[44] But what are the basic ideals of a nation, how are they formed, and to what extent do they shape policy at any particular time in history?

In his important recent studies, Iriye tends to define the role of culture in American foreign policy in terms of Wilsonian internationalism, meaning, in Iriye's view, that men and women everywhere have shared interests.[45] But culture alone hardly seems an

41 Lynn Boyd Hinds and Theodore Otto Windt, Jr., *The Cold War as Rhetoric: The Beginnings, 1945–1950* (New York, 1991), 7.

42 For the disregard of context see Appleby, Hunt, and Jacob, *Telling the Truth About History*, 207–31. The stress on "how" rather than "why," on process rather than causation, on identity and knowledge rather than interests and needs is embedded in the new criticism based on culture, gender, and rhetoric. See also Joan Wallach Scott, *Gender and the Politics of History* (New York, 1988), 4–11.

43 Hinds and Windt, *Cold War as Rhetoric*, 8.

44 Akira Iriye, "Culture and International History," in Hogan and Paterson, eds., *Explaining the History of American Foreign Relations*, 215 and 217.

45 Akira Iriye, *The Cambridge History of American Foreign Relations*, vol. 3, *The Globalizing of America, 1913–1945* (New York, 1993), esp. 71–72; idem, *Power and Culture: The Japanese-American War, 1941–1945* (Cambridge, MA, 1981).

independent variable capable of explaining, for example, the continuation of internationalism in the United States in the 1920s, or its demise in the 1930s, or its revival after World War II. Iriye juxtaposes power and culture in ways that are tantalizing and provocative, yet also elusive and confusing. The Japanese, he argues, possessed a vision of internationalism in the 1920s that receded in the 1930s and then reemerged after the Japanese-American war, never totally extinguished. But if cultures have autonomy that generates distinctive images and symbols, why does the imagery change so rapidly and culminate in such disparate policies? How does culture explain both the imperialism and racism of the war years and the cooperation and interdependence characteristic of much of the Cold War era?

John Dower, another brilliant student of Japanese culture and Japanese-American relations, shows that the same stereotypes, metaphors, and images that "fed superpatriotism and outright race hate were adaptable to cooperation." He argues that "code words and pet images of everyday life survive extreme vicissitudes: they are usually remarkably flexible and malleable, and can be turned about, even turned almost inside out, to legitimize a multitude of often contradictory purposes."[46] In other words, although culture may be autonomous, it also seems infinitely malleable and capable of giving shape to totally divergent policies; for example, to internationalism or isolationism in the United States, and to cooperative internationalism or race hatred in Japan. The malleability of culture suggests to me that in order to understand its impact on policy, one needs also to study the dynamics of political economy, the evolution of the international system, and the roles of technology and communication, among many other variables.

I am also struck that despite divergent cultures, policy outcomes can be rather similar. In their new book, *Uncertain Partners: Stalin, Mao, and the Korean War*, Sergei Goncharov, John Lewis, and Xue Litai conclude that when it came to particular external policy issues, "the ultimate concern of both sides [the

46 John W. Dower, *War without Mercy: Race and Power in the Pacific War* (New York, 1986), 302.

Soviet Union and the People's Republic of China] was not class struggle, but state interests.... In the final analysis, realpolitik governed their thinking and strained their relations."[47]

Likewise, I would suggest that the new materials emanating from China illustrate how, notwithstanding different cultural traditions and conflicting ideologies, Chinese and American leaders often shared certain mindsets. We have known for years how notions of credibility, dominoes, and bandwagons influenced policymakers in Washington.[48] We now see that Mao and his comrades shared quite similar notions. Pondering intervention in the Korean War on 4 August 1950, Mao wrote, "If the U.S. imperialists won the war, they would become more arrogant and threaten us." On 12 October 1950, he repeated, "If we do not send our troops, the enemy will be swollen with arrogance. This will result in a variety of disadvantages to us, especially in the Northeast area."[49] Mao saw dominoes just as did Acheson; he saw bandwagons, just as did Kennan. Perhaps he even learned the same lessons from the Manchurian incident of 1931 and the Munich Conference of 1938. We must not appease, said Mao during the Taiwan Straits crisis in 1955. "If we show fear, the enemy will consider us weak and easy to bully. In other words, if we give them an inch, they will take a mile and intensify their military expansion. Only by adopting an unyielding, resolute, and calm stance can we force the enemy to retreat."[50]

47 Sergei N. Goncharov, John W. Lewis, and Xue Litai, *Uncertain Partners: Stalin, Mao, and the Korean War* (Stanford, 1993), 220.

48 See, for example, Robert J. McMahon, "Credibility and World Power: Exploring the Psychological Dimensions in Postwar American Diplomacy," *Diplomatic History* 15 (Fall 1991): 455–72.

49 Jian Chen, "China's Changing Aims during the Korean War, 1950–51," *Journal of American-East Asian Relations* 1 (Spring 1992): 13 and 21. Michael Hunt also sees parallels in the ways Truman and Mao reacted to developments in Korea. "The mix of calculations Mao applied to the Korean intervention in October brings to mind nothing so strongly as the outlook in Washington at the very same time." See Hunt, "Beijing and the Korean Crisis," 472–75, quotation is on p. 474.

50 Quoted in Gordon H. Chang and He Di, "The Absence of War in the U.S.-China Confrontation over Quemoy and Matsu in 1954–1955: Contingency, Luck, Deterrence?" *American Historical Review* 98 (December 1993): 1516. Culture and ideology, the authors claim, generated mistaken images. Although their argument contrasts with the one I am making here, it is interesting to note that Chinese and American misperceptions were akin to one another and that both governments faced difficult constraints, leading the authors to emphasize the overall "complexity" of the situation.

The Chinese, like the Americans, saw themselves acting defensively. This tendency is not culture-bound, although the form and character of defensive actions will be shaped by geography and national experience. Leaders everywhere usually see themselves acting defensively. Moreover, they often expect their adversaries to interpret their actions as they themselves see them. This, of course, is not likely to happen.[51] But the key to understanding their policies seems to be to grasp how particular leaders defined their interests (both domestic and international), conceived security, and perceived threats (also both domestic and international). Ideology, of course, would be a factor shaping the perception of threat, and culture would serve as a framework for defining that which was threatening as well as that which was desirable (interest). Language, resonant with cultural symbols, could then be molded to catalyze support for any number of diverse policies, dependent upon domestic political configurations, the state of the economy, and the distribution of power in the international system.

The above sketch is a plea to overcome fragmentation in our own field and an invitation to use one's imagination to show how the now-fashionable categories of analysis – culture, gender, language, and ideology – need to be linked with older interpretive modes – geopolitics, political economy, and public opinion – in order to come up with satisfactory syntheses that do justice to the complexity of reality.[52] I can assure you, for example, that the answers to our contested "truths" about the Cold War will not come from the opening of new archives. Recent conferences dealing with the Soviet Union, Germany, and Eastern Europe during the Cold War and recent books and articles on the Korean War show how new archival materials will continue to lend weight to divergent explanations.[53] Stalin's aims and motives remain

51 Robert Jervis, Richard Ned Lebow, and Janice Gross Stein, *Psychology and Deterrence* (Baltimore, 1985), 180–232; Robert Jervis, *Perception and Misperception in International Politics* (Princeton, 1976), 58–78 and 143–216.

52 I think this is also the point of Frank Ninkovich's article, "Interests and Discourse in Diplomatic History," *Diplomatic History* 13 (Spring 1989): 135–62.

53 The Cold War International History Project, housed at the Woodrow Wilson International Center in Washington, DC, has cosponsored three major conferences on the origins of the Cold War during the last two years. The papers given were based on the newly accessible materials in Russia, Eastern Europe, and Germany. In my view, the papers underscore the difficulty of making any clear-cut generalizations about the

unclear. Scholars dealing with Soviet-East German relations and looking at some of the very same materials, for example the diaries of German Communist leader Wilhelm Pieck, cannot agree on whether the Soviet dictator wanted a unified or divided Germany, a Communized eastern zone or a neutral country amenable to Soviet wishes and security concerns.[54]

If new archival materials will enrich but not resolve our controversies, the moral triumphalism emanating in some of the post-Cold War literature will do neither.[55] I would like nothing better than to be able to say that the moralism and idealism of U.S. officials led to the containment of Soviet communism. But the astonishing thing about reading the diaries and papers of President Harry S. Truman and his top advisers was to realize how little attention they initially paid to moral factors, that is, to the human travail of Stalin's Russia. Read the president's diary or his letters to his wife and you will encounter a moral indifference that is infuriating. What went on in Russia, the president noted, was Russia's business. The Soviet people had no democracy, but "they evidently like their government or they wouldn't die for it." Stalin was "honest – but smart as hell."[56] Reflecting on Truman's campaign goof in 1948 when he told reporters "I like old Joe," Clark Clifford, the president's friend, counsel, and

motives and objectives of the Soviet Union. These papers may be obtained from Jim Hershberg, the director of the Cold War International History Project. The emerging literature on the Korean War based on Russian, Chinese, and Korean sources also underscores that new archival evidence will not resolve old controversies but will enrich them and direct them along new and interesting lines. See, for example, Bruce Cumings, *Roaring of the Cataract*; Shu Guang Zhang, *Deterrence and Strategic Culture: Chinese-American Confrontations, 1949–1958* (Ithaca, 1992); Goncharov, Lewis, and Litai, *Uncertain Partners*; Hunt, "Beijing and the Korean Crisis"; Chen, "China's Changing Aims during the Korean War"; and Kathryn Weathersby, "The Soviet Role in the Early Phase of the Korean War: New Documentary Evidence," *Journal of American-East Asian Relations* 2 (Winter 1993): 425–58.

54 R. C. Raack, "Stalin Plans His Post-War Germany," *Journal of Contemporary History* 28 (January 1993): 53–74; Wilfried Loth, "Stalin's Plans for Postwar Germany," and Gerhard Wettig, "All-German Unity and East German Separation in Soviet Policy, 1947–1949," both papers delivered at the Conference on the "Soviet Union, Germany, and the Cold War, 1945–1962," Essen, 1994.

55 See, for example, John Lewis Gaddis, "The Tragedy of Cold War History," *Diplomatic History* 17 (Winter 1993): 1–16; and Francis Fukuyama, *The End of History and the Last Man* (New York, 1992).

56 Robert H. Ferrell, ed., *Off the Record: The Private Papers of Harry S. Truman* (New York, 1980), 44 and 53.

political consultant, acknowledged that Truman still had mixed feelings about Stalin, even after he had announced the Truman Doctrine and the Marshall Plan.[57] And those historians who wish to attribute this attitude to the naiveté of a typical provincial American politician need to deal with the fact that policymakers in England and America with widely divergent personal backgrounds shared the same moral obtuseness. If "it were possible to see him [Stalin] more frequently," W. Averell Harriman claimed, "many of our difficulties would be overcome."[58]

To repeat, I would love to assume a heroic view of American nobility at the outset of the Cold War, but such a view does not square with the facts.[59] The men who made American policy in 1945, and '46, and '47, were concerned with lots of things, but Stalin's crimes were not high on the list. And should we be terribly surprised by this? Had these same men spoken out in defense of or given refuge to the millions of persecuted Jews during the 1930s? Had they led a moral crusade against Hitler's barbarity? Had they been morally shocked by French slaughters in Algeria in 1945 or in Madagascar in 1947, by the murderous actions of Chinese nationalists, or by the institution of apartheid in South Africa a few years later?[60]

The best retort to these charges is that American officials could not have been so preoccupied with Stalin's crimes because the

57 Clark Clifford, *Counsel to the President: A Memoir* (New York, 1991), 200–201.

58 Harriman to Truman, 8 June 1945, U.S. Department of State, *Foreign Relations of the United States, Conference of Berlin (Potsdam)*, 2 vols. (Washington, 1970), 1:61; W. Averell Harriman and Elie Abel, *Special Envoy to Churchill and Stalin, 1941–46* (New York, 1975), 533–36. See also the comments by Frank Roberts, the British diplomat, in "A Diplomat Remembers Stalin," *The World Today* (November 1990): 210.

59 For an attack on my alleged disregard of American idealism and my supposed indifference to Stalinist barbarity see Jacob Heilbrunn, "The Revision Thing," *New Republic* 152 (15 August 1994): 31–38.

60 See, for example, David S. Wyman, *The Abandonment of the Jews: America and the Holocaust, 1941–1945* (New York, 1984); and Henry L. Feingold, *The Politics of Rescue: The Roosevelt Administration and the Holocaust, 1938–1945* (New Brunswick, 1970); for allusions to French actions see T. E. Vadney, *The World since 1945* (New York, 1992), 100; for Chinese Nationalist slaughters see R. J. Rummel, *Death by Government* (New Brunswick, 1994), 123–39; for the United States and South Africa see Thomas Borstelmann, *Apartheid's Reluctant Uncle: The United States and Southern Africa in the Early Cold War* (New York, 1993).

magnitude of the gulag was not then known. Nor was it clear that Stalin wanted to export his system abroad. The evidence emanating from Russian archives makes clear that Stalin's regime was as brutal and repressive as his fiercest critics charged,[61] but Russian archival papers do not yet demonstrate that Stalin's foreign policies were aimed at unlimited expansion, or that his vision of security meant "complete insecurity for everyone else."[62]

Insecurity and apprehension were endemic to the postwar world because of the legacy of fifteen years of depression, war, and mass slaughter. Economies were shattered; traditional trade patterns were deranged; and the distribution of power in the international system was transformed. Asian peoples wanted autonomy and nationhood; European peoples yearned for peace, prosperity, social justice, and freedom. The insecurities of the postwar world were multidimensional, dependent on one's nationality, race, ethnicity, class, and wartime experiences; the Kremlin's power was only one of many anxieties. In the cauldron of postwar national and transnational politics, the appeal of liberal capitalism was anything but certain. In England and northern Europe, social democrats were in the ascendancy; in France, Italy, and Czechoslovakia, Communists had substantial support; in Asia, revolutionary nationalists were on the march; and throughout Eurasia,

61 In their recent article, J. Arch Getty, Gabor T. Rittersporn, and Viktor N. Zemskov present low estimates of victims in Stalin's penal camps, but they do not address the appalling consequences of collectivization, starvation, resettlement, and mass murder during World War II. See "Victims of the Soviet Penal System in the Pre-War Years: A First Approach on the Basis of Archival Evidence," *American Historical Review* 98 (October 1993): 1017–49; for Stalin's crimes see, for example, Robert Conquest, *The Great Terror: A Reassessment* (New York, 1990); Anton Antonov-Ovseyenko, *The Time of Stalin: Portrait of a Tyranny*, trans. George Saunders (New York, 1983); Dmitri Volkogonov, *Stalin: Triumph and Tragedy*, ed. and trans. Harold Shukman (New York, 1988); and Rummel, *Death by Government*, 79–89.

62 One of my basic disagreements with John Gaddis is his tendency to equate Soviet repression at home with Soviet expansion abroad. American officials, I want to emphasize, were concerned with the latter much more than the former. They focused more attention on Soviet power than on Stalin's contempt for human rights. Although I do think that Stalin wanted control over his periphery and over German and Japanese power, the nature of the control was initially quite vague and did not necessarily mean "complete insecurity for everyone else," as Gaddis argues, although it did mean repression and circumscribed autonomy (especially in the realm of foreign relations) for many neighboring countries. Gaddis, "Tragedy of Cold War History," 10.

peoples yearned for revenge against former enemies even as they looked to their states for land reform, welfare, and social justice.[63]

To frame international politics in the initial postwar years as a struggle between Soviet tyranny and American freedom is to simplify reality and distort the way most peoples around the world understood events. And although many governments and groups came to look to the United States for aid and security, although the "empire by invitation" thesis contains important insights, it should not be understood to mean that those soliciting or accepting American assistance had the same motives or concerns as did the United States or shared the same values as did Americans.[64] Whereas U.S. officials were preoccupied with containing the expansion of the Kremlin, recipients were often most concerned with financing economic recovery or domestic reform, thwarting internal foes, or strengthening themselves against traditional regional enemies. Interests perhaps most often converged in efforts to contain indigenous Communists. The appeal of America, in other words, inhered not so much in the attractiveness of its political economy, which was veering toward the center while most of the world was heading toward the left, but in America's wealth and strength, that is, in its ability to offer aid, arms, and military guarantees.

Is there room in this analysis for a consideration of freedom and liberty, variables that I cautioned should not be overstated but that are nevertheless integral to American culture and ideology, rhetoric and language? The importance of these values to policymakers is easy to overlook, particularly if we focus on corporatist arrangements within the domestic political economy

63 These generalizations can be supported by reference to a vast literature, but I particularly recommend two of Christopher Thorne's last books, *Border Crossings*; and *The Issue of War: States, Societies, and the Far Eastern Conflict* (London, 1985). The opening pages of Thomas G. Paterson's *On Every Front: The Making of the Cold War* (New York, 1979) still provide a wonderful glimpse of the devastation and dislocation wrought by World War II.

64 For the very influential thesis that the postwar American empire was an "empire by invitation" see Geir Lundestad, "Empire by Invitation? The United States and Western Europe, 1945–1952," *Journal of Peace Research* 23 (September 1985): 263–77; and John Lewis Gaddis, "The Emerging Post-Revisionist Synthesis on the Origins of the Cold War," *Diplomatic History* 7 (Summer 1983): 176–78.

or on the dynamics of the world capitalist system. In the two seminal empirical studies of corporatism and world-systems in the foreign policies of the United States in the postwar years, Michael Hogan and Bruce Cumings rely primarily on the work of Thomas Ferguson to support their view that highly capitalized and technologically innovative firms thrust America into a global role. Such a role, they argue, was indispensable to reforming and preserving capitalism.[65]

These magisterial accounts rightly force us to ponder the role of social class, economic interest, and functional groups in the making of American foreign policy. But although we get a magnificent analysis of Marshall planners in the government and a fascinating glimpse of the machinations of soybean and silver speculators, we see no systematic assessment of the very industries, interests, and groups that allegedly inspired America's global role. And when we reexamine Ferguson's influential article, we see that however intriguing is his analysis of the political realignment of industrial groupings during the New Deal, he says nothing about their views of international relations or of Soviet Russia during the early stages of the Cold War.[66]

Some of my students have begun to explore the views of business groups and foreign policy during the late 1940s and 1950s, and the picture seems blurry. In key industries like automobiles, electrical machinery, and electronics, there were individuals who spoke out forcefully in behalf of a global role for the United States, but they do not seem to have spoken for their industries as a whole.[67] Even more surprising to me is the evidence that American raw materials industries in the 1950s seemed hardly interested in Southeast Asia at all, and that businessmen in general

65 Hogan, *Marshall Plan*; Cumings, *Roaring of the Cataract*; Thomas Ferguson, "From Normalcy to New Deal: Industrial Structure, Party Competition, and American Public Policy in the Great Depression," *International Organization* 38 (Winter 1984): 41–94. For the importance of Ferguson's article see Hogan, *Marshall Plan*, 11–12 ff.; and Cumings, *Roaring of the Cataract*, 18, 90–91.

66 Nor does Ferguson do so in his other article cited by Cumings. See Ferguson, "Party Realignment and American Industrial Structure: The Investment Theory of Political Parties in Historical Perspective," *Research in Political Economy* 6 (1983): 1–82.

67 Joe Thorndike, "Business and Public Policy, 1945–1955" (seminar paper, University of Virginia, Spring 1994).

demonstrated little concern with this region, even while U.S. commitments under Truman and Eisenhower mounted.[68]

I stress that these are not exhaustive studies and more research has to be done, but they raise questions about the extent to which functional elites and business interests were responsible for the policies leading to the Korean War, the Vietnam War, and the Cold War more generally. They underscore doubts that although Dean Acheson, Robert Lovett, Averell Harriman, and John Foster Dulles were aware of the dynamic interdependence of the world capitalist system, their policies toward the Soviet Union or Communist China can be explained primarily in these terms. For Cumings it is "as simple as Acheson saying 'defense perimeter' in public and 'great crescent' in private," but I would suggest that it is rather more complicated.[69] Nor, as Cumings claims, is it a matter of choosing between Kennan or Acheson, for I, like Cumings, think that Acheson was far more important than Kennan. But unlike Cumings, I find it difficult to reduce Acheson to an agent of world capitalism, albeit a sophisticated one. For me, Acheson was as concerned about the distribution of power in the international system as he was about the functioning of the world political economy, and he was more concerned about the threat of Soviet expansion than he was about the potency of his nationalist/isolationist opponents at home. Acheson possessed a vision typical of American officials, a view that imagined a favorable configuration of power abroad as indispensable to preserving a free political economy at home.[70] And unlike Cumings, I take the notion of freedom as seriously as I take the concept of capitalism, as when Dwight D. Eisenhower wrote a friend: "I believe fanatically in the American form of democracy – a system that recognizes and protects the rights of the individual and that ascribes to the individual a dignity accruing to him because of his

68 J. Lodge Gillespie, Jr., "Dollars and Dominoes: Corporate America and the Threat in Southeast Asia, 1950–61" (M.A. thesis, University of Virginia, 1993). A revised version of this thesis will be appearing in a forthcoming issue of *Business History Review*.

69 Cumings, "'Revising Postrevisionism.'"

70 For my assessment of Acheson see Leffler, "Negotiating from Strength: Acheson, the Russians, and American Power," in *Dean Acheson and the Making of U.S. Foreign Policy*, ed. Douglas Brinkley (London, 1993), 176–210.

creation in the image of a supreme being and which rests upon the conviction that only through a system of free enterprise can this type of democracy be preserved."[71]

Although recently some scholars have identified me with a "neorealism" that places primacy on geopolitics, this was *not* the theme of my book.[72] I used terms like "national security" and "power," but my purpose was not to dwell on spatial entities or on strategies for protecting the United States against a military attack. In my introduction, in fact, I stressed the opposite: National security, I wrote, "meant more than defending territory." It meant defending America's "core values, its organizing ideology, and its free political and economic institutions." "The good society," I went on to say, was believed to be one that "circumscribed the role of government in the nation's political economy; the good society was one that attributed primacy to the protection of civil liberties and individual rights. Yet that society would be difficult to sustain either in a world divided by trade blocs or, worse yet, in a world dominated by the Kremlin's power." And to highlight a paradox that I think critical to understanding American policy, I also stated that American officials were "driven less by a desire to help others than by an ideological conviction that their own political economy of freedom would be jeopardized if a totalitarian foe became too powerful."[73]

I quote so extensively because the intent of my book, as is my intent today, was to try to break down some of the old categories compartmentalizing geopolitics, ideology, and political economy. My point was to stress that the core values of individual liberty, free enterprise, private property, and democratic government were perceived to be linked to configurations of power in the international system and to configurations of power in other countries. If my preoccupation with efforts to safeguard liberal capitalism

71 Robert Griffith, ed., *Ike's Letters to a Friend, 1941–1958* (Lawrence, 1984), 40.

72 For comments on my book, *A Preponderance of Power: National Security, the Truman Administration, and the Cold War* (Stanford, 1992), see, for example, Cumings, "'Revising Postrevisionism'"; Michael J. Hogan, "The Vice Men of Foreign Policy," *Reviews in American History* 21 (June 1993): 326; Anders Stephanson, "Commentary: Ideology and Neorealist Mirrors," *Diplomatic History* 17 (Spring 1993): 288–95; and Barton J. Bernstein, "Commentary: The Challenge of 'National Security' – A Skeptical View," ibid., 296–310.

73 Leffler, *A Preponderance of Power*, 13–14.

at home rather than to defend freedom abroad resonated with the arguments of older revisionists, my emphasis that the principal threats emanated from the external world (rather than from domestic failures) sounded like orthodoxy and realism. Some readers questioned whether this synthesis smacked of ambivalence: a wishy-washiness between my inability to choose from the fixed categories of realism, revisionism, and postrevisionism.[74]

My hope was to reconfigure old categories, and, if anything, I would try even harder today. As critics pointed out, I did not do justice to domestic political culture; I did not sufficiently assess why different groups in society supported anticommunism and why they favored alternative strategies of dealing with it. To do so, I needed to take domestic politics more seriously, not because it was the driving force behind policy but because policy could not be implemented without galvanizing support within society. And to understand why that support ultimately was forthcoming, I needed to grapple more effectively with the dynamic interplay between culture, ideology, language, and policy.

The emphasis on culture and ideology has made me ever more sensitive to notions and images of personal liberty, equality of individual opportunity, free enterprise, and democratic government that are integral to the belief systems of Americans. Racism and sexism are also integral to our culture (probably to most cultures). These diverse beliefs coexist, conflict, and intersect. Within our heterogeneous society, different ethnic, religious, racial, gender, class, and professional groups contest the meaning of these cultural symbols and struggle to harness these concepts to serve their interests and promote their respective communal values. In the cauldron of clashing interests and competing ideas, foreign policy unfolds. For most Americans, foreign policy always has been a secondary or tertiary consideration. Indeed, we know too little about how subgroups within the populace sort out competing values and mesh them with precise domestic and foreign policies, policies themselves that often require tough

74 In addition to the citations in footnote 72 see Robert Jervis, "The End of the Cold War on the Cold War?" *Diplomatic History* 17 (Fall 1993): 651; and Lynn Eden, "The End of U.S. Cold War History? A Review Essay," *International Security* 18 (Summer 1993): 174–207.

tradeoffs between competing values. Thanks to pathbreaking work by Emily Rosenberg and Frank Costigliola, we do know, however, that officials partly consciously, partly subconsciously use gendered and racist language to mobilize support for and legitimize actions they wish to pursue.[75]

My plea is for more studies that try to link class, interest, and culture; geopolitics, political economy, and ideology; rhetoric, public opinion, and policy. These are separate categories of analysis; but they are also interactive. As we relate and compare them in new and innovative ways, we will enrich and reconfigure realism, revisionism, and postrevisionism, the modes of analysis that have set our interpretive boundaries for many years.

Some of us have a stake in these debates, and the reconfiguration of categories is emotionally wrenching and intellectually daunting. Some of us honestly do not believe that the new evidence or the new categories justify new reconfigurations. I can respect this position, and I think we should all welcome arguments that take note of new categories and configurations and demonstrate why the older ones remain more persuasive. I for one am convinced that however welcome are the new studies of culture, ideology, and rhetoric, their utility resides in their interaction with older categories of analysis that stressed political economy, geopolitics, and power – power both within particular societies and within the international arena.

We should, therefore, be reading, utilizing, and reconfiguring ideas from the many influential writers in our field. I say without hesitation that I have learned much from reading Bruce Cumings, Gabriel Kolko, and Walter LaFeber as well as John Gaddis, Geir Lundestad, and Ernest May, from reading Akira Iriye, Michael Hunt, Christopher Thorne, and Emily Rosenberg as well as Michael Hogan and Charles Maier. And if I am not always captivated by the new, I still find it useful to test the new against the old, and I continue to encourage students to read Samuel Flagg Bemis, Arthur P. Whitaker, Albert K. Weinberg, Thomas A. Bailey, and Frederick Merk. But students need not emulate either the new

75 Rosenberg, "Gendered Discourses in Dollar Diplomacy"; Costigliola, "The Nuclear Family: Cold War Gendered Discourse in the Western Alliance."

or the old; all of us simply have provided themes, arguments, and research agendas to explore and categories of analysis to reconfigure as the evidence dictates.

For me, however, the writings of William Appleman Williams still provide the best foundation for the architectural reconfigurations that I envision. Williams captured the essential truth that American foreign policy has revolved around the expansion of American territory, commerce, and culture. He understood that American foreign policy has been about preserving a way of life. He grasped the interrelationships between ideology and economics. And he demonstrated that we needed to look at social groupings, at farmers, businessmen, and missionaries, as well as at the state, in order to capture the totality of America's diplomatic experience.[76]

Yet there were problems with Williams's synthesis (as with any synthesis) that beckon for reconfiguration. He neglected the international system, understated threats and pressures that emanated from abroad, and discounted the real evil that existed in the world. He talked of an ideology and stressed a weltanschauung, but somehow the vitality of American cultural beliefs – of personal liberty, individual opportunity, and representative government – never gained the autonomy they merited and often were reduced to economic determinism. And lastly, he exaggerated the consensus that gathered around expansion as a solution to our domestic ills. As a result, he conflated the richness of domestic debates and the variety of reform movements, distorted the differences among interest groups, and overlooked the roles of self-interested bureaucracies.

Williams also suggested the destabilizing impact of American power and ideals on other societies and taught us to question both the wisdom of expansion and the virtue of American power.[77] During the Vietnam War those lessons resonated, as well they should have. But as we look at the world today, as we see the

76 See especially William A. Williams, *The Tragedy of American Diplomacy* (Cleveland, 1959); idem, *The Contours of American History* (Cleveland, 1961); and idem, *The Roots of the Modern American Empire: A Study of the Growth and Shaping of Social Consciousness in a Marketplace Society* (New York, 1969).

77 For a powerful recent reaffirmation of this viewpoint see LaFeber, *American Search for Opportunity*.

human travail in places like Bosnia and Rwanda, one can legitimately wonder whether a more interventionist orientation might promote a respect for the elemental rights of humanity that bind us as members of a world community. When we look at the appalling record of Communist rule, we may reflect that our record of opposing communism was not quite as ill-advised as Williams suggested.

Some observers will believe that these qualifications dilute the forcefulness of Williams's critique of American foreign relations. But I hardly think that is the case. Recognizing that American foreign policy has had great successes as well as failures seems to me simply a matter of common sense. Noting the accomplishments in places like Germany, Japan, and Western Europe, accomplishments that of course had their own costs and that were made possible by other governments and peoples as well as our own, in no way means that we need to forget the horrendous consequences of errors that our leaders made, for example, when they ordered UN troops across the 38th parallel in Korea or supplanted the French in Indochina.

Reconfigurations should take cognizance of successes and failures, of diverse motivations and ambiguous results. Triumphalism should be mooted even as we see the spread of liberal ideals. For ultimately, even our friends abroad have taken note that notwithstanding the appeal of our political ideals and mass consumption culture, something is lacking within our own society.[78]

In his recent book on the Cold War, Martin Walker, the well-known British correspondent, praises the role of the United States in the reconstruction of Western Europe and Japan yet sadly notes how different our societies have become. By the early 1990s, he writes, "the concept of the West as a series of liberal-capitalist democracies sharing common values was hardly tenable. In its attitudes to the death penalty, to the penal system, to the acceptance of violence, to abortion, to fundamental criteria of civilisation like health care for all, and in the wide disparity of incomes, the United States was sharply distinct from its European and Japanese allies. . . . No other NATO member used the death penalty. The

78 Thorne, *Border Crossings*, 275–306.

homicide rate among young males . . . was twenty times higher in the USA than in Britain, West Germany or France, and forty times higher than in Japan." A male black American, he goes on, was four times more likely to be in prison than his counterpart in South Africa, and if he lived in Harlem his life expectancy was worse than in Bangladesh. Moreover, during the 1980s, the number of children living in poverty increased by 22 percent; those in juvenile custody increased by 10 percent; and those experiencing violent death by 11 percent. In Britain and France there were four times as many poor people as rich people; in Japan, three times as many poor; in the United States, the figure was twelve times.[79]

This evidence illuminates how an examination of American foreign policy leads to transnational comparisons that, in turn, sharpen our understanding of our own society. We need to grasp how and why we have exercised power abroad and what have been the consequences of our actions both abroad and at home. In so doing we need to consider definitions of interest and perceptions of threat, the influence of ideology and the impact of culture, the role of language and the use of rhetoric. We need to look at the "state" and its constituent parts as well as its connections to society. We need to study the mediating influence of politics at home as well as analyze the constraints imposed by the distribution of power in the international system.

If we can assimilate the new approaches and reconfigure and integrate older interpretations, we will write monographs and syntheses for which our colleagues in other fields yearn. We will surprise ourselves by the fertility of our efforts and the utility of our work. No more will it be said that we were "marking time"; "thinking in time," we may even get ahead of our time.[80]

79 Martin Walker, *The Cold War: A History* (New York, 1994), 342–43.

80 I am referring to the influential essay by Charles S. Maier, "Marking Time: The Historiography of International Relations," in *The Past Before Us: Contemporary Historical Writing in the United States*, ed. Michael Kammen (Ithaca, 1980), 355–87; and to the prize-winning book by Richard E. Neustadt and Ernest R. May, *Thinking in Time: The Uses of History for Decision-Makers* (New York, 1986).

4

The Long Crisis in U.S. Diplomatic History: Coming to Closure

MICHAEL H. HUNT

Gordon A. Craig recently warned "historians are really more interesting when they are writing history than when they are talking about it."[1] Craig is undoubtedly right, but diplomatic historians, gripped by a long crisis of confidence, have had little choice.

Our remarkably sustained exercise in self-reflection and self-criticism spanning the last two decades was a defensive response to the pointed criticism, if not wounding indifference, directed at diplomatic topics by a historical profession in transformation. Social historians flogged diplomatic history, and political history more generally, for seemingly old-fashioned methods and concerns, especially the tendency to identify with the political elite and to ignore the links between policy and the patterns of privilege and power within American society and culture. The new cultural history added its own charges: epistemological naiveté and an impoverished sense of the importance of language for an

Michael S. Sherry, Otis Graham, and Leon Fink created opportunities for trying out some of the ideas laid out here. John W. Coogan, George C. Herring, Michael J. Hogan, Richard H. Immerman, Warren F. Kimball, William E. Leuchtenburg, Bradford Perkins, Thomas Schmitz, Russel Van Wyk, Odd Arne Westad, and several anonymous reviewers offered helpful comments as this paper has evolved over the last few years.

I use "diplomatic history" in the title and throughout the text as a familiar shorthand for work done on a variety of aspects of U.S. relations with the outside world. Readers who prefer some other label such as "history of foreign relations," "history of international relations," or even "international history" are welcome to make the appropriate substitution wherever "diplomatic history" appears.

1 Gordon A. Craig, "The War of the German Historians," *New York Review of Books*, 15 January 1987, 19. Craig had by then already offered his own reflections on diplomatic history – in "The Historian and the Study of International Relations," *American Historical Review* 88 (February 1983): 1–11.

understanding of both historical evidence and historians' discourse. Those with a strong theoretical bent consigned diplomatic historians to the role of the hewers-of-wood and the drawers-of-water in their world of international relations theory. The historians were to toil in the archives, constructing detailed case studies on which real social scientists were to raise grand explanatory structures that would account for the enduring patterns in international relations and that would command the respect of policymakers.[2]

The steady reflection on the state of the field, which has built to a crescendo in the last year or so, has been beneficial. The field is less beleaguered, and the long crisis seems to be drawing to a close. On the inside, diplomatic historians are writing about the field with a fresh confidence.[3] Other signs of strength are the growing membership of the Society for Historians of American Foreign Relations (now over thirteen hundred) and the liveliness of its journal *Diplomatic History*. On the outside, critics in other fields are experiencing their own self-doubts or are finding their claims to special insight contested.[4]

2 Self-criticisms by diplomatic historians are noted below. On vulnerabilities of the field as seen from outside see William E. Leuchtenburg, "The Pertinence of Political History: Reflections on the Significance of the State in America," *Journal of American History* 73 (December 1986): 485–87; Lynn Hunt, ed., *The New Cultural History* (Berkeley, 1989), esp. Hunt, "Introduction: History, Culture, and Text," 1–22, Patricia O'Brien, "Michel Foucault's History of Culture," 25–46, and Lloyd Kramer, "Literature, Criticism, and Historical Imagination: The Literary Challenge of Hayden White and Dominick La Capra," 97–128; John E. Toews, "Intellectual History after the Linguistic Turn: The Autonomy of Meaning and Irreducibility of Experience," *American Historical Review* 92 (October 1987): 879–907; Paul G. Lauren, ed., *Diplomacy: New Approaches in History, Theory, and Policy* (New York, 1979); and Michael G. Fry, *History and International Studies* (pamphlet; Washington, 1987).

3 For evidence of this newfound confidence and range see the contributions to "A Roundtable: Explaining the History of American Foreign Relations," *Journal of American History* 77 (June 1990): 93–180; and to "Writing the History of U.S. Foreign Relations: A Symposium," *Diplomatic History* 14 (Fall 1990): 553–605. Michael J. Hogan and Thomas G. Paterson, eds., *Explaining the History of American Foreign Relations* (Cambridge, England, 1991), reprints most of those contributions and supplements them with a few additional essays.

4 Leuchtenburg, "The Pertinence of Political History," 587–88; Joyce O. Appleby, "One Good Turn Deserves Another: Moving beyond the Linguistic: A Response to David Harlan," *American Historical Review* 94 (December 1989): 1326–32; Bryan D. Palmer, *Descent into Discourse: The Reification of Language and the Writing of Social History* (Philadelphia, 1990); Stanley Hoffmann, "An American Social Science: International Relations," *Daedalus* 106 (Summer 1977): 51–59; Susan Strange, "Cave! hic dragones: A Critique of Regime Analysis," *International Organization* 36 (Spring

Diplomatic history has reached a watershed whose significance justifies yet another act of introspection. Now is a good time to reflect on how the field has evolved and how it might further develop. No longer driven to meditate on whether it will survive or how to rescue it, we can turn now to the happier task of surveying the topography of a transformed field and identifying the variety of historical concerns that have come to define it.

The practical returns on such an attempt at stock taking add further to the argument for attempting it. As always, some shared understanding of the field is essential to corporate identity and in turn to our ability to orient newcomers and to explain ourselves to interested outsiders in history and international relations. The newcomers are a special concern. The process of training graduate students and ultimately helping them to develop a fruitful research agenda depends to a large degree on our ability to supply a clear and accessible picture of the major tendencies and developments at work within their chosen specialty. Above all, knowing the broad parameters of the field is indispensable if they are to locate their special research interests within the broader concerns of the field, identify assistance or provocation that may come from adjacent areas of investigation, and recognize questions that may for the moment lie beyond their technical competence or interpretive reach.

This effort at capturing the current condition of the field rests on a basic proposition – that U.S. diplomatic history has fragmented into three fairly distinct yet interdependent realms of inquiry. This fragmentation has occurred over the last three decades as increased attention to the domestic and international dimensions of policy has slowly diluted diplomatic history's preoccupations with policy and policymakers as a thing apart and left us with an expanded sense of the potentials and parameters

1982): 479–96; Robert W. Cox, "Social Forces, States and World Orders: Beyond International Relations Theory," in *Neorealism and Its Critics*, ed. Robert O. Keohane (New York, 1986), 204–54; Joseph S. Nye, Jr., and Sean M. Lynn-Jones, "International Security Studies: A Report of a Conference on the State of the Field," *International Security* 12 (Spring 1988): 5–27; and the special issue of *International Studies Quarterly* 34 (September 1990), devoted to poststructuralism, especially the essay by Jim George and David Campbell and the conclusion by the editors of this issue, Richard K. Ashley and R. B. J. Walker.

of the field. As the boundaries have moved outward, three domains have come to dominate the terrain within. Each defines itself by the set of fundamental questions about U.S. foreign relations that it seeks to address and by the tools – methods, theories, concepts, and language – that it employs to answer those questions. While within each there is a variety of interpretive views, each domain contains a prominent group or outlook with which it is primarily associated.

It is worth stressing here at the outset that this essay is not intended to categorize the domains into the good and the bad, the outmoded and the up-to-date, or to give priority to particular concepts, methodologies, or interpretations. Rather, its essential point is that the basic questions we pose are all of primary and equal importance. Taken together, they fundamentally define our work and constitute the field as a whole. The tools we use and the positions we take are derivative of and secondary to those questions.

The most imposing domain – the oldest and most populous – belongs to the study of the foreign policy of the American state. Its inhabitants concern themselves primarily with time-honored questions about the policy process that have long defined the field. What policies has the U.S. government followed? How were they made? Who made them? And how were they implemented? Consistent with this set of preoccupations, the main industry of this domain is the mining of American diplomatic archives and the processing of archival nuggets, and much of the talk heard on the street relates to the hard struggle to dig out the ore, to reports of mines opening and closing, and rumors about bonanzas in the offing.

In this land of state policy the leading citizens might best be described as "realists." The elders among them make up a long and distinguished list. George F. Kennan, whose *American Diplomacy, 1900–1950* is a classic of realism, is perhaps the best known.[5] Warren I. Cohen, Robert A. Divine, Robert H. Ferrell,

5 George Kennan, *American Diplomacy, 1900–1950* (Chicago, 1951). For a discerning appraisal of Kennan the realist see Anders Stephanson, *Kennan and the Art of Foreign Policy* (Cambridge, MA, 1989), chap. 6. The University of Chicago, where Hans Morgenthau and other political scientists did their work, has the best claim to being the home of realism. See especially Morgenthau's *Politics among Nations: The Struggle for Power and Peace* (New York, 1948); Robert E. Osgood, *Ideals and Self-Interest in America's Foreign Relations: The Great Transformation of the Twentieth Century*

John Lewis Gaddis, Norman A. Graebner, Arthur S. Link, Ernest R. May, and Gaddis Smith are others whose work at one time or other since the 1950s has taken on a pronounced realist orientation. The influence exercised by these established historians, not least as graduate mentors, has helped to make realism among diplomatic historians an extraordinarily influential syndrome.

If realism is a slippery term, assuming different meanings in a striking variety of contexts, its diplomatic history variant bears certain recurrent features.[6] Realists regard the state as the central actor in international relations and hence the primary unit of study. They contend that policymaking within the state is concerned with the pursuit and exercise of power, and therefore downplay or ignore economic forces and cultural influences. They see policymaking itself as a battleground between "realism" and "idealism" (or some similar set of evaluative categories used to distinguish good policy from bad). And they argue that in an anarchic international society marked by pervasive evil, "realism" is indispensable if political leaders are to maintain the national security. Realists in the field of diplomatic history, it must be stressed, draw on these interpretive concerns and analytic categories in a variety of ways that lead them to often divergent historical judgments.

Those in the realist domain reveal themselves most strikingly to us and to each other by their easily recognized language. Their discussions of the ultimate ends of American policy are marked by references to such self-evident concepts as "national interests," "vital interests," "international realities," "systemic pressures," and "geopolitical forces" to which policymakers are supposed to respond. They measure the soundness of policy by applying an "ends-means" calculus, by which they can judge whether policymakers, having identified the national interest, took the steps to mobilize the necessary resources. They deplore the intrusion of an "ignorant and emotional public" and "opportunistic politicians" into a policy process that should be the preserve of

(Chicago, 1953); and Tang Tsou, *America's Failure in China*, 1941–50 (Chicago, 1963). Appropriately, Kennan delivered at the University of Chicago the lectures that became *American Diplomacy*, and the University of Chicago Press published the volume.

6 For a sympathetically critical introduction see Michael J. Smith, *Realist Thought from Weber to Kissinger* (Baton Rouge, 1986).

realistic policymakers and their experts. They emphasize special American disabilities in foreign policy, the result of "moralism," "idealism," "legalism," and "isolationism." They celebrate "expertise" as the basis for a sound foreign policy and often personally identify with the "experts" who enjoy a prominent place in their studies.

This realist vocabulary facilitates discourse between U.S. diplomatic historians and those manning the foreign affairs bureaucracy in Washington, as well as the think tanks and foundations linked to that bureaucracy. Realism in the field grew up with the Cold War state as historians intent on understanding that state took its dominant language and dominant set of assumptions as their own. The result has been a much-traveled bridge between the world of scholarship and government. With their respect for and interest in the exercise of state power, realists have proven natural intermediaries between the scholarly community and an often indifferent or suspicious government. They have sought to establish the utility of history to policy formulation.[7] Their work and presence pervade government schools devoted to the training of the officer corps and the foreign service, no less than the schools of international service within the university. Their reassuring soundness makes them policymakers' natural ally in academe, where they serve as spokesmen for or explicators of official perspectives.

Realism is, moreover, marked by a sort of neo-Rankean style. It is given over either to the close examination of elite sources in an effort to find out what really happened or to attempts at synthesis drawing on works that directly tap official sources. Based directly or indirectly on careful, in-depth archival research, works in this genre develop a point of view as it emerges from the official record, using the language found in that record. The resulting publications offer guides to others wanting to make sense of the formidable official record and the complexities of official strategic doctrine and of the foreign affairs bureaucracy.

7 Ernest R. May has been at the forefront of this effort. See May, *"Lessons" of the Past: The Use and Misuse of History in American Foreign Policy* (New York, 1973); May, ed., *Knowing One's Enemies: Intelligence Assessment before the Two World Wars* (Princeton, 1984); and May and Richard Neustadt, *Thinking in Time: The Uses of History for Decision-Makers* (New York, 1986).

Preoccupied with an intricate policy process and structure, realists have energetically promoted the value of a more analytic approach by making use of strategic studies, bureaucratic politics, group and individual psychology, and the like. Some among the realists have even contended that by thus incorporating techniques and concepts pioneered by political scientists, diplomatic history could shed its old-fashioned image and become more respectable. As a rigorous and systematic endeavor, it would become more theoretical and policy relevant through its discovery of predictable patterns.[8]

But realism has its limits, which have become more evident as the field of diplomatic history expands and as its concerns become more diverse. The very identification with the state, with current policymaking, and with the underlying assumptions of the foreign policy elite that gives realism its strength also limits its intellectual range and analytic scope, in effect trapping realists (as their critics have argued) in a framework of inquiry that has a pronounced national as well as gender and class bias.

Perhaps the most troubling of realism's deficiencies are its questionable categories of analysis and its ahistorical interpretive themes. What is an informed public? How do we know one when we see one? Who are the experts that policymakers should listen to? Can real experts be expected to reach common conclusions? If they start from different premises and perhaps even have different political or organizational loyalties, then how do we determine who the real experts are? What is a realistic policy, and how can we tell if it meets the supposed requirements of the international system? What is the national interest, the knottiest no less than the most important notion in the realist lexicon? These large and

8 Among diplomatic historians, Ernest May, Gordon Craig, Melvin Small, Paul Lauren, and John Lewis Gaddis have advocated closer ties to political science. From the other side, Alexander George, Ole Holsti, Richard Ned Lebow, and Robert Jervis have advocated more contact with historians of the state. The outcome of this eclectic enterprise remains in some doubt. Thoughtful, even ingenious, attempts by political scientists to use history run the risk of making uncritical and derivative use of sources, retracing familiar historical ground to little effect, or arriving at obvious conclusions. Such at least seems to me the outcome evident in respectively David A. Lake, *Power, Protection, and Free Trade: International Sources of U.S. Commercial Strategy, 1887–1939* (Ithaca, 1988); Deborah Welch Larson, *Origins of Containment: A Psychological Explanation* (Princeton, 1981); and Stephen R. Rock, *Why Peace Breaks Out: Great Power Rapprochement in Historical Perspective* (Chapel Hill, 1989).

complicated questions cannot be resolved by obiter dicta or even by research in the archives of the American state.

The command of the archives can become for realists and others working in this realm of state policy a kind of tyranny that reinforces the tyranny of language noted above. The great temptation to which neophyte realists embarking on a doctoral dissertation often fall prey is to define projects not extrinsically but intrinsically – in relation to the government papers they most favor. Rather than first singling out a significant historical problem for study and then searching for the sources as well as methods appropriate to it, these historians are prone to look for a freshly opened or previously untapped set of government papers, to select a topic that corresponds to the contents and organization of those papers, and to end up exploring the official perspectives found there. The work proceeds on the questionable assumption that the resulting monographs will be important because the sources on which they draw are deemed important.

The preoccupation with the archives, especially the freshly opened ones, that is characteristic of scholars in this realm has also led to an increasingly serious problem of overemphasis on the post–World War II period to the neglect of earlier periods, especially the nineteenth century, and thus to an ironic diminution of historical perspective on the part of historians. A disproportionate number of dissertations and published monographs are now centered on the Eisenhower period as papers are opened for research. A fever for the Kennedy years is already on us, to be followed by a similar outbreak for the Johnson and Nixon presidencies. Archival research should not be regarded as pathological, but its grip can be so strong that it needlessly limits the range of concerns, chronological no less than topical, of those working on state policy.[9]

Finally, work done within this realm all too often suffers from a narrow conception of policy that makes a convincing evaluation

9 Of ninety-two articles, review essays, and notes/comments published in the inaugural issues of *Diplomatic History* (1977–1980), only twelve dealt with the years before 1898 and another ten looked at 1898–1913. The Cold War and above all the period 1945–1960, still claim the lion's share of attention according to recent reports by Michael J. Hogan, the current editor. See Hogan, "Annual Report of the Editor," *Diplomatic History* 13 (Spring 1989): 292–93; ibid. 14 (Spring 1990): 314–15; and ibid. 15 (Spring 1991): 313–14.

of that policy difficult if not impossible. This problem is strikingly evident in the work of the realists. They make much of a mercurial or intrusive public opinion but do not give public opinion data close, critical attention or bring to bear the insights from the relevant theoretical literature in a way that would render the argument compelling. Similarly, their evaluations of whether a particular policy served the nation well generally skirt such complex but crucial issues as the domestic resources diverted to foreign affairs or the domestic impact of policy decisions. Mastery of the American archives is invaluable, indeed essential, to the work of the field, but those who set themselves upon this task must recognize the limited horizons those archives define and guard against interpretive overreach.

The inhabitants of this realm of state policy have to date shown little creativity in responding to interpretive challenges to their narrow preoccupations. The first lost opportunity came in the 1960s and early 1970s when critics of realism made the case that economic calculations shaped U.S. policy. Some realists reacted by impugning the integrity of those historians and searching the archives for evidence to refute this slander.[10] No effort was made to engage the fundamental issue of where policy did come from (aside from the heads of policymakers and their advisers). Hobbled by what amounted to a naive positivism, they continued to treat official sources as final and authoritative. By taking them literally, realists spared themselves the task of considering social and economic influences, probing assumptions, wrestling with code words, and listening for evasions and silences. However much those working in the realm of the state wish to fend off those approaches, they will need to engage them directly if they are going to demonstrate, rather than just assume, state autonomy from society.

To the most recent challenge – posed by the revival of interest in the state in the 1980s – these diplomatic historians have responded with what seems almost studied avoidance. But like other elements in the realist faith, the state can no longer be taken for granted; it needs to be a structure of power, organized bureaucratically,

10 Peter Novick, *That Noble Dream: The "Objectivity Question" and the American Historical Profession* (Cambridge, England, 1988), 447–53.

deploying overwhelming coercive force, exercising an effective claim to legitimacy within a defined territory, and regularly laying claim to a substantial portion of the stream of income from the national economic product. Policy as an expression of state authority is better understood if viewed not in isolation but in relation to the distribution of power, intermediary institutions between state and society, resource flows, official recruitment and socialization, ideological formulations, and the maintenance of legitimacy.[11]

An overall evaluation of work done within the realm of state policy requires some care, because the shortcomings are closely wedded to the strengths. State policy is important, but so too is the impact of that policy in the real world, on the lives of real people. Bureaucratic paper may help us understand outlooks and decisions in Washington and its global outposts, but that paper may also at times constitute little more than the inconsequential by-product of large government organizations. The official archives are the most important single source for the field, but the preoccupation with those archives can lead to an unfortunate interpretive blinkering or its opposite, interpretive claims beyond the capacity of American state papers to sustain.

Those loyal to this realm of the state have suffered the most abuse as diplomatic history has undergone change, and they have had to give up the most ground as the other two realms have claimed a place for themselves. Critics have deemed the "diplomatic history" associated with this realm narrow, even anachronistic, and they have argued that the field needs a fresh designation such as "history of U.S. foreign relations" or even "U.S. international history" to make clear its break with the past. But a more expansive, less partisan view of the field as a whole would suggest that the state remains central. Even a radically reconstituted diplomatic

11 Pointing the way on this line of inquiry are Eric A. Nordlinger, *On the Autonomy of the Democratic State* (Cambridge, MA, 1981); Stephen Skowronek, *Building a New American State: The Expansion of National Administrative Capacities, 1877–1920* (Cambridge, England, 1982); Peter B. Evans, Dietrich Rueschmeyer, and Theda Skocpol, eds., *Bringing the State Back In* (New York, 1985), chaps. 1 and 11; Leuchtenburg, "The Pertinence of Political History," 589–600; James A. Smith, *The Idea Brokers: Think Tanks and the Rise of the New Policy Elite* (New York, 1991); and Louis Galambos, ed., *The New American State: Bureaucracies and Policies since World War II* (Baltimore, 1987), especially the essay by Charles Neu, "The Rise of the National Security Bureaucracy," 85–108.

history should not exclude "old" practices and concerns but rather accord them a place of respect alongside newer ones.

The second major domain lying within the confines of the new diplomatic history is devoted to linking policy to the domestic sphere. It emerged as questions about context and consequence increasingly jostled their way from the margins to a place of prominence in the field and demanded explicit and systematic treatment. What is the relationship between the foreign policies of the American state and the broader society? How have domestic economic systems, class structures, cultural values, political organizations and allegiances, and so forth shaped policy decisions? What impact have policy decisions had – immediate and long-term – on the domestic front?

The inhabitants of this domestic domain, laboring to account for origins and evaluate consequences, have not ignored government papers but instead have heavily supplemented them with other sources and extensively leavened them by use of the literature on American domestic history. The result has been studies developing a wide array of topics, including the intellectual roots of foreign policy,[12] its regional basis,[13] its impact on domestic culture,[14] its relationship to the world of science and technology,[15]

12 See, for example, on the early decades: Drew R. McCoy, *The Elusive Republic: Political Economy in Jeffersonian America* (Chapel Hill, 1980); Reginald Horsman, *Race and Manifest Destiny: The Origins of American Racial Anglo-Saxonism* (Cambridge, MA, 1981); Thomas R. Hietala, *Manifest Design: Anxious Aggrandizement in Late Jacksonian America* (Ithaca, 1985); Steven Watts, *The Republic Reborn: War and the Making of Liberal America, 1790–1820* (Baltimore, 1987); and Kinley Brauer, "The Great American Desert Revisited: Recent Literature and Prospects for the Study of American Foreign Relations, 1815–61," *Diplomatic History* 13 (Summer 1989): 395–417.

13 The South offers an intriguing example. For a recent contribution, which is also an introduction to the relevant literature, see Tennant S. McWilliams, *The New South Faces the World: Foreign Affairs and the Southern Sense of Self, 1877–1950* (Baton Rouge, 1988).

14 See, for example, for the Cold War era: Paul Boyer, *By the Bomb's Early Light: American Thought and Culture at the Dawn of the Atomic Age* (New York, 1985); Michael S. Sherry, *The Rise of American Air Power: The Creation of Armageddon* (New Haven, 1987); Spencer R. Weart, *Nuclear Fear: A History of Images* (Cambridge, MA, 1988); M. J. Heale, *American Anticommunism: Combating the Enemy Within, 1830–1970* (Baltimore, 1990); Stephen J. Whitfield, *The Culture of the Cold War* (Baltimore, 1991); and Susan Jeffords, *The Remasculinization of America: Gender and the Vietnam War* (Bloomington, 1989).

15 See, for example, Richard Rhodes, *The Making of the Atomic Bomb* (New York, 1986); Marek Thee, *Military Technology, Military Strategy, and the Arms Race* (London, 1986); and Walter A. McDougall, . . . *The Heavens and Earth: A Political History of the Space Age* (New York, 1985).

and the role of the media and public opinion.[16] Given the wide variety of directions their interests have taken, it should be no surprise to learn that historians associated with this domestic realm are a diverse lot, and some do not even think of themselves as diplomatic historians.

Among those who do, the most prominent are a loose group of "progressives." They share a preoccupation with the ways in which social privilege and economic power inform and sustain policy. They also share an antagonism toward realism – its incestuous and limiting relationship with policymakers, its treatment of the state as autonomous rather than intimately tied to the socioeconomic system, and its emphasis on the disruptive role of the public rather than on the public as the target of elite manipulation.

"Progressive" diplomatic history has its immediate roots in the interwar period and in the writings of Charles A. Beard. By the mid-1930s, Beard had come to argue that the economic system and those whose privileges depended on it had come to hold foreign policy hostage. Dependent on foreign markets for their prosperity, business interests, their allies in both political parties, and militarists had embraced a policy of economic expansion and entangled the country in foreign quarrels. The influence of Beard and like-minded historians such as Harry Elmer Barnes was to suffer eclipse in the early postwar period. The progressives were overwhelmed by a realist assault that questioned their intellectual sophistication and historical credentials.[17]

But in the 1960s the progressive impulse enjoyed a revival. William Appleman Williams, whose *Tragedy of American Diplomacy* proved an influential manifesto, played a leading role. Links to Beard were evident in Williams's 1959 work, with its emphasis on the economic roots of foreign policy and the rise of a market-oriented, open-door strategy that served the interests of corporate America. It was also evident in the writings of Walter LaFeber, Lloyd C. Gardner, Thomas J. McCormick, and Robert Freeman

16 See, for example, on the Vietnam War: Daniel C. Hallin, *The "Uncensored War": The Media and Vietnam* (New York, 1986); Kathleen J. Turner, *Lyndon Johnson's Dual War: Vietnam and the Press* (Chicago, 1985); and Melvin Small, *Johnson, Nixon, and the Doves* (New Brunswick, NJ, 1988).

17 Ellen Nore, *Charles A. Beard: An Intellectual Biography* (Carbondale, IL, 1983), chaps. 11, 13–15; Novick, *That Noble Dream*, 247–49, 291–92, 301–9.

Smith that appeared in the 1960s. These products of the seminars that Williams, and before him Fred Harvey Harrington, taught at the University of Wisconsin gave the open-door thesis a monographic underpinning. The Wisconsin group's position received additional support in the late 1960s and the early 1970s from other historians, also dubbed "new left" or "radical," such as Thomas G. Paterson, Gabriel Kolko, and N. Gordon Levin.[18]

The sudden outpouring of progressive work ignited a historical debate just as the Vietnam War began to break down the foreign policy consensus and to create growing interest in alternatives to realism. Much of the debate turned on the origins of the Cold War as progressives pounded away at what they took as the realist apologia for recent American policy. Washington's preoccupation with markets and the policy elite's fear of radical movements in the Third World not only explained the coming of the Cold War but also became a theme central to understanding earlier U.S. foreign policy.

This revival of the American progressive position and the historical warfare that it ignited invite comparison with contemporaneous developments in German historiography. German progressives such as Fritz Fischer and Hans-Ulrich Wehler emerged in the 1960s and engaged a well-entrenched historical establishment in a debate that still reverberates, much as the progressive-realist contest continues. The German historical establishment, which had survived the defeat in World War II and denazification, bore characteristics that call to mind American realists. It was strongly oriented to the study of the state, downplayed or ignored domestic social or economic forces, patriotically accepted the claims of *raison d'état*, eschewed questions of domestic costs, and displayed an aversion to systemic historical explanations. The outsiders wanted to broaden the research agenda – in the words of one, "to call attention to intrasocietal, socioeconomic

18 Williams's work and influence is best assessed in Bradford Perkins, "The Tragedy of American Diplomacy: Twenty-five Years After," *Reviews in American History* 12 (March 1984): 1–18. See also William G. Robbins, "William Appleman Williams: 'Doing History is Best of All. No Regrets.'" in *Redefining the Past: Essays in Diplomatic History in Honor of William Appleman Williams*, ed. Lloyd C. Gardner (Corvallis, OR, 1986), 3–19; and Walter LaFeber, "Fred Harvey Harrington," *Diplomatic History* 9 (Fall 1985): 311–19.

factors and to break up the ossified cliches of political history." Just as the spirit of Beard hovered over the American progressives of the 1960s, so Eckart Kehr with his emphasis on the role of class and bureaucratic interests in shaping of policy, inspired their German counterparts.[19] Taken together, the American and German cases serve as a powerful reminder that the treatment of anything as symbolically potent and politically consequential as the state is bound to give rise to profound tensions and divisions of opinion.

By the 1970s, progressive diplomatic history, which had never constituted an interpretive monolith, was moving along three distinctly divergent tracks. One sustained the emphatically economic interpretation of U.S. policy and recently has sought to bolster it by incorporating the insights of dependency and world-systems approaches.[20] But some established figures, along with younger progressives, began to explore alternative positions, moved in part by a barrage of critical evaluations that Marxist and business historians as well as realists had aimed at the economic interpretation with often telling results.[21] These historians thus began to move down a second track, putting aside systemic questions in favor of a critical examination of policy with an emphasis

19 Georg G. Iggers, *The German Conception of History: The National Tradition of Historical Thought from Herder to the Present*, rev. ed. (Middletown, CT, 1983); idem, *New Directions in European Historiography*, rev. ed. (Middletown, CT, 1984), chap. 3; Hans-Ulrich Wehler, "Historiography in Germany Today," in *Observations on "The Spiritual Situation of the Age": Contemporary German Perspectives*, ed. Jurgen Habermas and trans. Andrew Buchwalter (Cambridge, MA, 1984), 221–59 (quote from p. 238); Arthur Lloyd Skop, "The Primacy of Domestic Politics: Eckart Kehr and the Intellectual Development of Charles A. Beard," *History and Theory* 13:2 (1974): 119–31.

20 Gabriel Kolko, *Confronting the Third World: United States Foreign Policy, 1945–1980* (New York, 1988); Thomas J. McCormick, "'Every System Needs a Center Sometimes': An Essay on Hegemony and Modern American Foreign Policy," in Gardner, ed., *Redefining the Past*, 195–220, which summarizes the argument of his *America's Half-Century: United States Foreign Policy in the Cold War* (Baltimore, 1989).

21 Eugene Genovese, "William Appleman Williams on Marx and America," *Studies on the Left* 6 (January–February 1966): 70–86; Robert W. Tucker, *The Radical Left and American Foreign Policy* (Baltimore, 1971); William H. Becker, *The Dynamics of Business-Government Relations: Industry and Exports, 1893–1921* (Chicago, 1982); Becker and Samuel F. Wells, Jr., eds., *Economics and World Power: An Assessment of American Diplomacy since 1789* (New York, 1984); and Ernest R. May and John K. Fairbank, eds., *America's China Trade in Historical Perspective: The Chinese and American Performance* (Cambridge, MA, 1986).

on the role of expansionist ideas and of elite personalities.[22] Others set off on a third line of development, also influenced by the critics, by tempering but not abandoning claims that policy sprang from economic pressures.

This latter reformulation has come to be known as "corporatism." Initially focusing on the late 1910s and the 1920s but recently extending into the post–World War II period, the corporatists found a more manageable framework of inquiry in organized economic power blocs operating in intimate relationship with the state. Banks, industries, export associations, organized labor, and farm groups reflected and articulated the needs of a complex modern capitalism. This system of private and public power was managed by elites and sustained by a corporate ideology stressing compromise in the interest of overall growth and stability. The state played the critical role of coordinator among economic associations with sometimes divergent foreign policy needs, and the state in turn relied on its private allies to assist in the execution of policy.[23]

By making careful use of business and economic as well as political history, corporatists introduced a more complicated historical picture, one that saw no business consensus or monolith but rather diversity and that turned attention from social classes to a wide range of functional economic groups (including labor). While the corporatist shift has not silenced the critics of progressivism, it has drawn the two sides into a genuine dialogue of the sort generally absent earlier in the battle for interpretive preeminence, and has led to fruitful contacts with European historians

22 Lloyd C. Gardner, *Architects of Illusion: Men and Ideas in American Foreign Policy, 1941–1949* (Chicago, 1970); Walter LaFeber, *America, Russia, and the Cold War, 1945–1966* (New York, 1967); and Thomas G. Paterson, *Meeting the Communist Threat: Truman to Reagan* (New York, 1988).

23 For the most important attempts to delineate and defend the approach see Thomas J. McCormick, "Drift or Mastery? A Corporatist Synthesis for American Diplomatic History," *Reviews in American History* 10 (December 1982): 323–29; and Michael J. Hogan, "Corporatism: A Positive Appraisal," *Diplomatic History* 10 (Fall 1986): 363–72. Hogan has offered the most detailed corporatist treatment in *Informal Entente: The Private Structure of Cooperation in Anglo-American Economic Diplomacy, 1918–1928* (Columbia, MO, 1977); and *The Marshall Plan: America, Britain, and the Reconstruction of Western Europe, 1945–1952* (New York, 1987). For a general account with a corporatist slant see Emily S. Rosenberg, *Spreading the American Dream: American Economic and Cultural Expansion, 1890–1945* (New York, 1982).

also interested in state-society issues and in the impact of the international economy.[24]

The work of progressives and others in the domestic realm strikingly redresses the weaknesses of realism described above. Their most important contribution has been to call attention to the links between state and society and thus to break the bonds of the archives and a hermetic treatment of policy. In broadest terms, the progressives have argued that domestic forces are not to be dismissed as regrettable intrusions or recurrent nuisances but should be taken seriously as potentially potent forces that can give direction, as well as legitimacy, to policy. In particular, the progressives' insistence on the importance of material interests in policy calculations ended what Williams characterized as "the great evasion" and compelled even the most skeptical to wrestle with the progressive argument.

The progressives also deserve credit for directing greater attention to U.S. relations with the Third World and for arguing for a more empathetic and complex understanding of weak peoples confronting the claims of a Great Power. In their studies of American dominance, the progressives directly challenged development theory, the supposed benefits of multinational corporate presence, the rhetoric of benevolence, the pretensions to paternalism, and the frequent resort to military and covert intervention to block emergent nationalist forces.[25]

Out of the commendably broad and bold questions progressives ask come answers that leave them vulnerable to criticism.[26]

24 See John Lewis Gaddis, "The Corporatist Synthesis: A Skeptical View," *Diplomatic History* 10 (Fall 1986): 357–62; John Braeman's sympathetic appraisal in "The New Left and American Foreign Policy during the Age of Normalcy: A Reexamination," *Business History Review* 57 (Spring 1983): 73–104; and Warren I. Cohen, *Empire without Tears: America's Foreign Relations, 1921–1933* (Philadelphia, 1987), an effort to fit corporatist findings in a realist framework.

25 This progressive line of interpretation is still very much alive, as the following recent publications make clear: Jules R. Benjamin, *The United States and the Origins of the Cuban Revolution: An Empire of Liberty in an Age of National Liberation* (Princeton, 1990); James Schwoch, *The American Radio Industry and Its Latin American Activities, 1900–1939* (Urbana, 1990); Dennis Merrill, *Bread and the Ballot: The United States and India's Economic Development, 1947–1963* (Chapel Hill, 1990); and Marilyn B. Young, *The Vietnam Wars, 1945–1990* (New York, 1991).

26 Good points of entry for the criticisms summarized in this and the following paragraph are Perkins, "The Tragedy of American Diplomacy," and the works cited in footnote 21 above.

Progressives who contend that foreign policy arises from forces of production have not adequately grounded their accounts in economic and business history. For example, critics have repeatedly contended that the business community was far from monolithic in its strategies and its dependence on foreign markets, that overproduction elicited a variety of corporate responses of which only one was to look for new markets abroad, and that an expansionist foreign policy was largely irrelevant to the most important markets for American goods in Europe and Canada. Establishing greater congruence between economic developments and structure on the one hand and elite perspectives and policy on the other remains a major task for progressives.

Progressives who have turned from the economic system and accorded most of their attention to the views of the corporate and policy elite have encountered problems familiar to intellectual historians. If economic concerns are but one of a number of guiding notions in the heads of policymakers, then on what groods does the progressives' claim for the primacy of an open-door or corporatist ideology rest? Are noneconomic concerns necessarily marginal? Can the minds of policymakers or even businessmen be neatly compartmentalized into economic and noneconomic lobes? Critics preoccupied with these questions have noted with some distress the way progressives have handled the problem. Some have conceded the existence of other, noneconomic ideas, and after only summary treatment of them proclaim ex cathedra pride of place for the economic concerns. Others have established the predominance of economic ideas by pushing inconvenient or contradictory evidence to the background.

Whichever way progressives wish to take their argument, they will benefit from paying greater attention to neo-Marxist theory, to an anthropological concept of culture in which historians of the United States have taken a keen interest, and the new cultural history with its stress on the construction of reality. The first of these is certainly pertinent to the progressive preoccupation with the origins and nature of power. It touches, for example, on dependency, the relation of state (of which foreign policy is a major part) to civil society, and ideological hegemony. The concerns of anthropology could enrich a fundamentally materialist interpretation through its treatment of how the parts of a society fit together and adjust over time. Finally, the new cultural history would help bring germane but neglected topics into view, such as gender and the power of language. All approaches have something to offer a more complex and powerful progressivism.[27]

The progressive revival has restored a healthy tension to U.S. diplomatic history. It has stimulated debate over the form and intensity of economic interests and in general has encouraged a more systematic conception of U.S. policy. Now is a good time for progressives, who have regained a secure footing in the profession, to sharpen their treatment of the domestic roots of policy and to expand their agenda to give more attention to the domestic impact of policy. Such a more rounded treatment would add to the power and the progressive argument while helping to integrate topics now treated piecemeal within the new diplomatic history's domestic domain.

The third domain in the new diplomatic history is devoted to relating policymaking more rigorously and systematically to the international environment. The growing concern with context evident in the questions defining the domestic realm has also given rise to this domain. How have international developments influenced U.S. policy? And what consequences, unintended no less than intended, has that policy had for the broader world? While these questions are no less straightforward than the ones that command attention in the other realms, answers here can carry the historian in many different directions and require a wider range of research skills. In relating the United States to the world, practitioners of international history confront not only a host of governments interacting with Washington but also a great

27 My own *Ideology and U.S. Foreign Policy* (New Haven, 1987); and Enrico Augelli and Craig Murphy, *America's Quest for Supremacy and the Third World: A Gramscian Analysis* (London, 1988), attempt to exploit some of these insights, although at the expense of a more straightforward market interpretation. For additional discussion see Michael H. Hunt, "Ideology," and Emily S. Rosenberg, "Gender," both in "A Roundtable: Explaining the History of American Foreign Relations," *Journal of American History* 77 (June 1990): 109–10, 119–21; and Rosemary Foot, "Where Are the Women? The Gender Dimension in the Study of International Relations," *Diplomatic History* 14 (Fall 1990): 615–22. Rosenberg and Foot build on Joan W. Scott's observation in *Gender and the Politics of History* (New York, 1988), 48–49, that "high politics itself is a gendered concept."

multiplicity of societies and transnational social and economic processes that collectively define the global setting for U.S. policy.

The very diversity of this international research agenda has given rise to a rich array of interpretive frameworks and research strategies. The best known of these is the multiarchival approach to U.S. relations with the other Great Powers. Historians here have brought it up to date by paying more attention to the national political and international economic context in which U.S. policymakers and their foreign counterparts have acted.[28] The collaboration-resistance model formulated by Ronald Robinson from his study of the British imperial experience has offered a flexible framework for considering the origins and dynamics of the American imperium, especially in Latin America and Asia.[29] Comparative international relations, a subject in which British historians have also shown the way, has helped us to a fresh view of the American foreign policy experience while at the same time offering an antidote to lingering assumptions of American exceptionalism.[30] The dependency approach, with its strong neo-

28 The last fifteen years have brought an outpouring of multiarchival work, most of it on U.S.-European relations. The names of European-born or European-trained scholars, together with Americans more closely identified with European history than with U.S. diplomatic history, would dominate most reading lists. Christopher Thorne, Donald Cameron Watt, Rosemary Foot, David Reynolds, Kathleen Burk, Friedrich Katz, Klaus Schwabe, Geir Lundestad, Wm. Roger Louis, Charles S. Maier, Alan S. Milward, and Irwin M. Wall come immediately to mind.

29 The classic statement is Ronald Robinson, "Non-European Foundations of European Imperialism: Sketch for a Theory of Collaboration," in *Imperialism: The Robinson and Gallagher Controversy*, ed. Wm. Roger Louis (New York, 1976), 128–51. But see also Robinson, "The Excentric Idea of Imperialism, with or without Empire," in *Imperialism and After: Continuities and Discontinuities*, ed. Wolfgang J. Mommsen and Jürgen Osterhammel (London, 1986), 267–89; and J. Galtung, "A Structural Theory of Imperialism," *Journal of Peace Research* 8 (1971): 81–117. Ranajit Guha and Gayatri Chakravorty Spivak, eds., *Selected Subaltern Studies* (New York, 1988), particularly the two contributions by Guha, deserves attention for the way it extends Robinson's insights on the dynamics of dominion. For applications see "American Empire, 1898–1903," *Pacific Historical Review* 48 (November 1979): 467–605; Peter W. Stanley's survey of U.S.-Philippine relations in James C. Thomson, Jr., Peter W. Stanley, and John Curtis Perry, *Sentimental Imperialists: The American Experience in East Asia* (New York, 1981), chaps. 8 and 19; and Bruce J. Calder, *The Impact of Intervention: The Dominican Republic during the U.S. Occupation of 1916–1924* (Austin, 1984).

30 See, for example, Christopher Thorne, *The Issue of War: States, Societies, and the Far Eastern Conflict of 1941–1945* (London, 1985); Paul Kennedy, *The Rise and Fall of the Great Powers: Economic Change and Military Conflict from 1500 to 2000* (New York, 1987); and Phillip Darby, *Three Faces of Imperialism: British and American Approaches to Asia and Africa, 1870–1970* (New Haven, 1987).

Marxist thrust, coming out of Latin American studies, has proven attractive in thinking about the consequences of U.S. economic dominance.[31] The cultural-systems and social-structure orientations, with their strong anthropological and sociological points of view so appealing to those in Asian studies, have found their exponents among internationalists interested in identifying fundamental values and forces underlying international conflict.[32] Finally, some have stressed the importance of the transmission and impact overseas of American popular culture and of the hegemony of the U.S. media.[33] As this partial inventory suggests, the international domain is highly pluralistic, and some of the most striking work here (as in the domestic realm) has been done by scholars who think of themselves as diplomatic historians marginally if at all.

Of the internationalists, a group of Harvard-trained and Harvard-based historians have been the most consistent and articulate advocates of giving U.S. foreign relations a more global orientation. Over three generations they have made the case for "international history," thereby posing an increasingly formidable challenge to

31 See, for example, Gilbert M. Joseph, *Revolution from Without: Yucatan. Mexico, and the United States, 1880–1929* (New York, 1982); John Mason Hart, *Revolutionary Mexico: The Coming and Process of the Mexican Revolution* (Berkeley, 1987); and a series of studies of Cuba by Louis A. Pérez, Jr., including notably *Cuba between Empires, 1878–1902* (Pittsburgh, 1983). For recent evaluations of the dependency approach and attempts to move beyond it see Cristóbal Kay, *Latin American Theories of Development and Underdevelopment* (London, 1989); William B. Taylor, "Between Global Process and Local Knowledge: An Inquiry into Early Latin American Social History, 1500–1900," in *Reliving the Past: The Worlds of Social History*, ed. Oliver Zunz (Chapel Hill, 1985), 115–90; Steve J. Stern, "Feudalism, Capitalism, and the World System in the Perspective of Latin America and the Caribbean," *American Historical Review* 93 (October 1988): 829–72; and the penetrating and sensitive account by Piero Gleijeses, *Shattered Hope: The Guatemalan Revolution and the United States, 1944–1954* (Princeton, 1991).

32 For examples see Bruce Cumings, *The Origins of the Korean War*, 2 vols. (Princeton, 1981 and 1990); Glenn A. May, *Battle for Batangas: A Philippine Province at War* (New Haven, 1991); John W. Dower, *War without Mercy: Race and Power in the Pacific War* (New York, 1986); Michael H. Hunt, *The Making of a Special Relationship: The United States and China to 1914* (New York, 1983). For a discussion of research trends see Paul A. Cohen, *Doing History in China: American Historical Writing on the Recent Chinese Past* (New York, 1984).

33 For two fascinating case studies see Reinhold Wagnleitner, "The Irony of American Culture Abroad: Austria and the Cold War," in *Recasting America: Culture and Politics in the Age of the Cold War*, ed. Lary May (Chicago, 1989); and Hans Rogger, "*Amerikanizm* and the Economic Development of Russia," *Comparative Studies in Society and History* 23 (July 1981): 382–420.

the field's old identity. The pioneers, such as Archibald Cary Coolidge and William L. Langer, blazed trails that were broadened and extended by John K. Fairbank and Ernest R. May and by an impressively long list of younger historians trained at Harvard.[34]

The Harvard group itself drew on two major currents in the profession that have had an impact well beyond Cambridge. One was the Anglo-German tradition of studying state-to-state relations using the archives of each of the Great Powers. An early variant on historical realism, this approach was characterized by studies that crossed national boundaries. Out of close archival research came a detailed story of political and military leaders debating the national interest among themselves and negotiating the issues of war and peace with their opposite numbers. In Germany, the founding fathers of professional history, such as Leopold von Ranke and Wilhelm Humboldt, were themselves students of interstate relations. In Britain, internationally minded historians, most eminently Sir Charles Webster and F. H. Hinsley, were to gain sufficient autonomy to establish themselves in separate departments. Their international concerns fit nicely alongside the even older commitment of their colleagues to the study of the British empire.[35]

During the interwar period, Langer at Harvard and likeminded, Harvard-trained historians elsewhere, such as Samuel Flagg Bemis and Dexter Perkins, championed the ideal of multiarchival scholarship that would establish the place of the United States in the trans-Atlantic state system.[36] May's own early monographs and those of

34 These include Michael A. Barnhart, Roger Dingman, John W. Dower, Akira Iriye, Charles S. Maier, Charles E. Neu, Stephen E. Pelz, Peter W. Stanley, Joseph S. Tulchin, and Marilyn B. Young.

35 Iggers, *The German Conception of History*; Ronald Robinson, "Oxford in Imperial Historiography," in *Oxford and the Idea of Commonwealth: Essays Presented to Sir Edgar Williams*, ed. Frederick Madden and David K. Fieldhouse (London, 1982), 30–48; William C. Olson, "The Growth of a Discipline," in *The Aberystwyth Papers: International Politics, 1919–1969*, ed. Brian Porter (London, 1972), 3–29; Hedley Bull, "The Theory of International Politics, 1919–1969," in Porter, ed., *Aberystwyth Papers*, 30–55; Richard Langhorne, "Introduction," in *Diplomacy and Intelligence during the Second World War: Essays in Honour of F. H. Hinsley*, ed. Langhorne (Cambridge, England, 1985), 3–11; and Jonathan Steinberg, "F. H. Hinsley and a Rational World Order: An Essay in Bibliography," in ibid., 12–21.

36 William L. Langer, *In and Out of the Ivory Tower: The Autobiography of William L. Langer* (New York, 1977); Carl E. Schorske, "Introduction," in William L. Langer, *Explorations in Crisis: Papers on International History*, ed. Carl E. Schorske and

Bradford Perkins exploited the multiarchival method to illuminate the multiplicity of perspectives that the United States alongside European allies and antagonists brought to major crises.[37]

The second current that carried the Harvard group along was area studies, dedicated to an interdisciplinary investigation of both the Third World and the Second World, which comprised the Soviet bloc. Area studies began to develop in the interwar period and moved ahead rapidly after World War II, thanks to an infusion of foundation and government funds prompted by Cold War fears.[38] Area studies, most notably its East Asian and Latin American branches, introduced into the multiarchival method a sensitivity to the pervasive influence of international economic exchange, cultural systems and cultural values, images and stereotypes, the nonstate aspects of international relations, and the importance of cultural collision and cultural transmission. These area studies concerns, once largely foreign to diplomatic historians, have proven particularly helpful in dealing with U.S. interactions with countries and regions where sharp power differentials have existed and where official archives are less important because state structures are relatively weak.

At Harvard, Coolidge proved a foresighted entrepreneur who secured a place and the funds for research and instruction on neglected areas of the world. Following him, Fairbank established his own legend as an academic entrepreneur, building up a China field in which the study of Sino-American relations occupied an

Elizabeth Schorske (Cambridge, MA, 1969), ix–xliv; H. C. Allen, "Samuel Flagg Bemis," in *Pastmasters: Some Essays on American Historians*, ed. Marcus Cunliffe and Robin Winks (New York, 1969), 191–209; and Gaddis Smith, "The Two Worlds of Samuel Flagg Bemis," *Diplomatic History* 9 (Fall 1985): 295–302.

37 Ernest R. May, *The World War and American Isolationism, 1914–1917* (Cambridge, MA, 1959); idem, *Imperial Democracy: The Emergence of America as a Great Power* (New York, 1961); and Perkins's trilogy on Anglo-American relations, 1795–1823: *The First Rapprochement: England and the United States, 1795–1805* (Berkeley, 1967); *Prologue to War: England and the United States, 1805–1812* (Berkeley, 1961); and *Castlereagh and Adams: England and the United States, 1812–1823* (Berkeley, 1964).

38 Robert F. Byrnes, *Awakening American Education to the World: The Role of Archibald Cary Coolidge, 1866–1928* (Notre Dame, 1982); Robert A. McCaughey, "Four Academic Ambassadors: International Studies and the American University before the Second World War," *Perspectives in American History* 12 (1979): 561–607.

important place. Though trained himself along classic multiarchival lines, he would promote a broad cultural perspective.[39] To give a push to the study of trans-Pacific relations that emphasized both culture and archives, Fairbank together with May and Dorothy Borg launched the Committee on American-East Asian Relations. Their efforts helped to give rise to an important subfield that extended the international history approach into the difficult, non-European terrain where archives are often inadequate, language barriers are formidable, and the requisite training is more varied than that conventionally associated with diplomatic history. Those in this subfield took regular stock of their enterprise, sponsored international conferences that set a new standard for collaborative international history, and inspired a string of important studies dominated by the names of Harvard-trained students.[40]

From this group of Harvard internationalists have issued the most consistently critical appraisals and the most sweeping calls for transformation of U.S. diplomatic history. In 1962, May stepped forward as the champion of multiarchival international history. Such work, he argued, would promote a nonjudgmental, Rankean style of history and put to rest "parochial" single-nation studies excessively preoccupied by contemporary events, a flawed approach that he linked to Beard and other progressives. Almost a decade later in a seminal essay, May sharpened his critique, contending that traditional diplomatic history had lost its vitality and was perhaps "approaching demise." Once again he called for international history, though he had now expanded his conception of it to include notably the economic and ideological forces at work on policy. In 1980, after the passage of nearly another decade, Charles S. Maier glumly reported that diplomatic history had enjoyed "no wave of transforming research." Taking up May's call for international history to displace old-fashioned diplomatic history, Maier gave even more stress to the need for a broad

39 Paul M. Evans, *John Fairbank and the American Understanding of Modern China* (New York, 1988).

40 Warren I. Cohen, "The History of American-East Asian Relations: Cutting Edge of the Historical Profession," *Diplomatic History* 9 (Spring 1985): 101–12.

angle of vision to include "political structures, cultural systems, and economic arrangements."[41]

Since Maier's lament a decade ago, international history has securely established itself within U.S. diplomatic history. A wide range of voices has endorsed one or another of its variant approaches. *Diplomatic History*, the main journal in the field, offers good evidence that the internationalists have carved out a realm of their own and are now regularly and vigorously holding to account those with limited Washington perspectives or narrow diplomatic concerns who intrude on their turf.[42]

The emergence of this international realm has forced diplomatic historians in the other two realms to be more careful than ever in addressing questions about the global context for U.S. policy. Those focused on the American state must now think twice before positing the existence of some "international reality" to serve as an interpretive anchor for their accounts of U.S. policy, and eyebrows are sure to go up if their notion of that reality is extracted from and bears an unnerving resemblance to the evidence in the American archives. So long as students of the American state offer only perfunctory attention to the outside world, they cannot hope to make compelling (dare I say "realistic") estimates of the appropriateness of American perceptions and the efficacy of American actions to which they are habitually drawn. Progressives and others concerned with the domestic roots

41 Ernest R. May, "Emergence to World Power," in *The Reconstruction of American History*, ed. John Higham (New York, 1962), 180–96; idem, "The Decline of Diplomatic History," in *American History: Retrospect and Prospect*, ed. George Athan Billias and Gerald N. Grob (New York, 1971), 430; Charles S. Maier, "Marking Time: The Historiography of International Relations," in *The Past before Us: Contemporary Historical Writing in the United States*, ed. Michael G. Kammen (Ithaca, 1980), 355, 387.

42 See the extended reviews and historiographical surveys in *Diplomatic History*: Sally Marks, "The World According to Washington," *Diplomatic History* 11 (Summer 1987): 265–82; Christopher Thorne, "After the Europeans: American Designs for the Remaking of Southeast Asia," ibid. 12 (Spring 1988): 201–8; Donald Cameron Watt, "Britain and the Historiography of the Yalta Conference and the Cold War," ibid. 13 (Winter 1989): 67–98; Alan S. Milward, "Was the Marshall Plan Necessary?" ibid. (Spring 1989): 231–53; James Edward Miller, "That Admirable Italian Gentleman: The View from America (and from Italy)," ibid. (Fall 1989): 547–56; Geir Lundestad, "Moralism, Presentism, Exceptionalism, Provincialism, and Other Extravagances in American Writings on the Early Cold War," ibid. 527–45; and Lester D. Langley, "The United States and Latin America in the Eisenhower Era," ibid. 14 (Spring 1990): 257–64.

of policy must also be sensitive to the limits of their inquiries. In particular, those among them interested in empire have stressed the motives of the metropole to the neglect of the imperial relationship as it operates at the periphery. Their arguments need to pay more attention to the diverse pattern of economic and political penetration within the Third World and to the complicated dynamics at work within countries brought under imperial control.[43]

Cumulatively, the rise of an internationalist domain has made clear the importance of situating the United States in the global environment. Internationalists have successfully argued for according a place to other peoples on the international stage – not just because they deserve attention but also because their presence makes the U.S. role in the drama more comprehensible. By stressing class, ideology, and political culture in relation to the foreign policy of other countries, internationalists have also prompted students of American policy to take a closer look at those very forces within their own culture and have given them models and tools to help with the job. Finally, by revealing differences in cultural and national traditions and perspectives, internationalist work has highlighted the pervasiveness and dangers of ethnocentrism in historical writing no less than in policymaking.

This discussion should not suggest that the borders of the international realm are hermetically sealed. There has always been some movement into this realm from the others,[44] and attempts to migrate will be even more common in the future. But not all migrants have made the trip successfully, and those contemplating the journey would do well to obtain a visa indicating their ability to deal with the international issues their studies touch on, whether that means a good grasp of the international economy in the 1920s, of Soviet policy in the 1940s, or the nature of peasant mobilization in Vietnam in the 1960s. Those who set off without proper credentials now more than ever risk denunciation as interlopers.

43 Anyone wishing to invoke the notion of an "American empire" should first turn for conceptual orientation to Wolfgang J. Mommsen, *Theories of Imperialism*, trans. P. S. Falla (New York, 1980); and for historiographical guidance to Robin W. Winks, "The American Struggle with 'Imperialism': How Words Frighten," in *The American Identity*, ed. Rob Kroes (Amsterdam, 1980), 143–77.

44 Ernest R. May is a notable crossover from the realist side. Examples from the progressive side include Robert Freeman Smith, Gabriel Kolko, and Michael J. Hogan.

While their work has stimulated the imagination and extended the horizons of the field, the internationalists and especially the Harvard-based advocates have not thought through some of the unsettling implications of their approach. First, some have called for replacing narrow U.S. diplomatic history with a broad international history without considering in detail the feasibility or implications of such a shift. Why assume that U.S. diplomatic history need be narrow? Indeed, the problem of the field (at least as defined here) is its daunting breadth and complexity. There is a second response to the call for a total overhaul of the field: Any international history would consist, it is safe to say, of units of study broken down along national or cultural lines. It may be more useful to think of U.S. diplomatic history as one of those units, and hence to make the task of international history not the negation of but the fruitful engagement with nationally or culturally organized histories.

Second, most internationalist commentary on the field suggests that interstate relations should remain our fundamental concern. This position corresponds closely to the preferences in the other U.S. diplomatic history realms where the state is also the central, unquestioned point of reference. The resulting consensus would make U.S. diplomatic history essentially about understanding the state and setting it in the widest possible context, thereby revealing the sources as well as the consequences of policy decisions.

But other international historians, particularly those trained in area studies, have begun in their writings implicitly to raise questions about this state-centered conception of the field.[45] They would argue that nonstate actors do not assume importance only by virtue of their connections to state activity but that previously marginalized actors deserve a place in their own right on the international stage and deserve to be understood from their own sources and with the help of appropriate methodologies. Thus, we would not only pay more attention to but also look in a

45 I draw here on Charles R. Lilley and Michael H. Hunt, "On Social History, the State, and Foreign Relations," *Diplomatic History* 11 (Summer 1987): 246–50. For an early call for "diplomatic historians to also be social historians, and not only of our national society but others we treat as well," see Thomas J. McCormick, "The State of American Diplomatic History," in *The State of American History*, ed. Herbert J. Bass (Chicago, 1970), 139. McCormick repeats the point in "Drift or Mastery?" 319–21.

different way at immigrants subject to socioeconomic pushes and pulls as well as the restraints of nativists and policymakers, at refugees and their rescuers, at multinational firms with their networks to reach customers and obtain raw materials, at missionaries and the foreign communities they sought to create, and at agriculturalists caught up in commercialization. This redefined notion of what is international would allow, on the one hand, for a genuine social history in which "ordinary people" and their attempts to handle the opportunity and challenge found in unfamiliar settings would figure prominently. It would permit, on the other hand, a less constrained treatment of the international economy, one in which economic actors and those pulled within their orbit are not understood exclusively or even primarily in terms of state policy but through their own eyes and through their own sources.[46] If developments in either direction mean making room for nonstate actors in our research agenda no less than in our courses at the expense of the mighty who shape state policy, then so be it.

Internationalists and others skeptical of this line of argument are justified in asking if diplomatic historians, who have enough on their hands now, should branch out into arcane topics where economists, sociologists, and anthropologists would be more at home. If the field is essentially about the study of U.S. policy, then these social and economic actors really are incidental. To date, those committed to the study of the state have not offered a clear response to the challenge posed by those arguing for more attention to the social and economic forces promoting global interpenetration.

This tension within the internationalist realm needs more thought, for a field focused essentially on the state is markedly different from one guided by broader and more eclectic concerns. For the moment at least, it seems safe to predict that the state, considered from one perspective or another, will remain the

46 Two recent works, both intent on setting the current debt crisis in perspective, illustrate the importance of international history that moves beyond the state: Stephen A. Schuker, *American "Reparations" to Germany, 1919–33: Implications for the Third-World Debt Crisis* (Princeton, 1988); and Barbara Stallings, *Banker to the Third World: U.S. Portfolio Investment in Latin America, 1900–1986* (Berkeley, 1987).

dominant concern, claiming the bulk of our research and teaching energies. That would not be a particularly disappointing outcome as long as we keep in mind the broad framework in which the state operates *and* begin tentatively to explore ways of incorporating into our work social and economic insights.

Alongside the fundamental problem of defining the focus of international history, the third realm faces a variety of practical problems that are deserving of attention. Even an international realm that remains essentially state-centered places heavy demands on diplomatic historians and sows confusion among them. While making diplomatic history overall more spacious and more complex, the internationalist agenda has at the same time blurred field parameters, set in doubt the bases of community among specialists, and made difficult scholarly discourse. Who is a specialist in U.S. foreign relations? What kind of research and teaching does one do? How should the next generation of graduate students be trained? How should search committees define their ideal candidate?[47]

That we are now asking these unsettling questions should be seen as a tribute to the transformative impact internationally minded historians have had. For a field set in flux in the 1960s by the revival of progressivism, their own innovative work and their forceful critiques of the field have added fresh impetus for change. Their appearance on the scene has not only further broadened field boundaries but has also helped to defuse the conflict between progressives and realists. Internationalists have highlighted deficiencies in the claims and methods of both camps, and have suggested at least by example that the concerns of the three domains are at heart not mutually exclusive but complementary.

Out of the travails that U.S. diplomatic history has gone through has come a renewal. It has been characterized by a steady expansion of the questions that the field counts as central to its inquiry. The near monopoly the realists established in the early postwar period has broken down. The revival of progressive work first put in question the autonomy of the state and brought under

47 I have addressed these questions in "Internationalizing U.S. Diplomatic History: A Practical Agenda," *Diplomatic History* 15 (Winter 1991): 1–11.

scrutiny realist premises. The development of international history has in turn raised even more questions about the centrality of the state to the field, while underlining the need for both international and comparative dimensions. The resulting development of greater interpretive breadth and methodological diversity gives support to the claim that U.S. diplomatic history's long crisis is coming to an end.

The more expansive conception of our enterprise is expressed most clearly in the questions that we now self-consciously ask and attempt to tie together. These questions define the classical but sometimes neglected concerns by which the significance of all works may be judged. Where does policy ultimately come from – the international system or the domestic sphere? Are policymakers relatively autonomous actors? Through what lenses do they perceive the world? How does U.S. policy compare with that of other countries? Is there a common set of forces working on all policymakers, or does it vary significantly by country, culture, and time? How do we evaluate policy decisions, particularly when the consequences of those decisions are felt and must be understood in the context of another culture? While no single study can engage this full range of questions, they do define the broad parameters of the field: the range of problems that preoccupy specialists, the kind of research projects most eligible for support and publication, the kinds of literature to appear on reading lists, and the variety of topics to teach.

Putting emphasis on the questions we ask is the best way to clarify the altered structure of the field. To attempt to survey the field by following specific interpretive differences is to march into a historiographical morass. A plethora of labels – traditionalist, nationalist, isolationist and neo-isolationist, court historian, internationalist, orthodox, realist, New Left, the Wisconsin school, the open-door school, corporatist, postrevisionist, conservative, neoconservative, and so forth – have grown up, each carrying almost as many meanings as there are historians.[48] Outsiders understandably regard this complex and ambiguous system of naming as

48 The Cold War literature alone requires six categories of interpretation according to Jerald A. Combs, "Cold War Historiography: An Alternative to John Gaddis's Post-revisionism," in the SHAFR *Newsletter* 15 (June 1984): 9–19.

empty scholasticism, while those in the field squirm uncomfortably in the tangle.

If this babel of labels is not enough to undermine faith in using interpretations to assess the field, then incorporating the main insights from Jerald Combs's detailed, thorough historiographical survey is sure to bring on the final collapse. Combs demonstrates how public debate in the wake of each major American war has set diplomatic historians off on a relentless and far-reaching reinterpretation of the field.[49] Combs's findings make it easy to think of the field in terms of a collection of ill-defined labels rearranged from time to time in kaleidoscopic fashion. We would do well to avert our gaze from this dizzying, almost psychedelic vision.

Defining the field in terms of its basic lines of inquiry also has advantages over the tendency, evident in the most recent round of writing on the state-of-the-field,[50] to organize our understanding in terms of commanding methodologies, key topics, or levels of analysis. An awareness of the range of tools and the kinds of categories available is invaluable to the researcher. But as the tools, methodologies, and levels formally laid before us multiply, overlap, and call for clarification, we begin to re-create some of the semantic confusion and conceptual jumble associated with defining the field in terms of interpretive positions. The result is to leave unclear how parts of the field fit together and how once assembled the field as a whole looks.

The picture of the field advanced here is a simpler and more functional one – as a collection of complementary, not contending or mutually exclusive, lines of inquiry, which, taken together, help us know a large and complex whole. Realists and others working within the domain of the American state will help us maintain contact with archives and the intricacies of the policy process. Progressives and their fellows in the domestic realm will keep us in touch with developments in the literature of American history essential to dealing with the domestic origins and consequences of policy. Finally, internationalists, with their own diverse

49 Jerald A. Combs, *American Diplomatic History: Two Centuries of Changing Interpretations* (Berkeley, 1983).

50 See the works cited in footnote 3 above as well as Stephen E. Pelz, "A Taxonomy for American Diplomatic History," *Journal of Interdisciplinary History* 19 (Autumn 1988): 259–76.

set of concerns will make sure that we keep in sight the global environment within which Americans operate.

This vision bears important implications for the spirit in which we handle our differences. A field as fragmented yet intradependent as U.S. diplomatic history has become is best served by a genial tolerance. We need no civil war among the principal domains or a balkanization of the field that arbitrarily obstructs free movement from one domain to the other. We can well do without a confining and disruptive sectarianism that proclaims the primacy of one realm over others and seeks to deny the multiplicity of concerns that have come to define U.S. diplomatic history. The marvelous diversity of the questions that we now ask and of the resulting interpretations that we now offer is bound to defeat those promoting some simple synthesis or new stabilizing orthodoxy.

The framework proposed here for understanding the field seems particularly pertinent to the looming, politically charged debate over who won the Cold War. Polemicists and patriots may trumpet an American victory, but historians conscious of the concerns of each of our three domains will avoid a rush to judgment. Those in the first realm can remind us that less than half of the relevant American records are available and that covert operations and intelligence assessments are so ill documented as to leave a significant gap in the half that is open. By bringing the second realm into the equation, we complicate our evaluation by considerations of how domestic concerns informed Cold War policy and how in turn domestic values and institutions were themselves influenced by the alarms and mobilization of the time. An appraisal becomes still more difficult and complicated once we add the perspective of the third realm. Documentation on friends and foes is strikingly uneven, with virtually no period or major problem fully documented from all sides engaged in the Cold War struggle.[51] Beyond foreign archives, we need to know how Cold War pressures and policies changed foreign societies and economies. Thinking in terms of the three domains underlines the enormous amount of work left to do before we can

51 Albert Resis's thoughtful and fresh *Stalin, the Politburo, and the Onset of the Cold War, 1945–46* (pamphlet; Pittsburgh, 1988), is a sobering reminder that it has taken almost half a century to come to terms with postwar Soviet perceptions. Soviet sources remain problematic, though at the moment the foreign ministry is promising

provide a full and ample description of the Cold War, not to mention an evaluation of its costs. Once all this is done, announcing winners and losers will seem as misguided as the earlier, equally sterile effort to assign clear-cut responsibility for the origins of the Cold War.[52]

This vision of a three-realm field also carries implications for our individual research agendas. It argues paradoxically for seeing the field in its breadth yet recognizing personal limits. The realms discussed here do not imprison diplomatic historians. Movement from one to another is not only possible but desirable. By breaking out of conventionally defined limits of inquiry and breaking down barriers that compartmentalize scholarship, diplomatic historians would be contributing to the solution of a problem now widely recognized in the profession. In practice, however, the realms have limited our mobility and will continue to do so. Most historians have tended over the course of a career to inhabit one or at most two of those domains. A strong and understandable attachment to familiar issues, sources, and methodologies – a kind of comparative advantage that each historian develops – tends to offset any impulse to migrate. Those who do stray from familiar ground face the challenge of mastering new skills and tools – whether economic analysis, social theory, or a particular foreign language and culture – appropriate to their new place of residence. As we become more sensitive to the distinctions among the realms, we also become more aware of the difficulties of gaining and maintaining dual citizenship.

The growing specialization of labor discussed here raises the

fairly unfettered access to its archival materials thirty years or older. On the new possibilities for sketching in parts of China's Cold War history see Michael H. Hunt and Odd Arne Westad, "The Chinese Communist Party and International Affairs: A Field Report on New Historical Sources and Old Research Problems," *China Quarterly* no. 122 (Summer 1990): 258–72; and Hunt, "Beijing and the Korean Crisis, June 1950–June 1951," *Political Science Quarterly* 107 (Fall 1992): 453–78.

52 Important initiatives aimed at promoting a broad appraisal include the 1990–91 meetings of the "Working Group on the Cold War" chaired by Gar Alperovitz and supported by the Institute for Policy Studies; a conference on "Rethinking the Cold War" convened by Allen Hunter and Richard McCormick at the University of Wisconsin in honor of William Appleman Williams in October 1991; and "The Program on the International History of the Cold War," an archives-oriented effort based at the Woodrow Wilson International Center for Scholars, funded by the John D. and Catherine T. MacArthur Foundation, and guided by a committee consisting of John Lewis Gaddis, William Taubman, and Warren I. Cohen.

risks of dilettantism for all researchers – from senior scholars to graduate students working with their advisers and dissertation committees – who seek to address simultaneously basic questions from several realms. All need to confront this risk self-consciously and honestly. Cross-over research needs to be more than just plausible; it needs to offer and evaluate evidence with sufficient knowledge and rigor to stand up to the scrutiny of specialists. Thus, for example, students of U.S. policy convinced of Stalin's responsibility for the Cold War or of the effectiveness of the American strategy of driving a wedge between China and the Soviet Union must do more than rely on fragmentary or circumstantial evidence, a procedure they would quite rightly object to if applied by others to their own area of expertise. Similarly, an account of U.S. economic policy toward Latin America that seeks to generalize about impulse and impact should build on and be able to pass muster with economic historians and regional specialists. Or, to take a final example, works that argue for public constraints on policymaking should offer a picture of the "public" and the reciprocal influence between that public and policymakers that social and cultural historians can take seriously. It would be possible to draw up a long list of fine studies marred by the incorporation of dubious interpretive claims and of distinguished authors who have asked questions that they were not prepared to answer.

The crisis that has transformed U.S. diplomatic history has left a residue of disagreement on future directions. Some have been arguing since the early 1980s that the field is healthy and that fundamental changes have gone far enough.[53] Proponents of further change, who for the most part identify with international history, respond that many of the practices and outlooks associated with the old diplomatic history have proven distressingly tenacious. Too much of the research is still archivally driven. The

53 See, for example, Cohen, "The History of American-East Asian Relations"; the dominant response to Maier in *Diplomatic History* 5 (Fall 1981): 353–82; Stephen G. Rabe, "Marching Ahead (Slowly): The Historiography of Inter-American Relations," ibid. 13 (Summer 1989): 297–316; Ralph B. Levering, "The Importance of the History of American Foreign Relations," *OAH Newsletter* 12 (May 1984): 20–22; Alexander DeConde, *American Diplomatic History in Transition* (pamphlet; Washington, 1981), esp. 3, 46–48; and idem, "Essay and Reflection: On the Nature of International History," *International History Review* 10 (May 1988): 282–301.

sheer volume of documents on U.S. policy during the Cold War era particularly distorts the field. The growing quantity and complexity of the new documentation to track down, get declassified, survey, and digest could by itself monopolize much of the talent in the field for years to come, while at the same time directing dialogue into well-worn channels and discouraging the development of work outside the Cold War era and on nontraditional topics. Too many works, especially by younger scholars, still ignore social and economic processes and neglect non-American perspectives. Do we really need, for example, some half dozen accounts of the origins of U.S. involvement in Vietnam when we have so little talent within our own ranks devoted to translating the Vietnamese experience of revolution, war, and reconstruction and relating that experience to parallel developments on the American side? And while multiarchival research has grown apace, much of it remains confined to Anglo-American relations, much of it is written by European historians, and little of it can be found where papers are less conveniently handled than in the Public Record Office or the National Archives and where they are less conveniently cast in some language other than English.

This divided judgment about the current state of affairs should not be taken as simply a reflection of personality type – the habitual booster at odds with the congenitally cranky. This disagreement reflects the degree to which the rise of the two newer realms has raised questions about the future development of the field that deserve debate and discussion. How prominent a role is each realm to play, what standards of admission to each should apply, and what kind of studies deserve priority? This guide cannot resolve those questions, but it is offered as a commonsensical framework for further dialogue. A German historian, familiar with the dissension and confusion that changes in diplomatic history can stimulate, has made the case for ongoing discussion in language worth quoting. "Conflicts are not onerous disturbances of scholarly harmony that ought to be avoided. Rather, . . . conflicts further scholarly progress and contribute to a freer and more critical consciousness."[54] Good reasons to keep talking.

54 Wehler, "Historiography in Germany Today," 251.

5

Commentaries

BRUCE CUMINGS, MELVYN P. LEFFLER, AND MICHAEL H. HUNT

"Revising Postrevisionism" Revisited

BRUCE CUMINGS

After *Diplomatic History* published my essay, "'Revising Postrevisionism,'" I got the impression that John Lewis Gaddis, Melvyn P. Leffler, and others I had criticized had trouble working up enthusiasm for what I had said. Perhaps they felt like the German composer Max Reger who, upon reading a critical review, wrote to the critic as follows: "I am sitting in the smallest room in my house. I have your review in front of me. Soon it will be behind me." Or perhaps they would agree with Samuel Johnson when he said, "I found your essay to be good and original. However the part that was original was not good and the part that was good was not original."

In the time that has since passed, Gaddis's distaste has grown not just for my essay but for the journal and the editor who published it: Now (not before, but only now) he thinks that sound editorial policy at *DH* has given way to incivility, unbalanced judgment, and unfair procedure.[1] It is a pity, because my essay was not so much a critique of John Gaddis or Mel Leffler as of the discipline of diplomatic history, and especially the keepers of

These are edited but essentially unexpurgated remarks that I made during the plenary session debate between yours truly and John Lewis Gaddis at the SHAFR Annual Meeting in June 1994 at Bentley College. I have added or updated a few things, and taken account of Mel Leffler's essay in this volume, but otherwise have not revised the text much.

1 The reference would be to the hundreds of pages of communications by fax, mail, and other means that John and his friends have sent to Michael Hogan and copied to many other historians. I would like to thank John, with a special thanks to Alonzo Hamby and Arthur Schlesinger, Jr., for enlivening my fax machine.

the field. Those I singled out included my acquaintances, my friends, and people I do not know, as well as Gaddis and Leffler. It was in a sense an old, anachronistic critique, one I could have imagined myself writing in the 1970s or early 1980s. It was really the persistence of certain ways of thinking down to the present, in spite of a generation of new scholarship and a lot of fully lived history, that struck me as odd and in need of the intellectual weapon of critique. Above all, perhaps, I came to write it because of the ideological consequences of the passing of the Cold War, particularly its eye-opening endnote of victorious crowing and liberal self-congratulation.

I did not want to say of the field that "there is no there there," merely to paraphrase once again Gertrude Stein on Oakland, California. I wanted to say what the *San Francisco Chronicle*'s venerable columnist Herb Caen said about Oakland: "The trouble with Oakland is that when you get there . . . it's there!" The trouble with the field is that it is still *there*, still scribbling commentaries on *FRUS* documents. Some of those who are "there" are my best friends (these are the people who are particularly happy that I did not mention their names in my essay). But in spite of these friendships, and even though I have also been known to scribble on *FRUS* documents, my intention was to rake through the field and beat about the underbrush beneath many practitioners, not to single out Gaddis as a test case of bland ambition.

Nor Melvyn Leffler, for that matter, although he, too, seemed less than enthusiastic about my critique, both at the time and in the presidential address included in this volume. Leffler has now joined Gaddis in arguing that "postmodernists" do not care about truth. First we need to ask, what is "postmodernism"? There is the long answer to this question, but here let me suggest the relevant short answer: "postmodernism" should not be yet another label affixed to that work which diplomatic historians abhor or do not understand. Nietzsche, Foucault, Derrida, Lacan, Baudrillard, and Virilio, to list a few prominent names, are very different thinkers. I think Baudrillard is the least of them, and yet he would be the only one happy with the label "postmodern." For my money, David Harvey has called the postmodern Rumpelstiltskin by its real name, that is, a relatively new political economy of "flexible accumulation" on a world scale that systematically disorders every national economy and every attempt at national regulation, right before our mid-1990s eyes.[2] A global hyper-capitalism of incessant change and dislocation moving with blinding speed into huge new markets (China, the former Soviet bloc, Indonesia, Mexico) is the "non-discursive" element that shapes the postmodern discourse. Yet more than a century ago we find Friedrich Nietzsche articulating a logic not of postmodernity but of *modernity*, and finding in this logic the same disordering principle. He wrote in 1888 that "what is attacked deep down today is the instinct and will of tradition: all institutions that owe their origins to this instinct violate the taste of the modern spirit.... One considers tradition a fatality; one studies it, recognizes it (as 'heredity'), but one does not *want* it.... It is the disorganizing principles that give our age its character."[3]

Think about American politics in 1995: We have a man going by the name of Newt with what he thinks is a contractual agreement to organize our age, while claiming simultaneously to be historian, conservative, traditionalist, free trader, futurologist, cyberspace fanatic, and champion of "family values." This is the same man who presented his first wife with divorce papers when she was recuperating from breast cancer treatment and whose sister is a gay/lesbian activist who disagrees with him on everything, big and small. This man is also an untiring lobbyist for the defense industries located in his congressional district, but somehow that is one of the last things we learn about him in our media. Surely a Nietzsche, if not a "postmodernist," wrote this absurd American script. Nietzsche was a genius, and his work is simultaneously complex, brilliant, repellent, deeply learned, shaped (as all human thought must be) by the time in which he wrote, and thoroughly honest and critical in the best sense. One cannot read his work in our time without the uncanny sense that one is in the presence of prophecy, just as one can find in it nearly

2 David Harvey, *The Condition of Postmodernity: An Inquiry into the Origins of Cultural Change* (Oxford, 1989). See also Frederic Jameson, *Postmodernism, Or, The Cultural Logic of Late Capitalism* (Durham, 1991).

3 Friedrich Nietzsche, *The Will to Power*, trans. Walter Kaufmann and R. J. Hollingdale (New York, 1967), 43.

everything that Foucault brought to bear on his own archival inquiries (as the latter frequently admitted).

Meanwhile, in a recent round-robin letter to me and several others, John Gaddis refers to Nietzsche as a "protofascist" and says I denied in my critique of his work "that there is any basis for making judgements about truth in history."[4] To confuse a great philosopher about whom there is a large library of postwar scholarship with events that came a half-century after his death is rather like a twenty-second-century historian blaming John Lewis Gaddis for a twenty-first-century dictator slaughtering millions in the name of "postrevisionist consensus." Furthermore, my point was not that truth in history is impossible, but that we can hardly make intelligent judgments about people like William Appleman Williams, Gabriel Kolko, Walter LaFeber, Thomas J. McCormick, or the "corporatists" if we appear to have no idea what they are talking about and consistently cubbyhole and caricature their thought. I can also replay one passage from my essay in case some convenient forgetting has transpired: "The diplomatic historian's code ought always to be this: 'The state never has any use for truth as such, but only for truth which is useful to it.' "[5] The state that Mel Leffler tells us "we deal with" has no use for the truth; it is not a question of whether there is truth in history.

Mel Leffler has a different reading of my essay, saying that I lump him together with John Gaddis and labeling the name of my "particular theory" not proto-fascism but "world-systems theory." He then goes on to argue that "no single theory can explain the dynamics of American foreign relations" or provide the "types of syntheses" he is looking for. I suppose it would be nice if detractors focused on my own historical scholarship rather than one critical and often polemical essay; they will find there a minor and, in my view, judicious use of some aspects of world-system analysis, plus much else. Still, I would urge Professor Leffler to reread that essay, because I sharply *distinguish* him from Gaddis and have much praise for a book that I admire and

4 John Gaddis to Bruce Cumings, Michael Hogan, Michael Hunt, Melvyn Leffler, Robert Dallek, et al., 1 February 1995.

5 Nietzsche continues, "more precisely for anything whatever useful to it whether it be truth, half-truth, or error." "Schopenhauer as Educator," in *Untimely Meditations*, trans. R. J. Hollingdale (New York, 1983), 190.

now always require my students to read – in spite of the bulk and cost of *Preponderance of Power*. I do argue that it needed more theory, but not necessarily world-system analysis. He could have started not with Immanuel Wallerstein but with Dean Acheson, whose "theory" clearly places a conception of world economy above geopolitical and geostrategic approaches and distinguishes his thought and his early postwar foreign policy architecture from that of George Kennan and, it goes without saying, the Joint Chiefs of Staff. (This thought and the many pages I have written about it elsewhere become, in Leffler's rendering herein, my boneheaded notion that Acheson was "an agent of world capitalism," not to mention my stunning incapacity to "take the notion of freedom . . . seriously" – as did, no doubt, Mr. Acheson himself, not to mention Dwight David Eisenhower.)

Professor Leffler could also ask himself what a Nietzsche or a Foucault would say of the concluding remarks in his book *A Preponderance of Power* about how power insinuates itself into a "truth" that American policies toward the First World were "wise" while those policies made by the very same wise men toward the Third World were "foolish." But the last thing I want to do is offend Mel Leffler any more than I already have, so let me just say this: His is a fine book.

As for "postmodernism" and truth, we might better call it critical theory and urge diplomatic historians to become familiar with it sooner rather than later, because its march into the study of international history and politics is inexorable. Leffler argues that "we deal with power"; well, both Nietzsche and Foucault were philosophers of power. Foucault in particular made an indelible contribution to our understanding of that thing so essential to international relations, the stuff of politics itself, the incantation mesmerizing the "realists," and what "we deal with": *power*. Foucault did not say there is no truth, but that power produces its own truth, a "truth" visible in the state, in the textbooks, even in the daily-life body language of the powerful and the weak.[6] The difference between the work of John Gaddis

6 See Michel Foucault, *Power/Knowledge: Selected Interviews and Other Writings, 1972–1977*, ed. and trans. Colin Gordon et al. (New York, 1980). This book offers a good summary of his views, and the discussion on pp. 90–98 is particularly relevant to the notion that "postmodernists don't believe in truth."

and Gabriel Kolko is not one of truth or falsehood, but the relationship of the diplomatic historian to power. All this still does not mean Nietzsche or Foucault were necessarily "right," have a method we all must use, or give us a guide to life for anyone but the fully committed and self-conscious individualist (a character Nietzsche saw as the logical outcome of the modern project, and a type that Foucault embodied). It does mean that if "we deal with power" we must seek truth, speak it to power, and not bury our head in the sand when new and original conceptions of power come down the pike. A good start would be James Der Derian's fine book about our subject, *On Diplomacy: A Genealogy of Western Estrangement.*[7]

What was it that I wanted to say in "'Revising Postrevisionism,'" this "hit-and-run attack" in Schlesinger's rendering, in a few words? At best, the keepers of the field rarely go beyond a ménage à trois: something orthodox, something heterodox, and (maybe) a synthesis of the two. At worst, the keepers betray their own lack of understanding of the work they deal with, a certain handcuffing of the self at the point of comprehension, which by no means inhibits subsequent criticism and censure. Or they indulge in an exclusionary discourse that wants to draw lines, establish between self and other a comfortable middle, thus to condemn those beyond the lines just drawn (although typically only one line, the line of most resistance, the purported left extreme). If this is not a McCarthyite practice, ultimately it nonetheless communicates – especially to students – the idea that there are good, responsible historians, and then there are the people we hereby warn you against. The combination of misreading and exclusion ultimately infuriates for its unfairness, its complacency, and its elemental lack of collegiality.

To refer in a scholarly publication to William Appleman Williams as a "Leninist" or a follower of "Lenin's theory" is badly to misread, but also readily to accept the ideological parameters of the Cold War that so blighted our minds – more than that, to prolong them into the post-Cold War 1990s as if we needed

7 James Der Derian, *On Diplomacy: A Genealogy of Western Estrangement* (New York, 1987).

more blight. Such malignant naming also betrays a complete insensitivity to what Williams and people like him suffered in our beloved US of A for their iconoclasm and independence: FBI inquiries, IRS audits, subpoenas of the scholar *and* his books by HUAC, and so on and so forth.

The first thing that ought to be said before a criticism of Williams is that he had one of the finest minds Midwestern progressivism has ever produced, that he was one of a handful of truly influential historians in his generation (inside and outside the discipline), and that his work will always remain compelling to some if not all of our students. After that you are free to criticize him, misread him, call him what you will, or learn from him.

A second point in my essay had to do with theory: What does it mean to say that the field is *atheoretical*? Theory, as Mao Tse-tung once said, is merely useful or not. If not, he said, it is dung – merely another Montana frisbee. Theory helps to conjure up for us a different explanation than the one we are used to hearing; it gives us something we can share with intellectuals outside our field; it gives us a useful and different searchlight when we spelunk into the archives. Mark Twain once wrote that "you can't depend on your eyes when your imagination is out of focus," which is a very good admonition for the American historian with a deep and natural empiricist bent. A kind of parallax, off-center, "second sight" can make of the diplomatic archives not something a part of which we assign to the aspiring doctoral student, in search of materials "no one has used before," but an archive that can be put to good use time and again through multiple and different "readings."

Why was it that as a young scholar I had the frequent experience of finding golden nuggets in archival boxes where other (more senior) prospectors had already been? For years I thought I had at least a different eye if not a better one, an eye that had seen many interesting things in the middle and late 1960s, a lens polished in scholarly and political activity in a time of crisis. Now I find that notion merely amusing, since I was just recapitulating the experience of many young scholars in the past. It was also true, however, that the golden nuggets meant nothing without a context in which to place them (so many dollars for an ounce of it), and that context, for me, was laid out and made intelligible by American intellects like Gabriel Kolko, Dorothy Borg, Walter LaFeber, Louis Hartz, James Kurth, Lloyd Gardner, James Palais, Tom McCormick, Barrington Moore, Jr., Bill Williams, Tom Ferguson, Charles Beard, Franz Schurmann, and Immanuel Wallerstein – but perhaps above all by makers of 1940s American foreign policy like Dean Acheson, George Kennan, John Reed Hodge, and John Foster Dulles. In the first group we have theorists, historians, and social scientists, but the last group merged theory with practice. As "Leninists" always told us, that makes a difference.

Someone once said that "prisons will not work until we send a better class of people there." I would say the same about the discipline called history, and especially those branches standing close to the seat of American power. My career to this point has taught me that we can find a better class of person, inside and outside the discipline, by reading those people we are warned against. Several of them are listed above.

It is an American curiosity that some of the scholars I just named have also been labeled "conspiracy theorists." This raises a third problem: Diplomatic historians often cannot distinguish human intentionality from conspiracy. Sometimes even to find, develop, and for all intents and purposes prove a consistent logic on the part of our policymakers is to attract this odious label: conspiracy theorist. Since my essay appeared, Gaddis has written that I am the Oliver Stone of the Korean War, or words to that effect, which might lead me to think this was praise if we speak of a film like *Born on the Fourth of July*, but of course he refers to the interesting but deeply flawed and ultimately stupid film, *JFK*. I am happy to debate the Korean War at any time and any place of John's choosing, but here I would rather point out the ad hominem quality of the remark, something by now habitual, not to mention its gratuitousness since he was reviewing somebody else's work on this war, and not my own. But let us ask the question, what is conspiracy theory?

It seems to be a theory that claims history to be moved forward, backward, or sideways by conspiracies. In other words, it is naive and stupid just like Stone's *JFK*. Does that mean that conspiracies do not exist? Yet we know they exist: Richard Nixon's entire career reflects a subconscious yearning to tell us they exist. What is a conspiracy? It is Richard Nixon at Watergate, Dean Rusk plotting a coup against Chiang Kai-shek or Ngo Dinh Diem, fifty-odd Chinese dumping soybeans on the Chicago Commodities Exchange in late June 1950 for some reason, the Pentagon figuring out the Inch'ôn landing before the Korean War began, a poorly plotted assassination in Mexico in 1994 that did its part to sorely test world currency markets in 1995, and so on and so forth. Conspiracies happen all the time. But we deny this because of a classic American fallacy, born of our relative unconnectedness to the old world: what I like to call the fallacy of insufficient cynicism. Or as William Burroughs, author of *Naked Lunch*, put it, "a paranoid is a man who knows a little of what is going on."

Still, conspiracies in the legal definition are far less frequent than the daily life and career of human intentionality. I remember once asking a historian, albeit over lunch, how he could live in and interpret a world that, so far as I could tell from his work, struck him as confusing and unpredictable if not purely random. I was afraid I might be insulting him, until he responded that yes, history was largely unpredictable, confusing, and random. And so, even the retrospective positing of *intentionality* in foreign policy gets many historians to thinking that someone must be posing a conspiracy theory. If Dean Acheson did something other than muddle his way through his humdrum existence at the State Department from 1947 to 1953, that might qualify as dangerous territory (not to mention terra incognita) for some of our colleagues.

But with intentionality, there is also a problem. Perhaps "the decisive value of an action lies precisely in what is *unintentional* about it." This is Nietzsche's statement,[8] and it had a deep impact on Freud. It had a big impact on me, too, since I grew up in a household where one did not cry over spilt milk, but tried to figure out what motivated the perpetrator to spill it in the first place. If we think about it, though, we can judge a country's actions as much by what the *outcomes* are, as what the intention-

8 Friedrich Nietzsche, *Beyond Good and Evil: Prelude to a Philosophy of the Future*, trans. Walter Kauffman (New York, 1966), 44.

ality and the procedures for arriving at an intention (that is, a decision) might have been. If in a foreign policy decision the United States ends up in bed with a Syngman Rhee, perhaps it was unintentional, bad judgment, poor information, misperception, a failure to communicate. But when you end up in bed with Syngman Rhee, Bao Dai, Chiang Kai-shek, Ngo Dinh Diem, Rafael Trujillo, Fulgencio Batista, Anastasio Somoza, Park Chung Hee, Nguyen Cao Ky, Suharto, Mobutu, Pinochet, and Chun Doo Hwan, some observers might conclude that you not only were in bed with them, but intended to be in bed with them – or that, at a minimum, this list renders inconsequential what your intentions might have been in the first place.

Nietzsche typically has something more intelligent to say: "During the longest historical period," he wrote, "the value or disvalue of an action was derived from its consequences." What the act was, what its origin might have been, what the perpetrator was "feeling" when he did it, made no difference: The act had to be punished anyway.[9] It then developed, Nietzsche continued, that intentionality became the main thing, as a means of moral judgment, blame, censure, ferreting out good and evil; and so it was left to Nietzsche and Freud once again to attempt a reversal or "revaluation" of this value, and to Nietzsche characteristically to find in Christian piety, with its endless protestation of peaceful intent and innocent purpose, the denial and condemnation of the very drive whose expression one *is*. You have to come from a long line of Calvinists to understand the deep meaning of this idea, but it is a secret, a talisman, for understanding American behavior in the world – the "last, best hope of mankind," its virtues all self-evident, which marches out to the world only in the world's best interest – as Samuel Huntington said in the journal *International Security* recently. Anybody else hegemonic, and the world is in trouble: Therefore, best to let America be hegemonic.[10]

Now, of course, we still live in a capitalist country and a

9 Ibid., 43–44.

10 Samuel Huntington, "Why International Primacy Matters," *International Security* 17 (Spring 1993). Huntington claims that "no other country can make comparable contributions to international order and stability" and pays particular and baleful attention to contrasting American primacy with a Japan dangerously close to hegemonic predominance (pp. 72–73, 82).

capitalist world economy – that is the greatest field in which diplomacy occurs, just as today capitalism has the greatest field in world history in which to expand. So it is just possible that capitalist intentionality might also have something to do with American diplomacy, in addition to Huntington's notion that the world needs us to save it from itself. Rather than dwell on that business, however, I would merely urge scholars to try their best to get the analysis of capitalism right, but also to remember something Herbert Marcuse once said to a student, namely, that "not every problem you're having with your girlfriend is necessarily due to the capitalist mode of production." It is more a matter of *not forgetting* that so many of the American figures that we study in our work spent a great deal of their lives understanding, representing, and profiting from the largest players in the market in this century, namely, the multinational corporations.

Some years ago I was on a committee that invited John Johnson, president of *Ebony* Magazine and other enterprises, to the University of Chicago for a visit (to his alma mater as it happened). At lunch, when asked about Chicago politics and his role in it, Mr. Johnson responded that we all ought to remember the Golden Rule: He who has the gold makes the rules. That is the title of Tom Ferguson's new book (coincidentally published by the University of Chicago Press), and I would say that to follow the money trail is always a useful hypothesis in figuring out American politics and foreign policy. But it is not the only hypothesis.

George Kennan ended a recent essay by saying of the origins of the Cold War, "We will never know who was right and who was wrong. . . . The one course was tried . . . the other course [a general negotiation circa 1950] remained hypothetical. Its results will never be known." I think that is the proper place to conclude. History is not a retrospective moral exercise in constructing right and wrong, but one of explaining and debating the past – what happened and what might be a good account of what happened – and imagining what might have been, thus to instruct the present and give a direction to the future. Nor is it an *impartial* discipline, legions of Rankean disciples to the contrary. An English judge, Lord Gordon Hewart, once wrote that "the only impartiality possible to the human mind is that which arises from understanding neither side of the case." Of course there are always two sides to every issue, we all know that: The correct side and the wrong side. For example, I know in my bones that Stalin had very little to do with the coming of the Korean War. And as Molière once wrote, "it infuriates me to be wrong when I know I'm right."

It is precisely Bill Williams's *partiality* that makes him so interesting – not as a "Leninist" but as an American progressive who knew a good historian when he read one (in his case Charles Beard), who cared deeply about his country, and who burned with a desire to love his country and love justice at the same time (as Camus once said). For him that meant that it should not have taken on, and ought now to disabuse itself of, the requirements of empire. There is a touching naiveté at work here, not a foreign doctrine but something as American as apple pie: *idealism.*

But what sort of a country is it that Williams loved so much? It *is* an exceptional country, as I argued at the end of my essay in *DH.* Fine: But what is the nature of its exceptionalism? Not that it is better, more virtuous, more idealistic, or "naturally inclined to hegemony," as Huntington might have it, than other countries; not that it can call back its empire if it wanted to, as Bill Williams said the Chinese did of the voyages to the Middle East and Africa of Admiral Cheng Ho. That too, is naiveté. We get closer with Clemenceau's remark that "America is the only nation in history which miraculously has gone directly from barbarism to degeneration without the usual interval of civilization." Or with Louis Hartz's central idea that America was an exception *to Europe*, or Karl Marx's on North America occupying the global horizon-cum-vacuum of capitalism, or with the United States as a country that goes both ways, moving toward Europe and away from it simultaneously. An old Hindi proverb had it that "he who speaks the truth should have one foot in the stirrup." Whatever you may think of his views, Williams was independent: And it is not easy to be independent, as a principle. Nietzsche's teaching was that this is the hardest thing: "Independence is for the very few; it is a privilege of the strong. And whoever attempts it without an inner constraint . . . enters into a labyrinth, he multiplies a thousandfold the dangers which life brings, . . . he becomes lonely, and is torn piecemeal by some minotaur of conscience." This is Uncle Friedrich talking to himself, but he also speaks to the loneliness of Bill Williams after he moved to Oregon and to everyone who has tried to tell the truth about U.S. foreign policy, knowing that someone already is preparing an ad hominem assault on their integrity. But the "inner constraint" is perhaps hardest to come by in a country where, when all is said and done, we agree on so many of the fundamentals.

There is still a great benefit to independence, though, and that is you can look yourself in the mirror when you are shaving. You can experience the emotion of a woman in a *New Yorker* cartoon from the 1950s: She is marooned on a desert island with a man encouraged by this unexpected outcome. The caption reads, "I'll know, that's who."

Assessing the Assessments

MELVYN P. LEFFLER

I shall comment here on the essays by Michael H. Hunt and Bruce Cumings as well as on the provocative presidential address by John Lewis Gaddis. Hunt seeks to survey the historiography of the last several decades and to assess the state of the field. Gaddis focuses on the evidence of repression and oppression in the former Soviet Union and suggests that we reconfigure our understanding of twentieth-century American foreign relations in terms of American resistance to authoritarian and totalitarian regimes. Bruce Cumings focuses on the works of four historians, labels their scholarship "postrevisionist," and uses his attack on their writings to laud his own world-systems approach.

I admire Hunt's survey of the literature. I especially like his enumeration of the key questions that historians of international relations should address:

> Where does policy ultimately come from – the international system or the domestic sphere? Are policymakers relatively autonomous actors? Through what lenses do they perceive the world? How does U.S. policy compare with that of other countries? Is there a common set of forces working on all policymakers, or does it vary significantly by country, culture, and time? How do we evaluate policy decisions, particularly

when the consequences of those decisions are felt and must be understood in the context of another culture?

Answers to these questions do require, as Hunt emphasizes, different approaches that focus on the state, the connections between state and society, the nature of the "global environment," and the distribution of power within other nations as well as within the international system. I concur both with his belief that a "genial tolerance" is needed among diplomatic historians who take different approaches and with his warning that a "balkanization of the field" would be counterproductive.

But I disagree with some aspects of Hunt's argument. I do not share his view that a "long crisis" actually existed in the field. In 1981 I wrote a dissent to Charles S. Maier's influential critique of the historiography. I believed, and I still believe, that important work was then being done, although it was not consonant with trends toward social and cultural history elsewhere in the profession.[1] Hunt's excellent survey of the literature, in fact, underscores my view because much of the "progressive" work on the state and society that he welcomes and many of the books of the "internationalist" school that he praises actually appeared while the "long crisis" supposedly engulfed the field.

Indeed, the whole notion of a "long crisis" emanates from a stereotyped view of the field. There once was a time, the fable goes, when diplomatic historians believed that states acted autonomously; accordingly, they concentrated their energies on describing what one white, male government clerk said to another. This characterization always trivialized what historians of American foreign relations were doing. Indeed, anyone familiar with the works of the generation of historians who came of age in the interwar years knows that they antedated both the "state/society" school and the "internationalist" school. Samuel Flagg Bemis, for example, did multiarchival, multinational research before most of the members of Hunt's "Harvard school" were born. Bemis also dealt with the economic and sectional influences that motivated the policies of the Adamses of Massachusetts and

1 Melvyn P. Leffler, "Responses to Charles S. Maier," *Dipomatic History* 5 (Fall 1981): 365–71.

the Pinckneys of South Carolina as well as Benjamin Franklin, John Jay, Alexander Hamilton, and other founders of the republic. Bemis, of course, was not alone. Many of his contemporaries who shared his political beliefs, and many who did not, agreed that they needed to probe the domestic factors that shaped American foreign policy. In the course of their work Frederick Merk, Julius Pratt, Arthur Whitaker, Albert Weinberg, and Thomas A. Bailey all examined business, religious, and sectional influences on foreign policy as well as illuminated the force of public opinion and popular ideology.

Without their work the so-called realist school would not have become quite so influential. Although the "realists" believed that foreign policy was about the quest for power and assumed that states might pursue power most effectvely if not beleaguered by interest groups and public opinion, they nevertheless argued that such propitious conditions had not existed since John Quincy Adams retired from the State Department. In short, realists believed that the American state should deal with other nations on the basis of rational calculations of interest and power, but they noted that the vagaries of domestic public opinion and the legalism and moralism inherent in American ideology made such approaches unusual in the American diplomatic experience. In short, realist historians did not simply focus on the state; they built on and contributed to a scholarly tradition that stressed the salience of public opinion, ideological commitments, and ethnic pressures.

"Progressive" scholarship, to use Hunt's word, therefore, did not shift the focus away from the state and toward society as much as it reconfigured the meaning of the domestic forces shaping policy. Public opinion, progressive historians suggested, needed to be studied more systematically in terms of social forces, especially in terms of the farm, business, and commercial interests seeking to shape policy. Idealism, they argued, was not divorced from self-interest. A legalistic bent meant the institutionalization of procedures for the peaceful settlement of international disputes and therefore comported well with the practical desire to promote world stability, augment trade, and enhance profits.

I agree with Hunt that progressive/revisionist/corporatist scholarship made important contributions to the understanding of the connections between state and society, but I disagree with his suggestion that success was achieved at the expense of archival research. Indeed, scholars in this tradition actually expanded the use of archives because they realized that the "state" could not be defined simply as the State Department or the White House. They engaged in extensive research in the records of such governmental agencies as the Commerce Department, the Treasury Department, the Economic Cooperation Administration, and the Federal Trade Commission. In so doing they often illuminated the far-reaching links that different groups within society maintained with different components of the American "state." In this way, archival research actually enhanced our knowledge of the connections between state and society, as did the concomitant research in the records of business, banking, religious, and philanthropic organizations.

As much as I disagree with Hunt's assessment of the role of archival research in "progressive" scholarship, I fully endorse his evaluation of the utility of "international" history. Such scholars as Hunt himself, as well as Akira Iriye, Christopher Thorne, Charles Maier, Stephen Pelz, Stephen Schuker, Roger Dingman, Shuguang Zhang, and many others, have brilliantly illuminated the international context in which American policy unfolds as well as demonstrated the great utility of comparative approaches to decision making. They also have underscored the importance of studying the impact of American policies, institutions, and culture on other societies. Although "international" approaches are not inherently better geared to analyze American motivations, assumptions, and processes than other schools of interpretation, such approaches do help us judge the comparative efficacy of American policies at a given time in history.

In this respect, John Gaddis's provocative article suggests that the opening of Soviet and East European archives may provide us with a new lens for viewing and judging the efficacy of American foreign policy during the Cold War.[2] Stressing the monstrosity of Stalin's regime, Gaddis argues that the role played by the U.S.

2 John Lewis Gaddis, "The Tragedy of Cold War History," *Diplomatic History* 17 (Winter 1993): 1–16.

government in resisting authoritarianism and totalitarianism should trigger a renewed appreciation of the wisdom and utility of containment. Revisionists, he intimates, have tragically underestimated the cruelty of Communist regimes in general and the Soviet regime in particular. They have discounted the ideological impulses underlying Stalin's foreign policies, disregarded his (undefined) "ultimate objectives," and ignored the reality that his vision of security "meant complete insecurity for everyone else."

In my presidential address to SHAFR (included in this volume) I outline some of the reasons why I question these conclusions. Please note that Gaddis and I do not dispute the barbarity of Stalin's regime (and Mao's as well), but I do disagree with him about the implications of the new documents from Soviet archives. The meaning of these documents is clearly an area of legitimate controversy, but I would submit that the information we have so far does not confirm that Stalin had "ultimate objectives" (whatever such words might mean). Nor does the information demonstrate that he was motivated to accomplish ideological ends (except the survival of his own hideous regime), although I do think that ideology influenced his perception of threat and his understanding of the international environment. I tend to agree with the characterization of both Stalin and Mao put forth by Sergei N. Goncharov, John W. Lewis, and Xue Litai (no revisionists they) in their book, *Uncertain Partners*. "The ultimate concern on both sides," they write, "was not class struggle but state interests (though the arguments were sometimes couched in revolutionary terms). In the final analysis, realpolitik governed their thinking and strained their relations."[3]

Such conclusions have a bearing on Gaddis's judgment about the role of the United States in resisting the spread of totalitarianism. Did containment, as practiced, actually ameliorate the international situation in general and conditions within the Soviet sphere in particular, or did American policies trigger the security dilemma, engender greater fears than need have existed, and intensify the clampdown in Eastern Europe as well as the globalization

3 Sergei N. Goncharov, John W. Lewis, and Xue Litai, *Uncertain Partners: Stalin, Mao, and the Korean War* (Stanford, 1993), 220.

of the Cold War? Did the institutionalization of containment after Stalin's death unnecessarily prolong the Cold War? Did American policies provide the rationale the men in the Kremlin needed to justify the nature of their regime and their policies? I am not suggesting that such questions have easy answers; anyone who has read the conclusion of my book, *A Preponderance of Power*, knows that I think that judgments must be nuanced. But such questions need to be pondered carefully before Gaddis's assessment is widely accepted.

Similarly, before praising U.S. officials for their stand in resisting totalitarianism one must examine the motives of U.S. officials. As I have indicated elsewhere, I do not think the evidence suggests that Truman administration policy was motivated by any particular concern with individual rights and civil society in the Soviet Union and the Eastern bloc. Notwithstanding my disagreement with Gaddis on this point, I like his stress on the so-called tectonic forces shaping history. Gaddis writes that

> tectonic forces – industrialization, the emergence of class-consciousness, and the alienation that flowed from it – undermined liberal democratic bourgeois market capitalism late in the nineteenth and early in the twentieth centuries, thus paving the way for fascism, communism, and the authoritarianism that accompanied them. But during the second half of the twentieth century these tectonic forces evolved into something else – post-industrialization, the emergence of communications consciousness, and the alienation that flowed from it – which then undermined the foundations of authoritarianism and brought us around to our next historically determined phase, which turned out to be liberal, democratic, bourgeois market capitalism all over again.

In certain important ways, American officials in the 1940s grasped the implications of some of these "tectonic forces." They understood that in the aftermath of the Great Depression and World War II, peoples everywhere yearned for a better future. They knew they had to revitalize liberal capitalism after its tarnished record in the first part of this century. They knew the Soviets capitalized not simply on their military power, but upon the hopes of peoples in both the developed and underdeveloped worlds that communism might offer a brighter future. They focused on reconstructing and integrating the world economy because they knew that doing so was indispensable to thwarting the spread of Communist influence, preserving a favorable balance of power abroad, and maintaining a free political economy and polity at home. But I do not think American officials had a great faith that Gaddis's "tectonic forces" would undermine communism from within; if they had had such confidence, they probably would have spent less money on strategic arms, less effort on covert actions, and less blood on limited wars.

How is Gaddis's stress on "tectonic forces" related to Cumings's emphasis on the functioning of the world capitalist system? This strikes me as an interesting question, but one that Cumings chose not to explore in his attack on Gaddis and postrevisionism. Cumings's polemic lacks the "geniality" of spirit that Hunt calls for in his essay. Anyone meditating on the flawed logic of Cumings's essay would have difficulty imagining the high quality of his scholarship in his area of expertise and the justified prominence he has achieved in the profession.

Cumings assails postrevisionism. Yet he makes no effort to define postrevisionism precisely or to outline the importance of the work of Gaddis or Hunt. Ostensibly there is one thing that unites the work of postrevisionists, namely their inattention to theory. But this generalization is not only mistaken, because Gaddis in particular has been attentive to theory, but is also without meaning. Most historians show little attention to theory: Does that make them all postrevisionists? Marilyn Blatt Young, Lloyd C. Gardner, Thomas G. Paterson, Walter LaFeber, and William S. Borden have written many important books without displaying any special interest in theory. Are they to be regarded as postrevisionists? Is it the lack of attention to theory that really bothers Cumings, or is it something else?

Cumings appears agitated by the inclination of postrevisionists to label and categorize other historians in ways that he deplores. Ironically, Cumings is guilty of the same sin. He lumps together four quite disparate historians, labels them all postrevisionists, and then lambasts them for their presumed inattention to theory. Meanwhile, he remains strangely silent about the atheoretical bent of historians who happen to share his own interpretive orientation.

Does Cumings really take objection to the lack of theory in the writings of Gaddis, Hunt, Combs, or myself? Or does he rather object to the fact that we do not subscribe to his world-systems interpretation? One could easily conclude from the essay that if you believe in world-systems, Cumings is likely to admire your work no matter how little research you have done in the primary sources; on the other hand, if you doubt the validity of a world-systems approach, your logic must be flawed or your sources unreliable. Note, for example, how Cumings chastises me for not researching in foreign archives and then praises Thomas McCormick for having found the right approach "through the lenses of world-systems theory" without having set foot in any archive. I happen to be an admirer of McCormick's book; indeed, I was the "referee" when Johns Hopkins University Press reviewed it for publication. But I cannot embrace the teleology holding that world-systems theory can serve as the holy grail for decoding all of American foreign policy.

Cumings would lead you to believe that the existence of Soviet totalitarianism played virtually no role in the unfolding of American foreign policy. American officials, he says, were more worried about the health of the world economy than they were fearful of the Soviets. How does Cumings know this? The secret, he says, is knowing how to read the evidence, such as Acheson's allusions to the "great crescent." And if you are wondering how the term "great crescent" demonstrates the veracity of the world-systems approach, you need only look, says Cumings, to Friedrich Nietzsche for the answer. Truth, asserts Nietzsche, is "an unrecognized motivation serving unacknowledged purpose." And what do you need to identify the recognized motivations and the acknowledged purposes? According to Cumings, you need a theory! Certainly, you would not want to tarry over the reams of interdepartmental committee reports, CIA assessments, and NSC studies which, in Cumings's revealing phrase, "clutter the archives." Why bother with such clutter, if you can snatch a serviceable theory from Nietzsche, or is it Wallerstein? Why bother, if you yourself can impose the acknowledged purposes and recognized motivations, or if you can cite people like Mary Kaldor and Thomas McCormick, who have written interesting books, but who have spent little time looking at manuscript materials and archival records?

My own view is that the archival evidence, in all its inevitable contradiction and ambiguity, suggests a most complicated relationship between the perception of a Soviet threat, the preoccupation with the functioning of the world economy, and a commitment to preserving a democratic polity and a free market economy at home. This may not be the place to argue the merits of our different approaches at length. My point here is that, because the evidence is so refractory, historians have an obligation to treat one another's work and attempts to get at the truth with respect and objectivity. I confess that Cumings, whose earlier archival studies I greatly admire, disappoints me by his cavalier treatment of Hunt's and Gaddis's scholarship and by what I regard as his simplification of my own arguments.

In this respect, it is more than a little ironic to see Michael J. Hogan reiterating Cumings's charges against "gatekeepers." Should the field have a gatekeeper, Hogan, the gifted and powerful editor of *Diplomatic History*, would surely be the number one candidate for the position. He makes the final choices on what appears in the journal. He selects the articles from the journal for the volumes (like this one) that are becoming "primers" for graduate students in the field. And he uses his position as editor of these volumes to put his own "spin" on what other people are trying to say.

Hogan claims, if I read him correctly, that the aim of my presidential address was to assert the primacy of geopolitics and to deny that other approaches can discover "reality." With all due respect, I hope that readers will allow me to have my own voice. Let me reiterate that my purpose was not to champion geopolitics, but to advocate the importance of reconfiguring and integrating existing approaches, old and new (including my own). Whether the syntheses I call for will amount to more, or less, than the sum of their parts will be open to future assessments.

On what criteria should these assessments be based? New theories and new methodologies do not make good history just because they are novel. Our task is not to adopt theories and methodologies for their own sake, but to inquire whether they comport with the evidence. If we misconstrue the purpose of theory or denigrate the utility of archival research, we risk compromising our mission as historians – to explain the past as it really was and with all its tantalizing ambiguities and confounding contradictions.

The Three Realms Revisited

MICHAEL H. HUNT

My 1992 field survey, published here in its original form, contended that "diplomatic history" had gained notably in its vitality thanks to a more catholic sense of subject matter and a concomitant diversification in the interests that defined the field. It was, I argued, helpful to think of the field's diversity in terms of three fairly distinct realms, each with its own basic question: What is policy, and how is it made? How does policy interact with domestic affairs, and particularly what are its societal sources and consequences? And how do U.S. policymakers but also other Americans not connected to the state interact with the outside world and with what import for other states and peoples?

Three practical implications flow from understanding our collective enterprise in terms not of contending sets of interpretations but rather of something more commonsensical and basic – the different kinds of questions that engage us. Most obviously, those working in different realms of U.S. foreign relations pursue different interpretive issues, methodologies, and bodies of evidence depending on their guiding questions. Those in the same realm will have a great deal to say to each other, while cross-border discourse may need the services of a translator so that communications do not miscarry. Second, those within the field are well served by being self-conscious about which realm their own work is situated in. Such a sense of place helps us keep in mind that each of us addresses only part of the full foreign relations puzzle; it promotes tolerance of work in other realms guided by other agendas; and it alerts us to the risks of trespassing into other realms without the requisite credentials ("interpretive overreach"). Finally, focusing on distinct, functionally defined, and hence relatively stable realms offers a way to alleviate the confusion spawned by the proliferation and overlapping of interpretive categories.[1] Such an approach would also put a damper on empty interpretive strife that was ostensibly over specific interpretive questions or "schools" but in fact turned on which realm had the right approach or should enjoy the dominant position.

The more I thought about the field as a collection of realms each with strengths and limits, the more I realized that diplomatic history did not need a kind of one-size-fits-all prescription for its scholarship, indeed that it was ill served by any champion of one right question, one right method, and one right body of evidence. As a genial tolerance for diversity took hold (so I hoped), competing schools of interpretation and the attendant bouts of internal strife might yield to a kind of collective security arrangement in which the legitimacy of each realm was guaranteed through tolerance granted to all realms.

These ideas were far from my mind when recently tensions within the field erupted, nominally over that venerable and still politically sensitive issue of who started the Cold War (given fresh edge by the equally sensitive issue of who won the Cold War). Like any street corner brawl, the punches thrown by John Lewis Gaddis and Bruce Cumings drew a crowd.[2] The fisticuffs first struck me as a kind of exuberance, if not good clean fun that anyone enjoying their work might occasionally be indulged.

But my attitude changed when, at the end of the spring 1994 term, I presented the essays at the center of the controversy to my graduate class in foreign relations, a group whose special interests spanned U.S. history and in a few cases fell outside the American field. Readings that I had expected to spark a lively discussion instead evoked almost uniform exasperation. The students expressed dismay with what they saw as "historical McCarthyism" and "sandlot historiography." "Fixed opinions

1 My article did invoke some labels but only to help readers see how much-discussed "schools" of interpretation could be placed in the context of one or the other of these realms and viewed as prominent examplars of the kind of work being done there.

2 John Lewis Gaddis, "The Tragedy of Cold War History," *Diplomatic History* 17 (Winter 1993): 1–16.

and closed minds," observed some in the class, had given rise to the controversy and would, they predicted, direct the field toward a "dead end."[3]

The papers this group subsequently offered on their term readings provided a hint of where the field is headed – or at least where one critical constituency within it thought it should go. While they noted the importance of conventional policy studies, they overwhelmingly found greater interpretive payoffs in works that sought either to link policy systematically to its broader American setting or to put policy in some international context. Thus, Geoffrey S. Smith's article exploring the domestic dimensions of "national security," Gregory E. Dowd's ethnocultural perspective on the other side of continental expansion by Europeans, and Piero Gleijeses's skillfully crafted tale of a small country caught in the U.S. Cold War vise earned special praise for the ways they broadened the picture beyond the narrow Washington world of policymakers.[4] Only by stepping outside that world, so the argument repeatedly went, was it possible to gain the critical interpretive leverage over the broad issues that mattered – where policy came from and what impact it had. While the policy studies by Melvyn P. Leffler and John Gaddis were impressive in their own right, these studies did not themselves successfully engage the issues of why policy mattered either to Americans generally or to people abroad.[5]

These student reactions, followed by a recent rereading of Gaddis and Cumings, reminded me why I had penned "Coming to Closure" in the first place and got me to worrying about the potential mischief this and similar controversies can do. Behind the good clean fun of a sandlot tussle are often clashing

3 From this class I would like particularly to acknowledge Gavin J. Campbell, S. Parker Doig, Carter S. Dougherty, Michael J. Flynn, Natalie M. Fousekis, Kelly L. Hughes, and Xiaodong Wang for helping me understand this reaction.

4 Geoffrey S. Smith, "National Security and Personal Isolation: Sex, Gender, and Disease in the Cold-War United States," *International History Review* 16 (May 1992): 221–40; Gregory E. Dowd, *A Spirited Resistance: The North American Indian Struggle for Unity, 1745–1815* (Baltimore, 1991); Piero Gleijeses, *Shattered Hope: The Guatemalan Revolution and the United States, 1944–1954* (Princeton, 1991).

5 Melvyn P. Leffler, *A Preponderance of Power: National Security, the Truman Administration, and the Cold War* (Stanford, 1992); John Lewis Gaddis, *Strategies of Containment: A Critical Appraisal of Postwar American National Security Policy* (New York, 1982).

aspirations to dominance and by extension to marginalize or even exclude. Realizing such aspirations would come at the substantial cost of narrowing a field that has benefited from diversity and breadth.

John Gaddis's presidential address promoted a vision of the field that was no longer haunted by the ghost of William Appleman Williams, in which writing about U.S. policy would be a moral or perhaps more precisely a nationalist act, and in which realist formulations would provide the best tool for interpreting and evaluating policy. To clear up the confusion spawned by Williams and like-minded historians, Gaddis identified the villains of the Cold War (not coincidentally the foes of the very Washington policymakers that Gaddis has devoted himself to studying). The chief villain was Josef Stalin, that sinister figure presiding over an illegitimate Soviet system. But his guilt was to be shared with little Stalins all over the world and with those who embraced the economic absurdities associated with socialism. In Gaddis's estimate, those Socialist-bloc leaders sinned not just against liberal values but also against the no less fundamental verities of realism by failing to balance ends and means and by taking a romantic (as opposed to a hard-nosed) approach to world affairs. In this world of dark and light (or idealism and realism), U.S. policymakers stood on the side of the angels, or at least of Woodrow Wilson and the vision of a just, humane, liberal global order. The men who directed the Cold War struggle were not just right. They were also sophisticated in their ability to read the requirements of the international system that the United States play a hegemonic role. Williams seems to have gotten matters precisely backwards. Stalin stood for unmitigated evil, and American hegemony was necessary, good, and restrained.

In reaching beyond the realm of his expertise here as in his other works, Gaddis falls into sectarian ways and becomes a victim of interpretive overreach. His comments on Stalin are good polemics but poor international history. His credentials for operating in that realm are modest, and, in any case, the sources on Stalin's Cold War policy are still thin. Both points quickly become apparent from recent treatments of Stalin's policy by historians who have paid their dues – who, like most international historians, know the language, seek understanding, and eschew the fast and easy verdicts of the hanging judge.[6]

If Gaddis would like to coopt the international realm, he is dismissive of that other, domestic, realm that Williams did not create but did much to invigorate. Gaddis is indifferent, if not hostile, to the complicated and important state-society issues that so engaged Williams. To focus on Williams's treatment of Stalin is to misread Williams's major contribution to the field and ignore the importance of the issues raised by the progressives and others working in the domestic realm. Gaddis's judgments reveal – if there was any doubt – his own loyalties to the realm dedicated to the study of U.S. policy and illustrate the tendency of those most comfortable with American state papers not just to see the world through the eyes of the men who generated those papers but to see the field in terms most compatible with the outlook of those men.

A field appraisal informed by the certitudes of American moralism and nationalism makes for good polemics, buttressing the case for the triumphalists in the wake of Soviet collapse. But a premature and ahistorical summing up on the Cold War and an insistence on a narrow, judgmental notion of diplomatic history contributes little positive to any of the realms or to the field as a whole.

Cumings's warm defense of Williams and a progressive interpretation reveals how interpretive labeling and single sweeping prescriptions are bound to miscarry. Cumings's critical discussion of "postrevisionism" quickly becomes tangled, as such exercises usually do; indeed, it runs directly counter to his own concluding caution against the confusion that labeling generates.[7] His stress

6 Albert Resis, *Stalin, the Politburo, and the Onset of the Cold War, 1945–1946* (occasional paper, Pittsburgh, 1988); and Vladislav Zubok and Constantine Pleshakov, "The Soviet Union," in *The Origins of the Cold War in Europe*, ed. David Reynolds (New Haven, 1994). Gaddis's tendentious treatment of Stalin dates back to his first book, *The United States and the Origins of the Cold War, 1941–1947* (New York, 1972), a fine study of U.S. policy marred by a conclusion that turned abruptly international and used the Soviet leader deus-ex-machina fashion to shift any hint of blame for Cold War origins away from Washington.

7 My own first reaction to finding myself labeled (libeled?) a postrevisionist was to raise my right hand and intone, "I am not now nor have I ever been . . ."

on theory is equally unsettling not because he finds the field poor in that commodity (itself debatable) but because he puts forward world-systems theory with evangelical fervor. In a plural field, there are many roads to heaven, and each diplomatic historian needs to search for a "theoretical" way appropriate to his or her own faith. Sectarian certitude is not likely to settle the matter satisfactorily.

Cumings's call to theoretical arms brought to mind a remark attributed to Edmund Burke: "The bulk of mankind . . . are not excessively curious concerning any theory whilst they are really happy; and one sure symptom of an ill-conducted state is the propensity of the people to resort to them." There may be some insight in Burke's observation if we think of diplomatic history as a state very much in ferment and governed by no one center, no single research agenda or body of evidence, and certainly no single theory.

Melvyn Leffler's presidential address, mildly worded and largely indirect in its response to Gaddis and Cumings, has a calming, mediatory tone. There is much to praise in Leffler's call to end the interpretive warfare and to work toward an interpretive synthesis for diplomatic history, indeed, to help in the construction of the much-discussed new synthesis for American history. But notwithstanding his calls for tolerance, Leffler's notion of a field synthesis and his comments on the field share something of Gaddis's vision of the field. The making of U.S. policy occupies center stage. That policy is to be seen through a realist prism, with the help of such notions as national interest and the international system. And cultural approaches (attended by the bogeymen of fragmentation and interpretive confusion) are set safely on the margin. In other words, Leffler's vision is one in which the realm of the state stands suzerain and the other two realms serve as dutiful feudatories. Sectarianism booted out the front door returns quietly through the back.

Leffler's own recent, justly praised book offers a good illustration of the strengths and limits of state-centered accounts and hence why the realm of the state should neither crowd out nor dominate the other realms. On the basis of impressive, painstaking research and in a clear, well groomed exposition, *Preponderance of Power* provides a detailed picture of the national security establishment at a critical moment, complete with all its major figures, debates, and decisions. Leffler tells this group's story in its language and from its perspective – and like others specializing in this genre, he has difficulty transcending that language and perspective.

While Leffler claims in his introduction to integrate policymaking with the domestic realm,[8] a reader would be hard pressed to explain how *Preponderance* illuminates what is American about Washington's Cold War policy or how Cold War policy changed the country it sought to defend. So resolutely is the focus on Washington that the volume also falls short as international history. Leffler can only draw second hand from a historical literature still limited on the role of the Soviet Union and thus still frustrating the effort to write a history of emerging U.S.-Soviet rivalry as a reciprocal process. Precisely because *Preponderance* is immersed in the making of U.S. policy (the very merit of the volume), it cannot develop the alternative, external perspective – whether domestic or international – critical to understanding the sources of that policy and the consequences it unleashed. For this very reason the book's conclusion that U.S. policymakers were prudent, wise, and foolish proves disappointingly puzzling, even incoherent, because the reader lacks a domestic or international referent against which those or other qualities could be measured.

This reading of the book suggests that Leffler's address and especially its call for synthesis may be a *crie de coeur* to his colleagues in the other two realms to come to his aid in writing a kind of total Cold War history. But in doing so he may underestimate how cultural history, pursuing its own path rather than the one marked out by students of the state, may contribute to defining the context for understanding policy. He may also underestimate how his favored notions of strategy and interest may be complicated, if not undercut, by international history showing how national interest and security codes vary with cultural con-

8 In an interview in *The Chronicle of Higher Education*, 2 March 1994, p. A10, Leffler repeated the claim that his book sought "to integrate arguments about the importance of geopolitics and domestic factors in the Cold War."

text.[9] We do not need to reconfigure the field to serve policy studies; we need multiple lines of inquiry and an open mind about how or even whether a synthesis of the Cold War might be done. It is not beyond imagining that the inspiration for such a synthesis might come from the international or the domestic realm or perhaps some fusion of ideas from the two and that policy studies might provide the building blocks but not the conceptual framework.

U.S. diplomatic history needs no "hegemonic projects," which are probably foredoomed by the already well established diversity in the field. But so long as they do appear, they will create a spirit of dissension not only among individual scholars but within the field as a whole. Those with a single, sweeping prescription might keep in mind an observation made some twenty-five years ago by one of my graduate instructors, Arthur Wright. "Everybody has one good idea – and most scholars once they find it proceed to make a career of it." If it is true that historians may have only one good idea, or perhaps even several, it is equally true that a lively field grappling with the complex issues raised by the U.S. role in world affairs has to look beyond the guidance any single person can supply. The last thing diplomatic history needs is a single style, theory, or agenda that would narrow our vision and impoverish our discourse. An acceptance of our diversity seems the surest recipe for keeping cooperation within a common field fruitful and tempers sweet.

9 Leffler's discussion of national interest in the United States, the Soviet Union, and China seems to me to get conceptually tangled by equating features common to all policies (no matter the time or place) such as surprise or defensiveness with some primordial, universal notion of interest inherent in the international system. Leffler cites my study of "Beijing and the Korean Crisis, June 1950–June 1951," *Political Science Quarterly* 107 (Fall 1992): 453–78, to support his argument. But in fact, that piece argues for parallels in crisis behavior, not commonality of security codes. I hope my treatment of *The Genesis of Chinese Communist Foreign Policy* (Columbia University Press, forthcoming, 1995) will dispel any doubts that Mao Zedong occupied a moral and strategic universe that was distinctly different from Harry Truman's or Josef Stalin's.

Part Two

The Historiography of American Foreign Relations since 1941

6

The Historiography of American Foreign Relations: An Introduction

MICHAEL J. HOGAN

The essays in this section survey some of the literature on the history of American foreign relations published, for the most part, over the last fifteen years. Although publication constraints sometimes made it difficult for authors to take account of the most recent books and articles, their essays nevertheless present a handy snapshot of the field as it stands today. They tell us something about the influences, intellectual and otherwise, that operate on diplomatic historians, what questions they are asking, and what approaches tend to dominate. They give us an excellent indication of what diplomatic historians are doing best these days, and what is missing in the field. The following is my assessment of what these essays, taken as a whole, have to say about the state of diplomatic history.

These essays evaluate the literature on the period since 1941 – the period that increasingly preoccupies diplomatic historians. The overwhelming majority of articles published in *Diplomatic History*, the journal of record in the field, focus on the twentieth century, and most of them on the years after World War II. What is more, the latest indicators suggest that diplomatic historians are concentrating increasingly on the years since 1960 – the last thirty-five years of American history. What are the implications of this recent-mindedness? To begin with, it means that diplomatic historians are working in a historiographical vacuum. They are not able to draw insights from a rich body of historical literature in the same way that diplomatic historians working on the first decades of the nineteenth century can be guided by the literature on republicanism, or those working on the interwar period can borrow from the literature on associationalism. Instead, they increasingly turn for guidance to political science, especially to the literature in international relations, which is driven by a modeling process that is often, though not always, ahistorical.

Making matters worse, historians of the recent past are working on topics for which much of the American documentation remains closed or undigested. John Ferris makes this point about the literature on intelligence, to give one example. He notes the obstacles that keep historians from the official record and spells out many of the problems that arise in analyzing a topic, however important, for which the evidence is limited. Nor do these problems stem simply from the lack of American documentation. Many of the following essays also note the deplorable absence of non-American sources, which limits the ability of diplomatic historians to contextualize the recent history of American diplomacy. The end of the Cold War gives hope of access to the records of the former Soviet Union and its satellites in Eastern Europe. But a full record will be years in the making and, even when complete, will only plug one of the many holes in the evidentiary base that is the key to a truly international history of the Cold War. According to Rosemary Foot, for example, we still know little about the Chinese role in the Korean War or, for that matter, the role played by Japan. Other contributors make the same point about the historiography they analyze.

Because of these and other shortcomings, the literature on the last twenty-five years of American foreign policy, though voluminous, is not always sophisticated. It is often narrative in structure, dominated by popular writers and the personal accounts of former policymakers, and not highly interpretive or theoretical. The exceptions are few, though worth noting. The first is the literature surrounding the so-called declinist debate. That debate, touched off by Paul Kennedy's remarkable book, *The Rise and Fall of the Great Powers*, has raised some interesting theoretical questions regarding the connection between imperial ambitions, military spending, and the loss of economic competitiveness.[1] The

1 Paul M. Kennedy, *The Rise and Fall of the Great Powers: Economic Change and Military Conflict from 1500 to 2000* (New York, 1987). For a discussion of Kennedy in this volume see Diane Kunz's essay.

second exception is the literature on the Vietnam War, though it is an exception less because of new theoretical perspectives than because it is grounded in a body of documentation that is unusual for works on recent history.

As Gary Hess points out in his essay, American involvement in Vietnam has dominated diplomatic studies of the Johnson administration, to the exclusion of almost every other topic. The result is an enormous body of scholarship, much of it based on *The Pentagon Papers* and other documents opened under pressure from journalists and historians. Because of this evidence, the literature on the Vietnam War has developed ahead of the literature on other major subjects in the years after 1965. What is more, the development of the Vietnam literature highlights some truisms that are also evident in the literature on other topics. One of these is a persistent interest in the moral basis of American foreign policy. As Hess notes, the morality of American intervention and American military strategy remains central to the literature on the Vietnam War, more than two decades after the end of that conflict. The same thing is true of the literature on the origins of the Cold War and on the atomic bombing of Japan, as J. Samuel Walker notes in his survey of the historiography on that subject.

Another truism, captured in the following essays, is the obvious influence of contemporary events on the topics of choice in the field. The end of the Cold War prompted renewed interest in the beginning of that conflict. The lingering controversy over Vietnam has helped to sustain the interest of historians in that topic. As Mark Stoler notes, the resurgence of neo-conservative thinking in the 1980s also resurrected the old, conservative critique of President Roosevelt's wartime diplomacy, especially at the Yalta Conference. The Watergate scandal had a similar effect on studies of American intelligence. According to John Ferris, Watergate sparked interest among historians and popular writers in the role that intelligence has played in the formulation of American foreign policy and military strategy.

These essays also illustrate the reactive and cyclical nature of historical thinking in the field, probably more clearly than most diplomatic historians would like to admit. As Stephen Rabe suggests, the Eisenhower literature appears in many ways to be an extension of the well-rehearsed arguments over the origins of the Cold War in the Truman administration. Even more interesting is an apparent pattern in the way the literature on a topic develops. The original accounts, often written by journalists, former policymakers, and historians writing at the time, give way to revisionist works, which in turn give way to some kind of postrevisionist synthesis reminiscent of the cycle of historiography on the origins of the Cold War. According to Rabe, for example, the original, critical accounts of Eisenhower and his diplomacy succumbed to a wave of Eisenhower revisionism, which carried in its wake a synthesis that is more balanced and complex than its predecessors. Rosemary Foot, Robert McMahon, Burton Kaufman, and Gary Hess, respectively, find the same pattern in the literature on the Korean War, U.S.-Asian relations, Kennedy's foreign policy, and the Vietnam War. Put differently, the first generation seems to identify the issues and stake out the positions to which subsequent generations react. Over time, historians hammer out a consensus on some basic points but remain at loggerheads on others. In some cases, the cycle even starts to repeat itself, usually in cases where the historiographical ground has been thoroughly chewed up, as Mark Stoler notes in his survey of the literature on Franklin Roosevelt's wartime diplomacy.

A quick reading of the following essays will demonstrate convincingly how completely the Cold War has dominated the literature on American foreign policy since 1939. This is the case with the literature on the foreign policy of presidential administrations and with the literature on U.S. policy toward particular regions of the world. Perhaps because of this preoccupation with the Soviet-American confrontation, the same literature tends to deal most often with issues of geopolitics, particularly geostrategy, including ways to contain communism, deter Soviet aggression, establish favorable balances of power, safeguard the national security, control vital resources, and deny those resources to potential adversaries. Even wartime diplomacy, as Stoler illustrates, has often been treated less on its own terms than in terms of the origins of the Cold War. The same is true of American relations with the developing world. As apparent in the essays by Robert McMahon and Douglas Little, these relations are invariably treated in an East-West, not a North-South, context. The opening of archives in the former Soviet world is likely to extend our preoccupation with the Soviet-American confrontation, particularly if historians follow the admonitions of John Lewis Gaddis.

There are dangers in this strategy. There is the danger that new evidence from Communist archives will be fitted into established historiographical categories and used to refight old battles. There is the danger that new evidence will be released so slowly and so spottily that it will produce incomplete and inaccurate accounts that must be revised with each new revelation. As Leffler argues, there is also the danger, evident from the Soviet documents released thus far, that new sources will not resolve old disputes but merely elaborate the evidence available to all sides in these controversies. Finally, but most importantly, there is the danger that new evidence from Communist archives will become a straight-jacket for diplomatic historians, locking them into well-established categories of analysis when they might be exploring new directions and asking new questions.

Do the essays that follow make a plea for new directions? Do they urge diplomatic historians to redefine their field to include not only topics traditional to the discipline but also such topics as ideology, culture, and discourse? Most do not. To be sure, some point to the exciting new work on the cultural aspects of diplomacy and warfare, including Michael S. Sherry's cultural analysis of air power, John W. Dower's brilliant book on the Pacific war, and Akira Iriye's pathbreaking analysis of culture and power.[2] For the most part, however, the authors in this section have not found a literature that takes up these new topics. Apparently, such topics are not yet part of the way most diplomatic historians think of their field, which may explain why they feel increasingly isolated from other historians.

Although many of the essays in this section argue for a new synthesis in diplomatic history, the word "synthesis" is often used as a synonym for "consensus" and seldom leaves room for

2 Michael S. Sherry, *The Rise of American Air Power: The Creation of Armageddon* (New Haven, 1987); John W. Dower, *War without Mercy: Race and Power in the Pacific War* (New York, 1986); Akira Iriye, *Power and Culture: The Japanese-American War, 1941–1945* (Cambridge, MA, 1981).

new ideas and topics. Diplomatic historians need to evaluate the role of gender in foreign policy, as well as race, write more comparative history, as well as more international history, and study the influence of nationalism and the North-South conflict, as well as communism and the Cold War. The relationship between political culture and foreign policy is another area to be explored, as is the influence on American policy of international information, advertising, and financial systems, which tend to globalize national cultures and economies. The study of nonstate actors should be broadened to include ethnic, racial, religious, and women's groups, as well as business and labor organizations. The connection between the Cold War and the modern state also deserves more attention than it has received. So does the impact of the Cold War on local communities and local politics; the role of international institutions, from multinational corporations, to UN agencies, to the International Red Cross; and the history of the international women's movement, the peace movement, the environmental movement, and the movement for human rights.

Equally pressing is the need for more broad overviews. If the historiographical essays that follow discover few new approaches, few pioneering works of theory, or few that bypass geostrategy for new topics, they also turn up few books that move beyond the discrete event or the bilateral study to an overview of scope and substance. One thinks quickly of Gaddis's *Strategies of Containment*, Thomas McCormick's *America's Half-Century*, Hunt's *Ideology and U.S. Foreign Policy*, and a few others, but not many others, considering the wealth of secondary literature that is now available on which synthesizers can build.[3]

So what is the conclusion? Traditional diplomatic history has never been written better, but that is not enough. Diplomatic historians must also write a new history, a new international history, a new comparative history, and a history of new topics, such as race, gender, culture, and discourse. They must read as much history as they do political science, begin to synthesize the

3 John Lewis Gaddis, *Strategies of Containment: A Critical Appraisal of Postwar American National Security Policy* (New York, 1982); Thomas J. McCormick, *America's Half-Century: United States Foreign Policy in the Cold War* (Baltimore, 1989); Michael H. Hunt, *Ideology and U.S. Foreign Policy* (New Haven, 1987).

work on the first three decades of the Cold War, and recognize that their preoccupation with the Soviet-American confrontation has left a hidden history waiting to be discovered. They must also write a history informed by new theory. It is wrong to fault any theoretical paradigm for not explaining everything, just as it is wrong to fault a synthesis for combining insights gleaned from different paradigms. But where would the best syntheses be without the theoretically driven literature from which insights are drawn? We need more not less theory, even the dreaded postmodernist theories that might help us wrestle with issues of discourse and culture, including gender, so that these issues, as Leffler says, can be included in the next great synthesis. These are the paths from margin to mainstream.

7

A Half-Century of Conflict: Interpretations of U.S. World War II Diplomacy

MARK A. STOLER

No event in U.S. history save the Civil War has assumed the mythic proportions of World War II, or resulted in such a deluge of scholarly as well as popular studies. Historiographical analyses of those scholarly studies, however, are in much shorter supply, especially in regard to U.S. wartime diplomacy. The recent fiftieth-anniversary commemorations of the war, along with the enormous number of publications that have preceded and accompanied those commemorations, make this a particularly appropriate time to provide such an analysis.[1]

In an earlier, 1981 assessment, I noted that the historiography of U.S. diplomacy during World War II possessed characteristics both similar to and different from other areas of intense historical dispute. Major similarities included the large volume of writings, the impact of contemporary concerns on evolving interpretations, and the effect of new schools of thought regarding U.S. foreign

The author wishes to thank Warren F. Kimball, David Reynolds, and Theodore A. Wilson for their invaluable criticism and advice regarding earlier drafts of this essay, as well as Michael J. Hogan for his encouragement and patience.

1 In light of both my own 1981 analysis of the literature and the volume of works to appear since then, much of this essay will focus on interpretations published between 1981 and 1994. For greater detail on earlier interpretations see my "World War II Diplomacy in Historical Writing: Prelude to Cold War," in *American Foreign Relations: A Historiographical Review*, ed. Gerald K. Haines and J. Samuel Walker (Westport, 1981), 187–206.

The first part of this essay essentially summarizes what I said in 1981 about those early interpretations. I have revised my assessments of works published during the 1970s, however, as well as focused on works of the 1980s and early 1990s; approximately two thirds of this essay is devoted to such works. Both the 1981 analysis and this one focus exclusively on U.S. wartime diplomacy after official U.S. entry into the conflict in December 1941.

relations in general. World War II diplomacy was a unique field, however, in at least two important respects. First, the combination of massive documentary evidence and continued popular interest in the war had already resulted by 1981 in a volume of literature so enormous and so rapidly growing as to merit special mention. Second, although the resulting schools of interpretation reflected to an extent those of U.S. diplomacy in general, they possessed a distinctive quality because of the enormous influence of the Cold War on the interpreters. That influence, I emphasized, had led most historians to analyze World War II diplomacy primarily in terms of its role in the postwar Soviet-American conflict.[2]

Interpretations of World War II diplomacy published since 1981 continued these trends. Of special noteworthiness is the ongoing and apparently insatiable public as well as scholarly interest in the war, fanned since 1989 by fiftieth anniversary commemorations, and the ensuing enormous volume of works being published. One historian has recently predicted that in the next two decades, World War II will replace the Civil War as "the most popular war in the public imagination."[3] Equally noteworthy is the continued impact of the Cold War on World War II interpretations. Highly illustrative of this impact is the fact that in numerous historiographical and bibliographical studies published during the 1980s, World War II diplomacy was combined with the origins of the Cold War rather than receiving separate treatment.[4]

The early 1980s witnessed a sharp deterioration in Soviet-American relations, however, as well as dramatic, related changes in the domestic American environment. In the wake of these developments, what had appeared in 1981 to be a promising interpretive synthesis was replaced by renewed interpretive controversy.

2 Ibid.

3 Ronald Spector comments in "The Scholarship on World War II: Its Present Condition and Future Possibilities," ed. Richard H. Kohn, *Journal of Military History* 55 (July 1991): 382.

4 See, for example, Robert L. Messer, "World War II and the Coming of the Cold War," in *Modern American Diplomacy*, ed. John M. Carroll and George C. Herring (Wilmington, DE, 1986), 107–25; Joseph A. Fry, "United States Diplomacy: A Bibliography of Historiographical Works," SHAFR *Newsletter* 20 (September 1989): 26–29; and Donald Cameron Watt, "Britain and the Historiography of the Yalta Conference and the Cold War," *Diplomatic History* 13 (Winter 1989): 67–98.

Neither the ensuing return of détente nor the unexpected conclusion of the Cold War in 1989–1991 ended these controversies. But they no longer monopolize the historiographical agenda. The simultaneous development during the 1980s of new schools of interpretation regarding U.S. foreign relations in general led to important new approaches to the years 1941–1945, some of which have clearly begun to shift the focus away from the Cold War.

Early interpretations viewed U.S. diplomacy during World War II as the first round in the Cold War and thus did not follow the standard historiographical pattern of official version, revisionism, response, and synthesis.[5] Instead, scholarship highly critical of U.S. policy surfaced first and practically became the official version. Although defenses of U.S. World War II diplomacy did appear during the first twenty years after the war, most of them accepted revisionist arguments to an extraordinary extent.

The focal points of this early criticism were the supposed blunders and naiveté of President Franklin D. Roosevelt and other U.S. policymakers in their wartime relations with the Soviet Union, which had resulted in a massive and unnecessary extension of Soviet power. Early proponents of this interpretation included Roosevelt's prewar domestic as well as foreign policy opponents and former advisers, such as Ambassador William C. Bullitt and General John R. Deane, who had disagreed with the president's cooperative wartime policies toward the Soviets. The group also included British and American journalists, such as Chester Wilmot and Hanson Baldwin, who saw British Prime Minister Winston S. Churchill's rejected wartime proposals and policies as the ones the United States should have followed vis-à-vis the Soviets.[6] Although Churchill himself consciously downplayed Anglo-

5 See Warren F. Kimball, "The Cold War Warmed Over," *American Historical Review* 79 (October 1974): 1119. See also Watt, "The Yalta Conference and the Cold War," 70–73, for an alternative, six-stage historiographical pattern.

6 See William Henry Chamberlin, *America's Second Crusade* (Chicago, 1950); Harry Elmer Barnes, ed., *Perpetual War for Perpetual Peace* (Caldwell, ID, 1953); William C. Bullitt, "How We Won the War and Lost the Peace," *Life* 25 (30 August 1948): 82–97; John R. Deane, *The Strange Alliance: The Story of Our Efforts at Wartime Co-operation with Russia* (New York, 1947); Hanson W. Baldwin, *Great Mistakes of the War* (New York, 1949); and Chester Wilmot, *The Struggle for Europe* (New York, 1952). See also Stoler, "World War II Diplomacy," 188–90.

American wartime differences in his memoirs so as not to damage postwar relations between the two countries, those memoirs nevertheless provided substantial ammunition for such attacks on U.S. policies and exercised an extraordinary influence over historians because of their high quality and early publication before the release of many documents. This impact was far from accidental. "History will bear me out," Churchill had boasted, "particularly as I shall write that history myself." He did indeed, albeit with an attitude, as paraphrased by Sir William Deakin, that "this is not history; this is my case."[7]

International and domestic events in the decade following World War II made this assault on U.S. wartime diplomacy not only popular but also an extremely powerful and emotional political issue. Indeed, the frustrations of perceived Cold War defeats in China and Korea, combined with loss of the U.S. nuclear monopoly and revelations regarding wartime Soviet spies, led Republican politicians such as Joseph R. McCarthy to fame and power by accusing Roosevelt and his associates of treason rather than mere naiveté. By the early 1950s the wartime Yalta Conference in the Crimea had become virtually synonymous with such charges and had acquired, as Donald Cameron Watt has noted, "a connotation of shameful failure, if not outright treason, matching that attached to the Munich Conference of September 1938."[8]

Roosevelt's supporters and numerous historians within the emerging realist school criticized the ahistorical framework upon which such assaults were based. The framework of 1941–1945 had not been the Cold War, they pointedly noted, but military necessity and the need to maintain the Grand Alliance in order to defeat the Axis. That defeat and military realities, most notably

7 Quoted in Warren F. Kimball, "Wheel within a Wheel: Churchill, Roosevelt and the Special Relationship," in *Churchill*, ed. Robert Blake and Wm. Roger Louis (New York, 1993), 294. See also Winston S. Churchill, *The Second World War*, 6 vols. (Boston, 1948–53). For Churchill's downplaying of Anglo-American differences see John Colville, *The Fringes of Power: Downing Street Diaries, 1939–1955* (New York, 1985), 658; and David Reynolds, "Roosevelt, Churchill, and the Wartime Anglo-American Alliance: Towards a New Synthesis," in *The "Special Relationship": Anglo-American Relations since 1945*, ed. Wm. Roger Louis and Hedley Bull (Oxford, 1986), 17–18.

8 Watt, "Yalta and the Cold War," 79. See also Athan G. Theoharis, *The Yalta Myths: An Issue in U.S. Politics, 1945–1955* (Columbia, MO, 1970).

those created by the advancing Red Army, rather than blunders, naiveté, or treason, had led inevitably to an enormous increase in Soviet power. Josef Stalin's supposed territorial gains at Yalta, historians John L. Snell, Forrest C. Pogue, Charles F. Delzell, and George A. Lensen emphasized in this regard in their 1956 *The Meaning of Yalta*, preceded and resulted from these realities rather than from Roosevelt's policies.[9]

Other defenses of U.S. wartime diplomacy published from 1945–1965 exhibited a fascinating duality, however, for most of the writers agreed with the charges of naiveté being leveled against Roosevelt and his advisers if not with the more extreme partisan charges of treason being leveled by the McCarthyites. Naiveté was one of the basic characteristics of all U.S. foreign policy, according to the realist critique then being expounded.[10] It was also a key component of traditional American self-perception. Furthermore, most of Roosevelt's defenders had by this time become Cold Warriors themselves and were thus neither willing nor able to defend his cooperative approach toward the Soviets during the war. Hence, in the process of defending U.S. wartime diplomacy against its extreme critics, most of these individuals wound up attacking it on grounds similar to those the critics had used.

This duality clearly affected the comprehensive and excellent "first generation" histories of the wartime alliance by William H. McNeill and Herbert Feis,[11] as well as the numerous interpretive assessments of U.S. foreign and military policies in general written between 1945 and 1965. During these two decades most scholars modified their general support of U.S. policy during the war by criticizing the policymakers' separation of military from political issues, their single-minded devotion to military victory,

9 John L. Snell, ed., *The Meaning of Yalta: Big Three Diplomacy and the New Balance of Power* (Baton Rouge, 1956).

10 See, for example, George F. Kennan, *American Diplomacy, 1900–1950* (Chicago, 1951).

11 William Hardy McNeill, *America, Britain, & Russia: Their Cooperation and Conflict, 1941–1946*, a volume in *Survey of International Affairs, 1939–1946*, ed. Arnold Toynbee (London, 1953); Herbert Feis, *Churchill, Roosevelt, Stalin: The War They Waged and the Peace They Sought* (Princeton, 1957). McNeill did see the breakup of the Grand Alliance as a natural result of victory rather than anyone's fault, but he still criticized FDR along the lines discussed above.

and their naive Wilsonianism regarding the postwar world. Roosevelt was further criticized for placing too much faith in Stalin's goodwill and in his own powers of persuasion. All of these criticisms had originally been made by Roosevelt's detractors, and by the early 1960s this view thus constituted the dominant consensus. Indeed, by that time scholars such as Anne Armstrong, Tang Tsou, and Gaddis Smith appeared to be agreeing with Roosevelt's severest critics in the process of supposedly attacking them.[12]

This historical consensus was clearly related to the Cold War consensus that had come to dominate American politics. And just as that latter consensus was shattered by the events of the 1960s, most importantly the war in Vietnam, so too was the historical one as two new schools of interpretation emerged in that decade to challenge the prevailing wisdom.

The first of these, which included historians preparing the U.S. Army's massive official military history of the war as well as others who made use of these volumes and/or the enormous documentary record then becoming available, argued that U.S. wartime policies and strategies had been highly realistic rather than naive and that the president had clearly controlled his military advisers rather than vice versa.[13] John L. Snell went even further in 1963, arguing in a brief, comparative history of wartime diplomacy that Axis leaders, rather than Roosevelt, had based their policies on illusions, and thereby lost the war. The president's policies, on the other hand, had been highly realistic

12 Anne Armstrong, *Unconditional Surrender: The Impact of the Casablanca Policy in World War II* (New Brunswick, 1961); Tang Tsou, *America's Failure in China, 1941–50* (Chicago, 1963); Gaddis Smith, *American Diplomacy during the Second World War, 1941–1945*, 1st ed. (New York, 1965). See also Samuel P. Huntington, *The Soldier and the State: The Theory and Politics of Civil-Military Relationships* (Cambridge, MA, 1957), 315–44, for a similar critique of Roosevelt's military advisers.

13 See, for example, William Emerson, "Franklin Roosevelt as Commander-in-Chief in World War II," *Military Affairs* 22 (Winter 1958–59): 181–207; Maurice Matloff, "Franklin Delano Roosevelt as War Leader," in *Total War and Cold War: Problems in Civilian Control of the Military*, ed. Harry L. Coles (Columbus, OH, 1962), 42–65; and Kent Roberts Greenfield, *American Strategy in World War II: A Reconsideration* (Baltimore, 1963), 49–84. See also Willard Range, *Franklin D. Roosevelt's World Order* (Athens, OH, 1959); and directly below. Entitled *United States Army in World War II*, the official army history eventually included some eighty volumes and a special collection of essays, *Command Decisions*, ed. Kent Roberts Greenfield (Washington, 1960).

and resulted in total military victory. Because cooperation with the Soviets was essential to that victory and expanded postwar Soviet power was an inevitable outcome of it, Roosevelt's cooperative approach was "virtually imposed by necessity." Snell further defended Roosevelt's much-maligned unconditional surrender policy and his postponement of all territorial settlements as highly realistic and pragmatic attempts to promote U.S. interests while simultaneously reconciling Allied differences and maintaining domestic support. In pursuing these policies, the president had concurrently established the key prerequisites for both wartime victory and postwar cooperation with the Soviets and placed limits on their expansion should cooperation not occur – limits clearly illustrated by the fact that Stalin's territorial gains did not exceed those Czar Nicholas II would have obtained at the end of World War I had he remained in power.[14]

This thesis received reinforcement in the late 1960s from two directions. In major reassessments of Roosevelt, Robert A. Divine and James M. Burns argued that the president had been highly pragmatic and realistic. Rather than FDR being duped by Stalin, Divine argued, historians and the public had been duped by the president's Wilsonian public statements, which were delivered to protect his domestic flank but which were contradicted by his pragmatic private comments and actions. Such pragmatism, both historians argued, had helped the Grand Alliance maintain itself during the war but ironically doomed Roosevelt's hopes for postwar cooperation – because it led him to misunderstand Stalin, according to Divine; and/or because it increased Soviet suspicions, according to Burns.[15] Simultaneously, British as well as U.S. historians began to reexamine the supposedly realistic alternative strategies and policies that Churchill had provided. Many of them concluded that fear of postwar Soviet power was a much less important motivation than the British prime minister had led his readers to believe, and that irrational as well as narrowly

14 John L. Snell, *Illusion and Necessity: The Diplomacy of Global War, 1939–1945* (Boston, 1963), 116, 137–43, 209–16. See also Raymond G. O'Connor, *Diplomacy for Victory: FDR and Unconditional Surrender* (New York, 1971).

15 Robert A. Divine, *Roosevelt and World War II* (Baltimore, 1969); James MacGregor Burns, *Roosevelt: The Soldier of Freedom, 1940–1945* (New York, 1970). See also Geoffrey Warner, "From Teheran to Yalta: Reflections on F. D. R.'s Foreign Policy," *International Affairs* 43 (July 1967): 530–36.

nationalistic motivations lay behind his proposals. Some argued that those proposals had been politically as well as militarily unsound, and that Churchill had in fact been more willing than Roosevelt to grant Stalin territorial concessions.[16]

The second school of interpretation to challenge the prevailing consensus on U.S. wartime diplomacy during the 1960s was the so-called New Left. It, too, made extensive use of the massive documentation then becoming available to attack the notion of American blunders and naiveté during the war, but in such a way as to sharply condemn rather than defend U.S. policy and to assert that aggressive U.S. behavior during the war had been a, if not the, primary cause of the ensuing Cold War.

This New Left assault was far from monolithic, however. Basing their work on the Open Door thesis that William Appleman Williams (and Charles Beard before him) had developed to critique U.S. foreign policy in general, historians such as Lloyd C. Gardner published broad and highly critical economic interpretations of all of Roosevelt's foreign policies. Gabriel Kolko provided the most extensive and extreme socioeconomic criticism of U.S. wartime diplomacy, maintaining that Washington had realistically and aggressively attempted to promote its own postwar capitalist expansion at the expense of the British Empire, the Soviet Union, and the indigenous Left throughout the world.[17] In more specialized revisionist works, however, other scholars, such as Gar Alperovitz and Diane Shaver Clemens, harkened back to D. F. Fleming's earlier and more specific Cold War revisionism, rather than to Williams's general economic approach, to defend Roosevelt's cooperative policy with the Soviet Union and to blame his successor, Harry S. Truman, for reversing it. Alperovitz saw such a reversal in Truman's decision to drop the atomic bomb on

16 See Michael Howard, *The Mediterranean Strategy in the Second World War* (London, 1968); Stephen E. Ambrose, *Eisenhower and Berlin, 1945: The Decision to Halt at the Elbe* (New York, 1967); O'Connor, *Diplomacy for Victory* and *Force and Diplomacy: Essays Military and Diplomatic* (Coral Gables, 1972), 11–25; and Trumbull Higgins, *Soft Underbelly: The Anglo-American Controversy over the Italian Campaign, 1943–1945* (New York, 1968).

17 William Appleman Williams, *The Tragedy of American Diplomacy*, enlarged rev. ed. (New York, 1962); Lloyd C. Gardner, *Economic Aspects of New Deal Diplomacy* (Madison, 1964); idem, *Architects of Illusion: Men and Ideas in American Foreign Policy, 1941–1949* (Chicago, 1970); Gabriel Kolko, *The Politics of War: The World and United States Foreign Policy, 1943–1945* (New York, 1968).

Hiroshima, a decision motivated primarily by a desire to blackmail the Soviets, rather than to end the war quickly, as Herbert Feis had earlier claimed. Clemens concluded her detailed revisionist analysis of Yalta by maintaining that Truman, rather than Stalin, had broken the accords, even though Stalin, rather than Roosevelt, had made the bulk of the concessions at the conference.[18]

Consensus historians sharply attacked this New Left assault on prevailing interpretations of World War II diplomacy and the origins of the Cold War, with the debate often as heated as the larger political one on the Vietnam War. By 1973, it included name calling and accusations of gross distortion and misuse of historical evidence that spilled beyond the confines of the profession and onto the pages of the *New York Times*.[19] Ironically, however, new works on U.S. diplomacy during World War II as well as during the Cold War were by that time moving far beyond such polarized confrontations and into an era of detailed monographs, attempted synthesis, and entirely new approaches.

Numerous factors accounted for this shift. The early debate had clearly reached a stalemate by the mid-1970s, while many historians had begun to realize that the divergent schools did share some important conclusions – such as the universalistic nature of U.S. policies during the war as compared with those of the other Allied powers. As the years passed, such shared conclusions became more visible, partially as a result of the calmer political environment that followed Watergate and the end of the Vietnam War, and partially as a result of the emergence of a new generation of historians not personally linked to the older battles – or to the personal experience of World War II for that matter.[20]

18 Gar Alperovitz, *Atomic Diplomacy: Hiroshima and Potsdam: The Use of the Atomic Bomb and the American Confrontation with Soviet Power*, 1st ed. (New York, 1965); D. F. Fleming, *The Cold War and Its Origins, 1917–1960* (New York, 1961); Herbert Feis, *Japan Subdued: The Atomic Bomb and the End of the War in the Far East* (Princeton, 1961); Diane Shaver Clemens, *Yalta* (New York, 1970). Secretary of State Edward R. Stettinius had first argued that Stalin made most of the concessions in *Roosevelt and the Russians: The Yalta Conference* (Garden City, 1949). See also Stoler, "World War II Diplomacy," 196–98.

19 See Robert James Maddox, *The New Left and the Origins of the Cold War* (Princeton, 1973); and *New York Times Book Review*, 17 June 1973.

20 See, for example, Lloyd C. Gardner, Arthur Schlesinger, Jr., and Hans Morgenthau, *Origins of the Cold War* (Waltham, MA, 1970). For early attempted syntheses from the revisionist and traditionalist perspectives, respectively, see Gardner, *Architects of*

This new generation in turn possessed new documentary evidence not available to its predecessors. The works of the 1960s had been based primarily on documentary information in the numerous volumes published during those years within the State Department's *Foreign Relations* series and the British and American official history series, as well as memoirs and recently opened manuscript collections.[21] The bulk of the official World War II documentary record remained classified until the early 1970s, however, when most of it was opened in both England and the United States. The result was quantitatively and qualitatively staggering. U.S. Army files alone weighed 17,120 tons, enough to fill 188 miles of filing cases end to end.[22] And within those files lay not only enormously detailed evidence to revise previous analyses

Illusion; and John Lewis Gaddis, *The United States and the Origins of the Cold War, 1941–1947* (New York, 1972). For the continuing enormous impact of the war on historians who lived through it see Richard Wrightman Fox et al., "A Round Table: The Living and Reliving of World War II," *Journal of American History* 77 (September 1990): 553–93.

21 As a result of the domestic political uproar over Yalta, a special *Foreign Relations* volume on that conference was published in 1955. Not until the 1960s, however, did the regular chronological series reach the war years and companion volumes begin to appear for the other wartime conferences; more than thirty volumes covering the period 1941–1945 would be published during the decade. The key British collections were the *Grand Strategy* military series of six volumes edited by J. R. M. Butler (London, 1956–76); and Sir Llewellyn Woodward's *British Foreign Policy in the Second World War*, published in an abridged single volume in 1962 and then in five volumes between 1970 and 1976. See also Wesley F. Craven and James L. Cate, eds., *The Army Air Forces in World War II*, 7 vols. (Chicago, 1948–49); Samuel Eliot Morison, *History of United States Naval Operations in World War II*, 15 vols. (Boston, 1947–62); and the previously cited eighty-volume *U.S. Army in World War II*. Most of Roosevelt's key advisers published memoirs in the three decades after the war. The last major one to appear was W. Averell Harriman's *Special Envoy to Churchill and Stalin, 1941–1946* (New York, 1975).

Roosevelt died before he could write any memoirs himself, but selections from his wartime diplomatic correspondence with Churchill and Stalin appeared in numerous volumes of the *Foreign Relations* series. Churchill's memoirs also contained extensive Big Three correspondence. In 1957 the Soviet Ministry for Foreign Affairs published Stalin's complete correspondence with Churchill and Roosevelt as *Russia: Correspondence between the Chairman of the Council of Ministers of the U.S.S.R. and the Presidents of the U.S.A. and the Prime Ministers of Great Britain during the Great Patriotic War of 1941–1945*, 2 vols. (Moscow, 1957). The Churchill-Roosevelt correspondence received separate, full-scale treatment only in the 1970s and 1980s. See Francis L. Lowenheim, Harold Langley, and Manfred Jonas, eds., *Roosevelt and Churchill: Their Secret Wartime Correspondence* (New York, 1975); and Warren F. Kimball, ed., *Churchill & Roosevelt: The Complete Correspondence*, 3 vols. (Princeton, 1984).

22 Kent Roberts Greenfield, *The Historian and the Army* (New Brunswick, 1954), 6.

but also revelations that opened entirely new areas of inquiry. Most publicized was the so-called Ultra Secret, the Anglo-American breaking of the highest German military code, which had remained unrevealed until 1974 and which after that date precipitated the creation of virtually a new subfield in World War II scholarship: cryptography and deception. The ramifications for the diplomatic history of the war of these and other aspects of intelligence, which one British diplomat labeled "the missing dimension of most diplomatic history," are still being explored.[23]

Two additional and related factors also deserve mention, although their full impact would not be felt until the 1980s. Historical study in general was being altered by the use of new social science models and the computer as well as by a new emphasis on social, cultural, and comparative history. Furthermore, diplomatic historians came under sharp attack for not participating in these changes and for limiting both their research and their focus to the United States. According to Alexander DeConde, diplomatic history underwent "perhaps . . . more criticism than any other comparable field of historical investigation." Although this criticism was overstated and ignored numerous pioneering efforts in the new areas and methods of inquiry, it clearly affected numerous scholars who attempted to incorporate such approaches into their work.[24]

23 See David Dilks, ed., *The Diaries of Sir Alexander Cadogan, 1938–1945* (New York, 1972), 21; and Christopher Andrew and David Dilks, eds., *The Missing Dimension: Governments and Intelligence Communities in the Twentieth Century* (Urbana, 1984).

The first work to reveal Ultra was F. W. Winterbotham's memoir, *The Ultra Secret* (New York, 1974). A complete note on all the related material published since would run many pages, and the interested reader is advised to consult both the *International Journal of Intelligence and Counterintelligence* and John Lewis Gaddis's "Intelligence, Espionage, and Cold War Origins," *Diplomatic History* 13 (Spring 1989): 191–212. Although primarily concerned with the impact of intelligence on the Cold War, Gaddis's article contains much information on the World War II years and a good summary of key works in the field. The most recent is Bradley F. Smith's *The Ultra-Magic Deals and the Most Secret Special Relationship, 1940–1946* (Novato, CA, 1993).

24 The most famous and cited of these attacks is Charles S. Maier's "Marking Time: The Historiography of International Relations," in *The Past before Us: Contemporary Historical Writing in the United States*, ed. Michael Kammen (Ithaca, 1980), 355–87. See also Sally Marks, "The World According to Washington," *Diplomatic History* 11 (Summer 1987): 281–82; and Christopher Thorne, "After the Europeans: American Designs for the Remaking of Southeast Asia," ibid. 12 (Spring 1988): 206–8. Excellent summaries of new approaches in the field can be found in Michael J.

The resultant outpouring during the 1970s of scholarship on World War II diplomacy cut in many directions. The new availability of military as well as diplomatic and British as well as U.S. documents led to numerous reexaminations of Anglo-American as well as Soviet-American wartime relations in general and of such highly controversial alliance issues as aid to Russia, the second front dispute, the Darlan affair, postwar decolonization and economic organization, Middle Eastern oil, the atomic bomb decision, and the treatment of postwar Germany.[25] Contradicting the image Churchill had sought to project in his memoirs, many of these studies emphasized intense Anglo-American as well as Soviet-American differences and tensions throughout the war. In his 1978 *Imperialism at Bay*, Wm. Roger Louis took such analyses a step further by using multiarchival research to examine

Hogan and Thomas G. Paterson, eds., *Explaining the History of American Foreign Relations* (New York, 1991), a compilation based upon earlier symposiums in *Journal of American History* 77 (June 1990): 93–182, and *Diplomatic History* 14 (Fall 1990): 553–605. Other attacks, as well as the DeConde quote, are in Stephen G. Rabe's review of *Explaining the History*, "Reports of Our Demise Are Greatly Exaggerated," *Diplomatic History* 16 (Summer 1992): 481–82. A summary of the attacks can also be found in Edward P. Crapol's recent historiographical essay, "Coming to Terms with Empire: The Historiography of Late-Nineteenth-Century American Foreign Relations," ibid. (Fall 1992): 573–76.

25 See, for example, Robert Beitzell, *The Uneasy Alliance: America, Britain, and Russia, 1941–1943* (New York, 1972); Gaddis, *The United States and the Origins of the Cold War*; Richard W. Steele, *The First Offensive, 1942: Roosevelt, Marshall and the Making of American Strategy* (Bloomington, 1973); Richard C. Lukas, *Eagles East: The Army Air Forces and the Soviet Union, 1941–1945* (Tallahassee, 1970); Arthur L. Funk, *The Politics of TORCH: The Allied Landings and the Algiers Putsch, 1942* (Lawrence, 1974); Mark A. Stoler, *The Politics of the Second Front: American Military Planning and Diplomacy in Coalition Warfare, 1941–1943* (Westport, 1977); Brian J. Villa, "The U.S. Army, Unconditional Surrender, and the Potsdam Declaration," *Journal of American History* 63 (June 1976): 66–92, idem, "The Atomic Bomb and the Normandy Invasion," *Perspectives in American History* 11 (1977–78): 463–502; Walter S. Dunn, Jr., *Second Front Now 1943* (University, AL, 1980); John Grigg, *1943: The Victory That Never Was* (New York, 1980); George C. Herring, *Aid to Russia, 1941–1946: Strategy, Diplomacy, and the Origins of the Cold War* (Baltimore, 1973); Thomas G. Paterson, *Soviet-American Confrontation: Postwar Reconstruction and the Origins of the Cold War* (Baltimore, 1973); Leon Martel, *Lend-Lease, Loans, and the Coming of the Cold War: A Study of the Implementation of Foreign Policy* (Boulder, 1979); Alfred E. Eckes, Jr., *A Search for Solvency: Bretton Woods and the International Monetary System, 1941–1971* (Austin, 1975); Armand Van Dormael, *Bretton Woods: Birth of a Monetary System* (London, 1978); Warren F. Kimball, *Swords or Ploughshares? The Morgenthau Plan for Defeated Nazi Germany, 1943–1946* (Philadelphia, 1976); and Bruce Kuklick, *American Policy and the Division of Germany: The Clash with Russia over Reparations* (Ithaca, 1972). See also directly below, footnotes 26–32.

intragovernmental as well as Anglo-American conflicts over postwar decolonization and trusteeships during the war.[26] Simultaneously, other scholars used the newly available material to shift the focus away from Anglo-American as well as Soviet-American relations and onto U.S. wartime policies vis-à-vis other nations during the war, as well as colonial areas. Once again, however, this shift reflected the consistent search for World War II roots to contemporary concerns. As the publication during the 1960s of studies on wartime Franco-American relations had coincided with Charles de Gaulle's return to power and removal of his country from the unified NATO military command,[27] so in the 1970s did the large number of studies on U.S. wartime policies regarding China, Indochina, and the Middle East parallel three areas of critical concern for U.S. foreign policy during that time period.[28] But the sheer volume of new documentation, combined with the rise of polycentrism and Third World issues in general during the 1970s, also led to a flood of specialized studies on wartime relations with a host of other countries.[29]

26 Wm. Roger Louis, *Imperialism at Bay, 1941–1945: The United States and the Decolonization of the British Empire* (New York, 1978). See below, footnotes 37 and 65, for additional works that focus on Anglo-American and/or intragovernmental conflicts during the war.

27 See Dorothy S. White, *Seeds of Discord: de Gaulle, Free France, and the Allies* (Syracuse, 1964); and Milton Viorst, *Hostile Allies: FDR and Charles de Gaulle* (New York, 1965).

28 See Barbara W. Tuchman, *Stilwell and the American Experience in China, 1911–1945* (New York, 1970); Michael Schaller, *The U.S. Crusade in China, 1938–1945* (New York, 1979); Edward R. Drachman, *United States Policy toward Vietnam, 1940–1945* (Rutherford, NJ, 1970); Gary R. Hess, "Franklin Roosevelt and Indochina," *Journal of American History* 59 (September 1972): 353–68; Walter LaFeber, "Roosevelt, Churchill, and Indochina, 1942–1945," *American Historical Review* 80 (December 1975): 1277–95; Christopher Thorne, "Indochina and Anglo-American Relations, 1942–1945," *Pacific Historical Revies* 45 (February 1976): 73–96; Phillip J. Baram, *The Department of State in the Middle East, 1919–1945* (Philadelphia, 1978); and John A. DeNovo, "The Culbertson Economic Mission and Anglo-American Tensions in the Middle East, 1944–1945," *Journal of American History* 63 (March 1977): 913–36.

29 See, for example, Walter R. Roberts, *Tito, Mihailovic, and the Allies, 1941–1945* (New Brunswick, 1973); Roger J. Bell, *Unequal Allies: Australian-American Relations and the Pacific War* (Melbourne, 1977); Richard C. Lukas, *The Strange Allies: The United States and Poland, 1941–1945* (Knoxville, 1978); James J. Dougherty, *The Politics of Wartime Aid: American Economic Assistance to France and French West Africa, 1940–1946* (Westport, 1978); Gary R. Hess, *America Encounters India, 1941–1947* (Baltimore, 1971); Frank D. McCann, Jr., *The Brazilian-American Alliance, 1937–1945* (Princeton, 1973); Randall B. Woods, *The Roosevelt Foreign-Policy*

On some issues the result was the creation of a new consensus. Most notable in this regard were works on the atomic bomb by Barton J. Bernstein and Martin J. Sherwin. Working with newly declassified material as well as with the existing and conflicting interpretations, each concluded independently that the United States had indeed practiced "atomic diplomacy" against the Soviets as Alperovitz had argued, but that this had been a secondary motive to ending the war quickly, as Feis had earlier maintained. They also emphasized that such atomic diplomacy had been a key component of Roosevelt's policy and that Truman had thus not reversed his predecessor's attitudes on the weapon vis-à-vis the Soviets.[30] A new consensus also began to emerge on wartime policy toward China, although here the result was more a reversal than a synthesis of previous interpretations. Those interpretations, written at the height of Sino-American conflict in the 1950s and 1960s, had criticized U.S. wartime policymakers for insufficient support of Jiang Jieshi (Chiang Kai-shek) and nonrecognition of the menace posed by the Communist Mao Zedong (Mao Tse-tung).[31] Writing in the 1970s, a decade of intense Sino-Soviet conflict and tremendously improved Sino-American relations, Barbara Tuchman and Michael Schaller criticized policymakers for not having dropped the hopeless Jiang in favor of Mao during the war.[32]

Establishment and the Good Neighbor: The United States and Argentina, 1941–1945 (Lawrence, 1979); Irwin F. Gellman, *Good Neighbor Diplomacy: United States Policies in Latin America, 1933–1945* (Baltimore, 1979); and Gerald K. Haines, "Under the Eagle's Wing: The Franklin Roosevelt Administration Forges an American Hemisphere," *Diplomatic History* 1 (Fall 1977): 373–88. This list is far from complete. For additional works see Richard Dean Burns, ed., *A Guide to American Foreign Relations since 1700* (Santa Barbara, 1982).

30 Barton J. Bernstein, "Roosevelt, Truman, and the Atomic Bomb, 1941–1945: A Reinterpretation," *Political Science Ouarterly* 90 (Spring 1975): 23–69; idem, "The Uneasy Alliance: Roosevelt, Churchill, and the Atomic Bomb, 1940–1945," *Western Political Quarterly* 29 (June 1976): 202–30; Martin J. Sherwin, *A World Destroyed: The Atomic Bomb and the Grand Alliance* (New York, 1975).

31 See Anthony Kubek, *How the Far East Was Lost: American Policy and the Creation of Communist China, 1941–1949* (Chicago, 1963); and Tsou, *America's Failure in China*. For an early defense of U.S. policies see Herbert Feis, *The China Tangle: The American Effort in China from Pearl Harbor to the Marshall Mission* (Princeton, 1953).

32 Tuchman, *Stilwell and the American Experience in China*; Schaller, *The U.S. Crusade in China*.

The decade ended with two major works that attempted both to synthesize the numerous recent monographs into a new consensus and to point the way for new lines of inquiry. In a detailed and exhaustive analysis of all of Franklin Roosevelt's foreign policies from 1932 to 1945, Robert Dallek sided with a decade of FDR defenders by dismissing all the supposed "blunders" listed by previous critics and by emphasizing both FDR's realism and the severe domestic as well as international constraints under which he had operated. Dallek's assessment was not uniformly positive, however. Echoing a series of recent studies, he criticized the president sharply for his "unnecessary and destructive compromises of legal and moral principles," most notably his sanctioning of illegal wiretaps and mail openings as well as the internment of Japanese-Americans, and his overly cautious response (or lack of response) to the Nazi destruction of European Jewry.[33] Simultaneously, British historian Christopher Thorne broke new ground by publishing the first diplomatic history of the Pacific war and by emphasizing within that pathbreaking work of multiarchival research racism, anticolonialism, Anglo-American friction, and relations with other Pacific nations as key themes.[34]

Additional studies soon appeared that both supported and filled in gaps within these two key works. Although his 1982 *Strategies of Containment* focused on the postwar years, John Lewis Gaddis began the work by crediting Roosevelt with a highly realistic though flawed wartime strategy of "containment by integration" of the Soviet Union into his proposed postwar order and by arguing, as had Dallek and a few others, that had Roosevelt lived longer he probably would have shifted to a tougher strategy after obtaining victory over the Axis.[35] Simultaneously, Martin Gilbert, David S.

33 Robert Dallek, *Franklin D. Roosevelt and American Foreign Policy, 1932–1945* (New York, 1979). Early works on the United States and the Holocaust include Arthur D. Morse, *While Six Million Died: A Chronicle of American Apathy* (New York, 1968); Henry L. Feingold, *The Politics of Rescue: The Roosevelt Administration and the Holocaust, 1938–1945* (New Brunswick, 1970); Saul S. Friedman, *No Haven for the Oppressed: United States Policy toward Jewish Refugees, 1938–1945* (Detroit, 1973); and David S. Wyman, *Paper Walls: America and the Refugee Crisis, 1938–1941* (Amherst, MA, 1968). See below, footnote 36, for more recent studies.

34 Christopher Thorne, *Allies of a Kind: The United States, Britain and the War against Japan, 1941–1945* (New York, 1978).

35 John Lewis Gaddis, *Strategies of Containment: A Critical Appraisal of Postwar American National Security Policy* (New York, 1982), 3–16. See also Terry H. Anderson, *The United States, Great Britain, and the Cold War, 1944–1947* (Columbia,

Wyman, and numerous other scholars expanded upon previous criticisms of U.S. and Allied refugee policy during the Holocaust in comprehensive, multiarchival works,[36] while Terry H. Anderson, Alan P. Dobson, Fraser J. Harbutt, Robert M. Hathaway, and John J. Sbrega explored Anglo-American wartime conflicts within their multiarchival analyses of U.S.-British relations during and immediately after World War II. So did David Reynolds and others, thereby completing the demolition of Churchill's one-sided interpretation and exposing a relationship that, although indeed "remarkable," had been marked by severe disagreements and became "special" only gradually, fitfully, and incompletely.[37]

In regard to other issues raised by Thorne in *Allies of a Kind*, Akira Iriye's 1981 *Power and Culture* offered an original and provocative comparative analysis of U.S. and Japanese societies and their values throughout the Pacific conflict, one that emphasized their similarities even in war. In his 1986 *War without Mercy*, John W. Dower made extensive use of evidence within popular culture to analyze in detail the racist views each nation held of the other and their consequences during the war. Thorne himself produced a comparative follow-up study in 1985, *The Issue of War*, a thematic analysis that attempted to remove the

MO, 1981), 41–51, 199–200n49. Interestingly, Gaddis in 1983 noted a parallel emerging consensus on the origins of the Cold War. See his "The Emerging Post-Revisionist Synthesis on the Origins of the Cold War," with responses by Lloyd C. Gardner, Lawrence S. Kaplan, Warren F. Kimball, and Bruce R. Kuniholm in *Diplomatic History* 7 (Summer 1983): 171–204.

36 See Martin Gilbert, *Auschwitz and the Allies* (New York, 1981); Walter Laqueur, *The Terrible Secret: Suppression of the Truth about Hitler's "Final Solution"* (Boston, 1980); David S. Wyman, *The Abandonment of the Jews: America and the Holocaust, 1941–1945* (New York, 1984); Monty Noam Penkower, *The Jews Were Expendable: Free World Diplomacy and the Holocaust* (Urbana, 1983); Richard Breitman and Alan M. Kraut, *American Refugee Policy and European Jewry, 1933–1945* (Bloomington, 1987); and Deborah Lipstadt, *Beyond Belief: The American Press and the Coming of the Holocaust, 1933–1945* (New York, 1985).

37 Reynolds, "Roosevelt, Churchill, and the Wartime Anglo-American Alliance, 1939–1945," 17–41. See also Anderson, *The United States, Great Britain, and the Cold War*; Alan P. Dobson, *U.S. Wartime Aid to Britain, 1940–1946* (London, 1986); Fraser J. Harbutt, *The Iron Curtain: Churchill, America and the Origins of the Cold War* (New York, 1986); Robert M. Hathaway, *Ambiguous Partnership: Britain and America, 1944–1947* (New York, 1981); John J. Sbrega, *Anglo-American Relations and Colonialism in East Asia, 1941–1945* (New York, 1983); as well as other works cited in Reynolds, 17–41; Reynolds, *The Creation of the Anglo-American Alliance, 1937–1941: A Study in Competitive Co-operation* (Chapel Hill, 1981); and idem, with David Dimbleby, *An Ocean Apart: The Relationship between Britain and America in the Twentieth Century* (New York, 1988), chap. 8.

boundaries between Western and non-Western history and to fuse diplomatic with economic and intellectual history as well as sociology and social psychology into a new "international history." Frank A. Ninkovich and Michael S. Sherry also made extensive use of cultural and intellectual history in their respective studies of U.S. foreign policy regarding cultural relations from 1938–1950 and the rise of American air power before and during World War II.[38]

Many of these themes and approaches were also evident in the continuing flood of studies on U.S. wartime relations with other nations and parts of the world. As in the 1970s, such studies continued to focus (although not exclusively) on areas of recent and contemporary concern, most notably Indochina and the Middle East. With the opening of Korean War documentation came an additional focus on the wartime origins of that conflict. Many of these new bilateral studies extended into the late 1940s or early 1950s rather than stopping in 1945, thereby continuing the tendency to focus on the diplomacy of the World War II years as a prelude to Cold War era policies.[39]

38 Akira Iriye, *Power and Culture: The Japanese-American War, 1941–1945* (Cambridge, MA, 1981); John W. Dower, *War without Mercy: Race and Power in the Pacific War* (New York, 1986); Christopher Thorne, *The Issue of War: States, Societies, and the Far Eastern Conflict of 1941–1945* (New York, 1985); Frank A. Ninkovich, *The Diplomacy of Ideas: U.S. Foreign Policy and Cultural Relations, 1938–1950* (New York, 1981); Michael S. Sherry, *The Rise of American Air Power: The Creation of Armageddon* (New Haven, 1987). See also Ronald Schaffer, *Wings of Judgment: American Bombing in World War II* (New York, 1985). On the new international/cultural history see Akira Iriye, "The Internationalization of History," *American Historical Review* 94 (February 1989): 1–10; idem, "Culture and Power: International Relations as Intercultural Relations," *Diplomatic History* 3 (Spring 1979): 115–28; Christopher Thorne, *Border Crossings: Studies in International History* (Oxford, 1988), a collection of previously published essays; and idem, "After the Europeans," a critique of traditional U.S. diplomatic history.

39 The number of pages in each work devoted to World War II rather than the early Cold War years varied enormously, with the 1941–1945 period providing merely an introduction to some and nearly all the content of others. See Lloyd C. Gardner, *Approaching Vietnam: From World War II through Dienbienphu* (New York, 1988); Gary R. Hess, *The United States' Emergence as a Southeast Asian Power, 1940–1950* (New York, 1987); Bruce Cumings, ed., *Child of Conflict: The Korean-American Relationship, 1943–1953* (Seattle, 1983); James I. Matray, *The Reluctant Crusade: American Foreign Policy in Korea, 1941–1950* (Honolulu, 1985); Marc S. Gallicchio, *The Cold War Begins in Asia: American East Asian Policy and the Fall of the Japanese Empire* (New York, 1988); Wesley M. Bagby, *The Eagle-Dragon Alliance: America's Relations with China in World War II* (Newark, DE, 1992); Irvine H. Anderson, *Aramco, the United States, and Saudi Arabia: A Study in the Dynamics of Foreign Oil Policy, 1933–1950* (Princeton, 1981): Michael B. Stoff, *Oil, War, and*

The 1980s also witnessed a major outpouring of biographical studies of key Roosevelt advisers, most notably Harry Hopkins and the much-maligned members of the wartime Joint Chiefs of Staff. These both represented and fueled a growing interest in the interaction between military and diplomatic issues during the war while providing substantial additional evidence of political astuteness by the president and his advisers.[40]

The tremendous impact of all of these studies, from the late 1960s through the mid-1980s, and the differences between the

American Security: The Search for a National Policy on Foreign Oil, 1941–1947 (New Haven, 1980); Aaron D. Miller, *Search for Security: Saudi Arabian Oil and American Foreign Policy, 1939–1949* (Chapel Hill, 1980); Bruce Robellet Kuniholm, *The Origins of the Cold War in the Near East: Great Power Conflict and Diplomacy in Iran, Turkey, and Greece* (Princeton, 1980); David S. Painter, *Oil and the American Century: The Political Economy of U.S. Foreign Oil Policy, 1941–1954* (Baltimore, 1986); Mark H. Lytle, *The Origins of the Iranian-American Alliance, 1941–1953* (New York, 1987); and Barry Rubin, *The Great Powers in the Middle East, 1941–1947: The Road to the Cold War* (London, 1980). For U.S. relations with European countries see Julian G. Hurstfield, *America and the French Nation, 1939–1945* (Chapel Hill, 1986); and James Edward Miller, *The United States and Italy, 1940–1950* (Chapel Hill, 1986).

40 An interesting set of articles that focuses on this interaction can be found in Walter Laqueur, ed., *The Second World War: Essays in Military and Political History* (London, 1982). On Hopkins see George T. McJimsey, *Harry Hopkins: Ally of the Poor and Defender of Democracy* (Cambridge, MA, 1987); Dwight William Tuttle, *Harry L. Hopkins and Anglo-American-Soviet Relations, 1941–1945* (New York, 1983); and the earlier Henry H. Adams, *Harry Hopkins* (New York, 1977).

Biographies of each of the four members of the wartime Joint Chiefs of Staff were published during the 1980s. Most notable was the fourth and final volume of Forrest C. Pogue's official biography of the army chief and later secretary of state, *George C. Marshall: Statesman, 1945–1959* (New York, 1987). Briefer works on Marshall include Ed Cray, *General of the Army, George C. Marshall, Soldier and Statesman* (New York, 1990); Thomas Parrish, *Roosevelt and Marshall: Partners in Politics and War* (New York, 1989); and Mark A. Stoler, *George C. Marshall: Soldier-Statesman of the American Century* (Boston, 1989). For the other Joint Chiefs see Thomas B. Bueel, *Master of Sea Power: A Biography of Fleet Admiral Ernest J. King* (Boston, 1980); Thomas M. Coffey, *HAP: The Story of the U.S. Air Force and the Man Who Built It, General Henry "Hap" Arnold* (New York, 1982); and Henry H. Adams, *Witness to Power: The Life of Fleet Admiral William D. Leahy* (Annapolis, 1985). See also Eric Larrabee, *Commander in Chief: Franklin Delano Roosevelt, His Lieutenants, and Their War* (New York, 1987); D. Clayton James, *A Time for Giants: The Politics of the American High Command in World War II* (New York, 1987); B. Mitchell Simpson III, *Admiral Harold R. Stark: Architect of Victory, 1939–1945* (Columbia, SC, 1989); and David Eisenhower, *Eisenhower: At War, 1943–1945* (New York, 1986). More critical were three works on Douglas MacArthur published in the 1980s: D. Clayton James's third volume, *The Years of MacArthur: Triumph and Disaster, 1945–1964* (Boston, 1985); Carol M. Petillo's *Douglas MacArthur: The Philippine Years* (Bloomington, 1981); and Michael Schaller's *Douglas MacArthur: The Far Eastern General* (New York, 1989). For Roosevelt's secretary of war see Godfrey Hodgson's *The Colonel: The Life and Wars of Henry Stimson, 1867–1950* (New York, 1990).

old consensus and the newly emerging one, could be most clearly seen in a comparison of the first and second editions of one of the major syntheses and undergraduate texts in the field, Gaddis Smith's *American Diplomacy during World War II.* When first published in 1965, that volume had clearly illustrated the extent to which Roosevelt's supposed defenders had accepted the critics' assault on his diplomacy. Although Smith had claimed he would analyze the issues in the context of the period 1941–1945 rather than the ensuing Cold War, he did the exact opposite by sharply attacking Roosevelt for placing military considerations before political ones, for having too much faith in a Wilsonian postwar collective security organization, and for efforts to "charm" Stalin that had been based on naive "hopes and illusions" instead of reality. In the preface to the second edition, published in 1985, however, Smith openly admitted that the environment of the early 1960s had led him to be "too harsh" in his judgments and "insufficiently appreciative of the limits of American power and of the intractable obstacles facing even the most conscientious, competent, and well-intentioned leader." Although he did not alter his overall assessment of Roosevelt's postwar policies as a failure, he did conclude that the president had been less naive than he originally thought. He also altered his tone so that there was "less stridency in condemnation" and "a greater effort to understand what Roosevelt sought and why he failed." While continuing to condemn Roosevelt for glossing over deep differences with Stalin and for equating international with domestic disputes (and thus conflicts over ends with conflicts over means), for example, Smith now openly questioned whether American interests, which focused first and foremost on Axis defeat, would have been better served by the open arguments within the tenuous alliance that would have flowed from different policies. He concluded in this regard that the president's approach might have been based on a "deeper realism." Equally noteworthy was the much greater emphasis in the second edition on decolonization as a major wartime issue and on U.S. policies regarding Latin America, the Middle East, and the Far East – especially Korea, China, and Indochina.[41]

41 Gaddis Smith, *American Diplomacy during the Second World War, 1941–1945*, 2d ed. (New York, 1985), vii–viii, 12–13.

Smith's work and others notwithstanding, the promising new synthesis did not continue far into the 1980s. Instead, the second half of that decade witnessed both extensive fragmentation and another massive interpretive debate over World War II diplomacy, one that in many ways repeated with equal intensity and heat those that had taken place in the early 1950s and late 1960s. The focus of the renewed debate was, once again, Franklin Roosevelt's policies toward the Soviet Union. Dallek's 1979 synthesis was essentially the capstone of the defense of Roosevelt-as-realist that had become more and more pronounced throughout the 1960s and 1970s. As such, it was able to subsume the earlier interpretations within this school and, to an extent, those of the New Left critics as well. The schools that had combined in the 1950s and early 1960s to form the original, negative assessment of Roosevelt remained only partially convinced at best, however, and in the mid-1980s they replied. So did some New Left historians from the late 1960s, such as Gar Alperovitz, who, in a second, 1985 edition to his 1965 *Atomic Diplomacy*, essentially reiterated and defended an updated version of his original interpretation against numerous critics.[42]

For the most part, however, the 1980s critique of U.S. wartime diplomacy echoed earlier criticisms from the right rather than the left and focused on Roosevelt's supposed blunders, naiveté, and failures vis-à-vis the Soviet Union. Smith, as previously noted, retained his 1965 critique of Roosevelt in this regard, albeit in milder form. Attacks also emerged in two 1985 studies of the previously neglected 1943 Cairo and Tehran summit conferences, Keith Eubank's *Summit at Teheran* and Keith Sainsbury's *The Turning Point*. Both historians saw Tehran as the pivotal wartime summit, one that in many ways determined both the agenda for and the results of the later Yalta meeting, and both in effect projected the old criticism of American and Rooseveltian naiveté at Yalta back to this earlier meeting – although for the British

42 Gar Alperovitz, *Atomic Diplomacy: Hiroshima and Potsdam*, expanded and updated ed. (New York, 1985). More recently, Diane S. Clemens has provided additional evidence of a policy reversal regarding the Soviets at the time of Roosevelt's death and Truman's ascension to the presidency in her "Averell Harriman, John Deane, the Joint Chiefs of Staff, and the 'Reversal of Co-Operation' with the Soviet Union in April 1945," *International History Review* 14 (May 1992): 277–306.

Sainsbury, as for Smith, with clear recognition of the numerous limits within which FDR had to work and the dangers posed by an alternative policy of confrontation. Russell D. Buhite revealed a similar depth of understanding in his 1988 *Decisions at Yalta*, while echoing similar criticisms of the president's poor diplomacy. He also criticized FDR for being too concerned with the domestic consequences of failure at Yalta and for even desiring the conference in the first place; summit conferences in general, Buhite concluded, were counterproductive and invited the sorts of misunderstandings and defeats that had taken place in the Crimea.[43]

Nineteen eighty-eight also witnessed the publication of two works more critical of Rooseveltian diplomacy than any published since the 1950s: Robert Nisbet's *Roosevelt and Stalin: The Failed Courtship*, and Frederick W. Marks III's *Wind over Sand*. Nisbet's brief volume essentially updated and reiterated the old assault on Roosevelt for extraordinary naiveté regarding Stalin, with the Tehran Conference replacing Yalta as the place where FDR "played essentially the role Chamberlain had at Munich" and where the Cold War had begun.[44] Marks went even further, arguing that Roosevelt's diplomacy from 1933–1945 had been marked by ambivalence, indecisiveness, narrow domestic motivation, parochialism, and failure. Although most of the volume concerned diplomacy before Pearl Harbor, one chapter extended this attack to the years 1941–1945. "Never was he the absolute prisoner of events," Marks insisted in countering Roosevelt's defenders on relations with Stalin during the war; rather, he "gave away much of his hand in a game whose rules he did not comprehend." Beyond that he "accumulated the largest overseas credibility gap of any president on record," was contemptuously disliked by his overseas contemporaries, and was the "fitting

43 Keith Eubank, *Summit at Teheran* (New York, 1985); Keith Sainsbury, *The Turning Point: Roosevelt, Stalin, Churchill, and Chiang Kai-shek, 1943: The Moscow, Cairo, and Teheran Conferences* (New York, 1985); Russell D. Buhite, *Decisions at Yalta: An Appraisal of Summit Diplomacy* (Wilmington, DE, 1986). See also Paul D. Mayle, *Eureka Summit: Agreement in Principle and the Big Three at Tehran, 1943* (Newark, DE, 1987).

44 Robert Nisbet, *Roosevelt and Stalin: The Failed Courtship* (Washington, 1988) , 12. See also directly below.

symbol" for an American "age of delayed adolescence in international affairs."[45]

This renewed assault on Roosevelt was clearly linked to the domestic and international environments of the 1980s, which differed substantially from those of the 1970s. Most important in this regard was the rise of the neoconservative movement and the revival of the Cold War that accompanied Ronald Reagan's election to the presidency in 1980 and the ensuing revival of a Manichaean worldview that labeled the Soviet Union the "evil empire." The late 1980s will probably be remembered in history as the time of the great "thaw" and the end of the Cold War, but the first half of the decade witnessed, as one popular college text in U.S. diplomatic history aptly noted in 1988, "some of the gloomiest and scariest times in the Cold War."[46] Along with this came a revival of the view that cooperation with the Soviet Union was and always had been impossible given its ideology, and that Roosevelt had thus been a fool to try it.

In 1985, the fortieth anniversary of the war's end, the neoconservative journal *Commentary* published a series of articles from Roosevelt's British and American critics that hammered away at these points. The British criticism came from Sir John Colville, Churchill's personal secretary, whose extensive and revealing diaries had just been published.[47] Although Colville carefully noted the impact of the decision-making vacuum created by Roosevelt's death in 1945, he also blasted the president's naiveté and blunders regarding the Soviets in terms that seemed to repeat verbatim the criticisms Bullitt, Wilmot, Baldwin, and others had uttered more than three decades earlier. The three Allies had won the war, Colville began in a virtual paraphrase of Bullitt's 1948 contention, but "it was the Soviets who won the peace" due to the president's naiveté, his "complete sellout to Stalin" at Yalta regarding Poland, the narrowly military and apolitical perspective of the admirals and generals who took over as his health

45 Frederick W. Marks III, *Wind over Sand: The Diplomacy of Franklin Roosevelt* (Athens, GA, 1988), 172, 260, 287.

46 Thomas G. Paterson, J. Garry Clifford, and Kenneth J. Hagan, *American Foreign Policy: A History*, vol. 2, *Since 1900*, 3d ed. (Lexington, MA, 1988), 658.

47 Colville, *The Fringes of Power*.

declined, and the anti-British bias of most U.S. policymakers due to their negative view of colonialism. In a *Commentary* symposium a few months later on U.S. foreign policy since 1945, four of the respondents directly or indirectly supported Colville. The indirect support came from neoconservative writer Irving Kristol, who ranked Yalta as one of the nation's three "major and costly mistakes" since 1945 (Suez and Vietnam were the other two), and former UN ambassador Jeane Kirkpatrick, who noted that the international organization so central to Roosevelt's position at Yalta had been based on a wartime American "falsification" regarding the nature of the Soviet Union. The direct support came from Lionel Abel and Robert Nisbet. Abel attacked the liberal view of foreign policy in general and held Roosevelt personally responsible for the "terrible" decisions Colville had described. Nisbet blasted Roosevelt for "credulity" regarding Stalin, "pathetic ignorance of political history and geopolitics," and "colossal naivete," while maintaining that his more realistic successors had been tremendously hampered in the Cold War by the "pro- or at least anti-anti-Soviet" view of "substantial parts" of the American public, that is, the liberals.[48]

In an early 1986 issue of the *New York Review of Books*, an aroused Theodore Draper launched a massive counterattack against this "neoconservative history," which he bluntly labeled, in a thinly veiled reference to McCarthyism, another effort to make history "serve current political extremism." Making extensive use of the previous decade's defenses of Roosevelt and attacks on Churchill as well as of Warren F. Kimball's recently published complete Roosevelt-Churchill correspondence,[49] Draper maintained that the Red Army, rather than Roosevelt, had given Stalin control of Eastern Europe, that conservatives such as John Foster Dulles had supported the same "illusions and compromises" as FDR, and that "the Western allies did not give away anything at Yalta that they actually had; they did get some promissory notes which they could not cash in once Stalin decided to stop payments." The "defamatory fury" of the neoconservative

48 John Colville, "How the West Lost the Peace in 1945," *Commentary* 80 (September 1985): 41–47; "How Has the United States Met Its Major Challenges since 1945: A Symposium," ibid. (November 1985): 25–28, 50–52, 56–60, 73–76.
49 Kimball, ed., *Churchill & Roosevelt.*

assault on Roosevelt, he bluntly concluded, an assault guilty of "ignorance and effrontery," had "less to do with the past than with the present" – that is, the neoconservative ideology and its hatred of "liberal internationalism." Despite the rhetorical similarity to earlier conservatism, this ideology was actually a new and extreme fusion of isolationism and interventionism whose real enemy and target were domestic liberals, a group the neoconservatives had once belonged to and one they were thus now attacking via historical character assassination as a means of displacing their own guilt for previous actions.[50]

The ensuing rejoinders made such language appear mild in comparison. Nisbet accused Draper of misreading and misrepresenting the Churchill-Roosevelt correspondence, while Abel labeled Roosevelt "the accomplice of Stalin – as is Mr. Draper by defending him – in the enslavement of Eastern Europe." Draper in turn labeled Abel's comments a McCarthyite "political obscenity," and Nisbet's a "largely fraudulent" misuse of documents that he doubted would be tolerated from an undergraduate.[51] In an only somewhat milder retrospective on this battle of words in *Commentary* a few months later, political scientist Paul Seabury attacked Draper's "near hysterical defamation" as well as his "tortured attempt" to paint Churchill as unrealistic and insisted that Roosevelt had "abandoned politics" and concerned himself solely with military victory.[52] These were far from the final words in the debate. Nisbet followed with a two-part article in *Modern Age*, which he expanded into his previously mentioned 1988 book, and Draper with a three-part review of David Eisenhower's wartime biography of his grandfather that emphasized his politico-military realism and the centrality of the Soviet war effort to all

50 Theodore Draper, "Neoconservative History," *New York Review of Books*, 16 January 1986. Melvyn P. Leffler went even further than Draper in "Adherents to Agreements: Yalta and the Experiences of the Early Cold War," *International Security* 11 (Summer 1986): 88–123, by questioning whether Stalin was the only one who decided to "stop payments" on the Yalta accords. In a balanced and detailed assessment clearly influenced by recent Soviet-American tensions and charges, he concluded that each power had complied with some components of the accords while disregarding others and that Washington had used supposed Soviet violations as a "convenient lever" to excuse its own.

51 *New York Review of Books*, 24 April 1986.

52 Paul Seabury, "Yalta and the Neoconservatives," *Commentary* 82 (August 1986): 47–49.

U.S. strategy and diplomacy; in 1988 he republished all these essays in *A Present of Things Past*.[53] Interestingly, although many of the participants in this debate were scholars, not one was a U.S. diplomatic historian. Clearly, World War II diplomacy remained a heated issue of concern to many beyond the profession and specialization, with this particular confrontation boldly revealing its continued link to both the state of the Cold War and domestic politics.

Draper, of course, was far from the only defender of Roosevelt and U.S. World War II diplomacy during the 1980s. Most of the previously cited works published during the decade provided at least partial defenses. They tended to echo Draper and Dallek, however, in emphasizing the domestic and international constraints under which the president had to work and thus his lack of viable alternatives regarding the Soviet Union. Warren F. Kimball, who in 1984 had published with detailed commentary the entire Churchill-Roosevelt correspondence, challenged this conclusion in his 1991 *The Juggler*, a series of essays seeking to comprehend Roosevelt's assumptions and worldview as well as his specific actions. Such an analysis was more an exploration and explanation than a defense of Roosevelt's ideas and policies, but in the environment of the 1980s simply to argue that FDR possessed an overall vision and made logical choices was to defend him from severe critics like Marks. Similarly, Kimball's use of "liberal" as a key descriptive term for the president's vision rather than as an epithet, and his equation of liberalism with "Americanism," constituted a powerful if indirect defense of Roosevelt against the neoconservative assault.[54]

53 Nisbet, *Roosevelt and Stalin*; Theodore Draper, "Eisenhower's War," *New York Review of Books*, 25 September and 9 and 23 October 1986, reproduced along with his "Neoconservative History" in *A Present of Things Past: Selected Essays* (New York, 1990), 3–66, 247–65.

54 Warren F. Kimball, *The Juggler: Franklin Roosevelt as Wartime Statesman* (Princeton, 1991); idem, *Churchill & Roosevelt*. See also Kimball's "Franklin D. Roosevelt: Dr. Win-the-War," in *Commanders in Chief: Presidential Leadership in Modern Wars*, ed. Joseph G. Dawson III (Lawrence, 1993), 87–105; and Gary R. Hess's defense of Roosevelt as a "practical idealist" in his brief survey, *The United States at War, 1941–1945* (Arlington Heights, IL, 1986). Roosevelt biographer Frank Freidel's final volume, *Franklin D. Roosevelt: A Rendezvous with Destiny* (Boston, 1990), offers a more traditional analysis and defense of Roosevelt's wartime diplomacy. See also directly below.

Reinforcement for both sides in this renewed debate came from scholars working with the thin but growing trickle of available Soviet sources. Many of them emphasized Stalin's caution, pragmatism, and lack of any overall "master plan" during the war years, as well as his desire to obtain limited gains within a framework of continued collaboration with his wartime allies. They disagreed, however, on how extensive his aims actually were and on whether a clear definition of acceptable limits by FDR and Churchill during the war would have made any difference. Vojtech Mastny and William Taubman saw those aims as quite extensive and were highly critical of Roosevelt's refusal to provide such a definition, although they held that postwar Soviet suspicion, hostility, and aggression would have resulted from any U.S. policy.[55] Similar criticisms and conclusions appeared in Edward Bennett's 1990 study of Roosevelt's wartime policy toward the Soviet Union, but alongside a strong defense of FDR's overall approach and record. Although he joined Mastny and others in criticizing Roosevelt for numerous errors in his dealings with Stalin, most notably his procrastination on territorial settlements that could have limited postwar Soviet influence in Eastern Europe and the excessive faith he placed in the ability of a postwar United Nations to settle great-power disputes, Bennett concluded that FDR's pragmatic approach to Soviet-American relations did secure his primary objectives of Axis defeat and "far more than the twenty-five years of peace he once said he hoped to ensure."[56]

Debate during the 1980s was by no means limited to assessments of Soviet-American diplomacy. The decade also witnessed an outpouring of scholarship on major British figures during the war, most notably Martin Gilbert's completion of the multivolume

55 Vojtech Mastny, *Russia's Road to the Cold War: Diplomacy, Warfare, and the Politics of Communism, 1941–1945* (New York, 1979); William Taubman, *Stalin's American Policy: From Entente to Detente to Cold War* (New York, 1982). For different conclusions see William O. McCagg, *Stalin Embattled, 1943–1948* (Detroit, 1978); Martin McCauley, *The Origins of the Cold War* (London, 1983); Albert Resis, "The Churchill-Stalin Secret 'Percentages' Agreement on the Balkans, Moscow, October 1944," *American Historical Review* 83 (April 1978): 368–87; and idem, "Spheres of Influence in Soviet Wartime Diplomacy," *Journal of Modern History* 53 (September 1981): 417–39.

56 Edward M. Bennett, *Franklin D. Roosevelt and the Search for Victory: American-Soviet Relations, 1939–1945* (Wilmington, DE, 1990), 183–88.

official biography of Churchill,[57] and on Anglo-Soviet as well as Anglo-American relations during the conflict. These also provided ammunition for both sides in the debate over U.S. policies. Although the biographical studies tended to defend the British position in Anglo-American wartime disputes, the studies of Anglo-Soviet relations were marked by detailed analyses of disagreements within the British government over Soviet policy and conclusions just as polarized as those to be found in the decade's studies of U.S.-Soviet diplomacy. Examining those relations during the early years of the war, for example, Gabriel Gorodetsky and Steven Merritt Miner reached diametrically opposed conclusions. Gorodetsky sharply criticized Churchill and some of his advisers for a virtual nonpolicy, if not an anti-Soviet one, and implied that the more cooperative approach supported by Ambassador Sir Stafford Cripps as well as by Roosevelt might have avoided the Cold War if implemented. Miner, on the other hand, sharply criticized the British for trying to appease Stalin and pointed to the hard-line American opposition to territorial settlements in 1942 as the policy London should have followed.[58]

57 See in particular Martin Gilbert, *Winston S. Churchill: Road to Victory, 1941–1945*, vol. 7 (Boston, 1986). See also Elisabeth Barker, *Churchill and Eden at War* (London, 1978); David Fraser, *Alanbrooke* (New York, 1982); Raymond A. Callahan, *Churchill: Retreat from Empire* (Wilmington, DE, 1984); and Alex Danchev, *Very Special Relationship: Field-Marshall Sir John Dill and the Anglo-American Alliance, 1941–1944* (London, 1986).

58 Gabriel Gorodetsky, *Stafford Cripps' Mission to Moscow, 1940–1942* (Cambridge, England, 1984); Steven Merritt Miner, *Between Churchill and Stalin: The Soviet Union, Great Britain, and the Origins of the Grand Alliance* (Chapel Hill, 1988). See also Arnold A. Offner, "Uncommon Ground: Anglo-American-Soviet Diplomacy, 1941–1942," *Soviet Union/Union Sovietique* 18 (1991): 237–57; Roy Douglas, *From War to Cold War, 1942–1948* (New York, 1981); Martin Kitchen, *British Policy towards the Soviet Union during the Second World War* (New York, 1986); Graham Ross, ed., *The Foreign Office and the Kremlin: British Documents on Anglo-Soviet Relations, 1941–1945* (Cambridge, England, 1984); Victor Rothwell, *Britain and the Cold War, 1941–1947* (London, 1982); Julian Lewis, *Changing Direction: British Military Planning for Post-war Strategic Defence, 1942–1947* (London, 1988); Ann Deighton, ed., *Britain and the First Cold War* (New York, 1990); P. M. H. Bell, *John Bull and the Bear: British Public Opinion, Foreign Policy and the Soviet Union, 1941–1945* (London 1990); David Reynolds, "The 'Big Three' and the Division of Europe, 1945–48: An Overview," *Diplomacy & Statecraft* 1 (July 1990): 111–36; and Watt, "Yalta and the Cold War," 85–98. Watt argues that British scholarship, unimpressed by New Left revisionism but deeply affected by events in Europe, moved in very different directions during the 1970s and 1980s and should continue to do so. "Failing the release of new evidence, which only the Soviet authorities can authorize," he concluded in 1989, "further debate will be only for the obsessed, not

Ironically, the procooperation Gorodetsky thereby indirectly provided Roosevelt's anticooperation critics with additional ammunition, while the anticooperation Miner did the same for Roosevelt's defenders.

As this irony clearly reveals, by the late 1980s the earlier conflicting schools of interpretation had become hopelessly confused as a result of this complex outpouring of scholarship and polemics. Indeed, by decade's end at least five separate positions on Roosevelt and U.S. wartime diplomacy, distinct from yet related to the earlier positions of the 1950s and 1960s, were clearly visible. At one extreme stood Roosevelt-as-ultimate-realist, a position supported by both FDR defenders who praised this realism while emphasizing the domestic and international limits under which he had to work and some New Left critics who attacked it as aggressive. At the other extreme was Roosevelt the naive and idealistic blunderer who had never understood the Soviet Union or international relations, a reiteration by neoconservatives and revisionists of the charges originally leveled during the late 1940s and 1950s. In between were at least three composites: Roosevelt the realist who actually had more maneuverability than he thought and who therefore could have done better than he did to check the Soviets; Roosevelt the skillful pragmatist who unfortunately worked under a series of mistaken conceptions regarding the Soviet Union; and Roosevelt the combined "idealist/realist" who possessed a clear and defensible vision of a reformed international order and who chose to compromise that vision because of wartime exigencies and dilemmas.

Where one stood on this spectrum seemed to depend not only on one's politics in the 1980s and reading of the documents but also on whether one was a believer in the "Yalta" or the "Riga" axioms regarding the USSR that Daniel Yergin had posited in 1977.[59] Although artificial and overstated, this dichotomy remains as useful for understanding contemporary World War II

for the most active and able of British historians today." The recent release of such evidence, discussed below, as well as the debate described above, obviously call into question such a conclusion.

59 Daniel Yergin, *Shattered Peace: The Origins of the Cold War and the National Security State* (Boston, 1977), rev. ed. (New York, 1990).

historiographical disputes as the origins of the Cold War – if not more so. For one's opinion of Roosevelt's policies vis-à-vis the Soviet Union does depend to a large extent upon whether one views that nation as simply a traditional Great Power with whom compromise was possible or as an ideological monstrosity incapable of cooperation or normal diplomatic behavior.

Reinforcing the importance of one's politics and preconceived notions regarding the USSR in assessing U.S. diplomacy during World War II was Roosevelt's notorious secrecy and deviousness, which, despite the enormous volume of his papers, resulted in a paucity of meaningful and clear statements of what he truly believed. In 1942 he revealingly told his military chiefs to alter strategic memorandums that he feared future historians would interpret as a proposal to abandon England. He also informed Secretary of State Cordell Hull that publication of notes taken at the 1919 Paris Peace Conference should be postponed and that such notes never should have been taken in the first place. And when the secretary of the Joint Chiefs of Staff tried to take notes at a wartime presidential meeting, Roosevelt, according to General George C. Marshall, "blew up."[60]

Even when FDR did break down and say something meaningful for the record, one was often unsure if it was what he really thought, or even of what it meant. One of the most notable examples in this regard was the president's comment to Churchill in March 1942 that he personally knew how to "handle" Stalin in regard to the demand for recognition of Soviet territorial conquests in Eastern Europe in 1939–40. In their 1986 debate, Nisbet and Draper both used this document, Nisbet to illustrate the president's naiveté vis-à-vis Stalin and Draper to illustrate his hard-headed realism in opposing recognition and in taking the

60 Mark A. Stoler, "The 'Pacific-First' Alternative in American World War II Strategy," *International History Review* 2 (July 1980): 422; Burns, *Roosevelt* 427–28; Larry I. Bland, ed., *George C. Marshall Interviews and Reminiscences* (Lexington, VA, 1991), 623. The very volume of Roosevelt's papers, according to adviser Rexford Tugwell, was "a gigantic trap for historians," who would be kept too busy "to ask embarrassing questions." Citing this quotation as well as FDR's tampering with the documentary record, one recent biographer has concluded that "Roosevelt was confident that he would enjoy a favorable historical reputation, to be sure; but just to be on the safe side, he took certain precautions." See Patrick J. Maney, *The Roosevelt Presence: A Biography of Franklin Delano Roosevelt* (New York, 1992), 194.

initiative from Churchill, who was ready to grant recognition.[61] One could almost hear the ghost of the Hyde Park squire laughing as scholars argued over what in the world he had meant by this and similar comments, as well as empathize with Henry Stimson's 1940 lament that speaking with FDR was "like chasing a vagrant beam of sunshine around a vacant room."[62] One of Roosevelt's recent biographers, relating a "recurrent and maddening dream" about card games with his subject during which FDR would from time to time "wink, take a card from his hand, and slip it inside his jacket," has aptly concluded that "it's safe to say . . . all of Franklin Roosevelt's cards were never on the table."[63]

While scholars of Roosevelt and the Grand Alliance continued to argue throughout the 1980s, other diplomatic historians proceeded during this time to explore the new areas and approaches being illuminated by social scientists and social/cultural historians as they applied to World War II. In doing so they began to alter the terms of the debate over wartime diplomacy by redefining the major issues, questions, and themes to be addressed. The pathbreaking works of Christopher Thorne, Akira Iriye, John Dower, and others in the realms of multiarchival research and the comparative cultural approach of the new international history have already been noted in this regard.[64] Equally notable was an increasing emphasis on bureaucratic politics as an explanation for U.S. wartime policies. While historians such as J. Garry Clifford, Theodore Wilson, Irvine Anderson, and Jonathan Utley focused on this mode of analysis to explain those policies prior to Pearl Harbor, others, such as Wm. Roger Louis, Philip J. Baram, Randall B. Woods, Leon Martel, and this author, used it as one of their major tools for analyzing wartime policies and disputes regarding

61 Kimball, *Churchill & Roosevelt* 1:421, and footnotes 49–51 above.

62 Stimson Diary, 18–19 December 1940, as quoted in Warren F. Kimball, *The Most Unsordid Act: Lend-Lease, 1939–1941* (Baltimore, 1969), 4.

63 Geoffrey Ward, "On Writing about FDR," *American Heritage* 23 (Summer 1991): 119.

64 See above, footnotes 34 and 38. See also Iriye's chapter on "Culture and International History" in Hogan and Paterson, eds., *Explaining the History of American Foreign Relations*, 214–25.

decolonization, global strategy, postwar allied relations, and relations with Latin America and the Middle East.[65]

In one sense, this was nothing new; analysis of disagreements within Roosevelt's notoriously chaotic bureaucracy had always been part of World War II diplomatic histories, and the archival openings of the 1970s enabled historians to trace in detail internal disagreements and their resolution within the policymaking process. Some scholars began to argue, however, that social science theories of bureaucratic behavior were central to understanding why as well as how specific policies had been initiated and implemented. This argument held profound consequences for the debate over Roosevelt and U.S. diplomacy in that it implicitly rejected FDR's centrality by denying his ability, or that of any other single individual, to dictate or implement policy. U.S. diplomacy, these scholars maintained, often emerged from a welter of bureaucratic desires and conflicts that bore little if any relationship to U.S. interests or to what Roosevelt had desired – or ordered.[66]

Political scientist Leon Sigal's 1988 *Fighting to a Finish* boldly illustrated the revolutionary consequences of such an analysis. Making use of the bureaucratic and "non-rational actor" models that Graham Allison had earlier developed to analyze the 1962 Cuban missile crisis, Sigal dismissed all previous interpretations of the atomic bomb/Japanese surrender controversy by arguing that neither the United States nor Japan had followed any rational

65 For a discussion of bureaucratic politics as a model and the relevant literature see J. Garry Clifford, "Bureaucratic Politics," in Hogan and Paterson, eds., *Explaining the History of American Foreign Relations*, 141–50. See also Irvine H. Anderson, Jr., *The Standard-Vacuum Oil Company and United States East Asian Policy* (Princeton, 1975); J. Garry Clifford and Samuel R. Spencer, *The First Peacetime Draft* (Lawrence, 1986); Jonathan G. Utley, *Going to War with Japan, 1937–1941* (Knoxville, 1985); Theodore A. Wilson, *The First Summit: Roosevelt and Churchill at Placentia Bay, 1941*, rev. ed. (Lawrence, 1991); Louis, *Imperialism at Bay*; Baram, *The Department of State and the Middle East*; Woods, *The Roosevelt Foreign Policy*; idem, *A Changing of the Guard: Anglo-American Relations, 1941–1946* (Chapel Hill, 1990); Martel, *Lend-Lease*; Stoler, *Politics of the Second Front*; idem, "The 'Pacific-First' Alternative," 432–52; and idem, "From Continentalism to Globalism: General Stanley D. Embick, the Joint Strategic Survey Committee, and the Military View of American National Policy during the Second World War," *Diplomatic History* 6 (Summer 1982): 303–21.

66 Gabriel Kolko had been one of the first scholars to reject Roosevelt's centrality in his 1968 *The Politics of War*, but hardly on the basis of bureaucratic politics or a split between U.S. policies and U.S. interests.

plan for ending the war. Rather, different segments of the bureaucracy in each country had proposed policies geared to their own worldviews and self-aggrandizement. Although Japanese army and navy leaders planned for a massive "final battle" to impress the Americans, they did so with different times and different locations in mind. Similarly, each segment of the U.S. defense establishment supported the dropping of atomic bombs for different bureaucratic reasons, none of which constituted a rational strategy to bring about Japan's surrender.[67]

Culture and bureaucratic politics were by no means the only new areas to be explored in the 1970s and 1980s. Major analyses focusing on gender, ideology, psychology, corporatism, "mental maps," public opinion, world systems, national security, balance of power, and international organization as explanations of U.S. foreign relations in general also emerged during these decades.[68] Although only a few of the new studies focused exclusively on World War II, that conflict played an important role in many of them. Numerous gender studies, for example, emphasized the complex impact of the war on American women as well as the relationship among gender, ideology, and war in general. In a fascinating 1975 article, Alan Henrikson explored the dramatic shift that had occurred in the American mental map of the globe during World War II and its impact on the origins of the Cold War.[69] Thomas G. Paterson, Les Adler, and Edward Mark similarly analyzed the impact of World War II on American ideological perceptions of Stalin and the Soviet Union, while Melvin Small, Ralph Levering, and others focused on wartime public opinion of the Soviet Union. Scholars also examined numerous other aspects of public opinion, with more than one asking if this

67 Leon V. Sigal, *Fighting to a Finish: The Politics of War Termination in the United States and Japan, 1945* (Ithaca, 1988). See also J. Samuel Walker, "The Decision to Use the Bomb: A Historiographical Update," *Diplomatic History* 14 (Winter 1990): 97–114; Graham T. Allison, *Essence of Decision: Explaining the Cuban Missile Crisis* (Boston, 1971); Martel, *Lend-Lease*; and Sherry, *The Rise of American Air Power*.

68 All of these approaches are summarized in Hogan and Paterson, eds., *Explaining the History of American Foreign Relations*. See also directly below.

69 Ibid., 33–35, 177–92; Alan Henrikson, "The Map as an 'Idea': The Role of Cartographic Imagery during the Second World War," *The American Cartographer* 2 (April 1975): 19–53.

might not have been the key motivating factor in FDR's postwar planning.[70] Thomas Campbell and, more recently, Robert Hilderbrand, explored the triumph of purely national over truly international definitions of security in the wartime formulation of the postwar international security organization, and Melvyn P. Leffler carefully noted the importance of the World War II experience in the new, global definition of American national security, which he viewed as central to the origins and development of the Cold War. Of related interest and focus were works by Lynn Davis, Geir Lundestad, Edward Mark, and, more recently, Lloyd Gardner that reassessed U.S. wartime attitudes toward spheres of influence.[71]

70 William C. Widenor, "American Planning for the United Nations: Have We Been Asking the Right Questions?" *Diplomatic History* 6 (Summer 1982): 245–65. On ideology see Les K. Adler and Thomas G. Paterson, "Red Fascism: The Merger of Nazi Germany and Soviet Russia in the American Image of Totalitarianism, 1930s–1950s," *American Historical Review* 75 (April 1970): 1046–64, revised and reprinted in Thomas G. Paterson, *Meeting the Communist Threat: Truman to Reagan* (New York, 1988); and Edward Mark, "October or Thermidor? Interpretations of Stalinism and the Perception of Soviet Foreign Policy in the United States, 1927–1947," *American Historical Review* 94 (October 1989): 937–62. See also Deborah Welch Larson, *Origins of Containment: A Psychological Explanation* (Princeton, 1985). On public opinion see Ralph B. Levering, *American Opinion and the Russian Alliance, 1939–1945* (Chapel Hill, 1976); and Melvin Small, "How We learned to Love the Russians: American Media and the Soviet Union during World War II," *The Historian* 36 (May 1974): 455–78. See also Allan M. Winkler, *The Politics of Propaganda: The Office of War Information, 1942–1945* (New Haven, 1978); Holly Cowan Shulman, *The Voice of America: Propaganda and Democracy, 1941–1945* (Madison, 1990); and Richard W. Steele, "American Popular Opinion and the War against Germany: The Issue of a Negotiated Peace, 1942," *Journal of American History* 65 (December 1978): 704–23.

71 Thomas M. Campbell, *Masquerade Peace: America's UN Policy, 1944–1945* (Tallahassee, 1973); Robert C. Hilderbrand, *Dumbarton Oaks: The Origins of the United Nations and the Search for Postwar Security* (Chapel Hill, 1990); Melvyn P. Leffler, *A Preponderance of Power: National Security, the Truman Administration, and the Cold War* (Stanford, 1992); Lynn Ethridge Davis, *The Cold War Begins: Soviet-American Conflict over Eastern Europe* (Princeton, 1974); Geir Lundestad, *The American Non-Policy towards Eastern Europe, 1943–1947: Universalism in an Area Not of Essential Interest to the United States* (New York, 1978); Edward Mark, "American Policy toward Eastern Europe and the Origins of the Cold War, 1941–1946: An Alternative Interpretation," *Journal of American History* 68 (September 1981): 313–36; and Lloyd C. Gardner, *Spheres of Influence: The Great Powers Partition Europe, from Munich to Yalta* (Chicago, 1993). On these issues see also Robert A. Divine, *Second Chance: The Triumph of Internationalism in America during World War II* (New York, 1971); Michael S. Sherry, *Preparing for the Next War: American Plans for Postwar Defense, 1941–1945* (New Haven, 1977); Charles F. Brower IV, "Sophisticated Strategist: General George A. Lincoln and the Defeat of Japan, 1944–1945," *Diplomatic History* 15 (Summer 1991): 317–37; and Stoler, "From Continentalism to Globalism," 303–21.

That these new approaches became increasingly voluminous as the decade of the 1980s came to an end and the 1990s began was far from accidental. Indeed, their rise coincided to an extent with the dramatic changes taking place within Eastern Europe, capped in the years 1989–1991 by the end not only of the Soviet empire but also of the Cold War and even of the Soviet Union itself. These extraordinary events, it appeared, were helping to break the virtual stranglehold the Cold War had held over interpretations of World War II diplomacy for the preceding forty to forty-five years.

Although this may have been true to an extent, it is important to note that all of these new approaches had first appeared while the Cold War was still in progress and that in many ways they reflected changes within America more than changes in its foreign relations. Furthermore, numerous scholars made use of many of these approaches to reassess and reargue the traditional questions about Roosevelt and the origins of the Cold War rather than to explore different themes. And although the dramatic events in Eastern Europe may have indirectly added to the popularity within the profession of different themes, those events were simultaneously laying the groundwork for another generation of Soviet-American World War II studies by accelerating both scholarly contact between the two countries and the long-desired opening of Soviet World War II archives. Without those archives all diplomatic histories of the Grand Alliance had been woefully incomplete; with them, scholars began to glimpse the possibility of researching and writing definitive histories of the coalition from all three national archives, rather than one or two. Consequently, the late 1980s and early 1990s witnessed a continued deluge of scholarship on the Grand Alliance that paralleled and often intersected with the deluge of new approaches to the World War II years.

It is still far too soon to ascertain the results. The past few years have witnessed the publication and translation of some key Soviet documents and reminiscences, as well as revelations regarding both Stalin and a few specific wartime episodes – most notably the Katyn Forest massacre of Polish officers.[72] Further-

72 For a useful but already dated summary see Walter Laqueur, *Stalin: The Glasnost Revelations* (New York, 1990). Recent translated Soviet works include Dmitrii Volkogonov, *Stalin: Triumph and Tragedy* (New York, 1991); Andrei Gromyko,

more, a small group of Soviet, American, and British World War II scholars has been meeting on a regular basis since 1986 to reanalyze the Grand Alliance, and the results of these meetings are in the process of being published in all three countries. The meetings have also influenced recent book-length studies by some of the participants.[73] Release of Soviet documents, however, remains highly erratic, incomplete, and unpredictable.[74] Furthermore, neither the documents released to date nor the post-Cold War international environment has resulted in any resolution of the existing historiographical disputes over U.S. wartime diplomacy. Indeed, two studies of Allied wartime diplomacy in general published in the early 1990s clearly illustrate that, far from resolving the debate, recent events and new Russian documents are merely providing additional ammunition to continue it. In his 1990 *Stalin, Churchill, and Roosevelt Divide Europe*, Remi Nadeau argued that recent revelations of Stalin's atrocities and the speed with which his Eastern European empire was dismantled serve only to reemphasize William Bullitt's 1948 charge that Roosevelt

Memoirs (New York, 1989); Albert Resis, ed., *Molotov Remembers: Inside Kremlin Politics; Conversations with Felix Chuev* (Chicago, 1993); Nataliya Lebedeva, "The Katyn Tragedy," *International Affairs* 6 (June 1990): 98–115, 144; and Vladimir Abarinov, *The Murderers of Katyn* (New York, 1993). I am grateful to Steven Miner for much of this information.

Also noteworthy are five still untranslated, pre-*glasnost* collections of wartime documents from the Soviet Ministry of Foreign Affairs. The most relevant one for U.S. diplomatic historians is *Sovetsko-amerikanskie otnosheniia vo vremia Velikoi Otechestvennoi voiny, 1941–1945: dokumenty i materialy* [Soviet-American relations during the Great Patriotic War, 1941–1945: Documents and materials], 2 vols. (Moscow, 1984). The others consist of parallel two-volume collections on Anglo-Soviet and Franco-Soviet relations, Soviet foreign policy in general during the war, and Soviet policy at the wartime conferences. See Watt, "Yalta and the Cold War," 74 n16, for these works and pre-*glasnost* Soviet diplomatic histories of the war that make use of them.

73 Selected and revised papers from the first, 1986 Soviet-American conference were published in Russian and English as *Soviet-U.S. Relations, 1933–1942*, ed. W. F. Kimball and G. N. Sevost'ianov (Moscow, 1989). A trilateral volume edited by David Reynolds, Warren F. Kimball, and A. O. Chubarian, *Allies at War: The Soviet, American, and British Experience, 1939–1945*, was published by St. Martin's Press in 1994. Recent and previously cited books by conference participants include Kimball, *The Juggler*; Gardner, *Spheres of Influence*; Bennett, *Roosevelt and the Search for Victory*; Miner, *Between Churchill and Stalin*; Woods, *A Changing of the Guard*; Elizabeth Kimball MacLean, *Joseph E. Davies: Envoy to the Soviets* (Westport, 1992); and Hugh D. Philipps, *Between the Revolution and the West: A Political Biography of Maxim M. Litvinov* (Boulder, 1992).

74 The Cold War International History Project of the Woodrow Wilson Center in Washington, DC, has been making a vigorous, though perhaps vain, effort to keep abreast of these documents insofar as they relate to the Cold War.

won the war but lost the peace because his innocence and misplaced idealism allowed Europe to be divided in the first place. In his 1991 biographical study of the Big Three, however, Robin Edmonds cited recently published Russian documents as well as U.S. and British sources and recent events to argue that a consistently pragmatic Roosevelt had been largely successful – as had his Big Three colleagues. Although the Grand Alliance had admittedly failed to resolve the contemporary issues of nuclear weapons and the future of Central Europe, he concluded, it had succeeded in totally destroying Nazism and establishing a sound UN structure – one that was now finally capable of fulfilling its potential.[75]

As of 1993, recent interpretations of U.S. diplomacy during World War II can thus be divided into two major and separate if overlapping categories: those that make use of the new documentation, approaches, and international environment to reargue the original debate over U.S. and Rooseveltian naiveté; and those that use the new documentation, approaches, and environment to redefine the questions being asked. Although historians have anything but a good track record in the realm of prophecy, it seems safe to conclude that both groups of studies will continue throughout the remainder of the 1990s and beyond. Furthermore, both sets of approaches will probably continue to be visible within a continuing flood of specialized studies that fill in the remaining gaps in the literature, as well as those that perceive new subjects to explore.[76]

75 Remi Nadeau, *Stalin, Churchill, and Roosevelt Divide Europe* (New York, 1990); Robin Edmonds, *The Big Three: Churchill, Roosevelt, and Stalin in Peace & War* (New York, 1991). See also the conflicting interpretations in the works cited in footnote 73.

The debate over Churchill's strategy that began in the late 1960s (see above footnote 16) has also continued into the 1990s. See, for example, Tuvia Ben-Moshe's highly critical *Churchill: Strategy and History* (Boulder, 1992) vs. Eliot Cohen's "Churchill and Coalition strategy in World War II," in *Grand Strategies in War and Peace*, ed. Paul Kennedy (New Haven, 1991), 43–67.

76 The author is well aware of the pitfalls of prophecy and presents these conclusions and projections with great trepidation. That trepidation is only increased by his recognition of how different these pages would have been had they been written in mid-1991, when they were originally due, rather than in 1993–94! The extraordinary and thoroughly unexpected events of the last few years have clearly influenced the analyses and conclusions expressed here while making clear to the author just how uncertain and subject to change they are.

Despite the deluge of studies in the 1970s and 1980s, those gaps are far more numerous than one might imagine. No recent biographies exist, for example, on such pivotal figures as Secretary of State Cordell Hull or Undersecretary of State Sumner Welles, although scholarly works are in progress on both. Similar gaps exist in the study of U.S. wartime relations with individual countries and parts of the world – especially within Africa. The Anglo-Soviet-American wartime conferences have each received multiple book-length treatments, but most of the Anglo-American summit conferences remain neglected.[77]

Within future works, one should expect continued debates over both Roosevelt's importance vis-à-vis the bureaucracy and his responsibility for the Cold War – despite the demise of that conflict and the Soviet Union. Indeed, although the opening of Soviet archives will enable scholars finally to analyze the alliance from a trilateral perspective, it will probably continue to reinforce rather than resolve the old debate. The present direction of Russian scholarship is toward sharper and sharper condemnation of Stalin's policies, condemnation that has already provided additional ammunition for Roosevelt's critics.[78] As previously noted, how-

77 Jonathan Utley is working on Cordell Hull, Michael Butler on his diplomacy during FDR's first term, Benjamin Welles on his father Sumner Welles, and Irwin Gellman on the personal interaction among Welles, Hull, and FDR. Old but useful is Julius W. Pratt, *Cordell Hull*, vol. 13 in *The American Secretaries of State and Their Diplomacy*, ed. Robert H. Ferrell and Samuel Flagg Bemis (New York, 1964); and Frank Warren Graff's posthumously published 1971 doctoral dissertation, *Strategy of Involvement: A Diplomatic Biography of Sumner Welles, 1933–1943* (New York, 1988). For studies of Tehran and Yalta see above, footnotes 4, 8, 9, 18, and 43. See also Richard F. Fenno, Jr., ed., *The Yalta Conference*, 2d ed. (Lexington, MA, 1972); Jean Laloy, *Yalta: Yesterday, Today, Tomorrow*, trans. William R. Tyler (New York, 1988); and Floyd H. Rodine, *Yalta—Responsibility and Response, January–March 1945* (Lawrence, 1974). On Potsdam see Herbert Feis, *Between War and Peace: The Potsdam Conference* (Princeton, 1960); and Charles L. Mee, Jr., *Meeting at Potsdam* (New York, 1975). On Anglo-American meetings, Theodore A. Wilson has completed a major revision of his 1969 study on the 1941 Atlantic Conference, *The First Summit*; and Keith Sainsbury covers the two 1943 Cairo Conferences in *The Turning Point*. The other Anglo-American summits have received no book-length treatment based on archival research. An analysis of some of them based on published documents can be found in Beitzell, *The Uneasy Alliance*, while books on specific issues associated with individual conferences (the atomic bomb and Potsdam; unconditional surrender and Casablanca; the Morgenthau Plan and the second Quebec Conference) often provide important if incomplete material on those meetings.

78 It also led to criticism of the view of Stalin as cautious and defensive in foreign affairs. For an example of that criticism based on older sources see R. C. Raack, "Stalin's Plans for World War II," *Journal of Contemporary History* 26 (April 1991): 215–27.

ever, it has also provided ammunition for Roosevelt's defenders. Furthermore, to assume that this anti-Stalin trend will continue indefinitely, or that all of the Soviet documents will support this approach, would be extraordinarily naive. As Russian scholarship develops and as additional archives are opened (assumptions that are in themselves questionable in light of the present uncertainty regarding Russia's political future), sharp disagreements should be expected to take place. Because Stalin was at least as secretive and confusing as Roosevelt, those documents will also in all likelihood be inconclusive. Thus, no final and definitive conclusions may be possible on numerous issues, and the debate over Soviet-American relations during World War II is far from over. A new synthesis does appear to be emerging on Anglo-American wartime relations,[79] but debates continue on Anglo-Soviet relations and Anglo-American wartime conflicts regarding the Soviets.

Along with the continuing debates over Roosevelt and the Cold War, one should expect to see new studies addressing areas of contemporary international concern. These would include, but by no means be limited to, U.S. wartime policies toward the different groups within the former Yugoslavia, Italy's African colonies, Palestine, the Islamic world, Japan, Germany, and international organization. Within these studies a myriad of the new approaches will be used, often in combination. These will tend to further blur the distinctions between diplomatic and other histories in terms of topics and research.

The limits of the new approaches for World War II diplomacy are as unclear as the results of the end of the Cold War. They raise important new questions and provide fresh perspectives, but presently they are not sufficiently numerous or complete to allow

Most of the archival revelations and condemnations have focused on Stalin's domestic policies, however, a fact that has led some Roosevelt critics and supporters to debate the relationship between Soviet domestic and foreign policies during the war. It has also led some writers to sweeping conclusions based upon very limited and insufficient evidence. Amos Perlmutter, *FDR & Stalin: A Not So Grand Alliance, 1943–1945* (Columbia, MO, 1993), is the most recent example of such over-generalization and misuse of very limited archival documentation.

79 See Reynolds, "Roosevelt, Churchill, and the Wartime Anglo-American Alliance," 17–41, for a detailed analysis.

substantial conclusions as to their overall impact. Furthermore, the previously mentioned works notwithstanding, many if not most of the diplomatic studies that emphasize these new approaches are strangely silent on the years 1941–1945, even though these years are pivotal for their approach. Corporatist scholars, for example, have so far focused on the years between the two world wars and the years after the second conflict, thereby creating a major gap in their efforts to achieve an overall synthesis in U.S. diplomatic history.[80] Specialists in other new areas have devoted greater attention to the years 1941–1945, as already noted. For most of them, however, as for their predecessors in the field, World War II seems to constitute merely a precursor or "seed time" to the really important years that followed.

Such a tendency is completely understandable – and perhaps inevitable. It also has positive consequences in that it links ideas and events in the war years to their full development and results after the achievement of victory in 1945. It is regrettable, however, in that it fails to deal with World War II on its own terms. Indeed, it often distorts U.S. policies during the war by ignoring wartime as opposed to postwar priorities and by sharply separating U.S. diplomacy into pre- and post-Pearl Harbor eras that seem to bear little if any relationship to each other. It also risks a continuation of the Cold War era tendency to project later conflicts, issues, and perspectives onto an earlier time period, as more than one scholar has warned.[81] Rather than more studies that try to cover wartime diplomacy as a precursor to what followed, one would hope to see more studies analyzing that diplomacy on its own, and/or as the result of what preceded it. Such a reconnection of the pre- with the post-Pearl Harbor years may

80 See Michael Hogan's "Corporatism" chapter in Hogan and Paterson, eds., *Explaining the History of American Foreign Relations*, 226–36. A recent symposium in the pages of *Diplomatic History* revealed a similar gap among scholars focusing on the roles of culture and gender in foreign relations; the two essays dealt with the pre-Pearl Harbor and the Cold War years, as did much of the ensuing commentary. The years 1942–1945 were thus neatly sandwiched – and either ignored or subordinated to what followed or preceded them. See "Culture, Gender, and Foreign Policy: A Symposium," *Diplomatic History* 18 (Winter 1994): 47–124.

81 See, for example, D'Ann Campbell, *Women at War with America: Private Lives in a Patriotic Era* (Cambridge, MA, 1984), 213–38; and Kitchen, *British Policy towards the Soviet Union.*

well enable historians not only to better understand World War II diplomacy but also to obtain a truly comprehensive perspective on what Warren Kimball has recently and aptly labeled the nation's wartime transition from "a major power to a superpower," as well as on the global expansion of American interests that took place throughout the 1930s and 1940s.[82]

The present lack of synthesis on U.S. diplomacy during World War II, or even a hint of future synthesis, is far from surprising. The multiple and often conflicting approaches, as well as conclusions, clearly reflect the fragmentation within both the discipline of history and U.S. society as a whole. Nor is this necessarily a sign of weakness. Thomas Paterson recently noted in this regard that the history of U.S. foreign relations in general possesses "a good number" of syntheses, but that diplomatic historians find them "contending or unsatisfying" and that "few subfields of history have produced syntheses that have remained dominant."[83] Clearly this is the case with U.S. diplomacy during World War II, and clearly, as with the history of U.S. foreign relations in general, the field is flourishing rather than floundering. Within the old framework, continued disagreements will remain linked to the state of Russian-American relations, domestic politics, and one's ideology as well as to the release of new documentation. Similarly, the new frameworks will in all likelihood be heavily influenced by these factors as we pass through the last decade of the century. One hopes that such influences will enlighten more than they distort the 1941–1945 record as we continue to try to come to terms with the enormous impact of World War II on our lives.

82 Warren F. Kimball, ed., *America Unbound: World War II and the Making of A Superpower* (New York, 1992), 1. Other recent notable efforts in this regard include Akira Iriye and Warren Cohen, eds., *American, Chinese, and Japanese Perspectives on Wartime Asia, 1931–1949* (Wilmington, DE, 1990); Hess, *The United States' Emergence as a Southeast Asian Power, 1940–1950*; Miller, *The United States and Italy, 1940–1950*; and Hurstfield, *The United States and the French Nation, 1939–1945*.

83 Hogan and Paterson, eds., *Explaining the History of American Foreign Relations*, 43–45.

8

The Decision to Use the Bomb: A Historiographical Update

J. SAMUEL WALKER

To commemorate the fiftieth anniversary of the end of World War II, the National Air and Space Museum, a part of the Smithsonian Institution, made plans for an exhibit featuring a section of the fuselage of the *Enola Gay*, the plane that dropped the atomic bomb on Hiroshima in August 1945. Curators consulted with an advisory committee of experts on the use of the bomb in an effort to ensure that the exhibit was historically accurate and consistent with recent scholarly findings. Although museum officials were acutely aware that the subject was controversial, they were ill-prepared for the outrage that early drafts of the script triggered. Veterans' groups led a fusillade of attacks that accused the Smithsonian of making the use of the bomb appear aggressive, immoral, and unjustified. The *Wall Street Journal*, for example, condemned "scriptwriters [who] disdain any belief that the decision to drop the bomb could have been inspired by something other than racism or blood-lust."

Eventually, the Smithsonian modified its script in response to the complaints of veterans, members of Congress, and a chorus of other critics. This, in turn, elicited protests from scholars that the museum had sacrificed historical accuracy to accommodate political pressures. The outcry over the Smithsonian's exhibit plans vividly demonstrated that the decision to use the bomb remained an emotionally charged issue, even nearly half a century after the end of World War II. It also graphically illustrated the wide gap

This article expresses the personal views of the author. It does not represent an official position of the U.S. Nuclear Regulatory Commission or any other agency of the federal government.

between popular and scholarly views of the reasons for the atomic attacks on Japanese cities. In an article on the "new battle of Hiroshima," *Newsweek* magazine summarized the interpretation that prevailed in popular perceptions: "The U.S. calculation, grimly momentous though it was, seems inescapable: an invasion of Japan would have been bloodier than the bombing." Scholarly investigations, however, have shown that President Harry S. Truman never faced a categorical choice between an invasion and the bomb and that the issues surrounding the use of atomic weapons were much more complex. They have produced a rich and controversial historiography that has debated those issues at length and in depth.[1]

Questions about the wisdom and morality of using the bomb arose shortly after Hiroshima. The central issue in a rather sporadic debate among scholars, journalists, former government officials, and publicists was whether the bomb was necessary to end the war against Japan promptly or whether other means were available to achieve the same goal. The prevailing view, advanced by former policymakers and supported by most scholars, held that the bomb obviated the need for an invasion of Japan, accelerated the conclusion of the war, and saved a vast number of American lives. But several writers, including Norman Cousins and Thomas K. Finletter, P. M. S. Blackett, Carl Marzani, William Appleman Williams, and D. F. Fleming, suggested that the bomb was not essential for a rapid end to the war and/or that its use was dictated more by political than by military considerations.[2]

1 *Wall Street Journal*, 29 August 1994; *Washington Post*, 26 and 30 September 1994; *New York Times*, 11 October 1994; Bill Powell with Daniel Glick, "The New Battle of Hiroshima," *Newsweek*, 29 August 1994, 36. For a discussion of popular views of the decision to use the bomb see J. Samuel Walker, "History, Collective Memory, and the Decision to Use the Bomb," *Diplomatic History* 19 (Spring 1995): 319–28.

2 For a valuable detailed essay on the literature before 1974 see Barton J. Bernstein, "The Atomic Bomb and American Foreign Policy, 1941–1945: An Historiographical Controversy," *Peace and Change* 2 (Spring 1974): 1–16. This essay focuses on publications that have appeared since that time.

The orthodox position on the use of the bomb is clearly outlined in Henry L. Stimson, "The Decision to Use the Atomic Bomb," *Harper's* 197 (February 1947): 97–107; Harry S. Truman, *Memoirs: Year of Decisions* (Garden City, 1955); and Samuel Eliot Morison, "Why Japan Surrendered," *The Atlantic* 206 (October 1960): 41–47. For early dissenting views see Norman Cousins and Thomas K. Finletter, "A Beginning for Sanity," *Saturday Review of Literature* 29 (15 June 1946): 5–9; P. M. S. Blackett, *Military and Political Consequences of Atomic Energy* (London, 1948);

In the first scholarly treatment of the subject based on extensive research in primary sources, Herbert Feis supplied an authoritative, though not definitive, evaluation of those issues. He declared without equivocation in 1961 that the bomb was not needed to force Japan's surrender "on [American] terms within a few months." Feis endorsed the U.S. Strategic Bombing Survey's conclusion that the war would have been over no later than the end of 1945 even without the bomb, Soviet entry into the war, or an invasion of the Japanese islands. But he argued that even though the bomb was not essential to end the war, its use was justified. American policymakers, he maintained, were convinced that dropping the bomb would save "probably tens of thousands" of American lives. Feis insisted that "the impelling reason for the decision to use [the bomb] was military – to end the war victoriously as soon as possible."[3]

Gar Alperovitz's *Atomic Diplomacy*, published in 1965, directly challenged Feis's conclusions and triggered a sharply contested historiographical dispute. Alperovitz contended that political rather than military considerations were the key to understanding the use of the bomb; he insisted that it was dropped primarily to impress the Soviets rather than to defeat the Japanese. His book received far more attention and stirred far greater discord than earlier works that had argued along the same lines, in part because he drew from recently opened sources to reconstruct events in unprecedented detail, in part because of growing uneasiness about the conduct of U.S. foreign policy in Vietnam, and in part because of the emerging scholarly debate over the origins of the Cold War.

Alperovitz agreed with Feis that the bomb was not needed to end the war in Asia but differed with him about the reasons that it was used. In his view, President Truman and his advisers saw the bomb as a diplomatic lever that could be employed to thwart Soviet ambitions in Eastern Europe and Asia. Soon after taking

Carl Marzani, *We Can Be Friends* (New York, 1952); William Appleman Williams, *The Tragedy of American Diplomacy* (Cleveland, 1959); and D. F. Fleming, *The Cold War and Its Origins* (Garden City, 1961).

3 Herbert Feis, *Japan Subdued: The Atomic Bomb and the End of the War in the Pacific* (Princeton, 1961).

office, Truman reversed Franklin D. Roosevelt's efforts to cooperate with the Soviets by condemning them for their actions in Poland. After learning about the prospects for the bomb, however, he adopted a "strategy of a delayed showdown" in order to avoid a confrontation with the Soviets and postpone the Potsdam meeting until the bomb was tested. If it proved successful, it could not only strengthen the diplomatic position of the United States in opposing Soviet policies in Eastern Europe but also end the war against Japan before the Soviets invaded and gained control of Manchuria.

Alperovitz argued that political considerations, not military ones, explained why the Truman administration did not explore alternatives to using the bomb to end the war, such as investigating the seriousness of Japanese peace initiatives, moderating the demand for unconditional surrender, or waiting for the Soviets to declare war on Japan. He further asserted that the bomb raised the confidence of American policymakers that they could successfully challenge Soviet expansionism in Europe and Asia, and that armed with the bomb, they mounted a "diplomatic offensive" after Hiroshima. In short, Alperovitz emphasized three main themes: the prospect of having the bomb was the guiding factor in the U.S. posture toward the Soviet Union in the spring and summer of 1945; the anticipated impact of the bomb on Soviet-American relations was crucial in motivating the Truman administration to use it; and the monopoly of atomic technology brought about policy shifts by the United States that played an important role in causing the Cold War.[4]

Alperovitz's "revisionist" thesis provoked a spirited reaction from a diverse array of scholars who agreed on little except that he was wrong. Gabriel Kolko, the most doctrinaire of New Left interpreters of the beginning of the Cold War, did not view use of the bomb as a major policy or moral issue and dismissed it as a factor in causing U.S.-Soviet discord. From a quite different perspective, Thomas T. Hammond, who found it "almost incredible that the United States failed to take fullest advantage of its atomic monopoly in 1945," described Alperovitz's findings as

4 Gar Alperovitz, *Atomic Diplomacy: Hiroshima and Potsdam* (New York, 1965).

"implausible, exaggerated, or unsupported by the evidence." Perhaps the harshest attack came from Robert James Maddox, who, after checking Alperovitz's footnotes, called *Atomic Diplomacy* a piece of "creative writing." He thought it "disconcerting ... that such a work could have come to be considered a contribution to the historical literature on the period." Despite the criticism, many scholars took Alperovitz's arguments seriously. His book spurred a great deal of scholarly effort that was designed, implicitly or explicitly, to test his hypothesis.[5]

By the mid-1970s, several important new studies, aided by the opening of key primary sources, had discounted parts of Alperovitz's position but substantiated others. Lisle A. Rose defended the Truman administration against some of Alperovitz's criticisms. He disagreed that Truman adopted a "strategy of delay" by postponing the Potsdam Conference in hopes that the bomb would be tested by the time the meeting began. He denied that the United States practiced any form of atomic diplomacy at Potsdam or bombed Hiroshima for political reasons. Despite his generally sympathetic view of Truman, however, Rose condemned the administration for attempting to take advantage of its atomic monopoly after the war to win diplomatic gains from the Soviet Union, and he denounced the destruction of Hiroshima and Nagasaki as "vile acts."[6]

Martin J. Sherwin found Alperovitz's interpretation more persuasive than did Rose, but he also took issue with some of the key points in *Atomic Diplomacy*. In *A World Destroyed*, Sherwin stressed that a full understanding of U.S. atomic policies required an examination of Roosevelt's as well as Truman's actions. He showed that from the beginning of the Manhattan Project, senior policymakers viewed the bomb as only a potential weapon and left any decisions about how it would be used for the future.

5 Gabriel Kolko, *The Politics of War: The World and United States Foreign Policy, 1943–1945* (New York, 1968); Thomas T. Hammond, "'Atomic Diplomacy' Revisited," *Orbis* 19 (Winter 1976): 1403–28; Robert James Maddox, "*Atomic Diplomacy*: A Study in Creative Writing," *Journal of American History* 59 (March 1973): 925–34; idem, *The New Left and the Origins of the Cold War* (Princeton, 1973); Bernstein, "Atomic Bomb and American Foreign Policy," 10–12.

6 Lisle A. Rose, *Dubious Victory: The United States and the End of World War II* (Kent, OH, 1973).

They never seriously questioned whether it would be used at all if it became available. Roosevelt was secretive in his treatment of atomic energy issues, and he ruled out sharing information about the bomb project with the Soviet Union. After assuming the presidency, Truman quickly adopted a firmer posture toward the Soviets than Roosevelt had taken, but Sherwin found no evidence of an elaborately planned showdown or "strategy of delay" in dealing with them.

Sherwin argued that the principal motive for using the bomb was to end the war as soon as possible. Policymakers saw no reason to reassess their assumption that the bomb would be dropped once it was ready. Sherwin agreed with Alperovitz that high-level officials viewed the bomb as a political weapon that could provide diplomatic leverage, but he regarded such considerations as secondary to the military ones. While denying any "diabolical motivations" on the part of the Truman administration, he regretted that it did not seriously weigh alternatives to the bomb. He suggested that modifying the unconditional surrender terms might have made the bombing of Hiroshima unnecessary and submitted that the attack on Nagasaki was indefensible.[7]

In an article published in 1975, Barton J. Bernstein, addressing Alperovitz's interpretation more directly than Sherwin, arrived at similar conclusions. Bernstein also emphasized the influence and momentum of Roosevelt's legacy in effectively narrowing the options available to Truman in dealing with the bomb. Like his predecessor, Truman assumed that the bomb was a legitimate weapon of war and was unlikely to change long-standing policies without any compelling reason to do so. Bernstein considered five possible alternatives to using the bomb to end the war: waiting for Soviet entry into the Far Eastern conflict; demonstrating the power of the bomb by setting off a warning shot in an uninhabited area; mitigating the demand for Japan's unconditional surrender; exploring the proposals of Japanese "peace feelers"; and relying solely on conventional weapons. He argued that each

7 Martin J. Sherwin, *A World Destroyed: The Atomic Bomb and the Grand Alliance* (New York, 1975). Sherwin introduced his major arguments in "The Atomic Bomb and the Origins of the Cold War: U.S. Atomic Energy Policy and Diplomacy, 1941–1945," *American Historical Review* 78 (October 1973): 945–68.

alternative seemed to policymakers to be less desirable, less feasible, or riskier than the atomic bomb option.

Bernstein emphasized that policymakers saw no reason to avoid dropping the bomb. They used it primarily to end the war and save American lives. They hoped the bomb would provide political gains by helping win diplomatic concessions from the Soviets, but this was, in Bernstein's estimation, "a bonus." He concurred with Alperovitz that the Truman administration wielded the bomb as a part of its diplomatic arsenal after the war, which he believed intensified but did not in itself cause the Cold War. Although he accepted parts of Alperovitz's thesis, Bernstein cast doubt on many of the arguments in and the emphasis of *Atomic Diplomacy*. Oddly enough, for a prominent Cold War revisionist, Bernstein came off in this article as a defender of the Truman administration, at least from much of the criticism that Alperovitz leveled against it.[8]

Other scholars who examined the question of the use of the bomb in the context of the developing Cold War agreed with the major points made by Sherwin and Bernstein. Several major works, in brief discussions of the decision to drop the bomb, supported the thesis that the Truman administration used it primarily for military reasons but also hoped that an additional result would be increased diplomatic power. Thus, John Lewis Gaddis, in a book that preceded the appearance of Sherwin's and Bernstein's analyses, and Daniel Yergin and Robert J. Donovan, in books that followed their publication, largely rejected Alperovitz's specific arguments but still accepted a key part of his overall framework. Gregg Herken concurred that the bomb served both military and diplomatic purposes, and stressed how Truman and Secretary of War Henry L. Stimson carefully weighed its political implications. In a study of James F. Byrnes, the most unabashed proponent of atomic diplomacy, Robert L. Messer took a similar view. While denying Alperovitz's contention that the bomb was a major consideration in American planning for the Potsdam Conference, he criticized Truman and Byrnes for harboring illusions

8 Barton J. Bernstein, "Roosevelt, Truman, and the Atomic Bomb, 1941–1945: A Reinterpretation," *Political Science Quarterly* 90 (Spring 1975): 23–69.

that possession of it "would save China, preserve the Open Door, make the Russians more manageable in Europe, and allow American leaders to dictate their own terms for the peace."[9]

Long after its publication, the impact of Alperovitz's *Atomic Diplomacy* on serious historical writing was apparent. In important ways, it shaped the debate over the bomb and how historians approached it. Before the book appeared, few scholars took seriously the argument that political objectives had played a vital role in the decision to use the bomb. After it appeared, a broad consensus viewed diplomatic considerations as an important part of the administration's view of the bomb's value. This would have been inconceivable before *Atomic Diplomacy*. The book redirected the focus of questions that scholars asked about the bomb. The major issue was no longer whether the bomb was necessary to end the war as soon as possible. Rather, the central questions had become: What factors were paramount in the decision to use the bomb and why was its use more attractive to policymakers than other alternatives? The best historical scholarship on the subject drew on a rich lode of recently opened sources, including the diary of Henry L. Stimson, the records of the Manhattan Project, the papers and diary of Joseph Davies, the notes of Byrnes's aide Walter Brown, and portions of the Roosevelt and Truman papers, to address those questions.

Scholars working on the subject did not offer unqualified comfort either to supporters or detractors of Alperovitz's point of view. They sharply criticized his thesis in some respects, especially his emphasis on the "strategy of delay," the primacy of diplomatic goals, and the carefully plotted coherence of the Truman administration's policies. In general, they found that Alperovitz had exaggerated the impact of the bomb on the thinking of American leaders. But most scholars still subscribed to important elements of his interpretation, especially his claims that the bomb influenced

9 John Lewis Gaddis, *The United States and the Origins of the Cold War, 1941–1947* (New York, 1972); Daniel Yergin, *Shattered Peace: The Origins of the Cold War and the National Security State* (Boston, 1977); Robert J. Donovan, *Conflict and Crisis: The Presidency of Harry S. Truman, 1945–1948* (New York, 1977); Gregg Herken, *The Winning Weapon: The Atomic Bomb and the Cold War, 1945–1950* (New York, 1980); Robert L. Messer, *The End of an Alliance: James F. Byrnes, Roosevelt, Truman, and the Origins of the Cold War* (Chapel Hill, 1982).

American attitudes toward the Soviet Union and that diplomatic considerations played a role in deliberations on using the bomb against Japan.

At that point, despite differences of opinion over some specific issues, the historiographical debate over the bomb seemed largely settled. The latest scholarship combined the traditional view that the United States dropped the bomb primarily for military reasons with the revisionist assertion that its inclusion in America's diplomatic arsenal aggravated tensions with the Soviet Union. The consensus did not go unchallenged for long, however. Important new evidence – Truman's handwritten diary notes of the Potsdam Conference, which were published in 1980, and private letters he had written to his wife, which were published in 1983 – prompted a reexamination of some important questions.

Truman's diary notes and letters provided the best available evidence about his understanding of and thoughts on the implications of the bomb at the time of Potsdam. But the new materials did not offer clear answers to the questions that had intrigued scholars. Indeed, as Robert Messer pointed out in a special issue of the *Bulletin of the Atomic Scientists* on the fortieth anniversary of Hiroshima, their implications for the historiographical debate over the use of the bomb were decidedly ambivalent. For example, after meeting with Josef Stalin for the first time, Truman recorded in his diary that the Soviet premier promised to enter the war against Japan on 15 August 1945, and added: "Fini Japs when that comes about." Here, then, was striking testimony that the president knew that the bomb was not needed to end the war quickly. This and other notations supported Alperovitz's contention that military requirements were not the primary reasons for using the bomb.[10]

10 Robert L. Messer, "New Evidence on Truman's Decision," *Bulletin of the Atomic Scientists* 41 (August 1985): 50–56. The diary notes are printed in Eduard Mark, "Today Has Been a Historical One: Harry S. Truman's Diary of the Potsdam Conference," *Diplomatic History* 4 (Summer 1980): 317–26; Barton J. Bernstein, "Truman at Potsdam: His Secret Diary," *Foreign Service Journal* 57 (July/August 1980): 29–36; and Robert H. Ferrell, ed., *Off the Record: The Private Papers of Harry S. Truman* (New York, 1980). Ferrell made no comment on the implications of the diary for the debate over the use of the bomb, but he did suggest that it provided evidence of duplicity on the part of Stalin. See Ferrell, ed., "Truman at Potsdam," *American Heritage* 31 (June/July 1980): 36–47. Truman's letters to his wife are published in Robert H. Ferrell, ed., *Dear Bess: The Letters from Harry to Bess Truman, 1910–1959* (New York, 1983).

But as Messer suggested, other statements Truman made seemed "to disprove the revisionist contention that he did not want 'the Russians' in the war at all." For a time, the president continued to express hope that the Soviets would enter the war promptly, which appeared to contradict the claim that one purpose of dropping the bomb was to keep the Soviets out of the war. This discrepancy can be resolved by the fact that Truman and his advisers decided shortly after learning details about the power of the bomb tested in New Mexico that Soviet entry into the war was neither necessary nor desirable.

Yet other Truman statements in his diary and his letters from Potsdam raise further questions about his views. He told his wife on 18 July (before receiving details about the test shot): "I've gotten what I came for – Stalin goes to war August 15 with no strings on it." He added: "I'll say that we'll end the war a year sooner now, and think of the kids who won't be killed!" Did Truman at that time really believe that the war could last another year? If so, in contrast to other of his comments, it could support the traditional argument that his principal motive for using the bomb was to shorten the war. But on the same day that the president wrote to his wife about ending the war a year early, he recorded in his diary: "Believe Japs will fold before Russia comes in. I am sure they will when Manhattan appears over their homeland." This seems to suggest that Truman saw the bomb as a way not only to end the war sooner than expected but also to keep the Soviets out of it. The Truman documents are fascinating but inconclusive and sometimes contradictory. As Messer pointed out: "The evidence of the Potsdam diary and letters does not close the book on the question of why the bomb was dropped. Rather it opens it to a previously unseen page."[11]

If Truman's notes and letters muddied the historiographical waters, three books published around the fortieth anniversary of Hiroshima did little to clear them. Each was written by a professional journalist who regretted the use of the bomb but did not directly address the issues debated by historians. The best of them was Richard Rhodes's *The Making of the Atomic Bomb*,

11 Messer, "New Evidence on Truman's Decision," 55–56; Ferrell, ed., *Off the Record*, 53–54; idem, ed., *Dear Bess*, 519.

which focused on the scientific and technical complexities that had to be overcome to build an atomic bomb. Rhodes delivered an absorbing narrative of the problems and personalities involved in the Manhattan Project but discussed the decision to drop the bomb only briefly. He maintained that once the weapon proved successful, "men discovered reasons to use it." In a brutal and barbaric war, the very existence of the bomb assured that it would be used without much thought of the long-range policy or human consequences. In *Day One*, Peter Wyden placed the primary burden for Hiroshima on the atomic scientists who plunged ahead with work on the bomb despite its potential dangers and the threat it posed to postwar peace. He largely absolved policymakers of ultimate responsibility for using the bomb because he believed that they were incapable of understanding the scientific principles or long-term political implications of nuclear weapons. Since Truman and his advisers were unable to control the speed or direction of events, the existence of the bomb guaranteed its use. In *Day of the Bomb*, Dan Kurzman described the developments leading to Hiroshima in a series of personality vignettes that never came together to form a thesis.[12]

Unlike Rhodes, Wyden, and Kurzman, Gar Alperovitz showed no reluctance to deal explicitly with historiographical issues. In an updated edition of *Atomic Diplomacy* published in 1985, he struck back at his critics. He dismissed Rose's work, and although both Sherwin's and Bernstein's conclusions were more to his liking, he still found them objectionable in important respects. Alperovitz contested their emphasis on the weight of Roosevelt's legacy in limiting Truman's options. He argued that the changing situation in Japan gave Truman wide latitude to revise policies he inherited from Roosevelt, and furthermore, that the president realized that the bomb was not necessary to end the war because

12 Richard Rhodes, *The Making of the Atomic Bomb* (New York, 1987); Peter Wyden, *Day One: Before Hiroshima and After* (New York, 1984); Dan Kurzman, *Day of the Bomb: Countdown to Hiroshima* (New York, 1986). For a review that criticized Rhodes for, among other things, neglecting key sources, embroidering the sources he used, and failing to analyze important issues surrounding the decision to use the bomb, see Barton J. Bernstein, "An Analysis of 'Two Cultures': Writing about the Making and Using of the Atomic Bombs," *Public Historian* 12 (Spring 1990): 83–107.

a number of prominent advisers, including chief of staff William D. Leahy, General Dwight D. Eisenhower, and Undersecretary of the Navy Ralph Bard, told him so. Reaffirming his belief in a "strategy of delay" and in the possibility of ending the war on favorable terms without the bomb, Alperovitz challenged the view that the United States dropped it primarily for military reasons. He insisted that there was no "overriding military necessity" for the bomb and that Truman and his closest aides knew it. Therefore, in his estimation, only the desire to impress the Soviets and to achieve diplomatic objectives could explain why Truman disdained alternatives to end the war and hastened to use the bomb. In short, after considering the new evidence and interpretations of other scholars, Alperovitz altered his opinions of twenty years earlier very little. In fact, the only changes he said he would make in his first edition would be to place greater stress on Byrnes's role in atomic policymaking and to move material originally located in an appendix into the main body of text.[13]

While Alperovitz was reasserting the correctness of his own position, other scholars were reexamining a number of old issues in the light of new evidence and arriving at some fresh conclusions. One such question was whether the bomb was necessary to save large numbers of American lives. Although several writers had addressed this matter by suggesting that the war could have ended and the loss of life averted without the bomb, new sources indicated that even in the worst case U.S. casualties would have been far fewer than former policymakers asserted after the war. In explaining why the United States had dropped the bomb, Truman, Stimson and others argued that an invasion of the Japanese islands could have caused half a million American deaths, one million American casualties, or some other appalling figure (the number varied from person to person and time to time). But Rufus E. Miles, Jr., pointed out in an article published in 1985 that during the war, military planners never projected casualty figures that were even close to those cited by Truman and his

13 Gar Alperovitz, *Atomic Diplomacy: Hiroshima and Potsdam*, rev. ed. (New York, 1985). Barton J. Bernstein argued that Eisenhower did not object to using the bomb against Japan in "Ike and Hiroshima: Did He Oppose It?" *Journal of Strategic Studies* 10 (September 1987): 377–89.

advisers after the war. Even in the unlikely event that an invasion had been necessary, the pre-surrender estimates did not exceed twenty thousand. Barton J. Bernstein, drawing on newly opened records, found the worst-case prediction to be a loss of forty-six thousand lives, still far short of the policymakers' claims. "The myth of the 500,000 American lives saved," he concluded, "thus seems to have no basis in fact." More recently, John Ray Skates, writing on plans for the invasion of Japan, offered the same view. "The record," he observed, "does not support the postwar claims of huge Allied casualties to be suffered in the invasion of Japan."[14]

The sparing of forty-six thousand or twenty thousand or many fewer lives might well have provided ample justification for using the bomb, but Truman and other high-level officials did not choose to make a case on those grounds. Indeed, as James G. Hershberg and Bernstein demonstrated, former government authorities

14 Rufus E. Miles, Jr., "Hiroshima: The Strange Myth of Half a Million American Lives Saved," *International Security* 10 (Fall 1985): 121–40; Barton J. Bernstein, "A Postwar Myth: 500,000 U.S. Lives Saved," *Bulletin of the Atomic Scientists* 42 (June/July 1986): 38–40; John Ray Skates, *The Invasion of Japan: Alternative to the Bomb* (Columbia, SC, 1994). In brief discussions of the same issue, Martin J. Sherwin and Michael S. Sherry offered support for the view set forth by Miles, Bernstein, and Skates. See Sherwin, *A World Destroyed: Hiroshima and the Origins of the Arms Race*, rev. ed. (New York, 1987); and Sherry, *The Rise of American Air Power: The Creation of Armageddon* (New Haven, 1987).

Edward J. Drea challenged the much lower estimates of Allied casualties in a brief discussion of the issue in his book *MacArthur's ULTRA: Codebreaking and the War against Japan, 1942–1945* (Lawrence, 1992). He based his argument largely on a letter that Truman sent in early 1953 to historians writing an official account of the role of the air force in the Pacific war. Drea suggested that a rapid Japanese buildup of forces on Kyushu so alarmed General Marshall that he told Truman at Potsdam that the invasion of Kyushu and later of Honshu would cost 250,000 to 1,000,000 American casualties. Robert H. Ferrell used this information to support his argument that Truman had received very large casualty projections before the bomb was dropped. In Ferrell's view, Truman "faced the dreadful choice of ordering the army and navy into an invasion of the home islands, with untold numbers of casualties, or ending the war as soon as possible" by using the bomb. See Ferrell, *Harry S. Truman: A Life* (Columbia, MO, 1994). But Truman's claim of hearing estimates of such large numbers from Marshall is very dubious. Bernstein has shown that the meeting at which Marshall supposedly gave the high estimates to Truman almost certainly never took place. The upper end of the casualty projections was a creation of White House staff officials, who wished to bring Truman's estimates into line with those published earlier by Stimson. See Bernstein, "Writing, Righting, or Wronging the Historical Record: President Truman's Letter on His Atomic-Bomb Decision," *Diplomatic History* 16 (Winter 1992): 163–73. To date, no contemporaneous evidence has been found to support estimates of deaths or casualties from an invasion in the range claimed by Stimson, Truman, and others after the war.

consciously and artfully constructed the history of the decision to discourage questions about it. The leader in this effort was James B. Conant, one of the key scientific administrators of the Manhattan Project, who persuaded Stimson to write an article explaining and justifying the use of the bomb as a way of heading off criticism of Truman's action. Stimson's article, which appeared in *Harper's* in 1947, suggested that the atomic attacks had prevented one million American casualties – a number that formed the basis for others' claims of U.S. lives saved by the bomb.[15]

Scholars have not provided a single explanation for why former policymakers felt compelled to exaggerate by several orders of magnitude the estimated casualties of an invasion of Japan. Presumably they believed that citing a huge number made the decision to use the bomb appear unassailable, or, at a minimum, less vulnerable to the ambiguities that smaller (and more accurate) estimates might have created. Hershberg found that Conant, in addition to his conviction that the bomb had shortened the war, worried about the impact of a loss of public support for nuclear weapons. Only if the American people demonstrated the will to use their atomic arsenal, he reasoned, would the Soviets be amenable to nuclear arms control agreements. Although Conant did not provide the estimates that Stimson cited – the source of the figure of one million casualties is unknown – he was the driving force behind the effort to persuade the public that the use of atomic weapons against Japan had been a sound and proper action.

Hershberg also suggested that Conant's position was influenced by unacknowledged feelings of guilt. "His bristling, his anxiety, and his marshaling of support for the decision to use the bomb reveal an intense personal sensitivity over how history would judge his role in the event," Hershberg submitted, "and a yearning to believe that Hiroshima's destruction was necessary to win both the war *and* the peace." Bernstein speculated that, in a similar manner, Truman felt more ambivalent about dropping the bomb than he ever admitted. This would explain, he argued,

15 James G. Hershberg, *James B. Conant: Harvard to Hiroshima and the Making of the Nuclear Age* (New York, 1993); Barton J. Bernstein, "Seizing the Contested Terrain of Early Nuclear History: Stimson, Conant, and Their Allies Explain the Decision to Use the Atomic Bomb," *Diplomatic History* 17 (Winter 1993): 35–72.

not only the need to inflate the number of lives saved by the bomb but also Truman's apparent self-delusion that it had been used on "purely military" targets. Robert L. Messer also addressed the intriguing question of Truman's state of mind regarding the bomb. He suggested that even though the president never acknowledged any feelings of remorse, he harbored a heavy burden of guilt arising from the discrepancy between the mass slaughter of civilians and his own moral convictions.[16]

The observations on the inner conflicts of Truman and other leading American officials added a new dimension to what was always a key, though often unstated, issue in the debate over the bomb: Was its use morally justified? This is, of course, a highly subjective judgment that has usually been implied more than explicitly discussed. If, as the defenders of the Truman administration maintained, the bomb shortened the war and saved lives, the morality of its use is defensible. But if, as many critics suggested, the bomb was not needed to end the war promptly or to save lives, then its morality seems highly questionable.[17] Some writers side-stepped this dichotomy by arguing that war is inherently immoral and that the atomic bombs were no more heinous than the firebombs and napalm that killed tens of thousands of civilians before Hiroshima. The moral desolation of the Pacific war was graphically illustrated by John Dower's *War without Mercy*, which described the atrocities carried out by both sides and reconstructed the cultural context in which the bomb was used. Dower showed that Americans viewed the Japanese as depraved, contemptible, ape-like subhumans, or alternatively, as fanatical, ruthless, and cruel superhumans. Although he said little about the bomb, it seems clear that both images he depicted discouraged open-minded consideration of the moral implications of using it.[18]

The moral aspects of the use of the bomb were addressed more

16 Hershberg, *James B. Conant*, 279–304; Bernstein, "A Postwar Myth," 40, and "Truman at Potsdam," 32; Robert L. Messer, "America's 'Sacred Trust': Truman and the Bomb, 1945–1949," paper presented at the annual meeting of the American Historical Association, 1987.

17 For a recent article that departs from the pattern by stating very clearly its argument that the use of the bomb was morally unjustified see Richard H. Minear, "Atomic Holocaust, Nazi Holocaust: Some Reflections," *Diplomatic History* 19 (Spring 1995).

18 John W. Dower, *War without Mercy: Race and Power in the Pacific War* (New York, 1986).

thoroughly and directly in two studies of American strategic bombing policy during World War II. Ronald Schaffer traced the evolution of bombing theory and practice from the precision strikes of the early war to the indiscriminate bombing of cities by the end of the war. The atomic attacks on Hiroshima and Nagasaki were a logical extension of the rationales developed for terror bombing with conventional weapons. Schaffer found that American leaders and scientists weighed the moral issues involved in the use of the atomic bomb. With the exception of the removal of the ancient city of Kyoto from the target list, however, he submitted that "moral constraints in the hearts and minds of those responsible for the American air war do not seem to have prevented them from employing any of the measures they contemplated using against Japan." Michael S. Sherry agreed that use of nuclear bombs could only be understood in the context of previous U.S. strategic policies. Although the moral aspects of American bombing were not the central theme of his book as they were with Schaffer's, they were an important and vivid part of it. Sherry suggested that scholars had focused too narrowly on the "sin of atomic bombing," which, "like the sin of the whole war's bombing," resulted from "a slow accretion of large fears, thoughtless assumptions, and incremental decisions."[19]

Assessing the moral implications of the bomb inevitably leads to examining the possible alternatives to it. Several scholars have raised anew the question of why the administration did not pursue, or explore more thoroughly, other options. One was to modify the demand for unconditional surrender and give clear assurances to the Japanese that they could retain the emperor. Sherry contended that the failure to do this was "the most tragic blunder in American surrender policy." Although he acknowledged that such an offer would not have guaranteed an immediate Japanese surrender, he argued that the risks were small and the "moral

19 Ronald Schaffer, *Wings of Judgment: American Bombing in World War II* (New York, 1985); Sherry, *Rise of American Air Power*, 301–41, 363. Conrad C. Crane took issue with Schaffer and Sherry by arguing that the United States remained committed to precision bombing throughout the European war. But he agreed that precision bombing in Japan gave way to indiscriminate terror bombing after Curtis LeMay took command of air operations against Japan in early 1945. The atomic bombings were a small step from the "fire raids" against Japanese cities. See Crane, *Bombs, Cities, and Civilians: American Airpower Strategy in World War II* (Lawrence, 1993).

risks . . . in pursuing an atomic solution . . . were large." Sherry did not view the refusal to soften unconditional surrender and the decision to drop the bomb as an effort to achieve political goals, however. He saw the use of the bomb as an outgrowth of momentum, confusion, and the "technological fanaticism" that had overtaken American bombing policy.[20]

Martin J. Sherwin criticized the Truman administration even more severely than Sherry and, indeed, more sharply than in his own *A World Destroyed*. He suggested that Truman rejected the idea of modifying the unconditional surrender terms partly for domestic political reasons and partly because "he preferred to use the atomic bomb" to strengthen America's diplomatic position. He further maintained that by electing to wait for the bomb, Truman prolonged the war; it might have ended sooner if the president had moderated the demand for unconditional surrender. Kai Erikson briefly explored another alternative to dropping the bomb on a densely populated city. He examined the question of why the United States did not fire a warning shot by dropping the bomb on a "relatively uninhabited" Japanese target. This would have given enemy leaders a graphic display of what would happen if they did not surrender promptly. The risks of this kind of demonstration were minimal; if it did not work other bombs could still be used on the cities on the target list. Erikson was troubled that neither this nor any other option received serious consideration from American policymakers. He attributed their aversion to any alternative to the bomb to a number of military and political factors, the most important of which was "the wish to make a loud announcement to the Russians."[21]

In a book he published forty years after coauthoring Henry L. Stimson's memoirs, McGeorge Bundy disagreed that the bomb's potential impact on the Soviet Union was a major factor in its use. But he, too, lamented that the highest officials in the Truman administration did not carefully weigh alternatives to the bomb; he acknowledged that Stimson had overstated the extent to which

20 Sherry, *Rise of American Air Power*, 255, 301–56.

21 Martin J. Sherwin, "Hiroshima and Modern Memory," *Nation* 233 (10 October 1981): 329, 349–53; Kai Erikson, "Of Accidental Judgments and Casual Slaughters," ibid. 241 (3/10 August 1985): 80–85.

the administration considered other options. In yet another twist on this theme, Bundy suggested that if the United States had admitted respected neutral observers to the successful atomic test shot at Alamogordo, New Mexico, they might have provided a convincing and effective warning to the Japanese about the power of the bomb. While a number of scholars reopened questions about alternatives to the bomb and faulted the Truman administration for not pursuing them, Akira Iriye argued that the Japanese government shared the blame for needlessly extending the war. He was particularly critical of Japanese leaders for sending peace feelers to the Soviet Union rather than attempting to deal directly with the United States.[22]

Barton Bernstein took issue with those who argued that the war could have ended as soon or even sooner than it did without using the bomb. He suggested that none of the alternatives available to U.S. policymakers – demonstrating the bomb in an isolated location, modifying the unconditional surrender demand, exploring the initiatives of Japanese peace feelers, waiting for Soviet entry into the Asian war, or continuing the naval blockade and intensifying conventional bombing – would have brought the war to a conclusion as rapidly as dropping the bomb. He doubted that any of the alternatives, taken alone, would have been sufficient to force a prompt Japanese surrender. Bernstein concluded that it seems "very likely, though certainly not definite" that a combination of alternatives would have ended the war before the planned invasion of Kyushu on 1 November 1945. Bernstein's disagreement with other scholars over the role of the bomb in determining how soon the war came to a close was necessarily speculative, and the question is unlikely to reach a definitive resolution. But it reopened a historiographical debate that had seemed to be settled, at least among scholars writing on the subject in the 1980s, who had suggested that the bomb was not necessary to end the war as quickly as possible.[23]

22 McGeorge Bundy, *Danger and Survival: Choices about the Bomb in the First Fifty Years* (New York, 1988); Akira Iriye, *Power and Culture: The Japanese-American War, 1941–1945* (Cambridge, MA, 1981).

23 Barton J. Bernstein, "Understanding the Atomic Bomb and the Japanese Surrender: Missed Opportunities, Little-Known Near Disasters, and Modern Memory," *Diplomatic History* 19 (Spring 1995): 227–73.

Key issues in this resurrected debate, particularly how American policymakers regarded the need for the planned invasion of Kyushu and the likelihood of an imminent Japanese surrender on the eve of Hiroshima, flared into a dispute between Bernstein on the one hand and Gar Alperovitz and Robert Messer on the other. In an article he published in 1991 on General Marshall's consideration of using tactical nuclear weapons as a part of the assault on Kyushu, Bernstein cautioned that Marshall's thinking "should give sober pause to analysts who conclude that American leaders believed that Japan was very near surrender before Hiroshima, and that these men dropped the bomb primarily to intimidate the Soviets." Alperovitz and Messer responded by insisting that in the minds of key U.S. officials, a Soviet invasion of Manchuria would probably eliminate the need for an American invasion of Japan. They also asserted that Truman's diary and letters indicated that he felt the same way. Bernstein remained unconvinced, and the disagreement reached a historiographical apogee of sorts by hinging in part on the possible placement of a comma in minutes of a meeting. Although the issue was not resolved with the evidence presented, its importance was sharply drawn by the exchange.[24]

24 Barton J. Bernstein, "Eclipsed by Hiroshima and Nagasaki: Early Thinking About Tactical Nuclear Weapons," *International Security* 15 (Spring 1991): 149–73; Gar Alperovitz and Robert Messer and Barton J. Bernstein, "Correspondence: Marshall, Truman, and the Decision to Use the Bomb," ibid. 16 (Winter 1991–92): 204–21.

Bernstein's argument received backing from Marc Gallicchio, who also concluded that Marshall's interest in tactical nuclear weapons even after Nagasaki indicated that he did not think that the atomic bombs would necessarily end the war and that an invasion might still be required. See Gallicchio, "After Nagasaki: General Marshall's Plan for Tactical Nuclear Weapons in Japan," *Prologue* 23 (Winter 1991): 396–404. The Alperovitz-Messer view was seconded in Kai Bird's biography of Stimson aide John J. McCloy. Bird maintained that McCloy and other American officials had concluded by the early summer of 1945 that an American invasion of Japan would not be necessary and that the war was virtually over. See Bird, *The Chairman: John J. McCloy, The Making of the American Establishment* (New York, 1992). The Alperovitz-Messer argument also won some indirect support in an article by Robert A. Pape, who contended that the atomic bombs were not decisive in causing the Japanese surrender. Rather, he cited the naval interdiction of Japan and the Soviet attack in Manchuria as the major considerations in persuading Japanese military leaders that they could not effectively resist a U.S. invasion of their homeland. This suggests that the war would have ended just as soon without using the bomb. But Pape did not deal with the perceptions of American leaders, and his article was too derivative and speculative to be conclusive. See Pape, "Why Japan Surrendered," *International Security* 18 (Fall 1993): 154–201.

One other issue that recent scholarship has revisited is whether or not the United States practiced atomic diplomacy. This is primarily a postwar question, and a discussion of the extent to which the Truman administration used its atomic monopoly for diplomatic purposes after Hiroshima extends far beyond the scope of this essay. But Melvyn P. Leffler suggested that even before the end of the war, the possession of the bomb influenced American foreign policy on one important matter. He argued that after learning about the power of the bomb, the administration not only lost interest in Soviet entry into the Asian war but also repudiated the sections of the Yalta agreement dealing with the Far East. "At the time of Japan's surrender," he wrote, "Stalin had more reason to question the American desire to comply with Yalta's Far East provisions than vice versa."[25]

Although recent analyses of the use of the bomb have raised probing questions, the answers they provided have often been tentative and suggestive. They have unsettled the historiography of the subject without redefining it or offering new directions that might clarify outstanding issues. Leon V. Sigal's *Fighting to a Finish*, however, published in 1988, did a little of both. By looking at the decision to drop the bomb from the perspective of bureaucratic politics, Sigal presented answers to some of the questions that had puzzled other scholars. His systematic discussion of bureaucratic factors produced some fresh insights into the use of the bomb.

Sigal suggested that the reason that Japanese leaders did not make direct contact with the United States, a point that Iriye raised, was that bitter factional rivalry prevented it. Army opposition foreclosed direct peace initiatives, so Japanese leaders seeking to end the war were limited to clandestine approaches in Moscow. "It was," Sigal wrote, "Moscow or nowhere for Japan's diplomats." The same kind of bureaucratic forces often, but not always, influenced American actions.

Sigal portrayed top American officials as largely powerless, ineffective, and ill-informed. Truman was too inexperienced and

25 Melvyn P. Leffler, "From Accommodation to Containment: The United States and the Far East Provisions of the Yalta Agreements," in *Yalta: Un Mito Che Resiste* [Yalta: A myth that endures], ed. Paola Brunda Olla (Rome, 1989).

insulated to grasp fully what was going on; his de facto authority was limited to halting the use of the bomb if he chose. But he had no compelling reason to do so. The key decisions on targeting and timing were made not by the president or the secretary of war but by General Leslie R. Groves and other military commanders. Groves, especially, was anxious to justify the effort and the expenditures of the Manhattan Project, and he avoided outlining alternatives to Truman that could change existing plans and frustrate his objectives. Thus, the bomb fell more because of bureaucratic imperatives than because of carefully considered questions of national interest. Weighing alternatives to bombing Japanese cities or seeking viable ways to reach Japanese peace advocates never received attentive review by the president or his closest advisers.[26]

Sigal's interpretation offered plausible answers to some important questions. It explained why the Japanese were so circumspect in their peace initiatives, why the United States did not pursue alternatives to the bomb, and why Truman often seemed so confused about issues relating to the bomb. Although much of the information he presented was well known, he offered a new and useful interpretive framework for it. But his interpretation was hardly definitive. It failed to show why Truman and other top policymakers did not act to assert greater control over decisions about the bomb or to overrule their subordinates. The ultimate authority remained at the top; historians still need to sort out what was critical and what was not in the thinking of key officials.

Careful scholarly treatment of the records and manuscripts opened over the past few years has greatly enhanced our understanding of why the Truman administration used atomic weapons against Japan. Experts continue to disagree on some issues, but critical questions have been answered. The consensus among scholars is that the bomb was not needed to avoid an invasion of Japan and to end the war within a relatively short time. It is clear that alternatives to the bomb existed and that Truman and his

26 Leon V. Sigal, *Fighting to a Finish: The Politics of War Termination in the United States and Japan, 1945* (Ithaca, 1988).

advisers knew it. Furthermore, most scholars, at least in retrospect, regard an invasion as a remote possibility. Whether the bomb shortened the war and saved lives among those who were fighting in the Pacific is much more difficult to ascertain. Some analysts have argued that the war would have ended just as soon, or even sooner, if American leaders had pursued available alternatives, but this is speculative and a matter of continuing debate. It is certain that the hoary claim that the bomb prevented a half million or more American combat deaths cannot be supported with available evidence. The issue of whether the use of the bomb was justified if it spared far fewer American lives belongs more in the realm of philosophy than history. But there are tantalizing hints that Truman had some unacknowledged doubts about the morality of his decision.

Since the United States did not drop the bomb to save hundreds of thousands of American lives, as policymakers later claimed, the key question and the source of most of the historiographical debate is why the bomb was used. No scholar of the subject accepts in unadulterated form Alperovitz's argument that political considerations dictated the decision. But nearly all students of the events leading to Hiroshima agree that, in addition to viewing it as the means to end the war quickly, the political implications of the bomb figured in the administration's deliberations. The consensus of the mid-1970s, which held that the bomb was used primarily for military reasons and secondarily for diplomatic ones, continues to prevail. It has been challenged and reassessed in some of its specific points. But the central theme in the consensus that has existed for the past two decades – that U.S. officials always assumed that the bomb would be used and saw no reason not to use it once it became available – remains intact. There were no moral, military, diplomatic, or bureaucratic considerations that carried enough weight to deter dropping the bomb and gaining its projected military and diplomatic benefits.

Since the mid-1970s, when the contention between traditional and revisionist views of why the United States used the bomb was largely resolved, scholarship on the subject has not divided into discrete or discernible schools of interpretation. Within the consensus that currently prevails, there is ample room for disagreement and differing emphases. And not all recent scholarship falls within the bounds of even such a broadly defined consensus. The most prominent dissent appeared in David McCullough's Pulitzer prize-winning biography of Truman. McCullough's presentation of the decision to use the bomb was a throwback to Stimson's *Harper's* article; he restated the traditional interpretation by arguing that Truman faced a stark choice between dropping the bomb and ordering an invasion. He added that by opting for the bomb the president saved large numbers of American lives, perhaps as many as one million. McCullough rejected the scholarship that took issue with this conclusion, and, if his bibliography is a fair guide, simply ignored most of it. His best-selling book was not only a strong reassertion of the rationale advanced by former policymakers but also, in terms of reinforcing popular views of their decision, almost certainly the most influential of recent studies.[27]

From quite a different perspective, Gar Alperovitz also remained outside of the prevailing consensus. In a series of articles he continued to insist that political considerations rather than military needs were the keys to explaining Truman's use of the bomb. The articles presented a preview of what promised to be a major new book, scheduled for publication in mid-1995, in which Alperovitz drew on important new sources to support his position. The appearance of the book seems likely to add new fuel to the historiographical controversy and help prompt careful reexamination of the developments and decisions of the summer of 1945.[28]

As the debate over the decision to drop the bomb continues, several issues merit more attention than they have received. One concerns the meaning of the test explosion of the first nuclear device (it was not, strictly speaking, a bomb) at Alamogordo. The consequences of the Trinity shot in symbolic and scientific terms are clear enough, but its significance for policy is less so. The test was made to prove the design of a weapon fueled with plutonium and detonated by an intricate system of implosion, which was

27 David McCullough, *Truman* (New York, 1992).

28 In addition to Alperovitz's publications cited above see his articles in the *Wall Street Journal*, 13 September 1994, and the *Washington Post*, 16 October 1994. For a response to Alperovitz and a preview of a rekindled historiographical debate see an essay by Robert Newman, *Washington Post*, 30 November 1994.

one of two different bombs being built in Los Alamos. The effectiveness of this method was in doubt until the experimental explosion lighted the New Mexico sky. But the atomic scientists were much more certain that the other design, a gun-type method in which one subcritical mass of highly enriched uranium-235 was fired at another, would succeed. Groves told Truman in their first meeting about the Manhattan Project in April 1945 that the uranium bomb would be ready without requiring a test around 1 August, and despite some qualms, scientists remained confident that it would work. Their confidence was justified – it was a uranium bomb that destroyed Hiroshima. This suggests that the Trinity test, for all its symbolic meaning, need not have been crucial to policymaking.

If Truman and his advisers realized during the summer of 1945 that the uranium bomb was almost ready and almost certain to work, it is curious that they reacted with so much surprise and elation to the news of the Trinity shot. If they did not understand that they would soon have an atomic bomb no matter what happened at Alamogordo, it suggests that they grasped or remembered little of what they were told about the details of the bomb project. Part of the explanation is that policymakers did not want to rely on the bomb until it definitely had proven to be successful, and they were unwilling to believe that it would make a major difference to them until they were shown what it could do. But they seemed to have little awareness that two types of bombs were being built. Even Stimson, the best-informed and most reflective senior official on matters regarding the bomb, appeared to think in terms of a single weapon that had to be tested at Alamogordo.[29] The issue is not one of transcending importance, but it could help to clarify the significance that Truman and his advisers attached to the bomb and its role in their planning. It might in that way resolve some of the contradictions and apparent confusion in Truman's diary.

The contradictions and confusion in Truman's notes and letters and in other sources have obscured another issue of importance

29 Sherwin, *A World Destroyed*, 3–6; Henry L. Stimson and McGeorge Bundy, *On Active Service in Peace and War* (New York, 1948), 618, 637.

in understanding the decision to use the bomb: Did leading American policymakers regard an invasion of Japan as likely or inevitable without the bomb? Scholars who have studied the end of the Pacific war have certainly not ignored the planning for an invasion. Indeed, many recent publications, including those of Alperovitz and Messer, Skates, Bird, Pape, Sherwin, Miles, and, with conditions, Bernstein, have concluded that the likelihood of an invasion of Japan was small. But the question of what policymakers believed at the time, before authorizing the use of atomic weapons, is more problematic. The debate between Bernstein on the one hand and Alperovitz and Messer on the other pointed out the uncertainties surrounding this issue. How much reliance can scholars place, for example, in Truman's diary and letters? Were they random and thoughtless jottings that captured the president's mood more accurately than factual information? Or were they based on reports and assessments that Truman had received from key advisers? If senior officials viewed an invasion as likely, or at least potentially necessary, to end the war, the case for the use of the bomb for military purposes is substantially strengthened, even if the number of lives saved was far less than several hundred thousand. If top American leaders regarded an invasion as unlikely, the political dimensions of the decision take on much greater significance. Even if Truman was confident that Japan was on the verge of surrender in early August 1945, however, it does not necessarily follow that he would have refrained from using the bomb as a means to end the war at the earliest possible moment – for military reasons. The outcome of scholarly investigation and debate on this issue is vital to a full understanding of the complex considerations that led to the atomic bombings.

Another subject that could benefit from further study is the role of scientists in the Manhattan Project. The ideas and activities of the atomic scientists, individually and corporately, have hardly suffered from neglect. Several scholars offered detailed accounts, particularly of the dissenting opinions of some of the Chicago scientists who wanted alternatives to the bomb explored and an approach to the Soviets seriously considered. William Lanouette provided a portrait of, arguably, the most engaging and eccentric of the atomic scientists, Leo Szilard, who was particularly outspoken in presenting his own ideas. The concerns of the scientists had no discernible impact on policy, which has led some scholars to reproach policymakers for failing to heed the warnings of the experts and others to chide the scientists for failing to press their views more effectively.[30]

Richard Rhodes, Peter Wyden, and Joseph Rotblat, a scientist who left Los Alamos in 1944 after learning that Nazi Germany had no atomic bomb, critically scrutinized the activities of the atomic scientists and raised, implicitly and explicitly, a number of difficult but important questions. What were the motivations of atomic scientists in building the bomb? Was their quest to prove their theories about the atom socially and politically irresponsible? Did they fail to provide moral leadership commensurate with their scientific leadership? What precisely was the relationship between the policies being framed in Washington and the process of building the bomb in Los Alamos? What, if any, were the political and moral obligations of the scientists involved in the bomb project? Were atomic scientists sedated by an assumption that their spokesmen or political leaders would have the foresight, wisdom, and power to control atomic energy once it became a reality?[31]

Another topic that deserves further attention is the role of the Russian bomb project in Soviet-American relations at the close of the war. David Holloway made a major contribution on this subject in his book *Stalin and the Bomb*. Even with unprecedented access to individuals who participated in the Soviet atomic program and sources that supplied a wealth of new information,

30 William Lanouette with Bela Silard, *Genius in the Shadows: A Biography of Leo Szilard, The Man Behind the Bomb* (New York, 1992). Alice Kimball Smith, *A Peril and a Hope: The Scientists' Movement in America, 1945–1947* (Chicago, 1965), portrayed the views of dissenting scientists sympathetically. Brian Loring Villa chided them for waiting too long to try to register their doubts about using the bomb with policymakers. See "A Confusion of Signals: James Franck, the Chicago Scientists, and Early Efforts to Stop the Bomb," *Bulletin of the Atomic Scientists* 31 (December 1975): 36–43.

31 Rhodes. *The Making of the Atomic Bomb*; Wyden, *Day One*; and Joseph Rotblat, "Leaving the Bomb Project," *Bulletin of the Atomic Scientists* 41 (August 1985): 16–19. For other useful discussions of the views of scientists see Martin J. Sherwin, "How Well They Meant," Victor F. Weisskopf, "Looking Back on Los Alamos," Robert R. Wilson, "Niels Bohr and the Young Scientists," and Rudolf Peierls, "Reflections of a British Participant," in ibid., 9–15, 20–29.

he regarded his findings as incomplete. Soviet records of potentially monumental importance remain out of the reach of scholars. Nevertheless, Holloway provided the fullest and richest account of the Soviet bomb project. He concluded that although Stalin had authorized the effort to build the bomb during the war, he did not recognize its political implications until after Hiroshima. At that point, he gave the bomb project top priority. Holloway suggested that, whatever Truman's motives were in dropping the bomb, Stalin viewed it as an anti-Soviet action that seriously distorted the balance of power. Therefore, attempts to achieve an American-Soviet agreement on nuclear arms control when only the United States had the bomb were doomed to failure.[32]

Walter A. McDougall offered a similar view on the question of whether Roosevelt and Truman could have done more to prevent a nuclear arms race. In a book on the space race, he described the Soviet Union as the original "technocracy," a nation in which technology was "a cold tool of the state." In a brief discussion of the Soviet atomic project, McDougall suggested that the bomb was an inevitable product of the Soviet system. His findings, along with those of Holloway, make clear that the debate over how the use of the bomb affected Soviet-American relations must be carefully and critically evaluated. If the Soviets were immutably committed to developing nuclear weapons, an attempt on the part of the United States to practice atomic diplomacy would have made little or no difference in their determination to build the bomb, though it might have in the urgency with which they proceeded and in their diplomatic posture. McGeorge Bundy added another perspective to this subject by submitting that even though Stalin's decision to build the bomb was irreversible, he was not unalterably opposed to negotiation of atomic issues. But Bundy provided little evidence to support his view that a sincere and unqualified diplomatic approach to the Soviets might have been fruitful, and Holloway took a quite different position. In any event, the issue of atomic diplomacy will remain open until a

32 David Holloway, *Stalin and the Bomb: The Soviet Union and Atomic Energy, 1939–1956* (New Haven, 1994).

more complete picture of Soviet atomic policies and progress emerges.[33]

The latest literature on the decision to use the atomic bomb has expanded and enriched our knowledge while at the same time raising new questions. The consensus that emerged in the mid-1970s still prevails, but it has been and surely will continue to be tested and reappraised. The events that led to Hiroshima are so innately interesting, so vital to understanding subsequent developments, so politically and morally ambiguous, and so much a part of popular mythology that it seems certain that they will perpetually occupy the attention of and stir discord among scholars of World War II and the nuclear age.

33 Walter A. McDougall, . . . *The Heavens and the Earth: A Political History of the Space Age* (New York, 1985); Bundy, *Danger and Survival*, 179–82.

9

Origins of the Cold War in Europe and the Near East: Recent Historiography and the National Security Imperative

HOWARD JONES
AND RANDALL B. WOODS

This essay examines materials published during the last decade or so on the origins of the Cold War in Europe and the Near East, with the goal of determining if something like a synthesis is emerging on the subject. Historians of America's foreign relations, particularly those of us writing on the Cold War, have struggled long and hard to forge a synthesis that integrates the domestic and international forces underlying American diplomacy. The results have not been encouraging, and there is even the possibility that such a grand, all-encompassing conceptual device does not exist.

Our analysis of recent works on the Cold War, however, does reveal a number of common factors that suggest if not a synthesis at least a dominant approach based on the national security imperative.[1] In other words, the bulk of this work demonstrates a

1 For the theme of national security see Daniel Yergin, *Shattered Peace: The Origins of the Cold War and the National Security State*, rev. ed. (New York, 1990); John Lewis Gaddis, *Strategies of Containment: A Critical Appraisal of Postwar American National Security Policy* (New York, 1982); Melvyn P. Leffler, "The American Conception of National Security and the Beginnings of the Cold War, 1945–48," *American Historical Review* 89 (April 1984): 346–81, plus comments by John Lewis Gaddis, ibid., 382–85, and Bruce R. Kuniholm, ibid., 385–90, followed by Leffler's reply, ibid., 391–400; Melvyn P. Leffler, "National Security," in "A Round Table: Explaining the History of American Foreign Relations," *Journal of American History* 77 (June 1990): 143–51; idem, *A Preponderance of Power: National Security, the Truman Administration, and the Cold War* (Stanford, 1992); and David F. Trask, "Past and Future of National Security History," SHAFR *Newsletter* 19 (March 1988): 6–16. See also Carl N. Degler, "Remaking American History," *Journal of American History* 67

pervasive concern with the way that policymakers perceived global threats to the nation's security and how they responded to those threats. In the best of this work, national security is defined broadly enough to show the relation between domestic and foreign elements affecting a country's safety and to include the social, economic, political, and military considerations that influence strategy, as well as the important and often subtle cross-cultural exchanges and the interworkings of the public and private sectors of society. Defined in this manner, the concept of national security encompasses not only the varied reasoned responses to danger but also those wide-ranging irrational impulses resulting from exaggerated or erroneous perceptions and from an often-obsessive concern with the credibility of the country's commitments abroad. Applied across national frontiers, the same concept can advance the cause of international history and enable us to avoid what Geir Lundestad has called the "moralism, presentism, exceptionalism, provincialism, and other extravagances" that have often permeated our work as American historians.[2]

(June 1980): 20. Joan Hoff-Wilson considers a consensus on the Cold War highly unlikely during this generation and argues that the real problem in history is an "ethical complacency" in our writing that is exacerbated by difficulties in accessing documents and by increasingly sophisticated methodology. See her article, "The Future of American Diplomatic History," SHAFR *Newsletter* 16 (June 1985): 19. For writings before the late 1970s see J. Samuel Walker, "Historians and Cold War Origins: The New Consensus," in *American Foreign Relations: A Historiographical Review*, ed. Gerald K. Haines and J. Samuel Walker (Westport, 1981), 207–36. See also Geir Lundestad, *America, Scandinavia, and the Cold War, 1945–1949* (New York, 1980), chap. 1.

2 Geir Lundestad, "Moralism, Presentism, Exceptionalism, Provincialism, and Other Extravagances in American Writings on the Early Cold War Years," *Diplomatic History* 13 (Fall 1989): 527–45. See also idem, *The American "Empire" and Other Studies of U.S. Foreign Policy in a Comparative Perspective* (Oxford, England, and Oslo, Norway, 1990), chap. 1. See Richard W. Leopold, "The History of United States Foreign Policy: Past, Present, and Future," in *The Future of History*, ed. Charles F. Delzell (Nashville, 1977), 242; "A Round Table: Explaining the History of American Foreign Relations," *Journal of American History* 77 (June 1990): 93–180; Thomas G. Paterson, "Introduction," ibid., 93, 96–98; idem, "Defining and Doing the History of American Foreign Relations: A Primer," 586–87, 590–91, in "Writing the History of U.S. Foreign Relations: A Symposium," *Diplomatic History* 14 (Fall 1990): 553–605. See also Knud Krakau, "American Foreign Relations: A National Style?" ibid. 8 (Summer 1984): 255; and Michael H. Hunt, *Ideology and U.S. Foreign Policy* (New Haven, 1987), 17–18. For a convenient collection of essays highlighting the different approaches to studying foreign relations see Michael J. Hogan and Thomas G. Paterson, eds., *Explaining the History of American Foreign Relations* (New York, 1991). Michael H. Hunt has declared that "the long crisis of confidence" in the field of American

Before the mid-1970s, most of the literature on the origins of the Cold War could be broken into two broad schools,[3] "Orthodox" or "Traditional,"[4] on one hand, and "Revisionist" or "New Left," on the other,[5] both of which concentrated heavily on the

foreign relations is coming to an end. Recent works, he argues, have demonstrated the interdependence and complementary nature of various approaches to the subject that include not only the foreign policy of the American state but also the impact of domestic considerations on the making of foreign policy and the relationship of policymaking to the international sphere. See "The Long Crisis in U.S. Diplomatic History: Coming to Closure," in this volume.

3 Division into only two schools will not satisfy many historians. Differences, of course, existed among historians within each school, underlining the complexities involved in interpreting the Cold War. See Walker "Historians and Cold War Origins," 207–12. David S. Patterson identifies four schools: the "conventional, liberal-realist, moderate revisionist, and radical (or New Left revisionist)." See his "What's Wrong (and Right) with American Diplomatic History? A Diagnosis and Prescription," SHAFR *Newsletter* 9 (September 1978): 4. Jerald A. Combs has delineated six schools: "right-wing idealists," "hard realists," "soft or restrained realists," "liberal moralists," "moderate revisionists," and "radical revisionists." See his "Cold War Historiography: An Alternative to John Gaddis's Post-Revisionism," ibid. 15 (June 1984): 11–16. For an even longer list of labels that, as the author suggests, approaches the absurd, see Hoff-Wilson, "Future of American Diplomatic History," 15.

4 Orthodox histories include Arthur M. Schlesinger, Jr., "Origins of the Cold War," *Foreign Affairs* 46 (October 1967): 22–52; Herbert Feis, *From Trust to Terror: The Onset of the Cold War, 1945–1950* (New York, 1970); Adam B. Ulam, *The Rivals: America and Russia since World War II* (New York, 1971); Robert J. Maddox, *The New Left and the Origins of the Cold War* (Princeton, 1973); and Robert H. Ferrell, "Truman Foreign Policy: A Traditionalist View," in *The Truman Period as a Research Field: A Reappraisal, 1972*, ed. Richard S. Kirkendall (Columbia, MO, 1974), 11–45.

5 Revisionist works include William Appleman Williams, *The Tragedy of American Diplomacy*, rev. ed. (New York, 1972); D. F. Fleming, *The Cold War and Its Origins, 1917–1960*, 2 vols. (Garden City, 1961); Gar Alperovitz, *Atomic Diplomacy: Hiroshima and Potsdam: The Use of the Atomic Bomb and the American Confrontation with Soviet Power* (New York, 1965); David Horowitz, *The Free World Colossus: A Critique of American Foreign Policy in the Cold War*, rev. ed. (New York, 1971); Walter LaFeber, *America, Russia, and the Cold War, 1945–1992*, 7th ed. (New York, 1993); Gabriel Kolko, *The Politics of War: The World and United States Foreign Policy, 1943–1945* (New York, 1968); Joyce and Gabriel Kolko, *The Limits of Power: The World and United States Foreign Policy, 1945–1954* (New York, 1972); Lloyd C. Gardner, *Architects of Illusion: Men and Ideas in American Foreign Policy, 1941–1949* (Chicago, 1970); Barton J. Bernstein, "American Foreign Policy and the Origins of the Cold War," in *Politics and Policies of the Truman Administration*, ed. Bernstein (Chicago, 1970), 15–77; and Thomas J. McCormick, *America's Half-Century: United States Foreign Policy in the Cold War* (Baltimore, 1989). Thomas G. Paterson, author of a widely used synthesis of the Cold War published more than a decade ago, has been referred to as a "soft revisionist." Though highlighting American exceptionalism, he deemphasizes economic considerations and focuses on the "conflict-ridden" post-war international system, the opposing ideologies and felt needs that led to competing spheres of influence, the differing tactics and conduct used in diplomacy, and the contrasting styles of Presidents Franklin D. Roosevelt and Harry S. Truman. Paterson is not stridently accusatory in tone and recognizes the complexities involved in examining the origins of the Cold War. See *On Every Front: The Making of the Cold War* (New York, 1979), x. Paterson has extensively revised this work to include material on the

issue of which superpower was primarily responsible for that epic conflict. In the aftermath of a visceral controversy between these two groups, most recent historians have avoided value-laden judgments and are now seeking an *understanding* of what happened and why. Rather than viewing the Cold War as a Manichean struggle between the forces of monopoly capitalism and Communist totalitarianism, increasing numbers of historians are focusing on key issues of the period and, using the wisdom afforded by hindsight, offering a critical perspective that heeds Richard Hofstadter's admonition against reducing history's complexity to simplicity.[6]

It seems safe to argue that not only did both the Soviet Union and the United States contribute to the beginnings of the Cold War but that other nations and other considerations played a role as well. The Iranian crisis of 1945–46 provides a revealing example. Stephen L. McFarland demonstrates how Iran's leaders indirectly encouraged the Cold War by playing off first the British against the Soviets and then the Americans against the Soviets, all in an effort to achieve Iranian independence. Mark Hamilton Lytle reaches similar conclusions and believes that the ensuing crisis convinced the State Department that Soviet Premier Josef Stalin intended to absorb Iran. The result was the first open encounter between the United States and the Soviet Union. American idealists in the State Department, Lytle claims, wanted to make Iran a model for democracy, while the War Department considered postwar Iran to be crucial to U.S. control of Persian Gulf oil. Neither division of government, he contends, questioned whether the Soviets actually intended to expand into the region, and both consequently overreacted to the perceived danger.[7]

end of the Cold War. See *On Every Front: The Making and Unmaking of the Cold War* (New York, 1993). See also John Lewis Gaddis, *The United States and the End of the Cold War* (New York, 1992). The negative impact of the Cold War on domestic America becomes plain in Edward Pessen, *Losing Our Souls: The American Experience in the Cold War* (Chicago, 1993).

6 Richard Hofstadter, *The Progressive Historians: Turner, Beard, Parrington* (New York, 1968), 442–43.

7 Stephen L. McFarland, "A Peripheral View of the Origins of the Cold War: The Crises in Iran, 1941–47," *Diplomatic History* 4 (Fall 1980): 333–51; Mark Hamilton Lytle, *The Origins of the Iranian-American Alliance, 1941–1953* (New York, 1987), xvi–xix, 138–40, 150–52, 216. Another recent study of the Iranian issue by James F. Goode does not focus on the origins of the Cold War but shows that growing bipolar tensions at first caused the Truman administration to concentrate on Europe and Asia

Much recent writing on the origins of the Cold War has grown out of the mixed reaction to John Lewis Gaddis's pronouncement in the early 1980s that a "post-revisionist synthesis" had begun to emerge. Critics complained that postrevisionism was merely orthodoxy under a new name because it still held the Soviet Union primarily accountable for the Cold War while attempting to excuse America's expansionist impulse. Gaddis responded by insisting that postrevisionism had gone "beyond both orthodoxy and revisionism" to incorporate the best from each camp and to point the way to the formation of a new consensus built upon a combination of the two.[8] But Gaddis was never able to describe the new synthesis satisfactorily, and thus indirectly demonstrated that much work lay ahead.

Several features of the new scholarship have now become clear. For instance, leaders in Washington were indeed apprehensive over the prospect of a postwar economic depression. But the evidence also shows that their apprehension was just one part of a general concern for national security and that a wide disparity of opinion existed within business and financial circles about how to avert a potentially disastrous economic downturn. As Joan Hoff has argued, and as Forrest C. Pogue has written about policymaking under Secretary of State George C. Marshall, the United States used economic power as an instrument for achieving political as well as economic objectives at home and abroad.

and leave Iran under British guardianship. By 1951, however, the British position in the Middle East had weakened and Washington's relations with the Iranians sharply deteriorated as it supported the shah's dictatorial rule in an effort to maintain order and undercut communism. See *The United States and Iran, 1946–51: The Diplomacy of Neglect* (New York, 1989), viii. See also James A. Bill's survey beginning with the 1940s, *The Eagle and the Lion: The Tragedy of American-Iranian Relations* (New Haven, 1988). French postwar policy also contributed to the heightened Cold War. Irwin M. Wall demonstrates how leaders in Paris exploited American fears of communism to secure assistance. See his study, *The United States and the Making of Postwar France, 1945–1954* (New York, 1991).

8 John Lewis Gaddis, "The Emerging Post-Revisionist Synthesis on the Origins of the Cold War," *Diplomatic History* 7 (Summer 1983): 171–90, quotes on pp. 172, 180, 183. In a followup section entitled, "Responses to John Lewis Gaddis, 'The Emerging Post-Revisionist Synthesis on the Origins of the Cold War,'" see positive responses by Lawrence S. Kaplan, ibid., 194–97, and Bruce R. Kuniholm, ibid., 201–4. For negative responses see Lloyd C. Gardner, ibid., 191–93, Warren F. Kimball, ibid., 198–200, and Combs, "Cold War Historiography," 9–19. Walker saw a postrevisionist synthesis well under way by 1981. See his "Historians and Cold War Origins," 207.

Both Mark A. Stoler's book on Marshall and Randall B. Woods's recent study of postwar Anglo-American relations assert that British and American diplomacy during and immediately after World War II focused on economic control of the non-Communist world rather than on how best to thwart Soviet ambitions. The Atlantic nations worked out a commercial and financial rapprochement only when a variety of factors converged to convince the Truman administration that Britain and the United States shared a community of interests in the eastern Mediterranean and that the Soviet Union posed a threat to those interests. Indeed, for a time it appeared that Washington's efforts to force Britain to accept a flawed multilateralism would undermine the latter's ability to restrain Stalin.[9]

James L. Gormly and Robert A. Pollard readily admit that the United States sought security by pushing for trade liberalization. The resulting international prosperity and political harmony, policymakers believed, would inevitably diminish the chances for war. Western economic interdependence, Pollard insists, was the intended outcome of the Bretton Woods financial agreements, the Marshall Plan, and postwar rearmament efforts. But the goal of America's containment policy was the preservation of regional economic organizations rather than the supplanting of socialism with capitalism throughout the world.[10]

9 Gaddis, "Emerging Post-Revisionist Synthesis," 173–75; Joan Hoff-Wilson, "Responses to Charles S. Maier, 'Marking Time: The Historiography of International Relations'" (Symposium), *Diplomatic History* 5 (Fall 1981): 379; Forrest C. Pogue, *George C. Marshall: Statesman, 1945–1959* (New York, 1987), 201, 204; Mark A. Stoler, *George C. Marshall: Soldier-Statesman of the American Century* (Boston, 1989), 158, 166–67; Randall B. Woods, *A Changing of the Guard: Anglo-American Relations, 1941–1946* (Chapel Hill, 1990), x, 1–8, 397–98.

10 James L. Gormly, *The Collapse of the Grand Alliance, 1945–1948* (Baton Rouge, 1987), 8–9, 155; Robert A. Pollard, "Economic Security and the Origins of the Cold War: Bretton Woods, the Marshall Plan, and American Rearmament, 1944–50," *Diplomatic History* 9 (Summer 1985): 271–89; idem, *Economic Security and the Origins of the Cold War, 1945–1950* (New York, 1985), ix–x, 3–4, 9, 247–49, 253. See also Donald R. McCoy, *The Presidency of Harry S. Truman* (Lawrence, 1984), 125–29. Lloyd C. Gardner shows how America's desire for an open commercial world and liberal ideas in the postwar world came into conflict with Churchill's determination to preserve the British Empire. See *Spheres of Influence: The Great Powers Partition Europe, from Munich to Yalta* (Chicago, 1993). For a critical work that is revisionist in tone see William E. Pemberton, *Harry S. Truman: Fair Dealer & Cold Warrior* (Boston, 1989). Public opinion and congressional attitudes, according to John Lewis Gaddis's earlier study, affected Truman's policy more than economic

Many new studies demonstrate that the Truman administration did indeed seek to spread American economic and political principles abroad but question whether its overriding motive was national self-aggrandizement and whether America's postwar search for order left no room for Soviet security. Eduard Mark argues that the United States by 1945 opposed "exclusive" Soviet spheres of influence in Eastern Europe but was willing to recognize "open" spheres that permitted smaller nations of the region to manage their domestic affairs while the Soviet Union controlled their foreign and defense policies. Lundestad admits to the usefulness of the two-sphere approach but insists that it does not adequately recognize that the acceptance of Soviet control in international affairs would probably also lead to its hegemony in domestic matters.[11]

Most recent works suggest, too, that American policymakers understood the strategic and economic aspects of postwar Eastern Europe and attempted to loosen the ties binding it to the Soviet Union, but that they made little headway in undermining Soviet control. Roberto G. Rabel insists that Truman and his

matters. See Gaddis, *The United States and the Origins of the Cold War, 1941–1947* (New York, 1972), 283, 315, 317–18, 351, 356, 360. Frank Ninkovich considers the open door construct a viable research tool only if it focuses on more than economic concerns. Indeed, he insists that in seeking an informal empire based on American cultural as well as commercial interests, the open door had an ideological basis in promoting peace through the avoidance of political or military involvement. Ninkovich observes that even though the outbreak of wars marked the failure of open door theory, it remains an important concept because it shows that political and economic interests were inseparable parts of the complex interplay of domestic elements on the international scene that together comprised culture. See "Ideology, the Open Door, and Foreign Policy," *Diplomatic History* 6 (Spring 1982): 186–92, 200, 208.

11 Gaddis, "Emerging Post-Revisionist Synthesis," 174–75; Eduard Mark, "American Policy toward Eastern Europe and the Origins of the Cold War, 1941–1946: An Alternative Interpretation," *Journal of American History* 68 (September 1981): 313–36; idem, "Charles E. Bohlen and the Acceptable Limits of Soviet Hegemony in Eastern Europe: A Memorandum of 18 October 1945," *Diplomatic History* 3 (Spring 1979): 201–13. Other historians agree that the United States resisted such closed spheres, particularly at Yalta. See Yergin, *Shattered Peace*, 42–68; Lundestad, *American "Empire,"* 169; Daniel F. Harrington, "Kennan, Bohlen, and the Riga Axioms," *Diplomatic History* 2 (Fall 1978): 423–37; Russell D. Buhite, *Decisions at Yalta: An Appraisal of Summit Diplomacy* (Wilmington, DE, 1986), 130–31; and Paterson, *On Every Front* (original ed.), chap. 3. For a critical review of Yergin's book see Carolyn Eisenberg, "Reflections on a Toothless Revisionism," *Diplomatic History* 2 (Summer 1978): 295–305. Lundestad also focuses on realpolitik at Yalta. See his *American "Empire,"* chap. 4. See also Diane S. Clemens, *Yalta* (New York, 1970).

advisers did, in fact, recognize limits on the capacity of the United States to determine Eastern European developments and yet acted decisively in the Yugoslav-Italian dispute over Trieste because that province lay outside of the Soviet sphere of influence as defined at Yalta. Poland, however, was an entirely different case. Richard C. Lukas argues that, even though the Truman administration recognized that its predecessor had conceded Poland to the forces of international communism, it nonetheless brought economic leverage to bear in an effort to establish American influence in that country. Means were unsuited to ends, however, and the United States emerged with an uncertain policy, one characteristic of U.S. relations with all of Eastern Europe, that deepened Soviet suspicions and guaranteed continuing Polish subjugation. Sheldon Anderson believes that the Truman administration overestimated the extent of Soviet economic control over Eastern Europe and failed to appreciate Poland's genuine interest in the Marshall Plan. Actually, Poland enjoyed enough economic latitude within Soviet restraints to export coal to Western Europe and was, in fact, partly responsible for the success of the American aid program. But the United States unwisely placed an embargo on Poland and thereby encouraged the economic partition of the Continent.[12]

As Mark S. Steinitz, Michael M. Boll, Stanley M. Max, and Henry W. Brands, Jr., have shown, America's policy toward Eastern Europe was neither consistently aggressive nor purely defensive. Often the two strains existed side by side and in conflict, thus undermining the notion that a single driving expansionist theme lay behind American foreign policy during the formative stages of the Cold War.[13]

12 Roberto G. Rabel, *Between East and West: Trieste, the United States, and the Cold War, 1941–1954* (Durham, 1988); Richard C. Lukas, *Bitter Legacy: Polish-American Relations in the Wake of World War II* (Lexington, KY, 1982), 1, 41, 136, 138; Roberto Rabel, "Prologue to Containment: The Truman Administration's Response to the Trieste Crisis of May 1945," *Diplomatic History* 10 (Spring 1986): 141–60; Sheldon Anderson, "Poland and the Marshall Plan, 1947–1949," ibid. 15 (Fall 1991): 473–94.

13 Mark S. Steinitz, "The U.S. Propaganda Effort in Czechoslovakia, 1945–48," *Diplomatic History* 6 (Fall 1982): 359–85; Michael M. Boll, "U.S. Plans for a Postwar Pro-Western Bulgaria: A Little-Known Wartime Initiative in Eastern Europe," ibid. 7 (Spring 1983): 117–38; idem, *Cold War in the Balkans: American Foreign Policy and the Emergence of Communist Bulgaria, 1943–1947* (Lexington, KY, 1984), vii,

A number of new studies have also established that several nations felt threatened by the Soviet Union and welcomed American intervention in Europe and the Near East. Geir Lundestad, Bruce R. Kuniholm, and Howard Jones have shown that rather than imposing its will on these regions, the United States was *invited* in by their leaders to extend economic and military assistance. Some of the regimes soliciting aid hoped to bring stability and ward off leftist insurrections or other troubles perceived as Soviet instigated. And not all of these regimes were autocratic and repressive. American policy toward the Near East, moreover, was more pragmatic and less rigidly anti-Communist than previously thought. In the case of Yugoslavia, Lorraine M. Lees and Brands show that the United States decided to assist Josip Broz Tito after he asked the West for economic assistance; the White House realized that, among other considerations, such a move would strengthen Tito's struggle for independence from Stalin while perhaps inducing the Yugoslav premier to cut off aid to the anti-government guerrillas in Greece.[14] Germany, too, according

1–4, 189–92; Stanley M. Max, "Cold War on the Danube: The Belgrade Conference of 1948 and Anglo-American Efforts to Reinternationalize the River," *Diplomatic History* 7 (Winter 1983): 57–77; idem, *The United States, Great Britain, and the Sovietization of Hungary, 1945–1948* (New York, 1985), 135, 137–38, 144; Henry W. Brands, Jr., "Redefining the Cold War: American Policy toward Yugoslavia, 1948–60," *Diplomatic History* 11 (Winter 1987): 41–53.

14 Geir Lundestad, "Empire by Invitation? The United States and Western Europe, 1945–1952," SHAFR *Newsletter* 15 (September 1984): 1–21 [also published under same title in *Journal of Peace Research* 23 (August 1986): 263–76]; idem, *America, Scandinavia, and Cold War*, 329–58; Bruce Robellet Kuniholm, *The Origins of the Cold War in the Near East: Great Power Conflict and Diplomacy in Iran, Turkey, and Greece* (Princeton, 1980); Howard Jones, *"A New Kind of War": America's Global Strategy and the Truman Doctrine in Greece* (New York, 1989). See also Gaddis, "Emerging Post-Revisionist Synthesis," 176–77, 181–82. As Lundestad also shows, the United States established the pattern for its own relative decline in world power by building an empire that overstretched Washington's capacities. See "Empire by Invitation," 16. On this point see also Paul Kennedy, *The Rise and Fall of the Great Powers: Economic Change and Military Conflict from 1500 to 2000* (New York, 1987), 514–35; and McCormick, *America's Half-Century*, 236–43. Lorraine M. Lees, "The American Decision to Assist Tito, 1948–1949," *Diplomatic History* 2 (Fall 1978): 407–22; H. W. Brands, *The Specter of Neutralism: The United States and the Emergence of the Third World, 1947–1960* (New York, 1989), 143–65. William Burr argues that the "empire by invitation" thesis does not work in France. In implementing the Marshall Plan in that country, the Truman administration used counterpart funds as leverage to push the French government to fight inflation, thereby demonstrating what Burr calls the "interrelated political-economic and strategic objectives" of the United States in Europe. See "Marshall Planners and the Politics of Empire: The United States and French Financial Policy, 1948," *Diplomatic History* 15 (Fall 1991): 495–522 (quote on p. 521).

to Thomas Alan Schwartz, saw a postoccupation American presence as the best defense against Soviet aggression as well as protection against subversive activity by both the Right and the Left. Further, as Peter G. Boyle, Terry H. Anderson, Robert M. Hathaway, Victor Rothwell, Fraser J. Harbutt, Martin H. Folly, Elisabeth Barker, and Randall B. Woods amply demonstrate, the British were the first to see a Soviet threat to the West and exerted pressure on the United States to realize that its national interest lay in accepting greater responsibility for protecting Western Europe from Soviet expansion. Finally, Alan Bullock shows in his study of British Foreign Secretary Ernest Bevin that the British impetus proved decisive in securing American involvement in the Marshall Plan and NATO as Stalin, in Harbutt's view, attempted to expand beyond his "protected sphere" of Eastern Europe.[15]

The central enigma in explaining the Cold War, according to Vojtech Mastny and William Taubman, continues to be Stalin. In

15 Thomas Alan Schwartz, *America's Germany: John J. McCloy and the Federal Republic of Germany* (Cambridge, MA, 1991), 299–300; Peter G. Boyle, "The British Foreign Office View of Soviet-American Relations, 1945–46," *Diplomatic History* 3 (Summer 1979): 307–20; Terry H. Anderson, *The United States, Great Britain, and the Cold War, 1944–1947* (Columbia, MO, 1981), 85, 108, 141–43, 176–84; Robert M. Hathaway, *Ambiguous Partnership: Britain and America, 1944–1947* (New York, 1981), 2, 50–53, 305; Victor Rothwell, *Britain and the Cold War, 1941–1947* (London, 1982); Fraser J. Harbutt, *The Iron Curtain: Churchill, America, and the Origins of the Cold War* (New York, 1986), 2 (quote), 283–85; Martin H. Folly, "Breaking the Vicious Circle: Britain, the United States, and the Genesis of the North Atlantic Treaty," *Diplomatic History* 12 (Winter 1988): 59–77; Elisabeth Barker, *The British between the Superpowers, 1945–50* (London, 1983), xi, 236–43; Woods, *Changing of Guard*; Alan Bullock, *Ernest Bevin: Foreign Secretary, 1945–1951* (New York, 1983), 116, 404–9, 582–85, 632–33, 655–56. See also Lawrence S. Kaplan, "Western Europe in 'The American Century': A Retrospective View," *Diplomatic History* 6 (Spring 1982): 120–21; Geoffrey Warner, "The Anglo-American Special Relationship," ibid. 13 (Fall 1989): 479–85; Henry Butterfield Ryan, *The Vision of Anglo-America: The US-UK Alliance and the Emerging Cold War, 1943–1946* (Cambridge, England, 1987), 2–7; Richard A. Best, *Co-operation with Like-Minded Peoples: British Influences on American Security Policy, 1945–1949* (New York, 1986); and Robin Edmonds, *Setting the Mould: The United States and Britain, 1945–1950* (New York, 1986). Edmonds, a British foreign service officer who was involved in many of the issues, used Public Record Office materials in characterizing the period as that of "confrontation" and "confusion." Ibid. 7. For a review of Harbutt, *The Iron Curtain*, see J. Samuel Walker, "The Beginning of the Cold War: Prize-Winning Perspectives," *Diplomatic History* 12 (Winter 1988): 95–101. Some American policymakers favored covert actions to undermine communism in postwar Europe. According to Sallie Pisani, the Marshall Plan was the Truman administration's first effort to combine secret economic help with secret political actions. See her study, *The CIA and the Marshall Plan* (Lawrence, 1991).

seeking his own nation's interests, the Soviet premier proved consistently opportunistic and suspicious of Western motives, thus encouraging the belief that the Soviets were not trustworthy. Mastny's reading of admittedly sparse Soviet and Eastern European materials along with Western sources leads him to conclude that Stalin intended during World War II to expand Soviet influence into Eastern Europe and other regions as far as the West would permit. In attempting to acquire only as much territory as Britain, the United States, and their allies would concede, Stalin practiced what Peter J. Stavrakis calls "prudent expansionism." Mastny and Taubman conclude that the West facilitated Soviet expansion into Eastern Europe by failing to pursue a firm policy of resistance before 1946.[16]

Historians have begun to examine, in a relatively sophisticated fashion, the influence of Stalin's personality upon the Cold War. Robert C. Tucker, who has completed the second of a three-volume biography of Stalin that takes his subject to 1941, uses a subtle psychoanalytical approach to show that the Soviet premier had by then embarked upon a vindictive and aggressive internal and external policy intended to establish himself as a cultlike, "revolutionary hero" in the eyes of the Soviet people and thus a worthy successor to Lenin. And yet, as Gaddis notes, Washington's policymakers after 1945 believed it possible to control Stalin's actions by taking advantage of both wartime damage to Russia and American technological advances that included a monopoly of the materials necessary to manufacture the atomic bomb. If Stalin's behavior was chiefly inner-directed, as Tucker believes, it nonetheless was reinforced by American policies. Mastny believes that Stalin militarized his foreign policy in

16 Vojtech Mastny, *Russia's Road to the Cold War: Diplomacy, Warfare, and the Politics of Communism, 1941–1945* (New York, 1979), 31, 40–44, 224, 265, 283, 305–6; William Taubman, *Stalin's American Policy: From Entente to Detente to Cold War* (New York, 1982), 8–9, 74–82, 94, 129; Peter J. Stavrakis, *Moscow and Greek Communism, 1944–1949* (Ithaca, 1989), 5, 214. Ulam made many of these same observations earlier. See *The Rivals*, 95, 97–101. See also Albert Resis, *Stalin, the Politburo, and the Onset of the Cold War, 1945–1946* (Pittsburgh, 1988). For similar conclusions see Remi Nadeau, *Stalin, Churchill, and Roosevelt Divide Europe* (New York, 1990), xii, 209–15. See also Gaddis, "Emerging Post-Revisionist Synthesis," 175–76; idem, *Russia, the Soviet Union, and the United States: An Interpretive History*, 2d ed. (New York, 1990), 197; and idem, "Intelligence, Espionage, and Cold War Origins," *Diplomatic History* 13 (Spring 1989): 208–9.

1948 primarily because of the perceived threats to Soviet security posed by European recovery under the Marshall Plan.[17] In contrast, William O. McCagg, Jr., insists that impending economic and political chaos inside the Soviet Union and neighboring Communist states forced Stalin to seek peace before 1948, but that in the early part of that year rebellious behavior in the Balkans (particularly on the part of Tito) and East Asia caused the Soviet premier to become more aggressive. Whatever the reasons for Stalin's hardened stance, he never clarified his country's security objectives and therefore seemed to the West to be committed to expansionist policies that threatened Europe and the Near East.[18]

If one aspect of Stalin's leadership seems unassailable, it is that his emphasis was more on national security than on some putative plan for a global Communist revolution. His willingness to forgo direct involvement in the affairs of European Communist parties, according to Paolo Spriano, Gregory W. Sandford, Charles Gati, John Coutouvidis, Jaime Reynolds, and Peter J. Stavrakis, suggests that the premier's approach to Communist ideology was

17 Robert C. Tucker, *Stalin in Power: The Revolution from Above, 1928–1941* (New York, 1990), 3–4, 45–48, 64, 146–47, 171, 549–50. For volume 1 of Tucker's work see *Stalin as Revolutionary, 1879–1929: A Study in History and Personality* (New York, 1973). See also Yergin, *Shattered Peace*, 324–26; Paterson, *On Every Front*, 58–67; Gaddis, *Long Peace*, 29–47; and idem, *U.S. and Origins of Cold War*, 355. Matthew A. Evangelista argues that the West greatly overestimated the strength of the Soviet army in 1947 and 1948 and that its troops were engaged in nonmilitary responsibilities, not preparations for an invasion of Western Europe. See "Stalin's Postwar Army Reappraised," *International Security* 7 (Winter 1982–83): 110–38. Susan J. Linz insists that foreign aid to the Soviet Union during the immediate postwar era would *not* have lessened its economic difficulties. See "Foreign Aid and Soviet Postwar Recovery," *Journal of Economic History* 45 (December 1985): 947–54. See also Kennedy, *Rise and Fall of Great Powers*, 362–64; and Gregg Herken, *The Winning Weapon: The Atomic Bomb in the Cold War, 1945–1950* (New York, 1980), 101–13. Herken shows that there was no "secret" about how to build the bomb and that the chief obstacle to Russian success was the acquisition of uranium ore, which the United States intended to monopolize. Ibid., and chap. 9. See also Taubman, *Stalin's American Policy*, 75, 171–79; Ulam. *The Rivals*, 130; Melvyn P. Leffler, "From the Truman Doctrine to the Carter Doctrine: Lessons and Dilemmas of the Cold War," *Diplomatic History* 7 (Fall 1983): 245–66; and Vojtech Mastny, "Stalin and the Militarization of the Cold War," *International Security* 9 (Winter 1984–85): 109–29.

18 William O. McCagg, Jr., *Stalin Embattled, 1943–1948* (Detroit, 1978), 237, 262–69, 279, 282–84, 301–3, 312. America's diplomats opposed giving up a monopoly on atomic weaponry that they considered essential to national security. See Larry G. Gerber, "The Baruch Plan and the Origins of the Cold War," *Diplomatic History* 6 (Winter 1982): 77; and Leffler, "American Conception of National Security," 371.

pragmatic. Stalin's decision to cave in to Western pressure and pull out of postwar Iran provides still another illustration.[19]

Nowhere does the nonideological nature of the early Cold War appear more clearly than in the East-West confrontation over postwar Germany. In a solid analysis of the origins and settlement of this international crisis, Avi Shlaim, a political scientist, reviews the multiple political, economic, and psychological factors responsible for the Berlin imbroglio. The Russians' motives in Germany, Shlaim shows, were complex and their tactics flexible. Indeed, it was never clear whether Stalin implemented the blockade to force the West out of Berlin and facilitate a Soviet takeover of the entire city, or to hold the city hostage in an effort to compel the Western powers to return to the wartime agreements dividing the city and thereby prevent integration of the Western sectors into one anti-Communist whole. Even though Stalin probably sought the latter because of the realization that he could not achieve the former short of an all-out war, his actions raised American and British fears that he was attempting to drive the West out of Berlin and perhaps off the Continent. The resulting Berlin crisis of 1948–49 provided a major impetus to the Western search for security through a military alliance that culminated in the establishment of NATO and a lasting, if uneasy, balance of power on the Continent.[20] Ideology, according to Shlaim and

19 Gaddis "Emerging Post-Revisionist Synthesis," 180–81; Paolo Spriano, *Stalin and the European Communists* (London, 1985), 220, 227, 260, 270–72, 289; Gregory W. Sandford, *From Hitler to Ulbricht: The Communist Reconstruction of East Germany, 1945–46* (Princeton, 1983), 221–23, 225; Charles Gati, *Hungary and the Soviet Bloc* (Durham, 1986), 4–5, 15–17; John Coutouvidis and Jaime Reynolds, *Poland, 1939–1947* (Leicester, England, 1986), 230, 265, 291, 308–9, 311, 313–14, 316; Stavrakis, *Moscow and Greek Communism*, 214.

20 McFarland, "Peripheral View of Origins of Cold War"; Avi Shlaim, *The United States and the Berlin Blockade, 1948–1949: A Study in Crisis Decision-Making* (Berkeley, 1983); Mastny, "Stalin and Militarization of Cold War," 120; Taubman, *Stalin's American Policy*, 182. See also John H. Backer, *The Decision to Divide Germany: American Foreign Policy in Transition* (Durham, 1978); Anton W. DePorte, *Europe between the Super-Powers: The Enduring Balance* (New Haven, 1979); Lawrence S. Kaplan, *A Community of Interests: NATO and the Military Assistance Program, 1948–1951* (Washington, 1980); Daniel F. Harrington, "The Berlin Blockade Revisited," *International History Review* 6 (February 1984): 88–112; John H. Backer, *Winds of History: The German Years of Lucius DuBignon Clay* (New York, 1983); Lawrence S. Kaplan, *The United States and NATO: The Formative Years* (Lexington, KY, 1984); idem, *NATO and the United States: The Enduring Alliance* (Boston, 1988); Ann and John Tusa, *The Berlin Airlift* (New York, 1988); and

Werner G. Hahn, provides little help in understanding Soviet behavior.[21]

Notwithstanding the calm discourse characterizing recent studies of the Cold War's origins, all is not yet quiet on the historiographical front. Among the more contentious issues are the Truman Doctrine and the crisis in the Near East, the impact of perceptions on policymaking, and the roles played by George F. Kennan and other prominent public figures.

The formulation of the Truman Doctrine in March 1947 constitutes an excellent example of how perceptions, quite honestly come by, frequently diverged from reality. Drawing on history, psychology, and political science, Deborah Welch Larson shows how policymakers categorize complex and varied information according to personal, political, and bureaucratic needs and thereby produce policy recommendations that are not always synonymous

Randall B. Woods and Howard Jones, *Dawning of the Cold War: The United States' Quest for Order* (Athens, 1991), xi–xii, 174–77, 195, 218. According to Heike Bungert, French policy toward postwar occupied Germany was not as recalcitrant as traditionally pictured. She shows that France aimed at improving relations with the United States by providing ideas and assuring support for a centralized Germany, but could not move fast because of political opposition at home. See "A New Perspective on French-American Relations during the Occupation of Germany, 1945–1948: Behind the Scenes Diplomatic Bargaining and the Zonal Merger," *Diplomatic History* 18 (Summer 1994): 333–52. Timothy P. Ireland shows that European nations viewed NATO not only as a means for restraining the Soviet Union but also for controlling Germany by incorporating it into the balance of power on the Continent. See *Creating the Entangling Alliance: The Origins of the North Atlantic Treaty Organization* (Westport, 1981), 159, 170. For Britain's role see John Baylis, *The Diplomacy of Pragmatism: Britain and the Formation of NATO, 1942–1949* (Kent, OH, 1993).

21 Shlaim, *U.S. and Berlin Blockade*; Werner G. Hahn, *Postwar Soviet Politics: The Fall of Zhdanov and the Defeat of Moderation, 1946–53* (Ithaca, 1982), 9–13, 57–58, 113. Daniel F. Harrington argues that policymakers from Britain, France, and Canada had to restrain Americans who wanted stronger action during the Berlin crisis. See "United States, United Nations and the Berlin Blockade," *Historian* 52 (February 1990): 262–85. Shlaim demonstrates that in the initial phase of the blockade, the British had a more determined policy. See "Britain, the Berlin Blockade, and the Cold War," *International Affairs* 60 (Winter 1983/84): 1–14. For the contentious aftermath of the Berlin crisis and the first days of the Federal Republic of Germany see Schwartz, *America's Germany*. In expressing the revisionist view of the German question, Bruce Kuklick argued some years ago that Germany's recovery was vital to Europe's economic rehabilitation and hence to America's economic expansion, thereby leaving little room for arguments pertaining to national security. See *American Policy and the Division of Germany: The Clash with Russia over Reparations* (Ithaca, 1972). For a balanced view that shows the complexities of the German issue at Potsdam see James L. Gormly, *From Potsdam to the Cold War: Big Three Diplomacy, 1945–1947* (Wilmington, DE, 1990), 30–31, 40–45, 55–58, 145–46.

with the national interest. Although the Truman administration recognized that indigenous social, economic, and political factors were responsible for many of the problems confronting Turkey and Greece, it nevertheless blamed the unrest on Soviet meddling in the wake of the British withdrawal from the Near East.[22] Without Soviet documentation, scholars can examine the Turkish and Greek issues only from the Western perspective, which during the Truman years was haunted by images of Soviet aggression. Reacting to the Munich analogy, Communist rhetoric, and British pressure, the White House assumed that the Kremlin was instigating and abetting troubles in the region and acted to contain the perceived Soviet threat.

Recent writings on the implementation of the Truman Doctrine in Greece provide a striking example of how historians using many of the same documents can arrive at markedly different conclusions even while accepting the premise that each participating nation acted in what it believed to be its national interest. Lawrence S. Wittner, Jon V. Kofas, John O. Iatrides, Peter J. Stavrakis, Bruce R. Kuniholm, and Howard Jones show that the Soviet danger was indirect at best, but on most other points these scholars sharply disagree.[23]

22 Deborah Welch Larson, *Origins of Containment: A Psychological Explanation* (Princeton, 1985). For British withdrawal from the Near East aimed at maintaining power there by nonintervention and partnership see Wm. Roger Louis, *The British Empire in the Middle East, 1945–1951: Arab Nationalism, the United States, and Postwar Imperialism* (Oxford, 1984), vii–viii, 1, 15, 46–47. See also Barry Rubin, *The Great Powers in the Middle East, 1941–1947: The Road to the Cold War* (London, 1980); and Daniel Silverfarb, *Twilight of British Ascendancy in the Middle East: A Case Study of Iraq, 1941–1950* (New York, 1994).

23 Lawrence S. Wittner, "The Truman Doctrine and the Defense of Freedom," *Diplomatic History* 4 (Spring 1980): 161–87; idem, *American Intervention in Greece, 1943–1949* (New York, 1982); Jon V. Kofas, *Intervention and Underdevelopment: Greece during the Cold War* (University Park, PA, 1989); John O. Iatrides, *Revolt in Athens: The Greek Communist "Second Round," 1944–1945* (Princeton, 1972); idem, "Perceptions of Soviet Involvement in the Greek Civil War, 1945–1949," in *Studies in the History of the Greek Civil War, 1945–1949*, ed. Lars Baerentzen, John O. Iatrides, and Ole L. Smith (Copenhagen, 1987), 225–48; Stavrakis, *Moscow and Greek Communism*; Kuniholm, *Origins of Cold War in Near East*; Jones, "*New Kind of War*." For the UN role in Greece see Amikam Nachmani, *International Intervention in the Greek Civil War: The United Nations Special Committee on the Balkans, 1947–1952* (New York, 1990). Robert Frazier unconvincingly asserts that if the United States had worked with Britain in liberating and rehabilitating Greece, there might not have been a December Revolution in 1944 and no Greek civil war in the period following World War II. See his study, *Anglo-American Relations with Greece: The Coming of the Cold War, 1942–47* (New York, 1991).

Wittner and Kofas have criticized Truman's March 1947 declaration as an unwarranted military and economic intervention in purely Greek concerns and have argued that the United States was supporting a rightist government that shunned needed economic and political reforms while brutally repressing all resistance. U.S. policymakers were willing to support autocracy and overlook human rights violations in an effort to ensure continued access to Middle Eastern oil, to establish commercial dominance in the eastern Mediterranean, and to carve out a strategic foothold in this crossroads between East and West. U.S. policy toward Greece established an interventionist pattern that would be repeated throughout the Third World. Ignoring military records in his research, Kofas does not discuss the dire military situation in Greece and, as a result, suggests that security considerations were inconsequential to White House decision making. Wittner simultaneously downplays terrorism by the Left and the importance of American intervention. He insists that the fighting ended as a result of the shifting balance of power within the Communist camp and not as a consequence of American aid. Wittner and Kofas conclude that with the collapse of the leftist revolution, Greece lost its chance for democracy and prosperity and, more provocatively, that continued political repression and economic exploitation by the government and its foreign allies bred chronic instability in postwar Greece. Indeed, they insist that America's perception of its experience reinforced strategic assumptions that led the United States into the Vietnam quagmire.[24]

In sharp contrast, Kuniholm, Iatrides, Stavrakis, and Jones have attempted to show how the Near East crisis developed and fit within a global context. The Truman administration was not responsible for the Greek government's inadequacies. That the regime in Athens was autocratic did not negate the reality of Greece's strategic importance. The United States intervened because

24 Wittner, "Truman Doctrine and Defense of Freedom"; idem, *American Intervention in Greece*, xi, 17–22, 56–64, 134–48, 166, 250–59, 284–85, 297–98, 307–12; Kofas, *Intervention and Underdevelopment*, xi, 16, 40–43, 65–66, 75, 85–87, 96, 105, 169, 179–80. Earlier revisionist studies attacked the Truman Doctrine for fomenting an irrational outburst of anticommunism that encouraged McCarthyism. See Richard M. Freeland, *The Truman Doctrine and the Origins of McCarthyism: Foreign Policy, Domestic Politics, and National Security, 1946–1948* (New York, 1970); and Athan Theoharis, *Seeds of Repression: Harry S. Truman and the Origins of McCarthyism* (Chicago, 1971).

meddling by the Soviet bloc had exacerbated longtime troubles in Greece; given the expansionist tendencies inherent in Stalinism, the Truman Doctrine was seen to be and was in fact vital to preserving stability along the Northern Tier of the eastern Mediterranean. Iatrides insists that even though Stalin abided by his wartime "percentages agreement" with Britain not to intervene in Greece, he would have coopted a Greek Communist state that emerged from the civil war. Stavrakis goes further. Drawing upon Greek Communist, British, and American sources, he holds that between mid-1945 and late 1946, Stalin pursued a careful, deliberate, yet unsuccessful, political infiltration of Greece that aimed at establishing Soviet influence. Jones agrees but places this "new kind of war," one based on infiltration, subversion, propaganda, and guerrilla tactics, in a multilateral perspective. The Truman Doctrine, a rallying point for the members of the forthcoming North Atlantic Alliance, demonstrated the effectiveness of a firm and yet flexible and restrained foreign policy built on multifaceted responses to different types and levels of perceived dangers.[25] That America would subsequently misapply the theory to Southeast Asia does not disprove its validity in the Near East in 1947 and 1948.

Beyond Greece and Turkey, a measure of historiographical consensus is emerging on the issue of oil. New studies by Irvine H. Anderson, Aaron David Miller, Michael B. Stoff, Stephen J. Randall, and David S. Painter have examined the Truman administration's quest for oil and security in the Middle East. They conclude that control over Arab oil constituted an integral part of America's search for security and that the economic interests of business and the strategic concerns of government paralleled each other. The oil industry never controlled the Truman admin-

25 Kuniholm, *Origins of Cold War in Near East*, xvi, xxi, 4–5, 98–99, 253, 353–55, 379–82, 404–5, 426–31; Iatrides, "Perceptions of Soviet Involvement in Greek Civil War," 234, 236–37; Stavrakis, *Moscow and Greek Communism*, 4–5, 53, 55, 102, 118–19, 206–7, 210, 213–14; Jones, "*New Kind of War*," viii–ix, 3–7, 15–16, 38, 58–60, 62, 66–69, 89, 93, 123, 134–35, 161–62, 220–26. The Northern Tier included Greece, Turkey, and Iran. Rabel's study of the Trieste issue demonstrates an early move toward what he calls "a relatively flexible and restrained policy of 'containment' which realistically matches means with end." See "Prologue to Containment," 73.

istration's policy toward the region. Indeed, the United States lacked a national policy on oil until after the Second World War. The most Randall is willing to admit is that "the emergence of the United States as a major military and economic power made a higher level of state intervention in the private sector essential for the ability of American firms to compete internationally." Although Painter goes further in arguing that big business controlled much of U.S. foreign policy, he, too, admits to the mutuality of public and private interests in the formation of a comprehensive oil policy.[26]

Conflict rather than consensus marks historical interpretations of the roles played by leading members of the American foreign service, particularly George F. Kennan, in the origins of the Cold War. Those who have studied the central figures have posed a number of important questions. By 1946, had Kennan ceased to view the Soviet Union as a conventional nation-state and Stalin as a pragmatic politician? Had he joined Charles E. Bohlen and Loy Henderson in depicting the Soviet Union as a totalitarian, ideologically driven state bent on global conquest? Or was Soviet ideology for Kennan the justification for and not the source of the Kremlin's behavior? Gaddis and David Mayers argue that Kennan was the quintessential student of the role of power and national interest in international affairs and thus advocated a measured response to the threat of Communist expansion, one that matched means with ends. A recent study by Wilson S. Miscamble, however, focuses on Kennan's role as director of the State Department's Policy Planning Staff and convincingly argues that he and his colleagues were uncertain about the strategy of containment and maintained flexibility in seeking to apply it on

26 Irvine H. Anderson, *Aramco, the United States, and Saudi Arabia: A Study of the Dynamics of Foreign Oil Policy, 1933–1950* (Princeton, 1981), 193, 197, 204–5; Aaron David Miller, *Search for Security: Saudi Arabian Oil and American Foreign Policy, 1939–1949* (Chapel Hill, 1980), xv–xvii, 175–79, 190–91, 208–12; Michael B. Stoff, *Oil, War, and American Security: The Search for a National Policy on Foreign Oil, 1941–1947* (New Haven, 1980), 211–15; Stephen J. Randall, *United States Foreign Oil Policy, 1919–1948: For Profits and Security* (Montreal, 1985), 4–6, 8–11, 253 (quote); David S. Painter, *Oil and the American Century: The Political Economy of U.S. Foreign Oil Policy, 1941–1954* (Baltimore, 1986), 1, 9–10, 91–92, 95, 110–16, 198, 202–10. See also Kuniholm, *Origins of Cold War in Near East*, 182–86.

a case-by-case basis. By no means did they possess a worldwide blueprint for peace.[27]

New studies of other important diplomatic figures also show that many of them viewed Soviet behavior with a healthy mistrust but were not dogmatic ideologues. Bohlen, according to T. Michael Ruddy, apparently did not believe that the Kremlin sought either world conquest or military conflict. And H. W. Brands demonstrates that Henderson, despite his staunch anticommunism, did not consider Stalin an irrational ideologue. The Soviet premier, both writers agree, recognized that limitations on Soviet power precluded a drive for global hegemony. Hugh DeSantis ascribes a large part to culture and psychology in explaining the changing worldviews of these three seminal figures together with twenty-seven of their colleagues in the foreign service. Professional diplomats, both "realists" and "Wilsonians," disagreed among themselves over whether to work with the Soviets. Those who served in Moscow and in southeastern Europe were more skeptical about an accommodation with the Soviets than were those assigned to Western Europe or Washington. According to DeSantis, Kennan after mid-1945 represented a minority view that urged realistic Soviet-American cooperation in the context of diplomatic firmness and military preparedness.[28]

27 Yergin, *Shattered Peace*, 11–12, 29–41, 92, 138–39, 152, 170–71; Harrington, "Kennan, Bohlen, and Riga Axioms"; Gaddis, *Strategies of Containment*, 23–53; David Mayers, *George Kennan and the Dilemmas of US Foreign Policy* (New York, 1988), 4, 6, 11–12; Wilson D. Miscamble, *George F. Kennan and the Making of American Foreign Policy, 1947–1950* (Princeton, 1992).

28 T. Michael Ruddy, *The Cautious Diplomat: Charles E. Bohlen and the Soviet Union, 1929–1969* (Kent, OH, 1986), x–xi, 56–57, 162–63, 165; H. W. Brands, *Inside the Cold War: Loy Henderson and the Rise of the American Empire, 1918–1961* (New York, 1991), 309–13; Hugh DeSantis, *The Diplomacy of Silence: The American Foreign Service, the Soviet Union, and the Cold War, 1933–1947* (Chicago, 1980), 3–9, 198–200, 204–10. Even though Truman relied on the advice of these professional diplomats more than did Roosevelt, they displayed their "silence," DeSantis declares, in disagreeing among themselves and *following* policy rather than leading its formulation. Ibid., 21–22. According to a recent study by Walter Isaacson and Evan Thomas, six men comprised the "core" of "the Establishment": Kennan, Bohlen, W. Averell Harriman, Robert A. Lovett, Dean Acheson, and John J. McCloy, Jr. In the public interest and not for private gain, they advocated an enlarged international role for the United States that rested on containment and foreign commitments. Their opposition to totalitarianism and support for liberal capitalism comprised a sound strategy that matched objectives and means. See *The Wise Men: Six Friends and the World They Made: Acheson, Bohlen, Harriman, Kennan, Lovett, McCloy* (New York, 1986).

Not all historians of the early Cold War find Kennan as balanced or detached. Walter L. Hixson argues that Kennan's anticommunism drove him to seek not a balance of power but Western supremacy over the Soviets. Kennan's alienation from American culture and society led to disenchantment with the global leadership role he had assigned to the United States in the containment article and ultimately made him an outsider, a "cold war iconoclast." Whereas Gaddis and Mayers argue that the Truman administration rejected Kennan's guidelines for limited containment, Hixson contends that his fellow historians both failed to recognize Kennan's consistent emphasis on rollback and missed "the global implications and contradictions of containment." But according to Anders Stephanson, Kennan's containment policy called merely for gradual liberation through peaceful means. Like Hixson, however, Stephanson argues that Kennan's cultural prejudices did not allow him to be a classical realist. Kennan's interest in a European balance of power stemmed from his desire to "delineate American interests within the larger framework of the West, the survival of whose civilization he always put before everything else."[29]

Hixson and Stephanson have provided thought-provoking analyses of their subject's behavior, but neither has succeeded in disproving the conventional characterization of Kennan as a realist who opposed Soviet expansion. As Gaddis shows, by the time Kennan's famous "X" article had appeared in July 1947, he was emphasizing the practical limitations on Soviet behavior and, during the debates over the Greek-Turkish crisis, was arguing against military assistance because he thought the Soviet threat at that time to be political and ideological rather than military in

29 Mayers, *Kennan*, 7–8, 10, 106, 134; Walter L. Hixson, *George F. Kennan: Cold War Iconoclast* (New York, 1989), x–xi, 36, 44–45, 47, 71–72, 222, 240–41, 300–301; Anders Stephanson, *Kennan and the Art of Foreign Policy* (Cambridge, MA, 1989), 50, 114–15, 148–49, 151, 155–56, 194. See Gaddis, *Strategies of Containment*, 238–39, 346, 354. Barton Gellman believes that Kennan regarded the major reality to be the series of power relationships lying within the realm of national security objectives. See his *Contending with Kennan: Toward a Philosophy of American Power* (New York, 1984), 33. See also Melvyn P. Leffler, "Was the Cold War Necessary?" *Diplomatic History* 15 (Spring 1991): 265–75. For a call to historians to examine the "credibility imperative" in U.S. postwar policymaking see Robert J. McMahon, "Credibility and World Power: Exploring the Psychological Dimension in Postwar American Diplomacy," ibid. (Fall 1991): 455–71.

nature. Kennan objected strenuously to the global burdens seemingly implicit in the Truman Doctrine. Indeed, in the years immediately following publication of his *Foreign Affairs* article, he demonstrated his own awareness of the limitations on American power by urging policymakers to match ends with means and to distinguish between vital and peripheral interests in determining foreign commitments. In the case of the Marshall Plan, Kennan recognized the wisdom of dividing Europe into two camps, thereby establishing a balance of power that would protect the peace. Although he believed that the political division of Germany would perpetuate the Cold War, he reluctantly endorsed Washington's refusal to respond to the Soviet Union's call for unification and approved the West's plans to integrate West Germany into a European alliance. In view of recent developments in Eastern Europe and the former Soviet Union, Hixson missed the mark in asserting that Kennan's "faith in liberation, or a Soviet capitulation, rested on dubious assumptions and was a major flaw of the containment strategy." The sharply differing interpretations of Kennan as policymaker and political observer have left the historiographical door open, and we still await a comprehensive and compelling biography.[30]

Less controversial than the works on Kennan and his colleagues is a series of new books dealing with the twin issues of perception and credibility. Several studies concern the enigmatic relationship between Truman and his secretary of state, James F. Byrnes. Robert L. Messer and Kendrick A. Clements argue that Truman appointed the South Carolinian in part out of a belief that he had been privy to the secret diplomacy of Yalta. Discovering that this was not the case, the president decided that his chief diplomat

30 See George F. Kennan, "Containment Then and Now," *Foreign Affairs* 65 (Spring 1987): 885–90; and Jones, "*New Kind of War*," 45–46. Dean Acheson repeatedly told congressional committees that some areas of the world fell into the Soviet sphere of influence and were therefore incapable of liberation through American assistance. Ibid., 49. See also Gaddis, *Strategies of Containment*, 23–24, 30–34, 39, 39n.*, 58–62, 64–65, 74–76; idem, "Containment: A Reassessment," *Foreign Affairs* 55 (July 1977): 873–87; Mayers, *Kennan*, 10, 121–24, 130–32, 137, 157, 159, 319, 331; and Hixson, *Kennan*, 256, 297, 299, 308. Gaddis defines symmetrical response as "acting wherever the Russians chose to challenge interests" and asymmetrical response as "acting only when interests at stake were vital, conditions favorable, and means accessible." See *Strategies of Containment*, 101.

had misled him. When Byrnes subsequently attempted to operate independently of the White House, his and Truman's relationship deteriorated and America's Soviet policy foundered. After the secret Yalta agreements became public, Messer continues, the American people soured on Roosevelt's conciliatory approach to the Kremlin. As it did, the Truman administration's attitude toward the Soviet Union hardened, thereby helping to bring on the Cold War. Clements goes beyond personality to detect a real distinction between Truman's and Byrnes's views on foreign policy. The president, Clements declares, moved toward a hard line because of his reading of the mistakes made at the Munich Conference and his desire to silence critics who claimed that he was unskilled in affairs of state. The secretary of state, however, was a Wilsonian whose idealism was constantly tempered by diplomatic and political realities. According to Patricia Dawson Ward, pressure from the White House, Congress, and public opinion forced Byrnes to abandon his initial attempts to reconcile Soviet-American differences. Despite his private attempts to negotiate contentious issues, she concludes, Byrnes's hard-line public behavior contributed to the Cold War.[31]

In the age of burgeoning national security states, policymakers struggled to anticipate their opponents' intentions and to stay a step ahead. It is therefore not surprising that, as Marc Trachtenberg and Russell D. Buhite and William Christopher Hamel have shown, more than a few of the administration's civilian and military spokesmen urged a preventive war before the Soviets could build their own bomb and, in so doing, doubtless intensified the Cold War by escalating Stalin's anxieties about the West. More work is needed, however, on whether these alleged calls for preventive war were authentic, were hollow attempts to establish credibility by demonstrating firmness, or were merely loose talk based on

31 Robert L. Messer, *The End of an Alliance: James F. Byrnes, Roosevelt, Truman, and the Origins of the Cold War* (Chapel Hill, 1982), 4, 8–10, 31, 55, 67–69, 239–40; Kendrick A. Clements, ed., *James F. Byrnes and the Origins of the Cold War* (Durham, 1982), 7–9; Patricia Dawson Ward, *The Threat of Peace: James F. Byrnes and the Council of Foreign Ministers, 1945–1946* (Kent, OH, 1979), ix–x, 175–79. For a British historian's view of the Yalta controversy see Donald Cameron Watt, "Britain and the Historiography of the Yalta Conference and the Cold War," *Diplomatic History* 13 (Winter 1989): 67–98.

contingency planning. Further, the claim that such measures unsettled Stalin remains problematic in light of the fact that his spies, Donald Maclean and Guy Burgess, sat in on the highest Anglo-American discussions (particularly those concerning NATO in the Pentagon in 1948) and heard the conferees admit that war, even initiated through a preemptive strike, was a dangerous gamble, given the weakness of Western military forces. This intelligence, along with the documents that Maclean pilfered, which showed how little uranium the West was mining and thus how few bombs were available, must have eased Stalin's anxieties.[32]

An increasing number of studies reveal that the Truman administration, like those that preceded and followed it, was a captive of twisted perceptions, circumstances beyond its control, a sometimes erroneous reading of history, and an inflated need to demonstrate reliability to friends. In general, White House leaders were products of a crisis-ridden period of history that resulted from the bitter legacy of the Great War and Versailles and, as Kendrick A. Clements and Göran Rystad show, of the rise of dictatorships and the failure of appeasement at Munich as well. They also were students of the "lessons" taught by the Great War, namely that social, political, and economic disorder made nation-states vulnerable to totalitarianism at home and to totalitarian

32 For the preventive war issue see Marc Trachtenberg, "A 'Wasting Asset': American Strategy and the Shifting Nuclear Balance, 1949–1954," *International Security* 13 (Winter 1988–89): 5–49; Russell D. Buhite and William Christopher Hamel, "War for Peace: The Question of an American Preventive War against the Soviet Union, 1945–1955," *Diplomatic History* 14 (Summer 1990): 367–84. For the spy issue see John Costello, *Mask of Treachery* (New York, 1988), 538–39, 572–73 (among many references to Maclean and Burgess); and Herken, *Winning Weapon*, 131, 323n.*, 340. Although many contemporary studies concluded that the Soviets would not invade Europe, the White House remained concerned about Communist infiltration in the midst of widespread European disorder. See Leffler's two articles, "American Conception of National Security," 374–75, 377, 379, and "The United States and the Strategic Dimensions of the Marshall Plan," *Diplomatic History* 12 (Summer 1988): 279–80. Consequently, according to Larry G. Gerber and James L. Gormly, the administration believed that the security of America and the rest of the world depended upon the establishment of a Wilsonian world order based on liberalism and capitalism and the maintenance of an atomic monopoly that belied the Baruch Plan's call for international control of atomic energy. See Gerber, "Baruch Plan and Origins of Cold War," 75, 77, 82–83, 93, 95; Gormly, "The Washington Declaration and the 'Poor Relation': Anglo-American Atomic Diplomacy, 1945–46," *Diplomatic History* 8 (Spring 1984): 125–43; and idem, *Collapse of Grand Alliance*, chap. 6. See also Herken, *Winning Weapon*, 101–13.

aggression from abroad. In postwar Egypt, Peter L. Hahn shows, the White House tried to achieve stability by pursuing conflicting strategic and political goals of containing the Soviet Union while satisfying Egyptian drives for nationalism. Some policymakers in Washington were obsessed with the Marxist-Leninist world revolution and the challenge it presented to capitalism. Others acted out of the belief that a brutally repressive government in Moscow was led by an even more brutally repressive premier determined to divert criticism of his dictatorial methods through a policy of expansion. According to Larson's psychological profile of Truman, the president saw Stalin as a prototype of Kansas City political boss Tom Pendergast and mistakenly believed that the Soviet premier would understand the importance of public opinion in America's policymaking process. When this perception proved erroneous, Truman then equated Stalin with Hitler. As John Lewis Gaddis and Randall B. Woods establish, the Truman administration could not persuade an isolationist and increasingly budget-conscious Republican Congress to support an activist foreign policy without portraying the Soviet Union as a mortal threat to American security and communism as a potential cancer that would eat away at American domestic institutions.[33]

Recent scholarship suggests that the Cold War grew out of a complex mixture of causes but that the common denominator in this equation was an East-West search for security made all the more urgent by a deep sense of mutual distrust and by the global disorder resulting from a devastating war. According to Robert C. Hilderbrand, the Dumbarton Oaks Conference of 1944 exposed

33 Clements, ed., *Brynes and Origins of Cold War*, 7; Göran Rystad, *Prisoners of the Past? The Munich Syndrome and Makers of American Foreign Policy in the Cold War Era* (Lund, Sweden, 1982), 26–30, 35; Peter L. Hahn, *The United States, Great Britain, and Egypt, 1945–1956: Strategy and Diplomacy in the Early Cold War* (Chapel Hill, 1991), 2–4, 242–47; Larson, *Origins of Containment*, 178; Paterson, *On Every Front*, 158; Gaddis, *U.S. and Origins of Cold War*, 283, 344–45, 351, 356; Woods, *Changing of Guard*, 289–90, 300, chap. 13. On the Stalin-Hitler comparison see Les K. Adler and Thomas G. Paterson, "Red Fascism: The Merger of Nazi Germany and Soviet Russia in the American Image of Totalitarianism, 1930's–1950's," *American Historical Review* 75 (April 1970): 1046–64. Gaddis Smith likewise agreed that Truman compared Stalin with Hitler. See *Dean Acheson* (New York, 1972), 423–24. On the Truman administration's Munich analogy see Ernest R. May, *"Lessons" of the Past: The Use and Misuse of History in American Foreign Policy* (New York, 1973), 32, 36, 49–51.

many of the problems that would besiege the postwar world as the Big Three and China gathered in Georgetown in an effort to achieve international security through the establishment of a United Nations organization. John Lewis Gaddis shows that the United States envisioned playing a central role in world affairs long before the Cold War and that this objective rested on the assumption that the Great Powers would cooperate in collective security. But an inherent contradiction bedeviled an approach that called for open markets, which was really economic integration, and self-determination, which was really political fragmentation. In the ensuing quest for order, the Truman administration publicly exaggerated the Soviet danger in an attempt to mobilize domestic support for its diplomatic goals; in the process, its own fears of Soviet means and objectives became exaggerated.[34]

Woods and Jones show the importance of perception and credibility in their recent study of the Cold War's origins by addressing a number of security related issues that were affected by mutual perceptions. One was the obsession with sovereignty and security among members of the Grand Alliance that made the erosion of the coalition predictable after Hitler's collapse. Another was the heightened anxiety and mistrust introduced into Soviet-American relations and international affairs by America's understandable decision to use the atomic bomb against Japan, albeit for primarily military reasons. Still another was the widespread destruction of Russia during World War II and the role it played in Stalin's determination to have "friendly neighbors" in Eastern Europe. Further, the Kremlin experienced great apprehension as a result of America's attempt to aid Greece and Turkey and subsequently, as Melvyn P. Leffler shows, to seek the latter's membership in NATO as part of an effort to deny Soviet access to the Mediterranean. Related to the preceding consideration was Stalin's overriding fear of a resurgent Germany, which

34 Robert C. Hilderbrand, *Dumbarton Oaks: The Origins of the United Nations and the Search for Postwar Security* (Chapel Hill, 1990); John Lewis Gaddis, "The Tragedy of Cold War History," *Diplomatic History* 17 (Winter 1993): 3–4, 16; idem, *U.S. and Origins of Cold War*, 351–52, 356; Evangelista, "Stalin's Postwar Army Reappraised," 111. See also Thomas G. Paterson, *Meeting the Communist Threat: Truman to Reagan* (New York, 1988), 35–36, 42–53.

was intensified by the Marshall Plan's call for the reintegration of that country into a unified Europe. Indeed, the Soviet leadership demonstrated a tendency to view every attempt by the West to rehabilitate Europe as part of a calculated effort to endanger the homeland. In many respects the fears and mistrust experienced by the Soviet Union and the West were mirror images that doubtless resulted from mutually mistaken perceptions of motives.[35]

The road to and from the first potential Armageddon of the Cold War, the Berlin blockade, was pockmarked with misperceptions. Despite the deep rift that occurred in Soviet-Western relations during and immediately following World War II, the Soviets quietly indicated their interest in a "peace offensive" just weeks before the outbreak of the Berlin crisis in June 1948. In addition, that same spring the Kremlin made private overtures to the United States about winding down the Greek civil war. With postwar Europe already divided into two camps, the Truman administration, perhaps too hurriedly, dismissed these Soviet moves as propaganda and insisted that negotiations were a cover for ongoing Communist expansion. Avi Shlaim shows that tensions ran so high over Berlin that the Truman administration considered using the atomic bomb, even though, as Gregg Herken, David Alan Rosenberg, and Harry R. Borowski have pointed out, America's nuclear arsenal was small and the likelihood of carrying out a successful nuclear attack was remote. Fearing a loss of credibility abroad and political attacks by anti-Communists at home, the administration never explored the possibility of negotiations. Such a move, argues J. Samuel Walker, might have divided the West, left the appearance of weakness, confused the American public, undermined the move for selective service, and hurt Truman's chances for reelection. As Walker implies, the

35 Woods and Jones, *Dawning of Cold War*; Gaddis, *U.S. and Origins of Cold War*, 245–46; Melvyn P. Leffler, "Strategy, Diplomacy, and the Cold War: The United States, Turkey, and NATO, 1945–1952," *Journal of American History* 71 (March 1985): 807–25; Anderson, "Poland and Marshall Plan," 493. On an integrated Europe that would alleviate the German problem see Armin Rappaport, "The United States and European Integration: The First Phase," *Diplomatic History* 5 (Spring 1981): 121–22. For an excellent review of the literature on America's use of the atomic bomb see J. Samuel Walker, "The Decision to Use the Bomb: A Historiographical Update," in this volume.

issue of credibility played a crucial role in policy formulation on both sides in the Cold War after 1948.[36]

An all-encompassing synthesis to explain the origins of the Cold War, if one exists, remains elusive. A major obstacle to the formulation of such a synthesis is the lack of systematic documentation from the archives of the Soviet Union and the other nations involved in early Cold War struggles. There is, moreover, the ever-present tendency among would-be architects of any synthesis to oversimplify events. Christopher Thorne has warned that generalized theories are "divorced from the complexities provided by historical evidence." Pitfalls await both those who attempt to synthesize and those who do not. On the one hand, Gaddis writes, generalizations can lead to "reductionism," attempts to explain complex events by identifying single causes or categories of causes, and thus threaten to result in what J. H. Hexter termed "tunnel history." On the other hand, the historian of the early Cold War must not attribute events to so many causes that the effort results in what Gaddis has called "mindless eclecticism."[37]

Michael H. Hunt argues that the key to broadening our

36 Jones, "*New Kind of War*," 205–13; Herken, *Winning Weapon*, 197–98; David Alan Rosenberg, "U.S. Nuclear Stockpile, 1945 to 1950," *Bulletin of the Atomic Scientists* 38 (May 1982): 25–30; Harry R. Borowski, *A Hollow Threat: Strategic Air Power and Containment before Korea* (Westport, 1982), 4–5, 37–39, 103–7. See also Shlaim, *U.S. and Berlin Blockade*, 228, 236–37, 245–46, 254–60, 294, 337–39, 341, 359; Gaddis, "Intelligence, Espionage, and Cold War Origins," 207; idem, *Long Peace*, 110–12; J. Samuel Walker, " 'No More Cold War': American Foreign Policy and the 1948 Soviet Peace offensive," *Diplomatic History* 5 (Winter 1981): 75–76, 89–91; Woods and Jones, *Dawning of Cold War*, 211–14, 226–27; and McMahon, "Credibility and World Power," 455–71.

37 Christopher Thorne, *Border Crossings: Studies in International History* (Oxford, 1988), 7; John Lewis Gaddis, "New Conceptual Approaches to the Study of American Foreign Relations: Interdisciplinary Perspectives," *Diplomatic History* 14 (Summer 1990): 406–10; J. H. Hexter, *Reappraisals in History* (Evanston, 1961), 194–95. See also Eric H. Monkkonen, "The Dangers of Synthesis," *American Historical Review* 91 (December 1986): 1155–56. On the continued paucity of Soviet documentation despite the high hopes of *glasnost* see "The Soviet Side of the Cold War: A Symposium," with introduction by John Lewis Gaddis and commentaries by George F. Kennan, William Taubman, Melvyn P. Leffler, Victor Mal'kov (Soviet historian at the Institute of World History in Moscow), and Steven Merritt Miner. The symposium focused on the Novikov Telegram (reprinted here), written on 27 September 1946 by the Soviet ambassador to the United States, Nikolai Novikov, to Soviet Foreign Minister Vyacheslav Molotov in Moscow. The telegram raised more questions than it answered. See *Diplomatic History* 15 (Fall 1991): 523–63.

understanding of the origins of the Cold War without distorting the past is to adopt an interdisciplinary and cross-cultural approach as part of an effort to become quasi-area specialists. Such a task requires multiarchival research, a broad perspective that will help to internationalize American diplomatic history, rigorous comparative efforts to provide more insights, increased attention to the role of nonstate actors, and greater emphasis on economic and social considerations. Only by borrowing from and collaborating with other fields, Hunt insists, can historians place the Cold War within its proper global context. In so doing, American ethnocentrism would give way to an international perspective derived from a comparative and systemic approach. The result, he concludes, would be a "more sophisticated appraisal" of America's international conduct.[38]

Hunt's recommendations have drawn wide support from within the profession. Robert J. McMahon notes that the study of foreign countries helps not only to delineate more precisely U.S. influence but also to place it in the proper context, and that area specialization enriches analyses of American policy by showing its impact on other countries. Geir Lundestad likewise advocates comparative studies that focus on the interplay between international and local factors and joins Hunt and Akira Iriye in calling for more collaborative work between American and non-American historians.[39]

Some writers have already begun to employ this broadened approach. An example of international history at its best is James Edward Miller's study of American-Italian relations during the 1940s. Grounded in archival research in both of these countries as well as in Great Britain, this work focuses on U.S. efforts to

38 Michael H. Hunt, "Internationalizing U.S. Diplomatic History: A Practical Agenda," *Diplomatic History* 15 (Winter 1991): 1–4, 7–8, 10–11; idem, "Responses to Maier," 355–56. Ernest R. May and Akira Iriye want the international approach extended to include all history. See May, "Writing Contemporary International History," *Diplomatic History* 8 (Spring 1984): 113; and Iriye, "The Internationalization of History," *American Historical Review* 94 (February 1989): 1–10. According to Iriye, historians must preserve "the totality of remembered pasts." Ibid., 10.

39 Robert J. McMahon, "The Study of American Foreign Relations: National History or International History?" *Diplomatic History* 14 (Fall 1990): 556–57; Lundestad, "Moralism, Presentism, and other Extravagances," 544–45; Iriye, "Responses to Maier," 359.

establish postwar political stability in Italy and to incorporate that country into the Western alliance. Relying primarily on economic assistance as leverage, U.S. policymakers overreacted to fears of Soviet communism by pursuing an interventionist course that shored up political forces on the Right while discouraging much-needed social and economic reforms. Another admirable cross-cultural work is Geir Lundestad's study of American-Scandinavian relations during the late 1940s. Using American and Norwegian archives along with other Scandinavian secondary materials, Lundestad shows how the United States after 1947 attempted to persuade the Scandinavian states to become part of the Western alliance. American policy toward the Soviet Union, Lundestad argues, was flexible and restrained, dependent upon technical and economic aid to achieve both political and economic objectives and not driven entirely by anticommunism.[40]

Multiarchival, culturally literate studies are not easily written. American archival material for the early Cold War period is generally open, but its volume is daunting.[41] Few other countries can match the United States in allowing access to government materials and, consequently, area studies are likely to be asymmetrical. Even in the United States, however, adequate records are not open past the mid-1950s. Moreover, beyond the question of documentation, would it not take a single historian a lifetime, Emily S. Rosenberg wonders, to complete a book that focused on nonstate actors and actions along with government leaders and power considerations, one that would be interdisciplinary and transnational in perspective and thus demonstrate the interplay of cultural factors? Hunt correctly admits that an individual historian's

40 James Edward Miller, *The United States and Italy, 1940–1950: The Politics and Diplomacy of Stabilization* (Chapel Hill, 1986), xiii, 3–7, 250–51, 263, 266–71, 274; idem, "Taking Off the Gloves: The United States and the Italian Elections of 1948," *Diplomatic History* 7 (Winter 1983): 35–55; Lundestad, *America, Scandinavia, and Cold War*, 33–35, 335. Regarding Italy, John Lamberton Harper argues that U.S. aid promoted its own strategic interests but that Italy's problems remained because only its people could solve them. See *America and the Reconstruction of Italy, 1945–1948* (Cambridge, England, 1986), vii–viii, 166–67. For an analysis of how Finland did not fit the Cold War model and instead maintained its good relations with the Soviet Union while keeping its democratic institutions see Jussi Hanhimäki, "'Containment' in a Borderland: The United States and Finland, 1948–49," *Diplomatic History* 18 (Summer 1994): 353–74.

41 May, "Writing Contemporary International History," 113.

search for knowledge can be only a single part of a necessarily cooperative enterprise.[42]

There are other pitfalls to this ambitious approach to writing history. Rosenberg insists that the United States resides at the center of the world system; hence, historians must "walk the borders of global power, analyzing power systems from various perspectives situated on the periphery." Walter LaFeber and Richard H. Immerman concur, arguing that, regardless of motive or method, the United States emerged from the war in 1945 as the central power in the world. The value of international history notwithstanding, Immerman insists that the "nationalist perspective" remains important if for no other reason than that it provides the basis for those who wish to specialize in comparative history.[43]

Despite Immerman's warnings against "conceptual imperialism," a number of recent studies have overarching theses, one of them being the corporatist model advocated by Michael J. Hogan. His study of the Marshall Plan demonstrates how collaboration among corporations, public and private agencies, and supranational organizations all affected American policy. As practitioners of scientific management, the Marshall planners used the New Deal as a blueprint in their struggle to assure international stability through the spread of liberal capitalism. Hogan offers corporatism as a multidimensional tool for analyzing political, economic, and public policies that promoted collective security through the establishment of a "corporative world order." In the case of the Marshall Plan, economic assistance provided the means for rebuilding a balance of power in Europe by establishing an organization that could simultaneously contain the Soviet Union in Eastern Europe and reintegrate Germany into an economically interdependent and politically stable Western Europe. Economic policy served geopolitical and strategic goals, just as NATO and

42 See Hoff-Wilson, "Responses to Maier," 378; Kaplan, "Responses to Gaddis," 197; and Emily S. Rosenberg, "Walking the Borders," *Diplomatic History* 14 (Fall 1990): 567.

43 Walter LaFeber, "Responses to Maier," 362; Rosenberg, "Walking the Borders," 568; Richard H. Immerman, "The History of U.S. Foreign Policy: A Plea for Pluralism," *Diplomatic History* 14 (Fall 1990): 577–78, 587–92.

the overall U.S. military assistance program bolstered the corporate order that provided the basis for the Marshall Plan.[44]

In emphasizing continuity, however, corporatist theory can give more weight to domestic forces than to geopolitical or external considerations. As even Hogan admits, its analysis begins with the domestic influences affecting foreign relations and then moves toward an examination of international forces. What is more, as Leffler contends, the dramatically altered power structure that emerged following World War II was more important than the New Deal in spawning and shaping the Marshall Plan. Gaddis warns that by assigning relative primacy to economic influences, corporatism emphasizes evolutionary change and obscures rather than accommodates the discontinuity in history. Indeed, he argues, corporatism focuses on geoeconomic forces and does not deal sufficiently with strategy, geopolitical needs, and perceptions of outside threats. Between 1941 and 1946, as Woods shows in his study of Anglo-American relations, American economic interests and U.S. national security policies worked at crosspurposes. Multilateralism, a system of freer trade buttressed by unrestricted international currency exchange, was undercut by bureaucratic imperialists and economic nationalists in Congress and the business community. In other words, corporatism may fall short on two counts: an overemphasis on the impact of domestic forces on the making of U.S. foreign policy and an underemphasis on the international balance of power.[45]

44 Immerman, "History of U.S. Foreign Policy," 583; Michael J. Hogan, "Corporatism," *Journal of American History* 77 (June 1990): 153–55, 159; idem, "The Search for a 'Creative Peace': The United States, European Unity, and the Origins of the Marshall Plan," *Diplomatic History* 6 (Summer 1982): 267–68; idem, "Revival and Reform: America's Twentieth-Century Search for a New Economic Order Abroad," ibid. 8 (Fall 1984): 287–310; idem, "Paths to Plenty: Marshall Planners and the Debate over European Integration, 1947–1948," *Pacific Historical Review* 53 (August 1984): 337–66; idem, "American Marshall Planners and the Search for a European Neocapitalism," *American Historical Review* 90 (February 1985): 44–72; idem, "Corporatism: A Positive Appraisal," *Diplomatic History* 10 (Fall 1986): 363–72; idem, *The Marshall Plan: America, Britain, and the Reconstruction of Western Europe, 1947–1952* (Cambridge, England, 1987); Rappaport, "U.S. and European Integration," 121–22, 149; Chester J. Pach, Jr., *Arming the Free World: The Origins of the United States Military Assistance Program, 1945–1950* (Chapel Hill, 1991), 202–4.

45 Leffler, "National Security," *Journal of American History* 77 (June 1990): 148–49; idem, "U.S. and Strategic Dimensions of Marshall Plan"; John Lewis Gaddis, "The Corporatist Synthesis: A Skeptical View," *Diplomatic History* 10 (Fall 1986): 357–62; idem, "New Conceptual Approaches," 408; Woods, *Changing of Guard*. It

Despite its limitations, the corporatist approach has promoted a broader understanding of the Marshall Plan. As Lawrence S. Kaplan observes, the European Recovery Program provided a great psychological boost to European morale during a period of intense disorder and insecurity. Also, as Lundestad argues, the postwar payments crisis posed a bigger problem than British historian Alan S. Milward has suggested; its resolution required Germany's economic and military participation in Europe's recovery, an arrangement necessitating the influence of the United States. Hogan's study of the Marshall Plan successfully relates domestic political and economic elements to foreign policy by placing the program within America's historic "search for order" at home. Corporatism also helps to right the balance between domestic and foreign influences on America's foreign relations by correcting the distortion caused by those historians whose focus has been on postwar forces outside the United States. And, despite Leffler's reservations about corporatist theory, he agrees with Hogan that the Marshall Plan provided the chief impetus to postwar European economic and political stability. It seems safe to regard corporatism as still another instrument by which historians can add to their understanding of the Cold War.[46]

In another helpful approach, Melvyn P. Leffler has taken the lead in arguing that national security must be the conceptual

should come as no surprise that corporatism works in an analysis of the development of a national oil policy. As shown earlier, economic (business, or private) and strategic (government, or public) interests paralleled each other. See Painter, *Oil and the American Century*, 2–3, 205–10.

46 Lawrence S. Kaplan, "The Cold War and European Revisionism," *Diplomatic History* 11 (Spring 1987): 146–49; Lundestad, *American "Empire,"* 25; Alan S. Milward, *The Reconstruction of Western Europe, 1945–1951* (London, 1984), xv, 2, 54, 90–92, 282, chap. 14; idem, "Was the Marshall Plan Necessary?" *Diplomatic History* 13 (Spring 1989): 231–53; Leffler, "U.S. and Strategic Dimensions of Marshall Plan," 277–78. See also William Diebold, Jr., "The Marshall Plan in Retrospect: A Review of Recent Scholarship," *Journal of International Affairs* 41 (Summer 1988): 421–45. For the economic aspects of the plan see Imanuel Wexler, *The Marshall Plan Revisited: The European Recovery Program in Economic Perspective* (Westport, 1983). For corporatism as a viable synthesis see Thomas J. McCormick, "Drift or Mastery? A Corporatist Synthesis for American Diplomatic History," *Reviews in American History* 10 (December 1982): 318–30. On corporatism as only a "methodology" or "research tool" and not "as a means to consensus" see Hoff-Wilson, "Future of American Diplomatic History," 11. For a "search for order" within the United States see Robert H. Wiebe, *The Search for Order, 1877–1920* (New York, 1967).

common denominator in any Cold War synthesis. Historians must focus on issues and crises that involve protection of domestic values from external danger. In so doing, their work will necessarily take into account the interdependence of domestic and foreign influences in shaping the nation's foreign relations. Power, Leffler argues, is the essential ingredient in national and international behavior, and in the postwar period, American power has had as its goal the establishment of political, social, and economic stability. In 1946 and 1947, geopolitical instability encouraged international disorder. Americans felt that their "core values," which Leffler defines as democracy, free enterprise, pluralism, and territorial security, were being threatened. As the Cold War progressed, American anxiety was intensified by the Soviet presence in Eastern Europe, the power vacuums in Western Europe and northeast Asia, and the prevalence of revolutionary nationalism in the Third World. By 1947, the Truman administration had dropped George F. Kennan's call for negotiations and asymmetrical containment and moved closer to globalism. Policymakers thereafter simplified their response to perceived Soviet aggression by expanding the definition of vital interests and increasing the nation's reliance upon a military solution to international problems.[47] Simply put, Truman and his advisers became concerned about Soviet behavior because they saw it as a threat both to the international system that they were trying to create and to the domestic system that they were charged to protect.

The principal problem confronting the Truman administration, Leffler argues, was to determine the extent to which it had to project American power beyond national boundaries to guarantee security and prosperity at home. In undertaking this elusive quest, the White House overzealously pursued strategic objectives along with ideological and economic expansion and thereby added to Stalin's fears. At a time when the Soviets posed no real military threat, the United States sought a "preponderance of power" that

47 Leffler, "National Security," 143–45, 147–48; idem, "American Conception of National Security," 348–49, 359–60, 362–63, plus comments by Gaddis and Kuniholm, followed by Leffler's reply, ibid., 382–400; Leffler, "From Truman Doctrine to Carter Doctrine," 250, 254, 266; idem, *Preponderance of Power*, 10–14, 55, 97–99, 237, 267–68, 310–11, 357, 488–89; Trask, "Past and Future of National Security History," 6–8, 12–13; Gaddis, *Strategies of Containment*, 25–109.

would make it the dominant voice in a global network in which the nation's security depended upon the safety of its friends everywhere. The State Department, Leffler insists, wanted to construct an international hierarchy of power based on world capitalism with the United States as the controlling power.[48] Leffler's argument raises some serious questions that remain unanswered. Where is the empirical evidence for his claim that America's drive for security was responsible for Soviet insecurity and, by logical extension, Soviet expansion? Did not the top secret material sent to the Soviet Union by Maclean and Burgess relieve much of Stalin's concern about a preemptive strike? Does not Leffler's allegation that the Soviets primarily *re*acted to American policies rest on the questionable premise that Stalin did not always operate on his own volition and in furtherance of his own interests, regardless of Washington's behavior? Indeed, did not Stalin's foreign policy goals stretch far beyond the Soviet Union's legitimate security needs to reflect what Robert C. Tucker sees as a raw drive for power?[49]

48 Leffler, "American Conception of National Security," 348–49; idem, "National Security," 150–51; idem, "From Truman Doctrine to Carter Doctrine," 263; idem, *Preponderance of Power*, 15–16, 18–19, 260–64, 493, 504, 513–17. See also idem, *The Specter of Communism: The United States and the Origins of the Cold War, 1917–1953* (New York, 1994).

49 Tucker, *Stalin in Power*. Other approaches to America's foreign relations have demonstrated their utility to understanding this period. Akira Iriye has argued that relations between peoples and societies – their "dreams, aspirations, and other manifestations of human consciousness" – comprise a cultural dimension that helps to explain international history. McCormick and Leffler have reminded us of the importance of examining relations between a country's domestic changes and those ongoing alterations in the international system in studying American policy. Another consideration, supported partly by Hogan's study of the Marshall Plan as well as by Pach's work on the military assistance program and Kaplan's extensive study of NATO, is the impact of bureaucratic conflict on policy. J. Garry Clifford draws attention to the clashes between personal and organizational interests and their impact on policymaking. Finally, Immerman and Larson have established the important relationship between psychology and foreign relations – particularly in the ways that personality factors can affect leaders' perceptions of problems. See Iriye, "Culture," *Journal of American History* 77 (June 1990): 99; idem, "Responses to Maier," 360–61; idem, "Internationalization of History," 5–6; idem, "Culture and Power: International Relations as Intercultural Relations," *Diplomatic History* 3 (Spring 1979): 115–28; Thomas J. McCormick, "World Systems," *Journal of American History* 77 (June 1990): 125–27; Leffler, "National Security," 143–45; Hogan, "Corporatism," 159; Pach, *Arming Free World*, 5; Kaplan, *Community of Interests*; J. Garry Clifford, "Bureaucratic Politics," *Journal of American History* 77 (June 1990): 161–62; Richard H. Immerman, "Psychology," ibid., 169–70, 174–75; and Larson, *Origins of Containment*.

Whereas in Leffler's work the influence of internal forces, especially capitalism, remains secondary to an emphasis on the external dangers to America's core values, the exact reverse is the case with the work of Thomas J. McCormick and other advocates of the "world-systems model." According to this model, the world capitalist system contains geographic regions suitable for markets, a metropolis as financial center, and core, periphery, and semiperiphery zones, each having certain responsibilities. Because economics is considered the essence of power, capitalist expansion is necessary. Such hegemony permits financial dominance, technological, industrial, and commercial advantages, military advances, and ideological unity. Thus does world-systems theory focus on geoeconomic rather than geopolitical considerations.[50]

Lest economics assume an undue position of dominance in American policymaking, new studies have demonstrated the strategic priorities of the Truman administration. Chester J. Pach, Jr., shows that the rush to security spawned poor judgment rather than imperial design. America's foreign policy became increasingly militarized, and yet, as Pach argues, Washington's policymakers never determined the amount of military aid needed, the time required to accomplish their aims, or the most feasible way to cut or terminate assistance without suggesting a lack of commitment. But ineptness does not equal lack of intent. In his study of Italo-American relations, E. Timothy Smith shows how in areas considered strategically crucial, economic interests were sacrificed to strategic considerations. Because the United States considered Italy militarily important to the fate of Europe and the Mediterranean, it soon revised the peace treaty of 1947 to allow that country's rearmament and eventual inclusion in NATO.[51]

50 See McCormick, "World Systems," 125–27; idem, *America's Half-Century*, 1–7, 72–73, 88–98; and Immanuel Wallerstein, *The Modern World System*, vol. 1, *Capitalist Agriculture and the Origins of the European World Economy in the Sixteenth Century* (New York, 1974). Wallerstein defines "world-economy" as a system held together by economic links but reinforced by cultural, political, and other elements. Ibid., 15. See also 38, 63.

51 Pach, *Arming Free World*, 5–6, 225–26, 229–32; E. Timothy Smith, "The Fear of Subversion: The United States and the Inclusion of Italy in the North Atlantic Treaty," *Diplomatic History* 7 (Spring 1983): 139–55; idem, "From Disarmament to Rearmament: The United States and the Revision of the Italian Peace Treaty of 1947," ibid. 13 (Summer 1989): 359–82; idem, *The United States, Italy and NATO, 1947–52* (New York, 1991).

Recent literature on the origins of the Cold War in Europe and the Near East indicates that historians of American foreign relations have not yet uncovered a conceptual synthesis but that a potential avenue to that goal might be the universal interest in national security. The only certainty is that if any sort of meaningful synthesis takes shape, it will be the *result* of a long process of research and not its cause. The new writers on the Cold War seem committed to broadening an understanding of America's foreign relations by using an interdisciplinary and multiarchival approach, and they have heeded Gordon A. Craig's warning against a type of "reductionism in which the State as an independent actor has disappeared and diplomatic history has been subsumed under social history." Of course, historians of America's foreign relations have moved beyond the state to nonstate actors and beyond elites to other participants in decision making; and they have incorporated the role of domestic factors in foreign policymaking while attempting to place that policy within the international context. At the same time, however, the great majority of these same historians have remained preoccupied with elites and the state. Thus, what is needed in Cold War historiography is exactly what is taking place today: research, depending upon the topic and availability of resources, that is multiarchival, interdisciplinary, cross-cultural, collaborative, and international.[52]

52 Gordon A. Craig, "The Historian and the Study of International Relations," *American Historical Review* 88 (February 1983): 3. See also Richard W. Leopold, "Historians and American Foreign Policy: A New Guide to the Field," *Diplomatic History* 8 (Summer 1984): 284; and Stephen G. Rabe, "Marching Ahead (Slowly): The Historiography of Inter-American Relations," ibid. 13 (Summer 1989): 304.

10

Making Known the Unknown War: Policy Analysis of the Korean Conflict since the Early 1980s

ROSEMARY FOOT

The Unknown War, *The Forgotten War*, *Korea: The War Before Vietnam*[1] – these titles and subtitles of studies of the Korean conflict published in the mid- to late 1980s give some indication of the perceived status of that event, especially in comparison with what many have seen as its offspring, or close relative, the war in Vietnam. Roger Dingman once described the neglect of Korea as resulting from its being sandwiched between the "good war" and the "bad war";[2] and Joseph Goulden attributed that neglect to the conflict's uninspiring nature. It was an event that most Americans were "eager to permit to slip through the crevices of memory."[3]

1 Jon Halliday and Bruce Cumings, *Korea: The Unknown War* (London, 1988). This book is a companion to the Thames Television series under the same name. Shown in Britain in 1988, the series was screened in the United States in late 1990. Clay Blair, *The Forgotten War: America in Korea, 1950–1953* (New York, 1987); Callum A. MacDonald, *Korea: The War Before Vietnam* (London, 1986). This chapter will not survey the literature that gives prominence to the military aspects of the war, of which Clay Blair's book is a valuable part. Further examples of studies emphasizing military matters include Bevin Alexander, *Korea: The First War We Lost* (New York, 1986); Anthony Farrar-Hockley, *The British Part in the Korean War*, vol. 1, *A Distant Obligation* (London, 1990); Max Hastings, *The Korean War* (London, 1987); Robert O'Neill, *Australia in the Korean War*, vol. 2, *Combat Operations* (Canberra, 1987); James L. Stokesbury, *A Short History of the Korean War* (New York, 1988); Harry G. Summers, Jr., *Korean War Almanac* (New York, 1990); and John Toland, *In Mortal Combat: Korea, 1950–1953* (New York, 1991). Oral histories provided by British and American soldiers are contained in Donald Knox, *The Korean War: An Oral History* (New York, 1985); and idem (with additional text by Alfred Coppel), *The Korean War: Uncertain Victory* (New York, 1988).

2 "The Korean War at Forty," Conference panel discussion, Organization of American Historians Meeting, Washington, March 1990.

3 Joseph C. Goulden, *Korea: The Untold Story of the War* (New York, 1982), xv.

The outcome has been that it has taken over thirty years for the moral and intellectual questions raised by these hostilities to be exposed and debated. For example, we have only recently discussed whether a domestic revolution with potentially regional repercussions was stopped on the peninsula in June 1950, whether the push into South Korea was a case of Southern entrapment, or of Soviet and/or North Korean aggression, whether U.S. threats to use atomic weapons were either effective or justified, and whether the costs suffered by all sides – but especially by the Koreans – in this enormously destructive war were commensurate with a negotiated settlement that plainly did not provide the basis for an eventual reunification of the peninsula.

For years, David Rees's book – an orthodox analysis that reflected and reinforced Washington's own interpretations of the war's origins and course – stood as the standard account of the war.[4] In the 1970s, revisionist literature, often in article form, challenged that orthodoxy and brought into the field a number of scholars who were primarily specialists on Asia.[5] In 1976, U.S. documents began to appear with the publication, in the series *Foreign Relations of the United States* (*FRUS*), of the first volume covering events in Korea during 1950. By 1984, all of the *FRUS* volumes for the war years were available, preceded in 1979 by the J. C. S. Historical Division's two volumes delineating the Joint Chiefs' contribution to policy formulation in the period. Finally, under the thirty-year rule, archives were steadily opening in Britain.[6]

4 David Rees, *Korea: The Limited War* (New York, 1964). See also idem, *A Short History of Modern Korea* (Port Erin, Isle of Man, 1988).

5 Examples include Frank Baldwin, ed., *Without Parallel: The American-Korean Relationship since 1945* (New York, 1975); John Gittings, "Talks, Bombs and Germs – Another Look at the Korean War," *Journal of Contemporary Asia* 5 (1975): 205–17; Jon Halliday, "The Korean War: Some Notes on Evidence and Solidarity," *Bulletin of Concerned Asian Scholars* 11 (July–September 1979): 2–18; and idem, "What Happened in Korea? Rethinking Korean History, 1945–1953," a review article for *Bulletin of Concerned Asian Scholars* 5 (November 1973): 36–44. See also Joyce Kolko and Gabriel Kolko, *The Limits of Power: The World and United States Foreign Policy, 1945–1954* (New York, 1972); Mark Selden and Edward Friedman, eds., *America's Asia: Dissenting Essays on Asian-American Relations* (New York, 1971); and Robert Simmons, *The Strained Alliance: Peking, Pyongyang, Moscow and the Politics of the Korean Civil War* (New York, 1975).

6 U.S. Department of State, *Foreign Relations of the United States, 1950* (Washington, 1976), 7 (hereafter *FRUS* with year and volume number); *FRUS, 1951* (Washington, 1983), 7; *FRUS, 1952–1954* (Washington, 1984), 15; James F. Schnabel and Robert

Not surprisingly, therefore, the 1980s witnessed a rapid increase in the number of studies of the war and its origins. In 1981 alone, four studies made their mark – those by Bruce Cumings, Charles Dobbs, Robert O'Neill, and William Stueck.[7] In 1983, Cumings edited a series of essays of such quality that they prompted further delving into the newly declassified materials.[8] James Matray's detailed study, tracing the origins of U.S. involvement in Korea from Pearl Harbor to 1950, and my analysis of the debate in Washington over the possible expansion of the conflict, appeared in 1985, and were followed in 1986 by three skillful, general studies of the war that have proven to be vital for teaching purposes.[9] In South Korea, too, there was an acceleration in research on the war, and in 1987 alone three conferences on the topic were held in the country.[10] More significant still, there has been

J. Watson, *The History of the Joint Chiefs of Staff. The Joint Chiefs of Staff and National Policy*, vol. 3, *The Korean War* (Wilmington, DE, 1979); Walter S. Poole, *The History of the Joint Chiefs of Staff. The Joint Chiefs of Staff and National Policy*, vol. 4, *1950–1952* (Wilmington, DE, 1979). Some parts of key State Department documents can also be found in Donald Stone Macdonald, *U.S.-Korean Relations from Liberation to Self-Reliance – The Twenty Year Record* (Boulder, 1992).

7 Bruce Cumings, *The Origins of the Korean War*, vol. 1, *Liberation and the Emergence of Separate Regimes, 1945–1947* (Princeton, 1981); Charles M. Dobbs, *The Unwanted Symbol: American Foreign Policy, the Cold War, and Korea, 1945–1950* (Kent, OH, 1981); Robert O'Neill, *Australia in the Korean War, 1950–1953*, vol. 1, *Strategy and Diplomacy* (Canberra, 1981); William Whitney Stueck, Jr., *The Road to Confrontation: American Foreign Policy toward China and Korea, 1947–1950* (Chapel Hill, 1981). The Dobbs volume provides a useful bibliographical essay. See also the bibliography compiled by Keith D. McFarland, *The Korean War: An Annotated Bibliography* (New York, 1986).

8 Bruce Cumings, ed., *Child of Conflict: The Korean-American Relationship, 1943–1953* (Seattle, 1983).

9 James Matray, *The Reluctant Crusade: American Foreign Policy in Korea, 1941–1950* (Honolulu, 1985). Matray has also edited a historical dictionary of the Korean War (New York, 1991). Rosemary Foot, *The Wrong War: American Policy and the Dimensions of the Korean Conflict, 1950–1953* (Ithaca, 1985); Burton I. Kaufman, *The Korean War: Challenges in Crisis, Credibility, and Command* (Philadelphia, 1986); MacDonald, *Korea.*

10 For details of various studies in Korean that were published in the 1980s, and an explanation for the spurt in interest in the war in South Korea itself, see Hakjoon Kim, "International Trends in Korean War Studies: A Review of the Documentary Literature," in *Korea and the Cold War: Division, Destruction, and Disarmament*, ed. Kim Chull Baum and James I. Matray (Claremont, CA, 1993). This book was itself the result of a conference held in Seoul in 1990. The conference demonstrated how preoccupied South Koreans remained with Dean Acheson's press club speech of January 1950 and whether the decision to place Korea outside the "defense perimeter" left the South open to attack. See, for example, Kim Chull Baum, "U.S. Policy on the Eve of the Korean War: Abandonment or Safeguard?" in ibid. John Edward

a veritable torrent of publications (many in Chinese) that focus on the Chinese role in the war, together with some that concentrate on Soviet actions, based on the partial opening of the archives, on memoirs, and on interviews, that are finding their way into academic writing. With the handing over to South Korean President Kim Young Sam on 2 June 1994 of several documents from the presidential and foreign ministry archive of the Russian Federation, documents that cover the period January 1949 to August 1953, we are on the cusp of a further deepening of our understanding of the decision-making processes in the Communist capitals of Beijing, Moscow, and Pyongyang.[11]

As a result of the originality of his contributions, his passionate commitment to the subject, and the historical and methodological sophistication of his work, Bruce Cumings strongly influenced the

Wilz, like many South Koreans, has been highly critical of the Truman administration for giving what he argues were repeated signals that it did not intend to defend the South militarily in the event of a North Korean attack. See "The Making of Mr. Truman's War," in *The Historical Re-Illumination of the Korean War: The Korean War Revisited on the Fortieth Anniversary*, ed. Lee Min Young (Seoul, 1991). The official North Korean interpretation is provided in *The US Imperialists Started the Korean War* (Pyongyang, 1977). See also Bruce Cumings's extensive discussion of the Acheson speech, including his evidence that the North Koreans believed Acheson had placed South Korea within the defense perimeter. Cumings, *The Origins of the Korean War*, vol. 2, *The Roaring of the Cataract, 1947–1950* (Princeton, 1990), chap. 13, an interpretation that is now challenged in Sergei N. Goncharov, John W. Lewis, and Xue Litai, *Uncertain Partners: Stalin, Mao, and the Korean War* (Stanford, 1993), esp. 142.

11 Four excellent historiographical essays that should be read in conjunction with this one are Bruce Cumings, "Korean-American Relations: A Century of Contact and Thirty-Five Years of Intimacy," in *New Frontiers in American-East Asian Relations: Essays Presented to Dorothy Borg*, ed. Warren I. Cohen (New York, 1983), 237–82; Robert J. McMahon, "The Cold War in Asia: The Elusive Synthesis," in this volume; Nancy Bernkopf Tucker, "Continuing Controversies in the Literature of U.S.-China Relations since 1945," and Chen Jian, "Sino-American Relations Studies in China: A Historiographical Review," the latter two of which are in *Pacific Passage: The Study of American-East Asian Relations on the Eve of the 21st Century*, ed. Warren I. Cohen (forthcoming). The essays by Chen and Tucker survey much of this new literature that details China's role in the Korean War. The Soviet side is best captured in Goncharov et al., *Uncertain Partners*; and Katherine Weathersby, "Soviet Aims in Korea and the Outbreak of the Korean War, 1945–1950: New Evidence from the Russian Archives," *Cold War International History Project*, working paper no. 8 (1993), and idem, "The Soviet Role in the Early Phase of the Korean War: New Documentary Evidence," *Journal of American-East Asian Relations* 2 (Winter 1993): 425–58. A useful evaluation of the new Chinese materials is provided in Steven M. Goldstein and He Di, "New Chinese Sources on the History of the Cold War," *Cold War International History Project Bulletin* (Spring 1992).

terms within which the Korean War's origins were subsequently debated. Even the very latest scholarship, it sometimes seems, has been engulfed in a polite – and occasionally not so polite – conversation with Cumings. In 1981, in a work that concentrated on the years 1945 to 1947, he argued that the outbreak of the fighting in June 1950 needed to be placed within the context of the civil struggle that was taking place on the peninsula, a struggle that had already claimed something in the order of one hundred thousand lives between 1945 and 1950. In the second volume of his study, published in late 1990, Cumings analyzed the period from 1947 to early 1951. He again gave primacy to the civil aspects of the conflict and sought to establish that the North Koreans planned and carried out the June attack with minimal external involvement and that they owed their initial successes to the widespread support they received from South Koreans. Cumings also provided a structuralist analysis of American foreign policy that allowed him to situate the American response in Korea within a larger strategy designed to expand and sustain the world market system. In Cumings's view, Korea intersected with the "grand global conflict between socialism and capitalism, and the internal struggle for the American state between nationalists and internationalists." Under "Acheson's hegemonic guidance and global vision," the victory went to a coalition of internationalists and containment advocates. Such a global vision meant that the events of 25 June 1950 could never be interpreted – or seen in the absurd light – as the moment when "Koreans invade Korea."[12]

This 1981 study shaped the literature of the 1980s in a number of direct ways. Many later studies, for example, incorporated Cumings's explanation of the war's antecedents but tended to combine (though rarely to discuss) his explanation of the local aspects of the conflict with its international dimensions. John Merrill's study, unusually and commendably, provided both a stimulating study of the peninsular origins of the war and evidence that suggested that the war "cannot be isolated either from its local context or from the complex resonances between events in the peninsular and the international environment." Burton I.

12 Cumings, *Origins of the Korean War*, vol. 1. See also idem, *Origins of the Korean War* 2:745, 630, 769.

Kaufman similarly described the war as "a great power struggle between the United States and the Soviet Union superimposed on a civil war between North and South Korea." Callum A. MacDonald saw the conflict at one level as the "latest act in a civil war" but at another level as a "clash between the Soviet and American power systems." And although Peter Lowe argued that "for the inhabitants of Korea, developments in June 1950 did not constitute the beginning of a war but rather the continuation of a civil war that had started in 1945," he added that the hostilities can best be understood "in the light of developments in the Korean peninsula, in China, Japan and in Europe."[13]

William Stueck, however, has long been dissatisfied with what he sees as the undue emphasis that has been given to local considerations. In an article published in 1986, he set about challenging that emerging consensus by focusing his lens on the international background to the conflict. Before much of the new Chinese and Soviet literature had become available, Stueck was already pointing to coordination among the Communist states on the eve of war. While he accepted that it had been Kim Il Sung's plan to attack the South, it was Mao who "provided him with experienced manpower, and Stalin [who] supplied the airplanes and heavy equipment that gave North Korea its margin of superiority over the South. North Korea may have been an assertive pawn in an international chess game," Stueck states, "but it was a pawn nonetheless."[14] Stueck's major international history of the Korean War, published in 1995, further develops these arguments concerning Communist coordination and integrates the work of, for example, Chen Jian, and Sergei Goncharov et al., with the Western materials that Stueck has been gathering and interpreting over many years. He remains convinced that without Soviet support there would have been no (international) Korean War.[15]

The predominant explanation for the American decision to

13 John Merrill, *Korea: The Peninsular Origins of the War* (Newark, 1989), 189; Kaufman, *Korean War*, 1; MacDonald, *Korea*, 3; Lowe, *Origins of the Korean War*, xii, x.

14 William Stueck, "The Korean War as International History," *Diplomatic History* 10 (Fall 1986): 294.

15 William W. Stueck, *The Necessary War: An International History of the Korean War* (Princeton, 1995). See also Chen Jian, *China's Road to the Korean War: The Making of the Sino-American Confrontation* (New York, 1994); and Goncharov, Lewis, and Xue, *Uncertain Partners.*

intervene in the fighting in June 1950 has been that South Korea was not important in and of itself, but that the South, "almost entirely an American creation," could be used to demonstrate to the Soviet Union as well as to America's allies that the United states would respond decisively to any Communist challenge.[16] Despite the general acceptance of the credibility argument, however, other interpretations have been advanced. Matray, for example, has pointed somewhat controversially to an American commitment since Pearl Harbor to the fostering in Korea of an independent, prosperous, and representative government, and Stephen Pelz has given primacy to the domestic storm clouds that were gathering over the Truman administration's Asian policy. In Pelz's view, "Truman and Acheson needed to interpret the North Korean attack as part of a global challenge to justify reversing their Asian policy," a reversal that was forced upon them by critics within the bureaucracy, such as Dean Rusk, John Foster Dulles, and Douglas MacArthur, and by opponents within Congress.[17]

More recently, the credibility argument has been questioned directly: Ronald McGlothlen has argued that such concerns were essentially subordinate to the issue of Korea's political and economic importance to Japan's future. It is an argument that he identifies with Acheson in particular and that pitted the U.S. secretary of state's "economic vision of containment" against the Pentagon's "global strategic vision," at least until the outbreak of the war.[18]

The Soviet role in the origins of the war, as noted above, has recently become somewhat better understood.[19] Prior to recent revelations, most authors had come to conclude that Kim Il Sung took the decision to attack the South largely alone, although it was assumed that Stalin and Mao were probably consulted. As

16 The phrase "American creation" is Cumings's own, from his introduction to *Child of Conflict*, 15. See also Dobbs, *Unwanted Symbol*; Kaufman, *Korean War*, 160–92; and Stueck, *The Road to Confrontation*.

17 Matray, *Reluctant Crusade*, 252; Stephen Pelz, "U.S. Decisions on Korean Policy, 1943–1950: Some Hypotheses," in Cumings, ed., *Child of Conflict*, 131.

18 Ronald McGlothlen, "Acheson, Economics, and the American Commitment in Korea, 1947–50," *Pacific Historical Review* 58 (February 1989): 24; and idem, *Controlling the Waves: Dean Acheson and U.S. Foreign Policy in Asia* (New York, 1993), esp. chap. 3.

19 One of the undoubted benefits of the ending of the Cold War has been the greatly improved prospects for international collaboration among scholars previously denied such opportunities and the partial opening of the archives (notwithstanding attendant difficulties) in the former Soviet Union.

MacDonald was to put it, it had become "clear that Stalin knew about Kim's plan without necessarily approving the timing." Gye-Dong Kim agreed with this interpretation, but added that it could well have been Syngman Rhee's war preparations and announced plans to march north that speeded up the reinforcement of the North Korean army and advanced the date of intervention.[20]

Until recently, many had relied upon Nikita Khrushchev's memoirs as the main source for establishing the communication channels between Kim, Mao, and Stalin. In a review of these memoirs, however, John Merrill had already cast serious doubt on the accuracy of the published text, arguing that it did not always reflect either the vagueness of or the hesitancy behind Khrushchev's remarks. Gromyko's *Memoirs*, published in 1989, failed to provide any additional information on the war's origins, although he did refer to Soviet "moral and material" assistance to the North. One intriguing detail he did offer, however, was that he had advised Stalin that the Soviet Union should return to the Security Council in late June in order to be in place to use the veto against the UN resolution calling for members to resist the attack on the South. But Stalin firmly rejected the idea. Was this because the Soviet leader hoped to see the United States drain its resources on the peninsula and even become embroiled with the Chinese, thus ensuring Beijing's dependence on Moscow and the potential exhaustion of Washington? Gromyko did not provide much support for this inference, because he described Stalin's decision as having been "guided for once by emotion."[21]

In his 1990 volume, Cumings also required us to contemplate the logic of Gromyko's request and Stalin's refusal. That logic led Cumings to conclude that the "Soviets did not have advance knowledge of the attack," for, if Moscow did have such advance

20 MacDonald, *Korea*, 28; Gye-Dong Kim, "Who Initiated the Korean War?" in *The Korean War in History*, ed. James Cotton and Ian Neary (Manchester, 1989), 44.

21 Nikita Khrushchev, *Khrushchev Remembers* (Boston, 1970), and *Khrushchev Remembers: The Glasnost Tapes*, trans. and ed. Jerrold L. Schecter with Vyacheslav V. Luchkov (Boston, 1990). John Merrill, review of *Khrushchev Remembers* in *Journal of Korean Studies* 3 (1981): 181–91; Andrei Gromyko, *Memories: from Stalin to Gorbachev* (London, 1989), 212 and 131–32. Stueck, in turn, has responded to Merrill's review of Khrushchev's memoirs. See "The Soviet Union and the Korean War," in Baum and Matray, eds., *Korea and the Cold War*, 113n5. An early argument that Stalin hoped to embroil the Chinese in the conflict is detailed in Mineo Nakajima, "The Sino-Soviet Confrontation: Its Roots in the International Background of the Korean War," *Australian Journal of Chinese Affairs* 1 (January 1979): 19–47.

knowledge, and given its probable anticipation that Washington would take the Korean question to the United Nations, "why would instructions – either to return or continue the boycott – not have been transmitted earlier? Why would Malik have not vetoed the UN resolution?" To further support his argument that Kim Il Sung largely took the decision to advance south alone, Cumings suggests that one corollary benefit for Moscow of its absence from the Security Council might have been "to teach a recalcitrant ally a lesson about moving independently."[22]

That interpretation of the Security Council decision, and a number of other aspects of the Sino-Soviet-North Korean roles in the war, have recently been challenged in the work of Katherine Weathersby and in the Goncharov, Lewis, and Xue volume referred to earlier. These authors argue that, while it was Kim's initiative to reunify the peninsula by force, the North Korean leader did eventually manage to persuade Stalin to give his support to this venture and to provide the weaponry needed to overcome any South Korean resistance. Stalin's concerns about possible U.S. entry into the fighting were apparently overcome by the combined force of Kim's argument that "(1) it would be a decisive surprise attack and the war would be won in three days; (2) there would be an uprising of 200,000 Party members in South Korea; (3) there were guerrillas in the southern provinces of South Korea; and (4) the United States would not have time to participate." Stalin, having acquiesced but still uneasy, urged Kim to consult with Mao and to gain his approval, which Kim did on 13 May 1950. According to the materials newly released to the South Korean government, Mao asked for an explanation from Stalin, who immediately replied to the effect that the final decision concerning Kim's reunification plan had to be made in collaboration with Beijing. Mao did give his support, according to Goncharov, Lewis, and Xue, because having previously argued that a Chinese attack on Taiwan would not trigger a U.S. response, he could not argue the reverse for the Korean case.[23]

22 Cumings, *Origins of the Korean War* 2:636–37.

23 Goncharov et al., *Uncertain Partners*, 144, 146–47; Kim Hak-Joon, "Russian Archives on Origins of Korean War," *Korea Focus* 2 (September–October 1994): 22–31. See also Weathersby, "Soviet Aims in Korea"; and idem, "The Soviet Role in the Early Phase."

Such revelations suggest not only a more prominent Soviet role in the origins of the war than had hitherto been assumed but also greater Chinese involvement. Zhai Zhihai and Hao Yufan, for example, in one of the earlier publications to use Chinese documents and interview material, categorically stated in 1990 that "only Stalin [and not Mao] was informed of Kim's detailed plan and the possible date for action, since, in Kim's mind, the Soviet Union was the only patron capable of helping him to carry out his reunification plan," and Goncharov, Lewis, and Xue also accept this.[24] But the newly released telegrams make that lack of detailed knowledge seem less likely, given that Stalin had attempted to make Soviet acceptance of Kim's aims conditional on Chinese agreement.

If China was, therefore, "embroiled" at an early stage, to include its agreement to redeploy several tens of thousands of Korean troops who had fought in the Chinese civil war,[25] we still need to understand its decision in October 1950 to intervene overtly in the fighting. Clearly, the older impression that Chinese leaders were preoccupied with domestic issues on the eve of the war can still be sustained despite the new material; nevertheless, serious military preparations did begin immediately to guard against unforeseen eventualities rendering the October decision as part of a more complex set of decisions.[26]

Jonathan Pollack, for example, focusing on the security aspects, has described the growing consternation in Beijing throughout July, August, and September and has provided evidence to

24 Zhai Zhihai and Hao Yufan, "China's Decision to Enter the Korean War: History Revisited," *China Quarterly* 121 (March 1990): 100; Goncharov et al., *Uncertain Partners*, 153. In September and October 1986, Warren I. Cohen interviewed several of Zhou Enlai's associates. The interviewees insisted that the Chinese were surprised by the outbreak of the war and their troops intervened because the Americans were bombing Manchuria and because U.S. ground forces were approaching the Yalu. See "Conversations with Chinese Friends: Zhou Enlai's Associates Reflect on Chinese-American Relations in the 1940s and the Korean War," *Diplomatic History* 11 (Summer 1987): 288.

25 Chen Jian, "The Sino-Soviet Alliance and China's Entry into the Korean War," CWIHP, Working Paper no. 1, 1992, 23; Cumings, *Origins of the Korean War* 2:350.

26 Michael H. Hunt, "Beijing and the Korean Crisis, June 1950–June 1951," *Political Science Quarterly* 107 (Fall 1992): 458. Hunt is a reliable and effective guide to many of the new Chinese materials. There is still much of value to be found in Allen Whiting, *China Crosses the Yalu: The Decision to Enter the Korean War* (Stanford, 1960).

show that the debate over intervention continued well into October, even after Zhou Enlai's famous late-night meeting with K. M. Panikkar, the Indian ambassador. It was only on 13 October that Mao and other leaders reaffirmed the necessity for the force deployment in Korea, having weighed once more the risks and costs of intervention against the perceived threats to the PRC's security if its forces did not intervene.[27]

Zhai and Hao fleshed out the argument that national security interests dominated the decision. By October, they state, Mao had come to see a direct conflict with the United States as inevitable and likely to emerge in the form of a U.S. attack either from Korea, Vietnam, or Taiwan. The party chairman, with the support of General Peng Dehuai, argued that if such a confrontation were inevitable, Korea was a more favorable battleground for China because of its short distance from the soviet Union and from the PRC's industrial center.[28]

Chen and Hunt, on the other hand, offer a more complex set of reasons for Chinese intervention, including not only the protection of China's national and physical security but also the argument that the war could be used to mobilize the Chinese population and thus contribute to the transformation of Chinese society, could contribute to the consolidation of Chinese Communist Party rule in the country, and could serve to bolster China's depiction of itself as the promoter of the revolution in the East. Chen does not see the Soviets as pressuring China to enter the

27 Jonathan Pollack, "The Korean War and Sino-American Relations," in *Sino-American Relations, 1945–1955: A Joint Reassessment of a Critical Decade*, ed. Yuan Ming and Harry Harding (Wilmington, DE, 1989), 213–37. See also Pollack's study, sponsored by the RAND Corporation: *Into the Vortex: China, the Sino-Soviet Alliance, and the Korean War* (Stanford, 1990). Russell Spurr also conducted interviews inside and outside of China on this topic and details leadership debates in Beijing in August and September 1950. He sees Mao as more ready to contemplate intervention than other Chinese leaders. See *Enter the Dragon: China's Undeclared War against the U.S. in Korea, 1950–1951* (New York, 1988). For a useful discussion of the repercussions for domestic policy of China's entry into the war see Lawrence S. Weiss, "Storm around the Cradle: The Korean War and the Early Years of the People's Republic of China, 1949–1953" (Ph.D. diss., Columbia University, 1981); for domestic influences on the policy decision to intervene see Byong-Moo Hwang and Melvin Gurtov, *China under Threat: The Politics of Strategy and Diplomacy* (Baltimore, 1980).

28 Zhai and Hao, "China's Decision," esp. 106–11. See also the security interests argument contained in Thomas J. Christensen, "Threats, Assurances, and the Last Chance for Peace: The Lessons of Mao's Korean War Telegrams," *International Security* 17 (Summer 1992).

war: in his view, Mao (in particular) was predisposed to do so once it became clear that Kim was in trouble. The Chinese leader was also willing to enter the fighting even without Soviet air support.[29]

Clearly, our understanding of China's decision to intervene and of Sino-Soviet relations on the eve of China's entry are advancing at a rapid pace, and this new evidence will need to be given close consideration in future studies of the Korean conflict.

The U.S. decision to cross the 38th parallel has long been seen as an unmitigated disaster. There is virtual unanimity among scholars that Beijing's overt entry into the fighting could have been averted and that the war could have been concluded in the autumn of 1950 if the United States had refrained from crossing that line. In explaining this myopia, Stueck emphasizes U.S. ethnocentrism, and he and Kaufman return to the powerful conditioning factor of "credibility" for the Truman administration, with both its domestic and international audiences. I have stressed the expected domestic political benefits to be derived from the movement north and the lack of strong restraints either in terms of dissenting allies, countermoves from Moscow, or objections within the U.S. bureaucracy.[30]

In his introduction to *Child of Conflict*, and in a far more developed form in the 1990 study, Cumings additionally urges us also to remember the presence of the "roll-back" coalition within the Truman administration. The rollback of North Korea, he argues, was prefigured in NSC-48, which described U.S. policy as designed not only to contain Soviet power and influence in Asia but also, where feasible, to reduce it. If the policy had been successful, Cumings suggests, the next debate within the rollback coalition might have been whether to go beyond the Yalu. The failure of rollback led, consequently, to bipartisan agreement that containment was the only possible policy.[31]

29 Chen, *China's Road to the Korean War*, esp. chap. 6; Hunt, "Beijing and the Korean Crisis," 459–65. An analysis that emphasizes Chinese efforts to deter the perceived threat to their borders is contained in Zhang Shuguang, *Deterrence and Strategic Culture: Chinese-American Confrontation, 1949–1958* (Ithaca, 1992), 94–99.

30 Stueck, *The Road to Confrontation*, 254–55; Kaufman, *Korean War*, 83–85; Foot, *The Wrong War*, 67–74.

31 Cumings, "Introduction: The Course of Korean-American Relations, 1943–1953," 32, 51; idem, *Origins of the Korean War*, vol. 2.

Although General Douglas A. MacArthur figures prominently in discussions of the crossing of the 38th parallel and of the agreement to press on to the Yalu, few studies would now claim that civilians within the Truman administration did not share fully in those decisions. Michael Schaller, in his highly readable biography of the "Far Eastern general," documents vividly the Joint Chiefs' timidity in the face of MacArthur's demands to launch his "end the war" offensive; but it is clear that many others were also in awe of MacArthur after the stunningly successful Inchon landing which, in Schaller's words, proved to be a "deceptively easy victory."[32]

After the debacle of December 1950, the general's complaints about his superiors' failure to see the conflict as the central struggle in the Cold War cost him his job, thus provoking a public outcry that Kaufman describes as "one of the singular events in modern American political history." The hearings into MacArthur's dismissal, preceded by careful coaching of Senators Richard Russell (D-GA) and Lyndon B. Johnson (D-TX), among others, ended with a whimper. But as Dingman rightly concludes, MacArthur continued to cast a long shadow over the conduct of the war in Truman's time, and to put the commander-in-chief "on the defensive." The general forged "an alliance between the White House and the Pentagon that demanded restraint in escalation beyond Korea but allowed intensification of the fighting within it," forced the administration to find a new legitimizing principle (the non-forcible repatriation policy), and helped to keep alive the military's belief that "force could still somehow be used to compell the enemy to compromise."[33]

The domestic political atmosphere in which policy toward Korea

32 Michael Schaller, *Douglas MacArthur: The Far Eastern General* (New York, 1989), 199.

33 Kaufman, *Korean War*, 163. Kaufman provides an illuminating portrait of the MacArthur hearings. For an analysis of those portions of the hearings deleted from the public record see John Edward Wilz, "The MacArthur Hearings of 1951: The Secret Testimony," *Military Affairs* 39 (December 1975): 167–73. Roger Dingman, "Why Wars Don't End: American Civil-Military Relations and Korean War Termination Policies, 1951–1953" (Paper presented at the International Studies Association conference, London, 1989), 13. See also D. Clayton James's three-volume study, *The Years of MacArthur*, esp. vol. 3, *Triumph and Disaster, 1945–1964* (Boston, 1985).

was formulated is best captured in Kaufman's excellent use of contemporary magazine and newspaper material, in Gary Reichard's analysis, and in biographies of Senator Joseph R. McCarthy (R-WI). McCarthy was at the height of his power during the war years, and his impact on the two U.S. administrations' ability to govern and on overseas perceptions of the United States was clearly enormous. "Asia-firsters" within Congress were only too willing to aid and abet McCarthy and were able to operate in the fertile ground of the congressional elections of November 1950 and during the presidential election campaign of 1952. As disillusionment with the conflict set in and casualties began to mount, the conflict was increasingly dubbed "Truman's war," a fact that contributed to a precipitate decline in Truman's popularity rating. Despite the contribution of the studies noted here, and of Ronald Caridi's 1968 account, there is still room for a fuller analysis of the relationship between domestic politics and the war in Korea.[34]

If domestic critics besieged U.S. policymakers, and particularly Truman and Acheson, no less troublesome to the Truman and Eisenhower presidencies were America's Western and Asian allies. The British role during the conflict has been covered most extensively, but important volumes also detail the Australian and Canadian perspectives. These studies serve to remind us that, however close the relationship with the United States, different priorities and different perceptions did exist. Australia, for example, had several other important strategic issues before it, including the greater threats to its security in the Middle East and Malaya, the pursuit of a security treaty with the United States, and the conclusion of a peace treaty with Japan. Britain was also more concerned about developments in Europe and the Middle East. Consequently, London and its Commonwealth partners

34 Kaufman, *Korean War*; Gary Reichard, *Politics as Usual: The Age of Truman and Eisenhower* (Arlington Heights, IL, 1988); David Oshinsky, *A Conspiracy So Immense: The World of Joe McCarthy* (New York, 1985); Thomas C. Reeves, *The Life and Times of Joe McCarthy* (New York, 1982); Ronald J. Caridi, *The Korean War and American Politics: The Republican Party as a Case Study* (Philadelphia, 1968). Useful analyses of the domestic environment are also contained in Frances H. Heller, ed., *The Korean War: A 25 Year Perspective* (Lawrence, 1977), in particular, John Edward Wilz, "The Korean War and American Society," 112–96, including comments and discussion.

sought throughout the war to find a means of bringing the hostilities to an end and to prevent the fighting from extending to the territory of the PRC. Rarely did the British offer any policy initiatives of their own, for their influence had been diminished to the point where they could only moderate the language the United States chose to adopt when formulating its policy positions and offer counsel designed to curb what the Foreign Office believed was a tendency for Washington to be "irresponsible" in the exercise of power.[35] Four episodes in Anglo-American relations have received detailed treatment, all of which show the essentially secondary role of the British and their unwillingness to risk a breach with the Americans: their tentative proposal to establish a buffer zone in Korea, some 60 to 120 miles south of the Yalu; their advice to the Truman administration concerning the crossing of the 38th parallel; Attlee's contributions at the summit with Truman in December 1950; and British activity over the Indian-sponsored resolution at the United Nations General Assembly in November 1952, concerning the prisoner of war (POW) repatriation issue.

Peter Farrar takes a number of us to task for failing to give the British proposal for a buffer zone its due place in the literature on the war. This move was important in his view because, if adopted, it might have prevented Chinese intervention in Korea and allowed for a cease-fire nearer the 39th than the 38th parallel.

35 Robert O'Neill, *Australia in the Korean War* 1:xv, 108; Denis Stairs, *The Diplomacy of Constraint: Canada, the Korean War and the United States* (Toronto, 1974); Paul M. Evans and B. Michael Frolic, *Reluctant Adversaries: Canada and the People's Republic of China, 1949–1970* (Toronto, 1991); Michael L. Dockrill, "The Foreign Office, Anglo-American Relations, and the Korean War, June 1950–June 1951," *International Affairs* 62 (Summer 1986): 475. An overview of British policy during the Korean War, designed for school and undergraduate use, has been written by Callum A. MacDonald. He summarizes Britain's task as being "to steer the United States away from isolationism, but to contain American power." See *Britain and the Korean War* (Oxford, 1990), 95. Ra Jong-yil, on the other hand, sees London's objectives (ultimately unrealizable) as developing the special relationship with the United States and reinforcing Britain's traditional great power role in the world. See "Special Relationship at War: The Anglo-American Relationship during the Korean War," *Journal of Strategic Studies* 7 (September 1984): 301–17. Another broad overview of the relationship between the United States and Britain is provided by Peter Lowe in "The Significance of the Korean War in Anglo-American Relations, 1950–1953," in *British Foreign Policy, 1945–1956*, ed. Michael Dockrill and John W. Young (London, 1989), 126–48. One volume of the British official history of the war has been published: Farrar-Hockley, *The British Part in the Korean War*, vol. 1.

But the scheme foundered on Beijing's disinterest and on its belief, which mirrored the thinking of MacArthur and of the Joint Chiefs at the time, that "force could win the day"– a view that could be reexamined in light of the new materials on the Chinese decision-making process. Britain's misgivings about the U.S. decision to cross the 38th parallel were also not promoted early or hard enough. With respect to the Truman-Attlee summit, Dingman and I both agree that it accomplished little of tangible benefit, except an increased sensitivity to each other's points of view, a renewed determination to manage the frictions over East Asian policy, and an elapse of time during which the Unified Command's military fortunes improved on the peninsula, thereby reducing the possibility that the United States would launch a wider war.[36]

In November 1952, Anglo-American relations probably reached their nadir. MacDonald's, Qiang Zhai's, and Roger Bullen's accounts of this episode at the United Nations clearly illustrate Acheson's irritation with British (and Canadian) attempts to build support for the Indian resolution in opposition to the U.S.-sponsored proposal. Once again, however, the result was a compromise that Bullen saw, incorrectly in my view, as evidence of American willingness to accommodate the British perspective.[37]

By this late stage of the war, Western allies had become restive and critical of America's inability to bring the armistice negotiations

36 Peter Farrar, "A Pause for Peace Negotiations: The British Buffer Zone Plan of November 1950," in Cotton and Neary, eds., *Korean War in History*, 66–79; William Stueck, "The Limits of Influence: British Policy and American Expansion of the War in Korea," *Pacific Historical Review* 55 (February 1986): 65–95; Roger Dingman, "Truman, Attlee, and the Korean War Crisis," in *The East Asian Crisis, 1945–1951, International Studies* (London, 1982): 1–42; Rosemary Foot, "Anglo-American Relations in the Korean Crisis: The British Effort to Avert an Expanded War, December 1950–January 1951," *Diplomatic History* 10 (Winter 1986): 43–57. For an analysis of British perceptions of South Korea's internal political problems see Ra Jong-yil, "Political Settlement in Korea: British Views and Policies, Autumn 1950," in Cotton and Neary, eds., *Korean War in History*, 51–65.

37 MacDonald, *Korea*, 169–73; Qiang Zhai, *The Dragon, the Lion, and the Eagle: Chinese-British-American Relations, 1949–1958* (Kent, OH, 1994), 121–22; Roger Bullen, "Great Britain, the United States and the Indian Armistice Resolution on the Korean War: November 1952," in *Aspects of Anglo-Korean Relations, International Studies* (London, 1984): 27–44. Bullen overlooks the Indian government's original intention – which London agreed with – to obscure the reference to non-forcible repatriation for prisoners of war, a matter that was made explicit in the resolution's final U.S.-supported form.

to a satisfactory conclusion and the fighting to an end. Syngman Rhee, on the other hand, balked at the notion of an armistice, seeing in that eventual step the end of his plan for reunifying the peninsula. All recent surveys of the war provide examples of Rhee's efforts to wreck the negotiations. Barton Bernstein outlines numerous occasions when Rhee undertook actions that endangered Unified Command troops, and he, John Kotch, and Edward Keefer analyze the Truman and Eisenhower administrations' consideration of a military coup against the South Korean president, occasioned in particular by the political crisis in the South in May 1952, the release of seventeen thousand non-repatriate North Korean prisoners from Unified Command camps in June 1953, and his continual threats to "march north."[38]

These and similar actions occasioned some harsh statements from Rhee's alleged allies. Winston Churchill, for instance, wrote in July 1953 that if he "were an American, as I might have been, I would vote for Rhee going to hell and taking Korea with him," and Eisenhower confided to his diary that "of course, the fact remains that the probable enemy is the Communists, but Rhee has been such an unsatisfactory ally that it is difficult indeed to avoid excoriating him in the strongest of terms."[39]

Rhee largely escaped such excoriation; instead, he was rewarded with a mutual defense treaty and extensive military and economic aid. Yet, even with the security treaty and generous U.S. funding, Rhee could still be obstructive, as his actions at the Geneva Conference on Korea and Indochina in 1954 showed. Fortunately for him, the continuing deterioration of the French military position in Indochina enhanced his role as an ally. In these circumstances, Dulles in particular became "more willing to overlook Rhee's

38 Barton Bernstein, "Syngman Rhee: The Pawn as Rook: The Struggle to End the Korean War," *Bulletin of Concerned Asian Scholars* 10 (January–March 1978): 38–47; John Kotch, "The Origins of the American Security Commitment to Korea," in Cumings, ed., *Child of Conflict*, 244–52; Edward C. Keefer, "The Truman Administration and the South Korean Political Crisis of 1952: Democracy's Failure" (Paper presented at the Annual SHAFR Conference, Williamsburg, Virginia, June 1989).

39 Churchill's remarks are quoted in Michael Dockrill, "The Foreign Office, Anglo-American Relations, and the Korean Truce Negotiations, July 1951–July 1953," in Cotton and Neary, eds., *Korean War in History*, 114, and Robert H. Ferrell, ed., *The Eisenhower Diaries* (New York, 1981), 248. Also relevant to this period is idem, ed., *The Diary of James C. Hagerty* (Bloomington, 1983); and idem, *Off the Record: The Private Papers of Harry S. Truman* (New York, 1980).

faults, especially since the Western allies were failing to cooperate with U.S. efforts elsewhere in Asia."[40]

Unfortunately for the historiography of the Korean War, the policies of the Asian countries with interests in the conflict have had relatively little exposure. The Indian government was active throughout, putting forward various negotiating proposals and relaying messages (not always successfully) between Beijing and Western capitals. Nothing could illustrate the value of its non-aligned stance better than the agreement that it should chair the Neutral Nations Repatriation Commission, set up to deal with the non-repatriate POWs, and the acceptance of the proposal that its troops alone should supervise the arrangements for the final disposal of the POWs. Though New Delhi often got bad press in the United States at the time for what was seen as its undue interference and so-called appeasement of the Chinese, it is hard to think of any other state that could have played such a valuable role in helping to bring the Korean conflict to an end.[41]

Tokyo's role in the war also rates further elaboration. Reinhard Drifte has pointed to Japan's position as a logistical base and to the use of its nationals in combat duties. In addition to acting as mercenaries in Korea, other Japanese were sent to that country to operate "dredges and lighters in the harbours, to run power plants and other essential industries in what had been their former work places when they ruled Korea." (Rhee objected to the presence of these technicians and workers, and he arrested and brought to trial as many as he could, which forced the Americans to keep them under escort or within U.S. installations.) Some forty-six Japanese vessels and twelve hundred former Imperial Navy personnel were also on combat duty in mine-sweeping operations in

40 Henry W. Brands, Jr., "The Dwight D. Eisenhower Administration, Syngman Rhee and the 'Other' Geneva Conference of 1954," *Pacific Historical Review* 61 (February 1987): 78.

41 One of the most useful sources remains Shiv Dayal, *India's Role in the Korean Question* (Delhi, 1959). See also Sarvepalli Gopal, *Jawaharlal Nehru: A Biography*, vol. 2, *1947–1956* (London, 1979); and Rosemary Foot, *A Substitute for Victory: The Politics of Peacemaking at the Korean Armistice Talks* (Ithaca, 1990). India's policies and their impact on Anglo-American relations during the Korean War are also discussed in Anita Inder Singh, *The Limits of British Influence: South Asia and the Anglo-American Relationship, 1947–1956* (London, 1993).

the Korean harbors of Wonsan, Kunsan, Inchon, Haeju, and Chimnampo.[42] Communist claims of direct Japanese involvement, made and dismissed at the time, can therefore be sustained.

This friction between the United States and its Western and Asian allies surfaced frequently during the Korean conflict, and especially during the truce talks. It caused the Americans to devote much attention not only to the demands of the adversary but also to the proposals of their friends.[43] Despite the length and complexity of these armistice negotiations, however, the process by which the war ended has tended to be neglected in comparison with analysis of the first year of hostilities. Fortunately, we do have Barton Bernstein's invaluable essay, and Sydney Bailey, Kaufman, MacDonald, O'Neill, and Stueck devote large parts of their studies to the period of "negotiating while fighting."[44] Issues that were controversial in the 1950s, such as whether the decision to hold the talks was taken at a time when the Chinese were capable of being pushed back to the Yalu, are less so now. Though the memoirs of Peng Dehuai point to the sorry plight of Chinese soldiers in April and May 1951, it has also been established that, as UN armies moved north, enemy resistance stiffened markedly and Western allied unity started to crumble. The Unified Command thus had good reason to seek a settlement at or near the 38th parallel, and the Chinese were not unrealistic in their assumption

42 Reinhard Drifte, "Japan's Involvement in the Korean War," in Cotton and Neary, eds., *Korean War in History*, 129–30. For an interesting argument that details the relative insignificance of the war for the Japanese and Japanese society see Roger Dingman, "The Dagger and the Gift: The Impact of the Korean War on Japan," in *A Revolutionary War: Korea and the Transformation of the Postwar World*, ed. William J. Williams (Chicago, 1993), 201–24.

43 This is one of the points that I have tried to establish in my book on the armistice negotiations, *A Substitute for Victory*. A Chinese interpretation of the talks has been written by Chai Chengwen and Zhao Yongtian, *Banmendian tanpan* (Beijing, 1989). See also Chen Jian, "China's Strategies to End the Korean War" (A paper prepared for the 1994 annual convention of the Association of Asian Studies, Boston, March, 1994).

44 Barton Bernstein, "The Struggle over the Korean Armistice: Prisoners of Repatriation?" in Cumings, ed., *Child of Conflict*, 261–307. See also Sydney D. Bailey, *The Korean Armistice* (London, 1992); Kaufman, *Korean War*; MacDonald, *Korea*; O'Neill, *Australia in the Korean War*, vol. 1; and Stueck, *The Necessary War*. Neglect of how wars are brought to an end is widespread. For a review of some of the literature on this topic see Francis A. Beer and Thomas F. Mayer, "Why Wars End: Some Hypotheses," *Review of International Studies* 12 (1986): 95–106. Useful points on Korea are also contained in Sydney Bailey, *How Wars End: The United Nations and the Termination of Armed Conflict* (Oxford, 1982).

that a cease-fire at that line would be an acceptable solution to both sides. In this respect, however, Beijing miscalculated, because Washington would not contemplate that divided line once Unified Command forces had established themselves above it in the central and eastern sectors. Most authors support this refusal to give up ground, except for Clay Blair, who reminds us that South Korea has never been deemed capable of holding line "Kansas" (as it was termed) on its own and that a tripwire could as well have been based on the 38th parallel as on Kansas,[45] a decision that might have speeded up the signature of the armistice agreement by several months.

Further valuable insight into the first year of these negotiations is provided in the diary of Admiral C. Turner Joy, who headed the Unified Command negotiating team until May 1952. This diary, available for some time in longhand form at the Hoover Institution, was published in 1978. As we might expect from such a source, Joy is more critical of Rhee within these pages and somewhat more sympathetic to Communist negotiating positions than in his published work of 1955.[46] The diary also provides graphic accounts of the plight of POWs in Unified Command camps and indications of Joy's unease with the non-forcible repatriation policy, especially during the period of the "screening" to determine POW "wishes" regarding repatriation. Bernstein, Kaufman, and MacDonald, using this and other documentary evidence, discuss how this policy came to be adopted and note Truman's crucial intervention in the debate. I have tried to determine the point at which the Truman administration had the information needed to conclude that a genuine choice regarding repatriation could no longer (if it ever could) be made and to ascertain whether there were opportunities to compromise over this flawed policy.[47]

The formulation of POW policy coincided with the height of

45 Peng Dehuai, *Memoirs of a Chinese Marshal: The Autobiographical Notes of Peng Dehuai* (Beijing, 1984), 480; Clay Blair, *The Forgotten War*, 935. Some thirty-seven thousand U.S. troops remain in South Korea.

46 Allen E. Goodman, ed., *Negotiating while Fighting: The Diary of Admiral C. Turner Joy at the Korean Armistice Conference* (Stanford, 1978); Admiral C. Turner Joy, *How Communists Negotiate* (New York, 1955).

47 Bernstein, "Struggle over the Korean Armistice"; Kaufman, *Korean War*, chap. 7; MacDonald, *Korea*, chap. 8; Foot, *A Substitute for Victory*, chaps. 4 and 5.

Communist accusations that the United States had used bacteriological weapons to fight the war. Chen's research in the Chinese archives suggested that "in early 1952 both C[hinese] P[eople's] V[olunteer] commanders and Beijing leaders *truly believed* that the Americans had used biological weapons against the Chinese and North Koreans." Yet no hard evidence has been unearthed to support this claim, and the evidence remains circumstantial: Washington did, after all, give protection after the Second World War to leading members of the Japanese and German germ warfare establishments; the International Scientific Commission's report, though denigrated, was never disproven; and the United States did develop huge stocks of nerve gas (Sarin) and considered its possible use after China's entry into the Korean conflict. For Jon Halliday, the use of bacteriological agents needed to be considered alongside other brutal behavior sanctioned by U.S. administrations, including the dropping of 635,000 tons of bombs on the North, the use of 32,000 tons of napalm, and the bombing of the North's irrigation dams. Could not such a nation have gone that one step further, he suggests.[48] Maybe, but there is still no direct evidence that it did.

The Korean War occurred at the height of U.S. power, even if one only measures that power in relational terms. Given Washington's political and economic strength, its nuclear and technological superiority, it is not surprising to find that, in the context of the inconclusive nature of the conflict, policymakers debated frequently the potential role of nuclear weapons during the war. The pioneering work of Roger Dingman has revealed Truman's attempts to engage in atomic diplomacy.[49] Eisenhower and Dulles's boasting that their use of nuclear threats had been instrumental

48 Chen, "China's Strategies," 35–36; Jon Halliday, "Anti-Communism and the Korean War, 1950–1953," in *The Socialist Register*, ed. Ralph Miliband et al. (London, 1984), 151; Gavan McCormack, *Cold War, Hot War: An Australian Perspective on the Korean War* (Sydney, 1983), 154–56.

49 Roger Dingman, "Atomic Diplomacy during the Korean War," *International Security* 13 (Winter 1988–89): 50–91. See also Roger M. Anders, "The Atomic Bomb and the Korean War: Gordon Dean and the Issue of Civilian Control," *Military Affairs* 52 (January 1988): 1–6. Anders details Truman's decision to transfer nine atomic bombs to the air force. It was a decision that marked the end of civilian control of part of the nation's war reserve of these weapons and it represented a change in "fundamental national policy established during peacetime by the Congress." See ibid., 1.

in bringing the conflict to a close has also invited investigation. Their decision to terminate the armistice negotiations in late May 1953 and to expand the war unless agreement was reached on the POW question has further attracted scholarly attention, in part because of the horrifying implications of this proposal.

To take the issue of Eisenhower's nuclear coercion first, several questions are embedded within this: namely, whether the Eisenhower administration truly attempted atomic diplomacy; if it did, the question remains whether such coercion was taken seriously or not; and if the threats were not made (or were made and not taken seriously) whether the explanation for the war's end lies more with internal conditions within the Communist states or with the astuteness of Eisenhower's non-nuclear diplomacy.

In response to the first question, Dingman has argued that the United States in 1953 did not engage in coercive diplomacy but in "milder, non-nuclear, persuasive diplomacy." Officials in the State Department, he states, "hoped to nudge Moscow into persuading Beijing and Pyongyang to accept a compromise on the prisoner of war issue." Kaufman also downplays the nuclear threat (although not to the same degree), arguing that the White House did not have to give the Chinese an explicit warning, because they "understood [Eisenhower] was thinking along these lines anyway."[50]

Conversely, Richard K. Betts, Daniel Calingaert, Keefer, MacDonald, and myself have argued that such a threat was made, although there remain areas of doubt as to the timing and number of signals sent.[51] Where members of the latter group differ is over the extent to which those threats were taken seriously or were instrumental in bringing the war to an end. Calingaert is persuaded that the threat achieved its objective; MacDonald, however, points out that both Washington and Beijing compromised at the negotiating table during the period when the threat was

50 Dingman, "Atomic Diplomacy," 85; Kaufman, *Korean War*, 319–20.

51 Richard K. Betts, *Nuclear Blackmail and Nuclear Balance* (Washington, 1987), 31–47; Daniel Calingaert, "Nuclear Weapons and the Korean War," *Journal of Strategic Studies* 11 (June 1988): 177–202; Edward C. Keefer, "President Dwight D. Eisenhower and the End of the Korean War," *Diplomatic History* 10 (Summer 1986): 267–89; MacDonald, *Korea*, 189; Foot, "Nuclear Coercion and the Ending of the Korean Conflict," *International Security* 13 (Winter 1988–89): 92–112.

being conveyed. In his view, "both sides compromised to end a struggle whose costs were out of all proportion to its benefits." Moreover, an important study of Chinese attitudes toward nuclear weapons during the war has argued that Beijing did not find U.S. threats credible. The Chinese had been combing Western sources to establish that U.S. officials had greatly exaggerated the destructive capabilities of nuclear weapons, and they believed that properly designed underground shelters and tunnels would prove as effective a defense against atomic bombs as they had proven to be against U.S. conventional bombing. Interviews in Beijing have added another twist to this explanation by revealing that Beijing's leaders thought that world and U.S. public opinion made it unlikely that America would make good on those threats. And more recently Zhang Shuguang has argued that the Chinese were preparing for a U.S.-led amphibious landing in Korea, not nuclear attack. When it did not come and, instead, the Americans offered final terms in May for the exchange of prisoners, the Chinese interpreted this as a U.S. concession forced as a result of the tactical offensives the CPV had launched. According to Zhang, CPV headquarters "neither had any information that atomic weapons had been deployed in the Far East, nor received any warning from the United States about the possibility that such weapons might be used."[52]

Evidence exists, therefore, to cast doubt on the claim that the Chinese were fully aware of Eisenhower's attempts at nuclear coercion or took them seriously if they were aware, and other suggestions need to be examined to explain why the POW issue was resolved on 8 June 1953. Dingman refers to Washington's subtle diplomacy; Kaufman puts more emphasis on the death of

52 Calingaert, "Nuclear Weapons," 197; MacDonald, *Korea*, 190; Mark A. Ryan, *Chinese Attitudes toward Nuclear Weapons: China and the United States during the Korean War* (Armonk, 1989); John Wilson Lewis and Xue Litai, *China Builds the Bomb* (Stanford, 1988), 15. Note also the remarks of Cohen's interviewees: "Beijing took Truman's threat to use the atomic bomb during the war seriously," but "Chinese leaders were not intimidated when Dwight Eisenhower's aides spread rumours that the bomb would be used." See "Conversations with Chinese Friends," 288–89. Zhai and Hao, "China's Decision," 107, argue that Mao and Peng believed in October 1950 that the "scarcity of atomic bombs meant it would be hard to use them in a peripheral area since they had been originally intended primarily to check the Soviet Union." In addition, see Zhang, *Deterrence and Strategic Culture*, 131–39.

Stalin and his successors' perceived need to improve their relations with the West. In his view, "Moscow probably pressured China and North Korea to end the conflict." MacDonald, on the other hand, believes it possible that the Communists' decision to wind down the war may have been made as early as October 1952, mainly for political and economic reasons, and that the process was simply accelerated after Stalin's death – a position that Chen's findings now endorse.[53] Certainly, most of these who have written recently on this topic agree that Eisenhower and Dulles's claims about the efficacy of their atomic threats were exaggerated.

What the Eisenhower administration would have done if agreement on the POW issue had not been reached is an intriguing and disturbing question. The UN commander during that period, General Mark Clark, subsequently reported that if the talks were terminated, he was authorized to step up air and naval operations, including launching "conventional attacks on bridges across the Yalu and on bases in Manchuria."[54] Whether the Eisenhower administration would have readied itself to use nuclear weapons against China and North Korea, as its contingency decision of 20 May suggested, is more difficult to determine because of the long lead-time (about a year) that was required before any nuclear plan could be put into operation.[55] Certainly, Eisenhower seemed to be preoccupied with finding a role for these weapons between February and May 1953. But he did send out contradictory signals over the matter from time to time, convincing those more charitable than myself that this was all part of his "hidden-hand" strategy to achieve peace and not to raise the stakes.[56]

53 Kaufman, *Korean War*, 306; MacDonald, *Korea*, 182; Chen, "China's Strategies," 40–42.

54 Barry M. Blechman and Robert Powell, "What in the Name of God is Strategic Superiority?" *Political Science Quarterly* 97 (Winter 1982–83): 595n17.

55 The National Security Council agreed on 20 May 1953 that "if conditions arise requiring more positive action in Korea," air and naval operations would be extended to China and ground operations in Korea intensified. The Joint Chiefs had already made it clear that none of these courses of action could be successfully carried out without the use of atomic weapons. See *FRUS, 1952–1954* 15:1066–68.

56 See, for example, Stephen E. Ambrose, *Eisenhower*, vol. 2, *The President* (London, 1984). The term "hidden-hand" is generally associated with Fred I. Greenstein's interpretation of the Eisenhower presidency. See his *The Hidden-Hand Presidency: Eisenhower as Leader* (New York, 1982).

This period of decision making reveals much about Eisenhower's presidential style and deserves to enter more fully into the revisionist debate on the quality of the leadership he provided. Stephen Ambrose and Dingman have praised Eisenhower's handling of these final months of the war, the latter seeing the president as cautious and circumspect, more of "an owl than a hawk." Keefer is more skeptical of this notion of Eisenhower proceeding wisely and deliberately and, although he acknowledges that the president deserves "full credit" for ending the conflict, Keefer argues that "he did so with misdirection and confusion."[57]

As for President Truman, some have seen a failure of leadership here, too. In a review of Kaufman's book on Korea, Michael H. Hunt takes Kaufman to task for not laying the blame for the confusion surrounding the administration's Korean War policy on Truman himself. The portrait that emerges for Hunt is of a president "playing a generally aloof but also a spasmodically disruptive role in the policy process." Certainly, Truman often did fail to think through positions, particularly his stance over POW repatriation; and there was a marked tendency to engage in what Deborah Larson, in her stimulating psychological study of Cold War decision makers, has referred to as "premature cognitive closure."[58]

Determining the intentions and thought processes of those charged with formulating policies is a complex task. But it is nevertheless one that many scholars have been willing to undertake. In Stanley Hoffmann's essay delineating some of the issues

57 Dingman, "Atomic Diplomacy," 84; Keefer, "Dwight D. Eisenhower," 268. U. Alexis Johnson who held the office of deputy assistant secretary of state for Far Eastern affairs subsequently argued in his memoirs that "instead of the finely crafted plan for ending the war the Republicans had intimated they possessed, both the President and Secretary were clearly groping their way." See *The Right Hand of Power* (Englewood Cliffs, 1984), 162. For a useful overview of the literature on Eisenhower and his era, and a powerful analysis of his thinking on "war, peace, and security in the nuclear age," see Richard H. Immerman, "Confessions of an Eisenhower Revisionist: An Agonizing Reappraisal," *Diplomatic History* 14 (Summer 1990): 319–42.

58 Michael H. Hunt, "Korea and Vietnam: State-of-the-Art Surveys of our Asian Wars," *Reviews in American History* 15 (June 1987): 322–23. See also his "Beijing and the Korean Crisis," 473. Deborah Welch Larson, *Origins of Containment: A Psychological Explanation* (Princeton, 1985), 146–47. Truman's presidency is also analyzed in Robert J. Donovan, *Tumultuous Years: The Presidency of Harry S. Truman, 1949–1953* (New York, 1982).

dividing orthodox and revisionist analyses of the Cold War, he argued that revisionists assumed that U.S. policymakers were "either mere puppets manipulated without their awareness . . . or else purposeful puppets conniving for, but carefully disguising, their real goals."[59] Postrevisionists, on the other hand, see the path that policymakers tread as being blocked or obscured at many points of the way as leaders are buffeted by domestic critics and pressured by wayward allies.[60]

This latter perspective has predominated because archival research encourages receptivity to multiple pressures and because the prevailing focus in foreign policy analysis models is on the level of the state and not on that of the international system. The consensus that emerged in the literature of the 1980s that debated whether the United States has been in decline as a hegemonic power, however, could provide a useful corrective to the postrevisionist position. This literature has argued that international processes since the advent of the first Cold War have facilitated the U.S. establishment of a structural position that has allowed Washington to exercise control over other peoples' security, to manage the system of production of goods and services and of finance and credit, and to determine the acquisition, communication, and storage of knowledge and information.[61] In light of these arguments, there is clearly an avenue that may allow a reconciliation between evidence of the constraints that plainly operated on American decision makers over particular issues and at particular times with the finding that processes also allowed the United States to establish an international order broadly compatible with its values and interests. Such a reconciliation may serve to remove the charge of reductionism that can be leveled not only at those who pitch their analyses at the level of the state

59 Stanley Hoffmann, "Revisionism Revisited," in *Reflections on the Cold War*, ed. Lynn Miller and Ronald Pruessen (Philadelphia, 1974), 12.

60 McMahon, "The Cold War in Asia," categorizes these different approaches as radical versus liberal. The modes of analysis associated with "rational actor" versus "governmental politics" also capture another area of difference among these authors.

61 See, for example, Susan Strange, "The Persistent Myth of Lost Hegemony," *International Organization* 41 (Autumn 1987): esp. 565; and Bruce Russett, "The Mysterious Case of Vanishing Hegemony; or, Is Mark Twain Really Dead?" ibid. 39 (Spring 1985): 207–31.

but also at those who place it at the level of the international system.[62]

For many, the Korean conflict was crucial to the establishment of U.S. hegemony. Korea's impact on U.S.-Third World relations, on U.S. policies toward the Soviet Union, on the size of America's military budgets, and on its security relations with its major allies, though moving us from a study of the whole to the parts of the system, have all been seen as crucial building blocks in the creation of the postwar international order. What remains in dispute, however, is the extent to which the hostilities in Korea should be seen as *the* crucial event in the Cold War, or as one that simply reinforced the underlying direction in U.S. policy toward making its containment policies global and its attitudes toward its Communist foes more rigid. Nancy B. Tucker, in her signal study of U.S.-Chinese relations, has clearly seen the Korean War as a critical turning point in that relationship. Lawrence S. Kaplan, in his study of NATO's formative years, described the changes that it brought about in Europe as "more profound" than those it wrought in Asia, because West Germany was assimilated and the United States shed "the substance as well as the language of isolationism." Stueck has argued that, where NATO is concerned, Korea provided political leaders with the necessary "sense of urgency." Robert Jervis, in an argument notable for its logical precision and clarity, went even further. In his view, "without Korea, U.S. policy would have been very different, and there were no events on the horizon which could have been functional substitutes for the war. The international or the American domestic system may have 'needed' high defense budgets, the globalization of American commitments, and the militarization of NATO, but these patterns arose only in the wake of Korea."[63]

62 See, for example, Theda Skocpol, "Wallerstein's World Capitalist System: A Theoretical and Historical Critique," *American Journal of Sociology* 82 (March 1977): 1075–90, for criticism of the reductionism inherent in this systemic approach.

63 Nancy B. Tucker, *Patterns in the Dust: Chinese-American Relations and the Recognition Controversy, 1949–1950* (New York, 1983), epilogue; Lawrence S. Kaplan, *The United States and NATO: The Formative Years* (Lexington, KY, 1984), 149–50; Stueck, "The Korean War, NATO, and Rearmament," in Williams, ed., *A Revolutionary War*, 174. Robert Jervis, "The Impact of the Korean War on the Cold War," *Journal of Conflict Resolution* 24 (December 1980): 563. Matray also sees the war as a "crucial turning point in postwar American diplomacy." See *Reluctant Crusade*, 257.

Other scholars have taken a different view of the meaning of the Korean conflict, arguing that it accelerated Cold War developments but was not pivotal. In Walter LaFeber's view, changes within NATO were less a response to the war than reactions to a deeper, systemic crisis that had been developing for over a year. Melvyn P. Leffler has argued that it was during 1947 and 1948 that the "Cold War assumed many of its most enduring characteristics . . . when American officials sought to cope with an array of challenges by implementing their own concepts of national security." Although he agrees with Jervis that it would have been difficult to obtain the large budgetary increases in the tight fiscal and election year of 1948, his point is that the mode of thinking about national security that subsequently accelerated the arms race and made military intervention in Asia possible was already in place. Gordon H. Chang and Andrew Rotter make similar points. Rotter, in his study of U.S. involvement in Southeast Asia, which adopts a political economy approach, contends that although Korea "accelerated" everything, the "major conceptual and practical shifts had occurred over the foregoing nine months."[64] For these authors, the perceptual parameters had been established prior to June 1950, and it was simply a matter of time before the actual policies were implemented.

Despite these differences, there is near universal agreement that the war had a regrettable impact on U.S. postwar diplomacy. While still acknowledging the tragic quality of the war, however,

64 Walter LaFeber, "NATO and the Korean War: A Context," *Diplomatic History* 13 (Fall 1989): 461; Melvyn P. Leffler, "The American Conception of National Security and the Beginnings of the Cold War, 1945–1948," *American Historical Review* 89 (April 1984): 349, 379, and his *A Preponderance of Power: National Security, the Truman Administration, and the Cold War* (Stanford, 1992); Gordon H. Chang, *Friends and Enemies: China, the United States, and the Soviet Union, 1948–1972* (Stanford, 1990), 75; Andrew J. Rotter, *The Path to Vietnam: Origins of the American Commitment to Southeast Asia* (Ithaca, 1987), 205. See also Stueck, *The Road to Confrontation*, 151–52. Cumings focuses on the meaning of the Korean War in the context of the development of the capitalist world order. See his article "The Origins and Development of the Northeast Asian Political Economy: Industrial Sectors, Product Cycles, and Political Consequences," *International Organization* 38 (Winter 1984): 1–40. He argues that the Korean War boosted Japan's economy and tied its future to South Korea and Taiwan, both of which became enmeshed in a system of American hegemony that brought them economic and military aid on a vast scale. In this connection, see also the political economy argument formulated in McGlothlen, *Controlling the Waves*.

some authors try to take a long-term perspective and to suggest some positive benefits from U.S. intervention as well. John Mueller has written that, because the conflict demonstrated the risk to the superpowers of limited war, it "may well have been an extremely important stabilizing event that vividly constrained methods each side could use in pursuing its policy." Stueck agrees, going so far as to title his major study of the conflict *The Necessary War*. In his view, U.S. action reduced the prospects of U.S.-Soviet confrontations in the future and "perhaps even set the stage for a modicum of détente."[65]

This view, in distinction to Jervis's, assumes that there were other areas where Communist states would seek to use force to expand their control and that U.S. intervention in Korea put a lid on these. Utilizing the work of Beatrice Heuser and Bela Kiraly – the latter a Hungarian exile formerly in Budapest's Ministry of Defence – Stueck has argued that the Balkans, and Yugoslavia in particular, were under serious threat. Yet, Stalin is said to have changed his mind about a lightning strike after Western mobilization in the period after June 1950.[66] This argument implies that a Soviet attack on Yugoslavia would have had more than local repercussions – a debatable proposition – and it leaves in place questions concerning the appropriateness of the American military response to Korean developments: whether the United States could have achieved the benefits of stability and a degree of détente at much lower costs, in terms of blood spilled and treasure lost.

Any argument for the stabilizing influence of the Korean War on superpower relations needs to include in the equation the number of proxy wars that have been fought in the Third World since 1953 and to assess the damage done by the conflict to the

65 John Mueller, *Retreat from Doomsday* (New York, 1989), 130. Stueck does also view Korea as a tragedy: *The Necessary War*, esp. chap. 10. See also his "Korean War as International History," 309.

66 Stueck, "Korea in Historical Perspective: The Necessary War, the Tragic War," in *The Korean War*, ed. Chae-Jin Lee (Claremont, CA, 1990). Beatrice Heuser, *Western "Containment" Policies in the Cold War: The Yugoslav Case, 1948–53* (London, 1989). See also Heuser's "NSC 68 and the Soviet Threat: A New Perspective on Western Threat Perception and Policy Making," in *Review of International Studies* 17 (1991): 17–40; and Bela Kiraly, "The Aborted Soviet Military Plans against Tito's Yugoslavia," in *At the Brink of War and Peace: The Tito-Stalin Split in a Historic Perspective*, ed. Wayne S. Vucinich (New York, 1982).

concept of collective security within the structure of the United Nations. In addition, we all need to contemplate more fully the consequences for Koreans of this bitter war. Preoccupation with the intricacies of big-power maneuvering has led to a neglect of the study of the impact of this war on Koreans, individually and communally, and on Korea itself, politically and institutionally.[67] Were there not other, less costly ways available to effect an end to or amelioration of superpower confrontation and to bring about a modicum of détente? Stueck now concludes: "It is a good bet . . . that Korea's contribution to international stability could have been achieved with a much shorter, less destructive course."[68] And I cannot but agree.

As one contemplates developments on the Korean peninsula over the period when the academic literature surveyed here was being produced, one is struck by the ironies that abound, and the business that remains unfinished. U.S. forces remain on the peninsula, and Washington retains a leading diplomatic role on issues affecting Korea, as demonstrated most recently by its direction of matters concerning the North Korean nuclear program. Russia's and China's positions, however, have been significantly transformed, for at the precise time that their roles in the origins of the Korean War were becoming better understood, their relations with the South were being normalized. Such normalization has clearly been at the expense of Pyongyang's interests, leaving it bereft of allies and facing a far more powerful South especially in economic and political terms. The international aspects of the Korean War are broadly over, therefore, but still the civil conflict remains unresolved. Reunification, when it occurs, is now perceived as likely to happen largely on the South's terms, either as a result of the collapse of the North or through its gradual incorporation into an international society whose norms Kim Il Sung, Mao, and Stalin once sought to challenge. Reconciliation between North and South Korea will thus carry a meaning well beyond the developments immediately affecting this divided country, much as did the outbreak of the war in June 1950.

67 On this point see, for example, B. C. Koh, "The War's Impact on the Korean Peninsula," in Williams, ed., *A Revolutionary War*.
68 Stueck, *The Necessary War*, 637.

11

Eisenhower Revisionism: The Scholarly Debate

STEPHEN G. RABE

For historians of U.S. foreign relations, the 1980s and early 1990s were the Eisenhower years. Books and articles on President Dwight D. Eisenhower's foreign policy appeared at an accelerating rate. In *Diplomatic History*, for example, only analyses of the origins of the Cold War surpassed the number of publications on Eisenhower and his diplomacy. The Eisenhower era was also a popular subject at scholarly conclaves. In 1988, Princeton University hosted an impressive conference on Secretary of State John Foster Dulles. And, in 1990, both the University of Kansas and Gettysburg College celebrated the centennial of Eisenhower's birth with major scholarly conferences.[1]

The Eisenhower boom can be readily explained. Scholarly output is influenced by access to documentary evidence. The Eisenhower Library in Abilene, Kansas, is a superb institution, and its knowledgeable archival staff manages a monumental collection of documents. The president and his staff were inveterate diarists, memoirists, notetakers, and recorders of conversation. Ann Whitman, Eisenhower's personal secretary, compiled a comprehensive record of Oval Office business, including copies of the president's diaries.[2] Aides meticulously kept minutes of the Eisenhower administration's

1 Three collections of papers presented at conferences on the Eisenhower years are Richard H. Immerman, ed., *John Foster Dulles and the Diplomacy of the Cold War* (Princeton, 1990); Joann P. Krieg, ed., *Dwight D. Eisenhower: Soldier, President, and Statesman* (New York, 1987); and Shirley Anne Warshaw, ed., *Reexamining the Eisenhower Presidency* (Westport, 1993).

2 For Whitman's role in the administration see Robert J. Donovan, *Confidential Secretary: Ann Whitman's 20 Years with Eisenhower and Rockefeller* (New York, 1988), 39–160.

366 National Security Council (NSC) meetings. General Andrew J. Goodpaster's memorandums of his boss's conversations with foreign policy officials are so precise, so replete with idiomatic expressions, that researchers believe that they can recover not only the president's words but also the tone and manner in which he spoke. Indeed, during their first day at the Eisenhower Library, a peculiar mixture of excitement and panic might well engulf scholars as they contemplate how rich but also how overwhelming are the library's holdings.[3]

The library's records are also unusually accessible for historians of the Cold War. During the 1970s, when government classification review policies were reasonable, archivists and scholars successfully declassified key records such as the Whitman File. By comparison, the restrictive classification policies that characterized the 1980s have retarded research for the post-Eisenhower period. To be sure, problems of access existed. Scholars had to wait until the late 1980s and early 1990s to read minutes of NSC meetings held during Eisenhower's second term.

Even though the Eisenhower Library's resources are impressive, historians would not have joined the pilgrimage to Abilene unless they judged the Eisenhower years worthy of study. As has been widely remarked, Eisenhower's reputation has grown as the popular mood has soured and as his successors have blundered. Eisenhower governed during a period that was presumably peaceful, prosperous, and predictable. In particular, the president avoided misadventures like the Bay of Pigs and debacles like Vietnam. He did not abuse presidential authority as other Republicans did in the Watergate and Iran-contra scandals. He also restrained military spending and balanced the federal budget during three fiscal years.[4] Eisenhower has accordingly become a man for all political seasons. To political conservatives, he is the leader

3 For a description of the Eisenhower Library's holdings see *Historical Materials in the Dwight D. Eisenhower Library* (Abilene, KS, 1989).

4 For fiscal politics in the Eisenhower era see Iwan W. Morgan, *Eisenhower versus "the Spenders": The Eisenhower Administration, the Democrats, and the Budget, 1953–1960* (New York, 1990); and John W. Sloan, *Eisenhower and the Management of Prosperity* (Lawrence, 1991). See also Robert Griffith, "Dwight D. Eisenhower and the Corporate Commonwealth," *American Historical Review* 87 (February 1982): 87–122.

who believed in limited government. As Alan Brinkley has noted, the resurgence of Eisenhower's popularity during the 1980s came at a time when many Americans questioned "the desirability of a powerful president and the feasibility of a large and active government."[5] On the other hand, Eisenhower's stewardship could serve, in Robert Burk's words, as a reaffirmation of the "Roosevelt-style assertive presidency." With the idealism and "hard-headed pragatic methods" that typified Franklin D. Roosevelt, Eisenhower took charge in promoting peace and nuclear disarmament.[6]

Historians have produced numerous historiographic pieces on the origins and development of Eisenhower revisionism.[7] What follows is an examination of how historians of U.S. foreign relations have worked with the new interpretation. The essay will first outline the theses of Robert A. Divine, Fred I. Greenstein, and Stephen E. Ambrose. At the beginning of the 1980s, these respected scholars published representative and influential studies that solidified Eisenhower's reputation as a wise and skillful global leader and defined the historiographical movement that has become known as Eisenhower revisionism.[8] The essay will then

5 Alan Brinkley, "A President for Certain Seasons," *Wilson Quarterly* 14 (Spring 1990): 119.

6 Robert Burk, "Eisenhower Revisionism Revisited: Reflections on Eisenhower Scholarship," *The Historian* 50 (February 1988): 197–98.

7 Barton Bernstein, "Foreign Policy in the Eisenhower Administration," *Foreign Service Journal* 50 (May 1973): 17–20, 29–30, 38; Vincent P. DeSantis, "Eisenhower Revisionism," *Review of Politics* 38 (April 1976): 190–207; Gary W. Reichard, "Eisenhower as President: The Changing View," *South Atlantic Quarterly* 77 (Summer 1978): 265–81; Mary S. McAuliffe, "Commentary/Eisenhower, the President," *Journal of American History* 68 (December 1981): 625–32; Arthur M. Schlesinger, Jr., "The Ike Age Revisited," *Reviews in American History* 11 (March 1983): 1–11; Anthony James Joes, "Eisenhower Revisionism: The Tide Comes In," *Presidential Studies Quarterly* 15 (Summer 1985): 561–71; Steve Neal, "Why We Were Right to Like Ike," *American Heritage* 37 (December 1985): 49–65; Robert J. McMahon, "Eisenhower and Third World Nationalism: A Critique of the Revisionists," *Political Science Quarterly* 101 (Fall 1986): 453–73; Burk, "Eisenhower Revisionism," 196–209; Bernard Sternsher, "Two Views of Eisenhower: Robert A. Divine and Piers Brendon," *Psychohistory Review* 17 (Winter 1989): 215–35; Brinkley, "A President for Certain Seasons," 110–19; Jeff Broadwater, "President Eisenhower and the Historians: Is the General in Retreat?" *Canadian Review of American Studies* 22 (Summer 1991): 47–59; John Robert Greene, "Bibliographic Essay: Eisenhower Revisionism, 1952–1992, A Reappraisal," in Warshaw, ed., *Reexamining the Eisenhower Presidency*, 209–20. For a useful annotated bibliography see R. Alton Lee, comp., *Dwight D. Eisenhower: A Bibliography of His Times and Presidency* (Wilmington, DE, 1991).

8 Important scholarly studies published in the 1970s that introduced Eisenhower revisionism include Herbert Parmet, *Eisenhower and the American Crusades* (New York, 1972); Blanche Wiesen Cook, *Dwight David Eisenhower: Antimilitarist in the White*

analyze how individual case studies have sustained or challenged the assumptions of Eisenhower revisionism.

Writing with "a basic sympathy for a badly underrated President," Divine has delivered a concise, compelling brief for Eisenhower, whose glory was that he kept the United States at peace during the 1950s. He ended the Korean War, avoided military intervention during crises over Indochina, Quemoy and Matsu, Suez, and Berlin, and stopped testing nuclear weapons in the atmosphere. Divine concedes that Eisenhower's accomplishments "were negative in nature," for he did not reach his objectives of reducing Cold War tensions and curbing the nuclear arms race. "But at the same time, his moderation and prudence served as an enduring model of presidential restraint – one that his successors ignored to their eventual regret" in Cuba and Vietnam. In presenting his striking thesis, Divine relied on secondary-source literature in the hope that his "essays will stimulate the archival research on which a mature understanding of Eisenhower's place in history must finally rest."[9] A decade later, Divine heeded his own call, offering a well-documented analysis of Eisenhower's response to the Soviet Union's successful 1957 launch of Sputnik. Divine again lauds the president for his "prudence and restraint" in trying to calm the public and for resisting congressional demands for massive increases in military spending.[10]

If Eisenhower so deserved the mantle of presidential greatness, why had scholars and pundits disdained him? In part, as Divine explains, these analysts, bred in the progressive tradition, had unfairly "applied an activist standard to Ike's negative record."[11] In political scientist Fred Greenstein's view, they also had failed to appreciate Eisenhower's "hidden-hand" style of leadership. In public, the president projected an image of warmth, goodwill,

House (St. Charles, MO, 1974); Peter Lyon, *Eisenhower: Portrait of the Hero* (Boston, 1974); Charles C. Alexander, *Holding the Line: The Eisenhower Era, 1952–1961* (Bloomington, 1975); Gary W. Reichard, *The Reaffirmation of Republicanism: Eisenhower and the Eighty-Third Congress* (Knoxville, 1975); and Elmo R. Richardson, *The Presidency of Dwight D. Eisenhower* (Lawrence, 1979).

9 Robert A. Divine, *Eisenhower and the Cold War* (New York, 1981), viii–ix, 11, 20–23, 153–55. See also idem, *Blowing on the Wind: The Nuclear Test Ban Debate, 1954–1960* (New York, 1978).

10 Robert A. Divine, *The Sputnik Challenge* (New York, 1993), viii, 191–96.

11 Divine, *Eisenhower and the Cold War*, 154.

and semantic confusion; in private, Eisenhower was a crafty politician who dominated the policymaking process. The documentary records, such as the minutes of NSC meetings, sustain the argument that Eisenhower, not his subordinates, made the critical decisions in his administration. Greenstein contends that Eisenhower was keen on protecting his personal standing and role as chief of state, the symbol of national unity. His garbled syntax was a public ruse designed to deflect criticism and avoid polarization. When he wanted to make his intentions clear, he delegated others, like Secretary of State Dulles, to serve as "lightning rods" for what were essentially his Cold War policies. With this leadership style, Eisenhower retained his popularity and credibility with the American public.[12] He was then free to promote the domestic tranquility commonly associated with the Eisenhower era.

Combining the insights of Divine and Greenstein along with extensive research at the Eisenhower Library, Stephen Ambrose has prepared perhaps the most widely read brief for Eisenhower revisionism. The heart of his case is in Eisenhower's boast that "the United States never lost a soldier or a foot of ground in my administration. We kept the peace. People ask how it happened – by God, it didn't just happen, I'll tell you that."[13] Ambrose agrees that Eisenhower "liked making decisions," that he was at "the center of events," and that "he ran the show." The show included ending the war in Korea and managing international crises without going to war. But beyond avoiding war, Eisenhower worked for peace. Ambrose judges the president's Atoms-for-Peace plan "the best chance mankind has had in the nuclear age to slow and redirect the arms race." And "almost single-handedly" Eisenhower restrained U.S. military spending. He did not, however, achieve an enduring peace. Ambrose faults Eisenhower for being unduly hostile toward the Soviet Union and for

12 Fred I. Greenstein, *The Hidden-Hand Presidency: Eisenhower as Leader* (New York, 1982), 5–9, 57–72, 87–91. Craig Allen argues that Eisenhower's "hidden-hand" style can also be detected in the president's successful use of mass communication for political purposes. Allen, *Eisenhower and the Mass Media: Peace, Prosperity, and Prime-Time TV* (Chapel Hill, 1993), 6–9, 204–13.

13 Eisenhower quoted in Stephen E. Ambrose, *Eisenhower*, vol. 2, *The President* (New York, 1984), 626.

allowing his distrust of the Communists to overwhelm his fear of an arms race. Eisenhower also too hastily equated Third World nationalism with communism. Nonetheless, Ambrose understands why "millions of Americans felt the country was damned lucky to have him": Eisenhower was "a great and good man."[14]

The core beliefs of Eisenhower revisionism can be summarized. Eisenhower approached the presidency in a thoughtful, systematic way. He had developed during his military career superb management skills and a comprehensive knowledge of international affairs, and he used those assets to master the presidency and dominate the policymaking process. Eisenhower's leadership was particularly apparent during foreign policy crises, when he astutely steered the nation away from potential disasters. In Ambrose's words, "what Eisenhower had done best was managing crises."[15] The president also worked, albeit unevenly, to reduce East-West tensions. Knowing that an accelerated arms race would destabilize Soviet-American relations and damage the American economy, at the very least, he successfully blocked massive increases in U.S. military expenditures.

Perhaps the least contested issue in Eisenhower revisionism is the emphasis on Eisenhower's central role within his administration. The traditional interpretation of an inept, bewildered president overwhelmed by his formidable secretary of state had been most scathingly put by Townsend Hoopes, who claimed that a strident, self-righteous, fanatical Dulles "was indisputably the conceptual fount, as well as the prime mover, of U.S. foreign policy during those years."[16] But even a cursory review of the presidential papers would lead scholars to challenge Hoopes's thesis. The papers reveal a diligent man with a lively mind, and even partisan critics like Arthur M. Schlesinger, Jr., concede that "Eisenhower showed more energy, interest, self-confidence, purpose, cunning, and command than many of us supposed in the 1950s."[17]

Eisenhower exercised his leadership through both formal

14 Ibid., 9–12, 150, 618–27.
15 Ibid., 626.
16 Townsend Hoopes, *The Devil and John Foster Dulles* (Boston, 1973), xiv.
17 Schlesinger, "Ike Age Revisited," 6.

mechanisms and informal arrangements. He used the NSC to set policy for the Cold War. Attending 339 of these often-lengthy meetings, he encouraged open debate, normally waiting until near the end of the meeting to offer his views and decide on policy. With its various boards, special assistants, and undersecretaries, the NSC apparatus had the potential to leave the president at the mercy of a ponderous bureaucracy. But, as Anna Kasten Nelson has demonstrated, Eisenhower supplemented and tamed the NSC process. To coordinate national security policy and diplomacy — the day-to-day conduct of international relations carried out by the State Department – Eisenhower, aided by his staff secretary, gathered regularly with foreign policy officials. The president also met often with Secretary Dulles in the late afternoon for cocktails and philosophical discussions on foreign policy. Wherever decisions were made, Nelson reminds us, "the man in the center was President Eisenhower."[18]

Scholars accept Nelson's insight; Eisenhower cannot be relegated to the sidelines. Richard H. Immerman wonders, however, whether scholars have overreacted to traditional interpretations of the Eisenhower-Dulles relationship. In 1979 in a pathbreaking article, Immerman labeled as "problematic" the popular assumption that Dulles had manipulated his boss. He further demonstrated in his *The CIA in Guatemala* that Eisenhower was the driving force in the destruction in 1954 of the popularly elected government of Jacobo Arbenz Guzman.[19] But after organizing the Dulles Centennial Conference and editing the conference's papers, Immerman asserts that the two men "were in a real sense a team." In some areas and issues, such as European economic and military unification, Dulles took the lead.[20] Deborah Welch

18 Anna Kasten Nelson, "'The Top of the Policy Hill': President Eisenhower and the National Security Council," *Diplomatic History* 7 (Fall 1983): 307–26. See also John W. Sloan, "The Management and Decision-Making Style of President Eisenhower," *Presidential Studies Quarterly* 20 (Spring 1990): 295–313.

19 Richard H. Immerman, "Eisenhower and Dulles: Who Made the Decisions?" *Political Psychology* 1 (Autumn 1979): 21–38; idem, *The CIA in Guatemala: The Foreign Policy of Intervention* (Austin, 1982), 14–19, 161–86.

20 Immerman, ed., *John Foster Dulles*, 9. See also Rolf Steininger, "John Foster Dulles, the European Defense Community, and the German Question," in ibid., 79–108; Hans-Jurgen Grabbe, 'Konrad Adenauer, John Foster Dulles, and West German-American Relations," in ibid., 109–32; and James G. Hershberg, "'Explosion in the Offing': German Rearmament and American Diplomacy, 1953–1955," *Diplomatic History* 16 (Fall 1992): 511–49.

Larson similarly sees an influential Dulles curbing Eisenhower's enthusiasm for détente with the Soviet Union. After Dulles had edited it, Eisenhower's "Chance for Peace" speech, delivered in the aftermath of Stalin's death, was less conciliatory than the president had proposed.[21] On the other hand, Frederick W. Marks III, taking a distinct stance, theorizes that Dulles restrained the president on issues such as Vietnam, China, and the use of nuclear weapons.[22] Despite these and his own reservations, Immerman reiterates that the "emerging paradigm" is that Eisenhower "did retain control of policy- and decision-making."[23]

The question of whether Eisenhower's management style produced effective policies generates more debate than the issue of who was in charge of U.S. foreign policy. Duane A. Tananbaum detects the hidden-hand presidency in the campaign against the Bricker Amendment, whereby Eisenhower helped defeat the amendment without alienating Senator John Bricker (R-OH) and his fellow conservatives. Eisenhower fought against restrictions on his presidential authority through the delaying tactic of appointing study commissions and by privately instructing aides like Sherman Adams and Dulles on how to lobby against the amendment. But Tananbaum questions whether the nation was well served by Eisenhower's low profile. The amendment's backers opposed U.S. adherence to international agreements on human rights such as the Genocide Convention. The Bricker Amendment, first introduced in 1951, was still alive in 1957, because Eisenhower would not firmly and publicly oppose it.[24]

Two studies on Eisenhower's foreign economic policy also debate the efficacy of Eisenhower's nonconfrontational style.

21 Deborah Welch Larson, "Crisis Prevention and the Austrian State Treaty," *International Organization* 41 (Winter 1987): 36–38.

22 Frederick W. Marks III, "The Real Hawk at Dienbienphu: Dulles or Eisenhower?" *Pacific Historical Review* 59 (August 1990): 297–322; idem, *Power and Peace: The Diplomacy of John Foster Dulles* (Westport, 1993), 25–46.

23 Immerman, ed., *John Foster Dulles*, 9.

24 Duane A. Tananbaum, "The Bricker Amendment Controversy: Its Origins and Eisenhower's Role," *Diplomatic History* 9 (Winter 1985): 73–93. See also idem, *The Bricker Amendment Controversy: A Test of Eisenhower's Political Leadership* (Ithaca, 1988). Cathal J. Nolan concedes Tananbaum's point that Eisenhower sacrificed U.S. support for international conventions on human rights but argues it was a "price well paid" to defeat the larger issue of isolationism inherent in the Bricker Amendment. Nolan, "The Last Hurrah of Conservative Isolationism: Eisenhower, Congress, and the Bricker Amendment," *Presidential Studies Quarterly* 22 (Spring 1992): 337–49.

Burton I. Kaufman credits Eisenhower for gradually transforming the Mutual Security Program from a military assistance to an economic aid program for Third World nations and for persuading high-tariff Republicans to accept the principle of free trade. But Congress consistently refused to appropriate adequate funds for international economic development and sharply restricted imports of Third World exports like lead, zinc, and petroleum. Kaufman faults Eisenhower for being "politically lazy," for refusing to confront protectionist Republicans and expend political capital to promote liberal trade practices.[25]

Tor Egil Førland also detects a gap between good intentions and results. Within the confines of the NSC, the president worked relentlessly to relax controls on trade with Communist countries, arguing that a restrictive policy was unworkable, that the allies opposed it, and that expanded East-West trade might undermine the Soviet Union's hold over Eastern Europe. Eisenhower seemed to have won the debate with the adoption in mid-1953 of a revised export control policy, NSC-152/2. But Eisenhower "could not persuade his own administration to carry out the policy he wanted." Cabinet officers, like Secretary of Defense Charles E. Wilson and Secretary of Commerce Sinclair Weeks, hamstrung trade expansion, and when elected officials objected to trading with Communists, Eisenhower again declined to risk his personal popularity with a public debate. As Førland has archly noted, "Eisenhower's failure to 'grasp the reins of power at all levels' meant that his so-called hidden-hand presidency could to some extent become a government by the many hidden hands in the Washington bureaucracy and that those hidden hands could turn policy in directions unintended by the commander in chief himself."[26]

25 Burton I. Kaufman, *Trade and Aid: Eisenhower's Foreign Economic Policy, 1953–1961* (Baltimore, 1982), 7–9, 140, 207–9. See also H. Richard Friman, "The Eisenhower Administration and the Demise of GATT: Dancing with Pandora," *American Journal of Economics and Sociology* 53 (July 1994): 257–71; W. W. Rostow, *Eisenhower, Kennedy, and Foreign Aid* (Austin, 1985), 198–201; and Thomas Zoumaras, "Eisenhower's Foreign Economic Policy: The Case of Latin America," in *Reevaluating Eisenhower: American Foreign Policy in the 1950s*, ed. Richard A. Melanson and David Mayers (Urbana, 1987), 155–91.

26 Tor Egil Førland, "'Selling Firearms to the Indians': Eisenhower's Export Control Policy, 1953–1954," *Diplomatic History* 15 (Spring 1991): 221–44. Robert Mark

Førland's insight that scholars must move beyond dissecting the decision-making process and consider the implementation and result of a decision can be used profitably to discuss scholarship on the core of Eisenhower revisionism, the president's handling of crises. Revisionists unreservedly praise Eisenhower for ending the Korean War. In Ambrose's judgment, "what stands out is Eisenhower the leader." After touring the battlefields as president-elect, Eisenhower decided on military grounds that victory was impossible and thereafter moved steadily and firmly to end the killing. In accepting an armistice, he overwhelmed Dulles, right-wing Republicans, and South Korean strongman Syngman Rhee. Eisenhower also grasped the insight "that unlimited war in the nuclear age was unimaginable, and limited war unwinnable."[27]

Although agreeing that peace in Korea was an impressive achievement, scholars have wondered whether Eisenhower's methods were as well conceived as revisionists have claimed. Edward C. Keefer has pointed out that, during the first months of 1953, Eisenhower repeatedly thought aloud about using atomic weapons against the North Koreans and the Chinese. In Keefer's mind, "these twelfth hour schemes seem to be evidence of an almost subconscious desire by Eisenhower for one final try for an easy solution to the Korean deadlock."[28] But whether Eisenhower explicitly threatened the enemy with atomic warfare, as Dulles later boasted, remains uncertain. Ambrose denies the claim, as does Roger Dingman, who notes that Eisenhower understood that, in lieu of a nuclear monopoly, "nuclear weapons were not easily usable tools of statecraft that produced predictable results."[29] Divine accepts the proposition, however, adding that the "impossibility

Spaulding, Jr., credits Eisenhower with more success on the export control issue than does Førland. Spaulding, "'A Gradual and Moderate Relaxation': Eisenhower and the Revision of American Export Control Policy, 1953–1955," ibid. 17 (Spring 1993): 223–49. Førland responds in "Eisenhower, Export Controls, and the Parochialism of Historians of American Foreign Relations," *Newsletter* 24 (December 1993): 4–17.

27 Ambrose, *Eisenhower: The President*, 31, 97–100, 104–7.

28 Edward C. Keefer, "President Dwight D. Eisenhower and the End of the Korean War," *Diplomatic History* 10 (Summer 1986): 277.

29 Roger Dingman, "Atomic Diplomacy during the Korean War," *International Security* 13 (Winter 1988/89): 79–91. See also Burton I. Kaufman, *The Korean War: Challenges in Crisis, Credibility, and Command* (Philadelphia, 1986), 319–20.

of telling even now whether or not he was bluffing" testifies to the "shrewdness" of Eisenhower's policy.[30] Rosemary Foot apparently agrees. According to her, in May 1953, Washington indirectly conveyed its nuclear resolve to the Chinese, not knowing that the Communists had already decided to compromise on such critical issues as the status of prisoners of war even without the threats.[31] As Foot sees it, although Eisenhower seemed preoccupied with using nuclear weapons, "he did send out contradictory signals over the matter from time to time, convincing those more charitable than myself that this was all part of his 'hidden-hand' strategy to achieve peace and not to raise the stakes."[32]

Eisenhower listed peace in Korea as his greatest achievement, but Eisenhower revisionists hold that his management of the Dienbienphu crisis ranks as a notable feat. As Immerman has observed, Eisenhower's Vietnam policy has "served as a principal catalyst to revise orthodox critiques of the president's diplomatic record."[33] Ambrose and Divine agree that Eisenhower again displayed mature professional judgment in rejecting the option of unilateral military intervention in Vietnam.[34] In Greenstein's view, Eisenhower's decision to stay out of Vietnam reflected the personal qualities "that led him to receive a rich stream of advice and opinion." Writing in conjunction with John Burke, Greenstein has compared how Eisenhower made decisions on Vietnam in 1954 with the way President Lyndon B. Johnson operated in 1965. Burke and Greenstein note that Eisenhower encouraged "spirited, no-holds barred debate" in the NSC and that he never intimidated subordinates. Aided by NSC official Robert Cutler, Eisenhower also kept discussions focused, reformulated questions, and analyzed policy tradeoffs and interdependencies. Eisenhower intuitively employed the "economist's logic of comparative

30 Divine, *Eisenhower and the Cold War*, 31.

31 Rosemary Foot, "Nuclear Coercion and the Ending of the Korean Conflict," *International Security* 13 (Winter 1988/89): 92–112; idem, *A Substitute for Victory: The Politics of Peacemaking at the Korean Armistice Talks* (Ithaca, 1990), 159–89.

32 Rosemary Foot, "Making Known the Unknown War: Policy Analysis of the Korean Conflict since the Early 1980s," in this volume.

33 Richard H. Immerman, "The United States and the Geneva Conference of 1954: A New Look," *Diplomatic History* 14 (Winter 1990): 43.

34 Divine, *Eisenhower and the Cold War*, 54–55; Ambrose, *Eisenhower: The President*, 185.

advantage." In contrast, the authors find the Johnson White House disorganized, characterized by "a great swirl of policy recommendations and analyses, much of which simply floated past the president." Moreover, Johnson did not foster within his administration an atmosphere that encouraged open debate.[35] Although the authors claim that their goal was to study the quality of decision making and not the intrinsic quality of the decisions themselves, a careful reader could nonetheless infer that Burke and Greenstein believe that Eisenhower would have steered clear of Johnson's disastrous course in Vietnam.

Melanie Billings-Yun, Laurent Césari and Jacques de Folin, Lloyd Gardner, George C. Herring and Immerman, Gary R. Hess, Marks, Gregory James Pemberton, John Prados, and Geoffrey Warner have dissected Eisenhower's decision not to relieve the besieged French garrison at Dienbienphu.[36] These historians debate whether Eisenhower seriously contemplated a military strike, in what ways the president and Dulles differed, in what forums critical decisions were made, and which of the allies – Great Britain, France, Australia – most influenced U.S. policy. What they do not quarrel with, however, is the "view that the administration acted wisely in staying out of war in 1954."[37]

Yet, even as they praised Eisenhower's crisis management, scholars questioned whether Eisenhower revisionists had neglected to

35 John P. Burke and Fred I. Greenstein, *How Presidents Test Reality: Decisions on Vietnam, 1954 and 1965* (New York, 1989), 54–59, 108, 257–64.

36 Melanie Billings-Yun, *Decision against War: Eisenhower and Dien Bien Phu, 1954* (New York, 1988); Laurent Césari and Jacques de Folin, "Military Necessity, Political Impossibility: The French Viewpoint on Operation *Vautour*," in *Dien Bien Phu and the Crisis of Franco-American Relations, 1954–1955*, ed. Lawrence S. Kaplan, Denise Artaud, and Mark R. Rubin (Wilmington, DE, 1990), 105–20; Lloyd Gardner, *Approaching Vietnam: From World War II through Dienbienphu, 1941–1954* (New York, 1988), 166–211; George C. Herring and Richard H. Immerman, "Eisenhower, Dulles, and Dienbienphu: 'The Day We Didn't Go to War' Revisited," *Journal of American History* 71 (September 1984): 343–63; Gary R. Hess, "Redefining the American Position in Southeast Asia: The United States and the Geneva and Manila Conferences," in Kaplan, Artaud, and Rubin, eds., *Dien Bien Phu*, 127–30; Marks, "The Real Hawk at Dienbienphu," 297–322; Gregory James Pemberton, "Australia, the United States, and the Indochina Crisis of 1954," *Diplomatic History* 13 (Winter 1989): 45–66; John Prados, *The Sky Would Fall: Operation Vulture and the U.S. Bombing Mission in Indochina, 1954* (New York, 1983), 152–65; Geoffrey Warner, "Britain and the Crisis over Dien Bien Phu, April 1954: The Failure of United Action," in Kaplan, Artaud, and Rubin, eds., *Dien Bien Phu*, 55–77.

37 Quoted in Herring and Immerman, "Eisenhower, Dulles, and Dienbienphu," 363.

analyze the political commitments to South Vietnam that the administration made after the Viet Minh's battlefield victory. The crucial Vietnam decisions may have come after the French military collapse and the Geneva Conference of 1954. The administration, led by Secretary of State Dulles, perceived the French defeat as an opportunity for the United States, presumably untainted by colonialism, to exercise leadership in the region. Overriding the objections of the U.S. military, the French, and U.S. Ambassador J. Lawton Collins, Dulles cast the American lot with the anti-Communist Ngo Dinh Diem in a "good stout effort" to build an independent, non-Communist South Vietnam. When, from 1955–1957, President Diem achieved a modicum of political stability in South Vietnam, the administration concluded that it had successfully constructed a bulwark against the spread of communism in Southeast Asia.[38]

Yet, in David L. Anderson's words, the administration and the United States had been "trapped by success." During the second presidential term, Eisenhower and his men declined to ask hard questions about whether Diem was an authentic representative of the Vietnamese people or whether Vietnam's village-based culture was receptive to American wealth and good intentions. Instead, the administration tied U.S. global credibility to the survival of the regime, pouring military aid into the region and lavishing praise on Diem. By the end of the decade, the "nation-building" enterprise had clearly failed; political discontent, economic turmoil, and civil war rocked South Vietnam. But as the crisis deepened, Anderson finds that the White House largely ignored it, other than to reaffirm its faith in containment and the domino theory. Assessing the 1955–1959 records that were declassified in 1987,

38 George C. Herring, "A Good Stout Effort: John Foster Dulles and the Indochina Crisis, 1954–1955," in Immerman, ed., *John Foster Dulles*, 213–33. See also David L. Anderson, "J. Lawton Collins, John Foster Dulles, and the Eisenhower Administration's 'Point of No Return' in Vietnam," *Diplomatic History* 12 (Spring 1988): 127–47; Roger Dingman, "John Foster Dulles and the Creation of the South-East Asia Treaty Organization in 1954," *International History Review* 11 (August 1989): 457–77; Gardner, *Approaching Vietnam*, 315–38; Gary R. Hess, "The American Search for Stability in Southeast Asia: The SEATO Structure of Containment," in *The Great Powers in East Asia, 1953–1960*, ed. Warren I. Cohen and Akira Iriye (New York, 1990), 272–95; and Immerman, "United States and Geneva Conference of 1954," 43–66.

Anderson notes that after 1955 "there is little evidence of the president's hand, hidden or otherwise, in Vietnam policymaking." The Eisenhower administration was "a creator and the captive of an illusion in Vietnam."[39] And, as Anderson and Henry William Brands, Jr., remind us, in the postpresidential years, Eisenhower continued to pursue that illusion, constantly urging President Johnson to use military force to defeat the Vietnamese Communists.[40]

Eisenhower also kept the United States out of war during the Taiwan Straits confrontations. But scholars have again asked whether the revisionists have exaggerated Eisenhower's diplomatic skill in managing relations with China. Revisionists have lauded Eisenhower for avoiding war through "deliberate ambiguity and deception," confusing the Chinese Communists about U.S. resolve. Divine writes that "the beauty of Eisenhower's policy is that to this day no one can be sure whether or not he would have responded militarily to an invasion of the offshore islands, and whether he would have used nuclear weapons."[41] Ambrose finds the president's handling of the Quemoy-Matsu crisis of 1954–55 similarly alluring, labeling it "a *tour de force*, one of the great triumphs of his long career." Eisenhower did not know how he would respond, because, as an experienced military commander, he wanted "to see the precise nature of the attack."[42]

Gordon H. Chang disputes the contention that Eisenhower kept his options open. Eisenhower's public accounts of his actions,

39 David L. Anderson, *Trapped by Success: The Eisenhower Administration and Vietnam, 1953–1961* (New York, 1991), 151–204. See also James R. Arnold, *The First Domino: Eisenhower, the Military, and America's Intervention in Vietnam* (New York, 1991), 225–377; Daniel P. O'C. Greene, "John Foster Dulles and the End of the Franco-American Entente in Indochina," *Diplomatic History* 16 (Fall 1992): 551–71; and George McT. Kahin, *Intervention: How America Became Involved in Vietnam* (New York, 1986), 93–121.

40 Anderson, *Trapped by Success*, 204–5; Henry William Brands, Jr., "Johnson and Eisenhower: The President, the Former President, and the War in Vietnam," *Presidential Studies Quarterly* 15 (Summer 1985): 597–99. See also Fred I. Greenstein and Richard H. Immerman, "What Did Eisenhower Tell Kennedy about Indochina? The Politics of Misperception," *Journal of American History* 79 (September 1992): 586.

41 Divine, *Eisenhower and the Cold War*, 65–66.

42 Ambrose, *Eisenhower: The President*, 245. See also Robert Accinelli, "Eisenhower, Congress, and the 1954–55 Offshore Island Crisis," *Presidential Studies Quarterly* 20 (Spring 1990): 329–48; and Bennett C. Rushkoff, "Eisenhower, Dulles, and the Quemoy-Matsu Crisis, 1954–1955," *Political Science Quarterly* 96 (Fall 1981): 465–80.

Chang asserts, are not supported by the documentary record. In January 1955, the administration secretly pledged to Chiang Kai-shek that it would defend Quemoy and Matsu and thereafter planned extensive nuclear attacks on China. At the height of the crisis in April 1955, Eisenhower adopted another strategy, endorsing Secretary Dulles's idea that the United States should offer to blockade the China coast along the Taiwan Strait, some five hundred miles long, if Chiang agreed to withdraw from the islands. In the judgment of Admiral William Radford and Ambassador to Taiwan Karl L. Rankin, this proposal meant war, for the Chinese were unlikely to permit the blockading and mining of their territorial waters. Chiang, however, turned down the U.S. scheme, and then, on 23 April, China unexpectedly offered to negotiate.[43] But the administration had escalated the crisis and lost control of events. As Chester J. Pach, Jr., has observed, "beauty may be in the eye of the beholder, but it is hard to be dazzled by policies that bring the world to the brink of nuclear war over territory whose value to American – or for that matter Taiwanese – security was close to nil."[44]

The administration continued to pursue provocative policies toward China in the aftermath of the first crisis. John Lewis Gaddis, Leonard H. D. Gordon, David Allan Mayers, Nancy Bernkopf Tucker, and Wang Jisi have discovered that the administration was not a prisoner of its own rhetoric. Officials privately understood that China fashioned its own agenda and that China and the Soviet Union were as much rivals as monolithic allies. Eisenhower and Dulles also increasingly distrusted Chiang, whom they knew favored entangling the United States in a military confrontation with the Communists. As such, the administration

43 Gordon H. Chang. *Friends and Enemies: The United States, China, and the Soviet Union, 1948–1972* (Stanford, 1990), 116–42. For China's perspective on the crisis see Gordon H. Chang and He Di, "The Absence of War in the U.S.-China Confrontation over Quemoy and Matsu in 1954–1955: Contingency, Luck, Deterrence?" *American Historical Review* 98 (December 1993): 1500–1524; and Thomas E. Stolper, *China, Taiwan, and the Offshore Islands: Together with an Implication for Outer Mongolia and Sino-Soviet Relations* (Armonk, NY, 1985).

44 Chester J. Pach, Jr., and Elmo Richardson, *The Presidency of Dwight D. Eisenhower*, rev. ed. (Lawrence, 1991), 104. See also H. W. Brands, Jr., "Testing Massive Retaliation: Credibility and Crisis Management in the Taiwan Strait," *International Security* 12 (Spring 1988): 124–51.

confidentially adopted a "two Chinas" policy.[45] But, as Tucker concedes, "the United States and China did remain enemies throughout the decade, and a careful reading of the new evidence will not change the fundamental realities."[46] The administration stationed B-52 bombers on Guam, installed intermediate range ballistic missiles on Taiwan, and gave Chiang's forces the capability to violate China's airspace by providing F-86 Sabre Jets equipped with Sidewinder missiles.[47] Between 1955 and 1957, the administration also turned aside conciliatory gestures, repeatedly rejecting, for example, China's offer to negotiate a settlement of the Taiwan problem. These stubborn measures and attitudes probably contributed to China's decision to develop a nuclear deterrent.[48]

Analyses of Eisenhower's policies during what Divine tags the "most severe crisis of his entire presidency," the Suez imbroglio of 1956, follow a pattern similar to interpretations of the Asian crises.[49] Scholars affirm the revisionist case that, in the heat of battle, Eisenhower displayed his characteristic calm judgment. But they again ask hard questions about the direction Eisenhower took in the aftermath of conflict. Writing with a transnational perspective, Wm. Roger Louis emphasizes that Eisenhower, not Dulles, controlled U.S. policy on Suez and that Great Britain, France, and Israel should have concluded that the United States

45 John Lewis Gaddis, *The Long Peace: Inquiries into the History of the Cold War* (New York, 1987), 183–87; Leonard H. D. Gordon, "United States Opposition to Use of Force in the Taiwan Strait, 1954–1962," *Journal of American History* 72 (December 1985): 637–60; David Allan Mayers, *Cracking the Monolith: U.S. Policy against the Sino-Soviet Alliance, 1949–1955* (Baton Rouge, 1986), 6, 142–49; Nancy Bernkopf Tucker, "John Foster Dulles and the Taiwan Roots of the 'Two Chinas' Policy," in Immerman, ed., *John Foster Dulles*, 235–62; Wang Jisi, "The Origins of America's 'Two Chinas' Policy," in *Sino-American Relations, 1945–1955: A Joint Reassessment of a Critical Decade*, ed. Harry Harding and Yuan Ming (Wilmington, DE, 1989), 204–8.

46 Nancy Bernkopf Tucker, "A House Divided: The United States, the Department of State, and China," in Cohen and Iriye, eds., *The Great Powers in East Asia*, 35.

47 Marc S. Gallicchio, "The Best Defense Is a Good Offense: Evolution of American Strategy in East Asia," in Cohen and Iriye, eds., *The Great Powers in East Asia*, 63–85; Waldo Heinrichs, "Eisenhower and Sino-American Confrontation," in ibid., 86–103.

48 Chang, *Friends and Enemies*, 141, 155–57; Jia Quingguo, "Searching for Peaceful Coexistence and Territorial Integrity," in Harding and Yuan Ming, eds., *Sino-American Relations*, 278–82.

49 Divine, *Eisenhower and the Cold War*, 79.

would oppose gunboat diplomacy.[50] Some scholars suggest, however, that Dulles should have been more explicit in conveying to British diplomats the president's opposition to force.[51] Nonetheless, in denouncing colonialism, the administration correctly gauged public opinion and the currents of international history. Peter L. Hahn agrees that Eisenhower acted boldly during the crisis but cautions that international justice was not the administration's primary concern. Eisenhower feared that Moscow would capitalize on the European and Israeli aggression. In Hahn's view, "the overriding objective during the crisis was containment of the Soviet Union, a strategic imperative, and not satisfaction of Egyptian aspirations."[52]

The administration's ambivalent attitude toward Arab nationalism became apparent in 1957 and 1958. Flush from its Suez triumph, the administration confidently set about to fashion a Middle East secure from colonialism and radical nationalism. Judging Egyptian leader Gamal Abdel Nasser as an "evil influence," Eisenhower pronounced his doctrine, in Robert D. Schulzinger's opinion, "to project the United States as the saviour of conservative Arabs from Nasserism."[53] The administration worried that an expansion of the Egyptian's hold on the Arab masses would inevitably accrue to the Soviet Union. But the practical effect of the Eisenhower Doctrine was to entangle the United States in intra-Arab politics. Between April 1957 and

50 Wm. Roger Louis, "Dulles, Suez, and the British," in Immerman, ed., *John Foster Dulles*, 133–58. See also Robert R. Bowie, "Eisenhower, Dulles, and the Suez Crisis," in *Suez 1956: The Crisis and Its Consequences*, ed. Wm. Roger Louis and Roger Owen (New York, 1989), 189–214; Diane B. Kunz, *The Economic Diplomacy of the Suez Crisis* (Chapel Hill, 1991), 138–52; Keith Kyle, *Suez* (New York, 1991), 224; and Donald Neff, *Warriors at Suez: Eisenhower Takes America into the Middle East* (New York, 1981), 365–423, 441–42.

51 Steven Z. Freiberger, *Dawn over Suez The Rise of American Power in the Middle East, 1953–1957* (Chicago, 1992), 160–86.

52 Peter L. Hahn, *The United States, Great Britain, and Egypt, 1945–1956: Strategy and Diplomacy in the Early Cold War* (Chapel Hill, 1991), 247. Isaac Alteras similarly argues that Cold War concerns dictated U.S. policy toward Israel. Alteras, *Eisenhower and Israel: U.S.-Israeli Relations, 1953–1960* (Gainesville, 1993), 125, 307.

53 Robert D. Schulzinger, "The Impact of Suez on United States Middle East Policy, 1957–1958," in *The Suez-Sinai Crisis, 1956: Retrospective and Reappraisal*, ed. Selwyn Ilan Troen and Moshe Shemesh (New York, 1990), 253–54. See also Egya N. Sangmuah, "Eisenhower and Containment in North Africa, 1956–1960," *Middle East Journal* 44 (Winter 1990): 76–91; and Freiberger, *Dawn over Suez*, 208–17.

August 1958, the administration bolstered King Hussein of Jordan with a naval show of force, covertly attempted to overthrow Syrian President Shukri Quwatly, and landed fourteen thousand U.S. Marines in Lebanon to rescue the conservative Christian government of Camille Chamoun.[54] These interventions helped to preserve the Middle Eastern status quo. But the Eisenhower administration had grossly exaggerated the Soviet threat, misunderstood Arab nationalism, and stimulated Arab anti-Americanism. By the end of the decade, the Eisenhower Doctrine had fallen into obscurity and the administration had retreated from the Middle East. Eisenhower had squandered his Suez triumph.[55]

Beyond extolling Eisenhower's crisis-management skills, revisionists commend the president for his commitment to peace and arms control. In the Atoms for Peace speech and the farewell address, Eisenhower spoke eloquently of the dangers of the nuclear arms race, and in October 1958 he unilaterally halted the testing of nuclear weapons. Scholars agree that Eisenhower understood the awful consequences of nuclear warfare and genuinely desired a Soviet-American nuclear accord. Immerman argues that Eisenhower did not consider the nuclear option viable, because he was the first postwar leader to recognize that the advent of nuclear weapons had inverted the traditional relationship between force and statecraft. The "New Look" basic national security policy, NSC-162/2 (1953), permitted the use of nuclear weapons. But Immerman believes that Eisenhower considered nuclear weapons to be militarily useless. Their deterrent value, however, would convey "to the Soviets the immutable lessons of life in the nuclear age."[56] John Gaddis adds that Eisenhower flatly rejected the idea of a preemptive nuclear strike against the Soviet Union.[57] And

54 Schulzinger, "Impact of Suez," 255–63; Douglas Little, "Cold War and Covert Action: The United States and Syria, 1945–1958," *Middle East Journal* 44 (Winter 1990): 51–75; Michael B. Bishku, "The 1958 American Intervention in Lebanon: A Historical Assessment," *American-Arab Affairs* 31 (Winter 1989–90): 106–19.

55 Thomas G. Paterson, *Meeting the Communist Threat: Truman to Reagan* (New York, 1988), 189–90; William Stivers, "Eisenhower and the Middle East," in Melanson and Mayers, eds., *Reevaluating Eisenhower*, 214–15; Little, "Cold War and Covert Action," 75; Schulzinger, "Impact of Suez," 263–64.

56 Richard H. Immerman, "Confessions of an Eisenhower Revisionist: An Agonizing Reappraisal," *Diplomatic History* 14 (Summer 1990): 319–42.

57 Gaddis, *Long Peace*, 142–43. See also Russell D. Buhite and Wm. Christopher Hamel, "War for Peace: The Question of an American Preventive War against the

Raymond L. Garthoff, a former intelligence analyst, approvingly notes that Eisenhower questioned alarmist studies purporting to show "missile gaps."[58]

Despite judicious attitudes and good intentions, Eisenhower presided over an accelerating nuclear arms race. His Atoms for Peace and "Open Skies" proposals did not spark serious international negotiations. In the ten months preceding the nuclear test moratorium, the United States exploded half as many nuclear weapons as it had in the previous twelve years.[59] By 1961, the United States had attained massive "overkill" capabilities with over 2,000 bombers, approximately 100 ballistic missiles, and contracts for over 650 additional land-based missiles and 14 Polaris submarines, each of which would carry 16 missiles. Between 1958 and 1960, the U.S. nuclear stockpile tripled from six thousand to eighteen thousand weapons.[60] Moreover, Eisenhower's hopes for a permanent test ban collapsed in the aftermath of the U-2 incident and the stormy Paris summit of 1960.[61] As Brands has observed, Eisenhower's farewell address should be interpreted less as a warning about the future and more as an admission of defeat, for "far more than any administration before or after, Eisenhower's promoted the growth of the military-industrial complex he decried."[62]

Eisenhower failed because arms control problems were complex and because he was indecisive and unable to overcome conventional Cold War attitudes. Eisenhower was understandably bedeviled by the conflicting advice he received on technical issues like verification. He governed at a time when thinking about

Soviet Union, 1945–1955," *Diplomatic History* 14 (Summer 1990): 382; and Richard D. Challener, "The Moralist as Pragmatist: John Foster Dulles as Cold War Strategist," in *The Diplomats, 1939–1979*, ed. Gordon A. Craig and Francis L. Lowenheim (Princeton, 1994), 136, 147–53.

58 Raymond L. Garthoff, *Assessing the Adversary: Estimates by the Eisenhower Administration of Soviet Intentions and Capabilities* (Washington, 1991), 46–49.

59 Ronald W. Powaski, *March to Armageddon: The United States and the Nuclear Arms Race, 1939 to the Present* (New York, 1987), 87.

60 David Allan Rosenberg, "The Origins of Overkill: Nuclear Weapons and American Strategy," in *The National Security: Its Theory and Practice, 1945–1960*, ed. Norman A. Graebner (New York, 1986), 173–74.

61 For the U-2 imbroglio see Michael R. Beschloss, *Mayday: Eisenhower, Khrushchev, and the U-2 Affair* (New York, 1986).

62 H. W. Brands, "The Age of Vulnerability: Eisenhower and the National Insecurity State," *American Historical Review* 94 (October 1989): 988–89.

nuclear weapons and arms control was going through an "intellectual and political adolescence."[63] Notwithstanding these dilemmas, Eisenhower acted inconsistently. Although he may have personally rejected the concept of limited nuclear war, he never explicitly ruled out the strategy of seeing nuclear weapons "as conventional weapons from a military point of view," as Brands demonstrates in his close reading of national security documents.[64] David Allan Rosenberg agrees with revisionists that Eisenhower became increasingly pessimistic about the outcome of a general war, but the president responded by strengthening rather than revising the national defense strategy of massive retaliation. As he noted in 1956 to the Joint Chiefs of Staff, a thermonuclear war was probably unwinnable, but "we don't want to lose any worse than we have to."[65] Such ambiguity created a climate in which bureaucracies like the Joint Chiefs, the Defense Department, and the Atomic Energy Commission could successfully lobby for new nuclear technologies and weapons.[66]

The Eisenhower administration's virulent anticommunism also undermined prospects for a Soviet-American accord. The Atoms for Peace and Open Skies proposals were "propaganda gestures and acts of political warfare." In internal memorandums, U.S. officials acknowledged that the proposals were one-sided, but they brazenly pushed ahead anyway, predicting that they would succeed in putting the Soviet Union on the defensive over its closed society.[67] In presenting these proposals publicly and without warning, Eisenhower, in McGeorge Bundy's view, also sharply reduced chances for serious negotiations.[68] Indeed, when the Soviets in May 1955 unexpectedly put forth what Matthew Evangelista,

63 Robert A. Strong, "Eisenhower and Arms Control," in Melanson and Mayers, eds., *Reevaluating Eisenhower*, 241.

64 Brands, "Age of Vulnerability," 987. William Burr finds Eisenhower displaying similarly ambiguous attitudes about nuclear weapons during the Berlin crisis. Burr, "Avoiding the Slippery Slope: The Eisenhower Administration and the Berlin Crisis, November 1958–January 1959," *Diplomatic History* 18 (Spring 1994): 177–205.

65 Rosenberg, "Origins of Overkill," 152.

66 McGeorge Bundy, *Danger and Survival: Choices about the Bomb in the First Fifty Years* (New York, 1988), 293–94, 304–5; Garthoff, *Assessing the Adversary*, 27; Richard G. Hewlett and Jack M. Holl, *Atoms for Peace and War, 1953–1961: Eisenhower and the Atomic Energy Commission* (Berkeley, 1989), 211.

67 Garthoff, *Assessing the Adversary*, 8–12. For a different view see W. W. Rostow, *Open Skies: Eisenhower's Proposal of July 21, 1955* (Austin, 1982).

68 Bundy, *Danger and Survival*, 303.

a student of Soviet politics, finds a meaningful disarmament proposal, the administration reacted suspiciously and then countered with the diversionary Open Skies initiative.[69] As Garthoff recalls, Eisenhower and his advisers concluded that the post-Stalin leaders of the Soviet Union were rational men. But U.S. officials could never suspend their conviction that the Soviets were implacably hostile and bent on global Communist domination. Moreover, their anticommunism prevented them from realizing that the unprecedented U.S. strategic buildup and U-2 overflights may have fostered some of the hostility they encountered.[70]

Extreme anticommunism also characterized the administration's policies toward Third World regions. Eisenhower's diplomacy toward the developing world is not an essential feature of Eisenhower revisionism. Many historians would reject the notion that a creditable interpretation of a postwar administration's policy can be assembled that excludes the Third World.[71] In any case, other scholars have critically examined Eisenhower and Third World nationalism. Reviewing studies published up to 1985 on U.S. relations with particular developing nations or regions, Robert J. McMahon finds that "the Eisenhower record appears one of persistent failure." The administration consistently was unable to distinguish nationalism from communism. Fearing that the Soviet Union would profit from disorder, the president backed authoritarian regimes and tied U.S. interests to a discredited status quo in areas yearning for change and development. That record may mean, McMahon opines, that Eisenhower revisionism is "a castle built on sand."[72] Irwin M. Wall holds, however, that McMahon

69 Matthew Evangelista, "Cooperation Theory and Disarmament Negotiations in the 1950s," *World Politics* 42 (June 1990): 502–28. For U.S. reaction to an earlier Soviet peace initiative see M. Steven Fish, "After Stalin's Death: The Anglo-American Debate over a New Cold War," *Diplomatic History* 10 (Fall 1986): 333–55; Peter G. Boyle, ed., *The Churchill-Eisenhower Correspondence, 1953–1955* (Chapel Hill, 1990), 30–55.

70 Garthoff, *Assessing the Adversary*, 29, 51. See also Thomas F. Soapes, "A Cold Warrior Seeks Peace: Eisenhower's Strategy for Nuclear Disarmament," *Diplomatic History* 4 (Winter 1980): 57–58, 68–69; and Strong, "Eisenhower and Arms Control," 242, 260.

71 This point is made in Richard H. Immerman's review of John Gaddis's *The Long Peace*. See "In Search of History – and Relevancy: Breaking through the 'Encrustations of Interpretation,'" *Diplomatic History* 12 (Summer 1988): 355.

72 McMahon, "Eisenhower and Third World Nationalism," 457.

unduly criticizes the revisionists. In Algeria, the administration opposed French colonialism, because it believed the Algerian National Liberation Front could be transformed into a democratic, anti-Communist movement.[73]

Analyses of the administration's policies toward Latin America, the Third World region most intensively examined by scholars, sustain McMahon's, not Wall's, evaluations. Blanche Wiesen Cook, Piero Gleijeses, Immerman, Sharon I. Meers, Stephen Schlesinger and Stephen Kinzer, and Bryce Wood have condemned the 1954 U.S. intervention in Guatemala. They believe that President Arbenz was directing an indigenous movement committed to a thoroughgoing reform of Guatemala's archaic socioeconomic structure. With little hard evidence, however, Eisenhower and Dulles succumbed to Cold War fears and concluded that Arbenz intended to transform his nation into a Soviet beachhead. The covert intervention set Guatemala on a ghastly course of political violence that has claimed perhaps one hundred thousand lives over the past four decades.[74]

Eisenhower's Cuban policy was similarly disastrous. Thomas G. Paterson forcefully argues that the administration created the preconditions for the bitter Cuban-American confrontation by violating its own pledges of neutrality and nonintervention during the Cuban Revolution. Once it decided to abandon its ally, dictator

73 Irwin M. Wall, "The United States, Algeria, and the Fall of the Fourth French Republic," *Diplomatic History* 18 (Fall 1994): 489–511. See also H. W. Brands, Jr., *The Specter of Neutralism: The United States and the Emergence of the Third World, 1947–1960* (New York, 1989), 9, 312–21. In response to Brands see Dennis Merrill, "America Encounters the Third World," *Diplomatic History* 16 (Spring 1992): 325–30.

74 Blanche Wiesen Cook, *The Declassified Eisenhower: A Divided Legacy* (Garden City, 1981), 217–92; Piero Gleijeses, *Shattered Hope: The Guatemalan Revolution and the United States, 1944–1954* (Princeton, 1991); Immerman, *The CIA in Guatemala*; Sharon I. Meers, "The British Connection: How the United States Covered Its Tracks in the 1954 Coup in Guatemala," *Diplomatic History* 16 (Summer 1992): 409–28; Stephen Schlesinger and Stephen Kinzer, *Bitter Fruit: The Untold Story of the American Coup in Guatemala* (Garden City, 1982); Bryce Wood, *The Dismantling of the Good Neighbor Policy* (Austin, 1985), 152–90. Frederick W. Marks III has disputed the assumption that the Eisenhower administration was primarily responsible for the overthrow of the Arbenz government. See Marks, "The CIA and Castillo Armas in Guatemala, 1954: New Clues to an Old Puzzle," *Diplomatic History* 14 (Winter 1990): 67–86. In response see Stephen G. Rabe, "The Clues Didn't Check Out: Commentary on 'The CIA and Castillo Armas,'" ibid., 87–95; and Meers, "The British Connection," 409.

Fulgencio Batista, the administration tried in 1958 to block Fidel Castro and his 26th of July Movement's road to power by sponsoring a series of "third-force" conspiracies.[75] Although most scholars do not assign sole blame to the administration for the rapid deterioration in relations in 1959–60, they do criticize it for overreacting to Castro's decision to conduct diplomatic and economic relations with the Soviet Union. Eisenhower's approval in March 1960 of a plan, modeled on the Guatemalan intervention, to overthrow Castro led directly to the Bay of Pigs fiasco.[76]

To be sure, the administration responded imaginatively in 1959 and 1960 to radicalism in Cuba, funding economic aid programs for progressive social and economic development in Latin America and laying the groundwork for the Alliance for Progress.[77] But, throughout the 1950s, Latin American democrats asked why the administration bestowed medals and military support on tyrants like Batista, Marcos Pérez Jiménez of Venezuela, and Rafael Trujillo of the Dominican Republic. Stephen G. Rabe answers that the imperatives of the Cold War led the Eisenhower administration to prize security and stability over democracy and human rights in Latin America.[78]

Eisenhower authorized the Central Intelligence Agency (CIA) to overthrow other Third World regimes, most notably the Iranian government of Mohammed Mossadegh. Middle Eastern experts argue that the administration again confused militant anticolonialism and nationalism with communism and left "a running wound

75 Thomas G. Paterson, *Contesting Castro: The United States and the Triumph of the Cuban Revolution* (New York, 1994), 206–25, 246.

76 Richard E. Welch, Jr., *Response to Revolution: The United States and the Cuban Revolution, 1959–1961* (Chapel Hill, 1985), 3–63; Alan H. Luxenberg, "Did Eisenhower Push Castro into the Arms of the Soviets," *Journal of Inter-American Studies and World Affairs* 30 (Spring 1988): 37–71; Morris H. Morley, *Imperial State and Revolution: The United States and Cuba, 1952–1986* (Cambridge, England, 1987), 40–130; Trumbull Higgins, *The Perfect Failure: Kennedy, Eisenhower, and the CIA at the Bay of Pigs* (New York, 1987), 78.

77 Stanley E. Hilton, "The United States, Brazil, and the Cold War, 1945–1960: End of the Special Relationship," *Journal of American History* 68 (December 1981): 599–624; Marvin R. Zahniser and W. Michael Weis, "A Diplomatic Pearl Harbor? Richard Nixon's Goodwill Mission to Latin America in 1958," *Diplomatic History* 13 (Spring 1989): 163–90; Thomas Zoumaras, "Containing Castro: Promoting Home Ownership in Peru, 1956–1961," ibid. 10 (Spring 1986): 161–81.

78 Stephen G. Rabe, *Eisenhower and Latin America: The Foreign Policy of Anticommunism* (Chapel Hill, 1988), 38–42, 84–92.

that bled for twenty-five years" by identifying U.S. interests with Mohammed Reza Shah Pahlavi.[79] CIA operations in Cuba, Guatemala, and Iran indicate that Eisenhower made covert activity a central feature of his foreign policy. However restrained the president may have been during international crises, Eisenhower and the CIA stealthily fought putative Communists in such far-flung areas as the Congo, Indonesia, Syria, and Tibet.[80] His subordinates, perhaps with Eisenhower's tacit approval, also hatched assassination plots against Castro, Trujillo, and Patrice Lumumba of the Congo.[81] Certain that international communism was aggressively pursuing a program of global subversion, Eisenhower ruled that covert operations were essential to national security. Even his scholarly admirers concede, however, that by adopting the tactics of covert intervention and assassination, Eisenhower and his men were undermining the democratic values that they aimed to preserve.[82]

79 James A. Bill, *The Eagle and the Lion: The Tragedy of American-Iranian Relations* (New Haven, 1988), 86. See also Barry Rubin, *Paved with Good Intentions: The American Experience and Iran* (New York, 1980), 54–90.

80 For accounts of CIA activity during the Eisenhower years see William Blum, *The CIA: A Forgotten History: U.S. Global Intervention since World War II* (London, 1986), 67–180; John Prados, *Presidents' Secret Wars: CIA and Pentagon Operations since World War II* (New York, 1986), 91–193; John Ranelagh, *The Agency: The Rise and Decline of the CIA* (New York, 1986), 229–348; and Gregory F. Treverton, *Covert Action: The Limits of Intervention in the Postwar World* (New York, 1987), 44–88.

81 The uncertainty that surrounds the issue of Eisenhower's knowledge of assassination plots is revealed in the conflicting interpretations offered by Stephen E. Ambrose. In 1981, Ambrose wrote that "it is highly unlikely, almost unbelievable," that Allen Dulles, the director of the CIA, would have approved assassination plots "unless he was certain he was acting in accord with the President's wishes." See Stephen E. Ambrose with Richard H. Immerman, *Ike's Spies: Eisenhower and the Espionage Establishment* (Garden City, 1981), 306. In 1984, noting that he had seen no documentary evidence directly linking Eisenhower with assassination attempts, Ambrose speculated that the president "could have given such orders verbally and privately to Dulles, but if he did he acted out of character." See Ambrose, *Eisenhower: The President*, 557. Eisenhower is absolved of responsibility for assassinations in William Bragg Ewald, Jr., *Eisenhower the President: Crucial Days, 1951–1960* (Englewood Cliffs, NJ, 1981), 265–80. But see also Madeleine G. Kalb, *The Congo Cables: The Cold War in Africa – From Eisenhower to Kennedy* (New York, 1982), 50–55, 63–67; and Stephen G. Rabe, "Eisenhower and the Overthrow of Rafael Trujillo," *Conflict Quarterly* 6 (Winter 1986): 34–44.

82 Richard M. Saunders, "Military Force in the Foreign Policy of the Eisenhower Presidency," *Political Science Quarterly* 100 (Spring 1985): 105, 115; H. W. Brands, Jr., *Cold Warriors: Eisenhower's Generation and American Foreign Policy* (New York, 1988), 68, 211. For an indictment of the administration's domestic antisubversive activities see Jeff Broadwater, *Eisenhower and the Anti-Communist Crusade* (Chapel Hill, 1992).

The past decade's intensive research and writing on Eisenhower have probably not produced a scholarly consensus, although it can be fairly said that the majority of case studies have not sustained Eisenhower revisionism. The revisionists have elevated process over policy. The making of foreign policy in the Eisenhower administration was orderly and rational. Bureaucratic coherence, however, does not guarantee either humane or generous foreign policies. President Eisenhower proved steady in crises. But praise for his leadership must be balanced by hard thinking about the long-range commitments he made in regions such as Vietnam, about his penchant for clandestine diplomacy, and his stout support for unsavory, anti-Communist tyrants. Tor Førland and Chester Pach have independently proposed a sobriquet – "Eisenhower postrevisionism" – to characterize the new historiography. They believe that historians accept the revisionist case that Eisenhower was a thoughtful, decent leader committed to international peace and prosperity. But the avoidance of war is not peace. Eisenhower's rigid anticommunism led him to sanction unwise, globalist adventures.[83] Indeed, Robert Divine, perhaps responding to the archivally based studies, agrees that the new task of scholars is to examine not only the Eisenhower administration's intentions and capabilities but also the nature and quality of its policies. Reviewing scholarship on Dulles, Divine notes that the administration discussed issues in a perceptive, deliberate, even sophisticated manner. Nonetheless, knowing this "does not change the fact that the United States pursued a narrowly anti-Communist foreign policy" throughout the 1950s.[84]

Historians of U.S. foreign relations can expect that their analyses of Eisenhower's foreign policies will be enriched by the continued declassification of official records and private papers. Access to

83 Førland, "Selling Firearms," 223 n.6; Pach and Richardson, *Presidency of Dwight D. Eisenhower*, xiii, 238–39. See also Piers Brendon, *Ike: His Life and Times* (New York, 1986), 13, 246–48.

84 Robert A. Divine, "John Foster Dulles: What You See Is What You Get," *Diplomatic History* 15 (Spring 1991): 279, 285. See also Ronald W. Pruessen, "Beyond the Cold War – Again: 1955 and the 1990s," *Political Science Quarterly* 108 (Spring 1993): 71, 82–83; Brian R. Duchin, "The 'Agonizing Reappraisal': Eisenhower, Dulles, and the EDC," *Diplomatic History* 16 (Spring 1992): 221; and Greene, "John Foster Dulles," 569 n.57. One Eisenhower revisionist who acknowledges the critical scholarly responses is William B. Pickett in his concise *Dwight David Eisenhower and American Power* (Wheeling, IL, 1995).

the archives of the former Soviet bloc and key Third World nations would be especially helpful. For example, a central tenet of Eisenhower revisionism is that scholars must separate rhetoric from reality and not define Dulles's fiery anti-Communist tirades as policy. But, because foreign leaders did not have access to the minutes of NSC meetings or General Goodpaster's memorandums of the president's conversations, could they make such precise distinctions? Did they attach meaning to public pronouncements or simply dismiss them as unlovely features of U.S. domestic politics? Moreover, how did foreign officials assess covert operations, such as the organization of paramilitary missions in Eastern Europe? Did such activities give substance to promises of "liberation"?[85]

While pursuing both old and new questions about U.S. foreign relations, historians might also want to ponder whether they want to continue to employ the "presidential synthesis" and place Eisenhower at the center of their research.[86] Eisenhower revisionism rests on the assumption that the president and his policies are unique and worthy of discrete inquiry. Scholars in other fields of U.S. history, however, offer other schemes of periodization. Gary W. Reichard asserts that the years 1945 to 1960 are, in the political realm, a distinct period, distinguished by political equilibrium and general voter contentment. Presidents Harry S. Truman and Eisenhower, he argues, shared similar goals and realized similar outcomes in both the domestic and foreign arenas.[87] For William H. Chafe, a social-cultural historian, it is the years between 1948 and 1963 that constitute a discrete period of study because anticommunism served during that time as both a barrier to domestic social change and as the guiding principle of U.S. foreign policy.[88] Whatever the merits of these various approaches, scholars will undoubtedly find it fruitful to analyze the Eisenhower years within the context of postwar U.S. history.

85 Garthoff, *Assessing the Adversary*, 51; Kenneth Kitts and Betty Glad, "Presidential Personality and Improvisational Decision Making: Eisenhower and the 1956 Hungarian Crisis," in Warshaw, ed., *Reexamining the Eisenhower Presidency*, 195–96.

86 On the problems of this approach see Thomas C. Cochran, "The 'Presidential Synthesis' in American History," *American Historical Review* 53 (July 1948): 748–59.

87 Gary W. Reichard, *Politics as Usual: The Age of Truman and Eisenhower* (Arlington Heights, IL, 1988), xii–xv, 168–73.

88 William H. Chafe, "America since 1945," in *The New American History*, ed. Eric Foner (Philadelphia, 1990), 143–60.

12

John F. Kennedy as World Leader: A Perspective on the Literature

BURTON I. KAUFMAN

In evaluating contemporary presidents, historians have often differed sharply from the American public. The gap over the last forty years between public perceptions and historical judgments of the Harry S. Truman presidency is a case in point, as is, to a lesser extent, the differences between public and historical assessments of the Eisenhower presidency. But there is probably no presidency on which public perceptions and historical evaluations have remained more at odds than that of John F. Kennedy.

Most Americans think of President Kennedy as the young, handsome, athletic, vibrant chief executive who was just coming into his own when he was cut down by an assassin's bullet in Dallas on 22 November 1963. Most historians, however, have painted quite another portrait of the nation's thirty-fifth president.[1] Those writing in the 1970s were particularly harsh in their criticism, characterizing Kennedy as a person of style rather than substance, of profile rather than courage, driven by ambition rather than commitment, physically handsome but intellectually and morally unattractive. With regard to foreign policy, they accused him of being a conventional Cold Warrior who brought the world to the brink of nuclear disaster during the Cuban missile crisis of 1962.

1 For a general discussion of Kennedy historiography and myth making see Thomas Brown, *JFK: History of an Image* (Bloomington, 1988). See also Walter LaFeber, "Kennedy, Johnson and the Revisionists," *Foreign Service Journal* 50 (May 1973): 31–33, 39; Kent M. Beck, "The Kennedy Image: Politics, Camelot, and Vietnam," *Wisconsin Magazine of History* 58 (Autumn 1974): 45–55; and William E. Leuchtenburg, "John F. Kennedy: Twenty Years Later," *American Heritage* 35 (December 1983): 51–59. For a bibliography of works on Kennedy, now somewhat dated, see also Joan I. Newcomb, *John F. Kennedy: An Annotated Bibliography* (Metuchen, NJ, 1977).

Such views are still much in evidence. Indeed, the latest Kennedy biography, by Thomas Reeves, is among the most damning, and is made all the more so by the fact that Reeves is a well-respected historian and biographer who grew up sharing the popular view of Kennedy. In his biography, Reeves notes, "the more I read, the more I became fascinated by what appeared to be a gap between JFK's image and the historical reality." As he studied Kennedy's life, he found that "many of [his] youthful observations from the 1950s and 1960s had to be revised."[2]

More recently, however, scholars have started to look at the Kennedy administration's foreign policy with more detachment and a better sense of balance. For the most part, they are still highly critical of the president. But they have moved away from simple Camelot bashing and have begun to stress the complexity of the foreign policy crises that the president faced and to challenge simplistic characterizations of Kennedy as a world leader.

The first important assessments of the Kennedy administration were written by administration officials like Arthur Schlesinger, Jr., who was special assistant to the president and served as unofficial White House chronicler; Theodore Sorensen, who was the president's special counsel and, along with Bobby Kennedy, one of his two closest advisers; and Roger Hilsman, who was director of intelligence and research at the State Department and a self-confessed member of Kennedy's inner circle. These men were lavish in their praise of the martyred president and did much to shape his popular image. They depicted Kennedy as a leader of almost heroic dimensions: a consummate pragmatist with an ironic sense of detachment, more concerned with protecting and promoting the national interest than with questions of ideology; yet an agent of worldwide social reform who became, in effect, his own secretary of state because of the ineffectiveness of the Department of State under Dean Rusk; a chief executive who early in his administration made mistakes, most notably the failed attempt in April 1961 to overthrow the Cuban government of Fidel Castro by landing a group of Cuban exiles at the Bay of

2 Thomas C. Reeves, *A Question of Character: A Life of John F. Kennedy* (New York, 1991), xi.

Pigs, but a person who learned from his mistakes and then successfully met Soviet challenges over Western access rights to Berlin and over Soviet missiles in Cuba.[3] While acknowledging with considerable regret the expanded American military commitment in Vietnam during his administration, they argued that he had been boxed in by a policy he had inherited from the previous administration and claimed that had he lived, he might have extricated the United States from Vietnam before it became a quagmire.

These accounts of Kennedy's presidency also promoted the idea that Kennedy's greatness as a world leader extended beyond his skill as a crisis manager. They asserted that his capacity to combine restraint of manner with toughness of purpose was surpassed only by his ability to energize diplomacy: to mobilize the spirit and will of peoples throughout the world; to understand and identify the United States with the forces of Third World nationalism; to fashion people-to-people programs like Food for Peace and the Peace Corps; and, near the end of his administration, to lessen the chances of nuclear proliferation by signing a limited nuclear test ban treaty with the Soviet Union. "[H]e had accomplished so much," Schleslinger concluded. He had brought about "the new hope for peace on earth, the elimination of nuclear

3 Arthur Schlesinger, Jr., declared that Dean Rusk's "mind, for all its strength and clarity, was irrevocably conventional." *A Thousand Days: John F. Kennedy in the White House* (Boston, 1965), 312. John Kenneth Galbraith, whom Kennedy appointed ambassador to India, remarked that he once got a sharp letter from McGeorge Bundy saying that Rusk "had come to suspect" that Galbraith did not hold him in high regard. Galbraith responded that this did "credit to [his] perception." Galbraith, *Ambassador's Journal: A Personal Account of the Kennedy Years* (Boston, 1969), 156. Rusk believed it was his job as secretary of state to support the president in his policies, not to be a public advocate for any particular position. His reticence and self-effacement annoyed Kennedy. The president is reported to have complained to one political journalist that Rusk "never gives me anything to chew on, never puts it on the line. You never know what he is thinking." See Michael Beschloss, *The Crisis Years: Kennedy and Khrushchev, 1960–1963* (New York, 1991), 17. According to Theodore C. Sorensen, "too often, Kennedy felt, neither the President nor the [State] Department knew the Secretary's views." Sorensen, *Kennedy* (New York, 1965), 270. On Rusk see also Warren I. Cohen, *Dean Rusk* (New York, 1980); and Thomas J. Schoenbaum, *Waging Peace and War: Dean Rusk in the Truman, Kennedy, and Johnson Years* (New York, 1988). Cohen and Schoenbaum are more sympathetic to Rusk than most authors, although both criticize him severely for his unswerving support of the Vietnam War. "In the end," writes Schoenbaum, "he was trapped by his adherence to his own deeply held principles; he was unable to judge their limitations." Schoenbaum, *Waging Peace and War*, 432.

testing in the atmosphere and the abolition of nuclear diplomacy, the new policies toward Latin America, the reordering of American defense."[4] To Hilsman, Kennedy was "a leader [and a] hero as well."[5] To Sorensen, he was a person of great wit and style, but one whom, Sorensen was confident, history would judge, not by his style, but by "what mattered most to him, [his] substance – the strength of his ideas and ideals, his courage and judgment."[6]

By portraying Kennedy in such hagiographic terms, his defenders probably did his subsequent reputation more harm than good. It would have been nearly impossible for any leader under careful scrutiny to live up to such an image. Opposition to a war for which Kennedy had to bear at least some responsibility and more general disapproval of a foreign policy that a whole school of historians considered imperialist in fact, if not in intent, also contributed to growing criticism of the Kennedy administration beginning in the early 1970s, as did the contrast between the Kennedy glitter of the early 1960s and the national discord of the late 1960s. But it was precisely the substance of Kennedy's statesmanship and "the strength of his ideas and ideals" alluded to by Sorensen that subsequent writers on his presidency have found most wanting and that are at the root of the Kennedy revisionism that has continued into the 1990s.

The first major assault on Kennedy's statesmanship came in 1972 with the publication of three important works on his foreign policy: David Halberstam's *The Best and the Brightest*, Louise Fitzsimons's *The Kennedy Doctrine*, and Richard J. Walton's *Cold War and Counter-Revolution: The Foreign Policy of John F. Kennedy*. These were followed the next year by Henry Fairlie's equally critical *The Kennedy Promise: The Politics of Expectation*. All four books attempted to address the question of what went wrong in the 1960s, and all four writers concluded that in one way or another Camelot had been a con game perpetrated on the American people.

Of the four books, Halberstam's *The Best and the Brightest*, a

4 Schlesinger, *A Thousand Days*, 857.
5 Roger Hilsman, *To Move a Nation: The Politics of Foreign Policy in the Administration of John F. Kennedy* (Garden City, 1967), 582.
6 Sorensen, *Kennedy*, 5–7.

best-seller, attracted the most national attention. A reporter for the *New York Times*, Halberstam had earlier received a Pulitzer Prize for his hard-hitting coverage of the Vietnam War, in which he challenged Washington's claims that the United States was winning the war. In *The Best and the Brightest* he sought to explain how the United States became involved in the conflict during the Kennedy and Johnson administrations. He placed much of the blame upon the intellectual and corporate elite (the "best and the brightest") who came to Washington with Kennedy in 1961. Arrogant and eager to test their new powers, these men were convinced that they could contain the Communist threat in Southeast Asia through the rational application of America's economic and military power. They lied and dissembled both to themselves and to the American people, twisting facts and creating truths, excising pessimistic reports of the war, inflating enemy body counts, and deflating North Vietnam's recuperative powers in order to justify a continuation and expansion of the war.

Although Halberstam regarded President Kennedy more favorably than he did the men who worked for him, the president, in his view, still embodied most of what was wrong with the "best and the brightest." He was "too cool, too hard-line in his foreign policies, too devoid of commitment." He was motivated solely by political considerations, "which made him cautious and almost timid," certainly too cautious to challenge conventional perceptions about Communist expansionism. This timidity resulted in the great irony of the Kennedy administration, "that John Kennedy, rationalist, pledged above all to rationality should continue the most irrational of all major foreign policies, the policy toward . . . Asia."[7]

It was left to Louise Fitzsimons and Richard Walton, however, to challenge the bulk of the assertions made by Kennedy apologists. In their view, Kennedy epitomized the Cold Warrior. He forsook diplomacy for confrontation during the Berlin and Cuban missile crises, heightened the arms race, brought the world to the brink of nuclear holocaust, and, on the basis of what Fitzsimons called the "Kennedy Doctrine" (the right to intervene

7 David Halberstam, *The Best and the Brightest* (New York, 1972), 12, 93, 96, 102.

politically and militarily in the internal affairs of other, less powerful, nations), engaged in counterrevolutionary activities and introduced counterinsurgency tactics into places like Laos and Vietnam.[8] Indeed, Walton referred to Kennedy as "the great counterrevolutionary of the postwar world," a leader who supported self-determination but "did not understand revolution" and "prosecuted the Cold War more vigorously, and thus more dangerously, than did Eisenhower and Dulles."[9] While Fitzsimons was less strident in her indictment of Kennedy, the thrust of her remarks was the same. With more sadness than bitterness, she stated that ten years after his eloquent and well-known inaugural address, in which he promised to "pay any price, bear any burden, meet any hardship, support any friend, oppose any foe, in order to assure the survival and success of liberty," his words rang out with "an ominous sound of recognition."[10]

Kennedy's rhetoric was also the subject of Henry Fairlie's *The Kennedy Promise.* A British reporter and commentator, Fairlie argued that from the time he took office, Kennedy spoke the language of a Cold Warrior. Instead of calling for policies based on reasoned and limited aims, he offered a prescription for the nation that exaggerated its international obligations. The American people, swept up by his rhetoric and charisma, accepted his definition of national purpose "without question." The result was a messianic "madness of empire" that proved "too exacting for a free society to bear without grievous dislocation."[11]

The assault on Kennedy's reputation as president and statesman elicted a strong response from Arthur Schlesinger, Jr., who in 1973 dismissed Walton's and Fitzsimons's work as not worthy of "extended coverage" and maintained that Fairlie portrayed Kennedy in a manner that bore little resemblance to reality.[12] But while revisionists did not go unchallenged, theirs remained the

8 Louise Fitzsimons, *The Kennedy Doctrine* (New York, 1972), 8–9.

9 Richard J. Walton, *Cold War and Counter-Revolution: The Foreign Policy of John F. Kennedy* (Baltimore, 1972), 34–35, 211.

10 Fitzsimons, *The Kennedy Doctrine*, 3–4.

11 Henry Fairlie, *The Kennedy Promise: The Politics of Expectation* (New York, 1973), 10–12.

12 Arthur Schlesinger, Jr., "J.F.K.: Promise and Reality," *Commonweal* (25 May 1978): 290–91.

most widely held view in the historical literature. For example, in his well-received *Pragmatic Illusions: The Presidential Politics of John F. Kennedy* (1976), Bruce Miroff remarks that Kennedy's ambition was "to assert control over not only the American global establishment, but also the course of events around the globe." In his important study, *J.F.K.: The Presidency of John F. Kennedy* (1983), Herbert Parmet concludes that Kennedy's "constant need to demonstrate toughness had helped to manufacture potential disasters everywhere." In *Kennedy's Quest for Victory: American Foreign Policy, 1961–1963* (1989), a collection of essays edited by Thomas G. Paterson, Paterson comments that "arrogance, ignorance, and impatience combined with familiar exaggerations of the Communist threat" to assure that Kennedy's foreign policy would fail. And in the most recent study of the Kennedy administration, *The Presidency of John F. Kennedy* (1991), James N. Giglio remarks that Kennedy "became a victim of his own rhetoric. Having promised to act tough and do more, he limited his options in foreign policy."[13]

Even though revisionism prevails, critics of Kennedy's foreign policy have become increasingly subtle and sophisticated in their arguments. They no longer engage in the same sort of frontal attacks on Kennedy's character. They interpret the Kennedy presidency as a transitional one facing the emergent problems of the 1960s. And even more important, they pay greater attention to the interplay of domestic and foreign concerns and their influence on Kennedy's foreign policy.

One question of considerable interest to a number of these scholars has been Kennedy's alleged manipulation of public opinion. In his book, Fairlie maintained that the president used rhetoric to mobilize the nation around his foreign and defense policies, creating crises when none existed and turning incidents into emergencies. In related fashion, Walton argued that Kennedy toyed with the media, engaging in a "policy of deception, distortion,

13 Bruce Miroff, *Pragmatic Illusions: The Presidential Politics of John F. Kennedy* (New York, 1976), 32; Herbert S. Parmet, *J.F.K.: The Presidency of John F. Kennedy* (New York, 1983), 352; Thomas G. Paterson, ed., *Kennedy's Quest for Victory: American Foreign Policy, 1961–1963* (New York, 1989), 23; James N. Giglio, *The Presidency of John F. Kennedy* (Lawrence, 1991), 45. Two other important revisionist accounts of Kennedy's foreign policy are Garry Wills, *The Kennedy Imprisonment: A Meditation on Power* (Boston, 1982); and Beschloss, *The Crisis Years.*

and secrecy" to fashion public opinion.[14] Few writers contest the fact that, like two other Democratic presidents, Woodrow Wilson and Franklin D. Roosevelt, Kennedy regarded and employed language as a political weapon. According to Kent H. Beck, in the 1960 campaign the Democratic candidate "set out to construct a rhetorical position [on the issue of Cuba] firm enough to offset [Richard] Nixon's advantage on foreign policy, yet so noncommittal that it would not frighten the public or antagonize Democratic liberals."[15] In "John F. Kennedy and the Green Berets," Justin Gustainis even argues that Kennedy engaged in the "rhetorical use of myth" to gain public and congressional support for the Army's Special Forces (the Green Berets), who were to have primary responsibility for counterinsurgency operations. By portraying the Green Berets as the modern equivalent of the "frontier hero," he also sought, according to Gustainis, to pacify the nation's political Right and bolster his own public image.[16] Even Schlesinger has acknowledged that the president was sometimes guilty of rhetorical overkill. In 1973 he termed as "unfortunate" the lines in Kennedy's inaugural address about paying any price, bearing any burden, and meeting any hardship. He also admitted that some of the president's programs, like the Alliance for Progress, were "oversold."[17]

It is one thing, however, to argue that Kennedy used rhetoric as part of his political arsenal and quite another to suggest, as Fairlie did, that Kennedy's hyperbole and rhetorical flourishes were responsible for the nation's combative foreign policy. Several writers, including Giglio, Parmet, and David Burner, have now qualified this view considerably. As they have reminded their readers, Kennedy was probably reflecting national opinion as much as crafting it in his remarks. After a series of humiliating foreign

14 Walton, *Cold War and Counter-Revolution*, 44–45, 54–57, 182–88.

15 Kent H. Beck, "The Kennedy Image: Politics, Camelot, and Vietnam," *Wisconsin Magazine of History* 58 (Autumn 1974): 45–55; idem, "Necessary Lies, Hidden Truths: Cuba in the 1960 Campaign," *Diplomatic History* 8 (Winter 1984): 37–59.

16 J. Justin Gustainis, "John F. Kennedy and the Green Berets: The Rhetorical Use of the Hero Myth," *Communications Studies* 40 (Spring 1989): 41–53. See also Fairlie, *The Kennedy Promise*, 187; William C. Cockerham, "Green Berets and the Symbolic Meaning of Heroism," *Urban Life* 8 (1979): 111; Alasdair Spark, "The Soldier at the Heart of the War: The Myth of the Green Berets in the Popular Culture of the Vietnam Era," *Journal of American Studies* 18 (April 1984): 29–30; and John Hellmann, *American Myth and the Legacy of Vietnam* (New York, 1986), 41–69.

17 Schlesinger, "J.F.K.: Promise and Reality," 290–91.

policy disasters, including the cancellation of Eisenhower's trip to Japan because the Japanese government could not guarantee his safety, the U-2 incident, and the subsequent cancellation of the Paris summit meeting between Eisenhower and Khrushchev, the president did not have to be much of a pied piper to lead the American people down the path of an aggressive foreign policy. Furthermore, Kennedy's rhetoric, when compared to the previous administration's talk about "brinkmanship" and "massive retaliation," does not seem all that menacing. His much-quoted inaugural address has been taken out of context. More than a call to arms, it was a response to a truculent speech Khrushchev had delivered two weeks earlier, in which he said that capitalism was retreating before communism. In fact, there was a dual theme throughout Kennedy's address. Giglio points out that "even though [Kennedy was] promoting military strength and global commitment," he was also seeking "peace through negotiation, cooperation, and arms limitation."[18]

It should also be noted that Kennedy's ability to mold public opinion appears also to have been limited. In their important study, *The Kennedy Crises: The Press, the Presidency, and Foreign Policy* (1984), Montague Kern, Patricia W. Levering, and Ralph B. Levering review over six thousand news stories from five of the nation's leading newspapers on the four major crises of the Kennedy administration (Laos, Vietnam, Berlin, and Cuba). They conclude that while Kennedy cultivated good relations with the press and was able, when there was policy consensus, to get the press coverage he wanted, he failed to command the news when there was strong opposition to his policies. They argue persuasively that the press is "a reflective institution," noting that if there are other political actors opposed to a policy, the press "will reflect, focus, and magnify their views, and the White House will feel the heat as it did during the prelude to the Cuban missile crisis."[19] All this suggests that while Kennedy may have been

18 Giglio, *The Presidency of John F. Kennedy*, 27–28; Beschloss, *The Crisis Years*, 63–64; David Burner, *John F. Kennedy and a New Generation* (Glenview, IL, 1988), 52–53, 76. See also Schlesinger, "J.F.K.: Promise and Reality," 290–91.

19 Montague Kern, Patricia W. Levering, and Ralph B. Levering, *The Kennedy Crises: The Press, the Presidency, and Foreign Policy* (Chapel Hill, 1984), esp. xi–xii, 195–203.

guilty of fueling existing crises, he did not manufacture them, and therefore the idea that he mobilized the nation to support an aggressive foreign policy by manipulating the media does not provide an adequate framework for understanding his foreign policy.

At the same time, though, the argument that Kennedy's foreign policy was circumscribed by the legacy he inherited from Eisenhower – a position Kennedy apologists have long maintained – also seems of limited utility. One immediate problem with this claim is that those who make it want to have it both ways, placing considerable responsibility for failures like the Bay of Pigs operation on the previous administration but ignoring the contributions of the Eisenhower administration to what they consider Kennedy's most significant achievements. An example of how they have slighted the previous administration is their treatment of economic development assistance programs like the Alliance for Progress for Latin America, which they attribute almost exclusively to Kennedy's concern about the pressing economic needs of Third World nations.[20] While it is true that even as a senator Kennedy played an important role in garnering congressional support for development aid and as president was responsible for the establishment of the Alliance for Progress, several authors, including Kennedy's former deputy national security adviser, Walt Rostow, have shown that these programs originated in the Eisenhower administration.[21]

Not only are Kennedy apologists unfairly selective in discussing the president's legacy from the previous administration, but they also fail to take proper note of the opportunities Kennedy had to cancel or fundamentally alter policies pursued by his predecessor. Certainly this was the case with respect to the Bay of Pigs operation. There can be no doubt that there was considerable institutional pressure on the new president to proceed with

20 On this point see footnote 69.

21 W. W. Rostow, *Eisenhower, Kennedy and Foreign Aid* (Austin, 1985), esp. 198–201 Compare also Schlesinger's *A Thousand Days*, 155–72, 427, and Sorensen's *Kennedy*, 350–51, 529–37, with my *Trade and Aid: Eisenhower's Foreign Economic Policy, 1953–1961* (Baltimore, 1982), esp. 209. In addition see James M. Hagen and Vernon W. Ruttan, "Development Policy under Eisenhower and Kennedy," *Journal of Developing Areas* 23 (October 1988): 1–30.

the invasion of Cuba. The director of the CIA, Allen Dulles, reassured Kennedy that the operation had a good chance of success, and there was no opposition to it from either the Department of State or the Pentagon. Although the Joint Chiefs of Staff did express some misgivings about the plan, no one seems to have offered any serious criticism of it at cabinet meetings. Reflecting upon the situation, Irving L. Janis, a psychologist, has emphasized the sometimes pernicious impact of groupthinking, or peer-group pressures, on crucial decisions like the Bay of Pigs.[22] Schlesinger and Sorensen also make a compelling argument when they point out the costs of canceling the operation. As Schlesinger has commented, the decision on whether to go forward with the attack was presented to the president in such a way that he had to choose between disbanding "a group of brave and idealistic Cubans, already trained and equipped, who wanted very much to return to Cuba on their own or permit[ting] them to go ahead."[23]

Nevertheless, the amphibious landing in Cuba involving fourteen hundred exiles trained in Guatemala had little chance of succeeding. One historian of the operation, Trumbull Higgins, recently referred to it as "the perfect failure," and argued that, contrary to claims by Kennedy's defenders, the president agreed with the CIA-sponsored plan when he first learned about it in November as president-elect.[24] As Schlesinger and Sorensen have maintained, one important reason why he continued to support the invasion after he took office was the faulty information he received from the CIA and the Pentagon.[25] But Joshua H. Sandman shows that this was due in part to the lack of proper lines of communication within the administration as a result of Kennedy's decision to dismantle the national security apparatus

22 Irving L. Janis, *Victims of Groupthink: A Psychological Study of Foreign-Policy Decisions and Fiascos* (Boston, 1972), 14–49.

23 Schlesinger, *A Thousand Days*, 215–16. See also Sorensen, *Kennedy*, 294–301; and Haynes Johnson, *The Bay of Pigs: The Leaders' Story of Brigade 2506* (New York, 1964). Johnson's early account of the invasion is based on conversations he had with leaders of the Bay of Pigs operation. Johnson places most of the responsibility for the botched invasion on the CIA rather than on the president.

24 Trumbull Higgins, *The Perfect Failure: Kennedy, Eisenhower, and the CIA at the Bay of Pigs* (New York, 1987), 66–67.

25 Schlesinger, *A Thousand Days*, 214–16; Sorensen, *Kennedy*, 294–96.

established by Eisenhower.[26] In the view of Thomas Paterson, who has written extensively on U.S.-Cuban relations since Castro came to power in 1959, an even more fundamental reason for the doomed operation was Kennedy's anti-Castro fixation, which blinded him, Paterson maintains, to the moral and legal – as well as the logistical and military – questions involved in "violently overthrowing a sovereign government."[27]

Clearly, then, it is wrong to attribute the Bay of Pigs fiasco primarily to the legacy Kennedy inherited from Eisenhower or even to his inexperience in office. The president was being historically accurate as well as politically responsible in assuming blame for the disaster. But Higgins and journalist Peter Wyden, in the two most recent books on the invasion, also emphasize the need to put Kennedy's part in the affair into a broader historical perspective than either Paterson or the earlier revisionists have done. Wyden agrees with Paterson's assertion that Kennedy sought to punish Castro. He notes that the president was determined to demonstrate to the Cuban leader "the smack of firm government." But he believes the president and his advisers never had a firm grip on the situation. Whereas most scholars portray Kennedy as a firm and decisive leader, Wyden claims that he was weak and indecisive and that the air strikes he canceled might have made a difference once the Cuban exiles were onshore.[28] In contrast, Higgins credits the president "for resisting the far greater folly of an open and indefinitely prolonged American military intervention, regardless of the immense pressure brought to bear and of the serious political consequences for himself."[29] Either way, Kennedy appears much more restrained and circumspect than earlier revisionists have suggested.

Historians generally agree that the failure at the Bay of Pigs had major consequences for the new administration. Having lost all confidence in the foreign policy apparatus outside the White

26 Joshua H. Sandman, "Analyzing Foreign Policy Crisis Situations: The Bay of Pigs," *Presidential Studies Quarterly* 16 (Spring 1986): 310–16. See also Beschloss, *The Crisis Years*, 133.

27 Thomas G. Paterson, "Fixation with Cuba: The Bay of Pigs, Missile Crisis, and Covert War against Castro," in Paterson, ed., *Kennedy's Quest for Victory*, 123–55.

28 Peter Wyden, *Bay of Pigs: The Untold Story* (New York, 1979).

29 Higgins, *The Perfect Failure*, 173.

House, Kennedy increased his own grasp over foreign policy. While the operation's failure prompted the president to launch Operation Mongoose (an effort to undermine Cuba through a systematic program of sabotage) and perhaps to conspire with the Mafia to assassinate Castro, it also made him wary about increasing America's military involvement in Laos, where the United States had already sent three hundred military advisers in an effort to keep the Communist Pathet Lao forces from overrunning the country.[30]

Kennedy's restraint was tested in the next major crisis of his young administration – Berlin. During a tense, two-day meeting with Kennedy in Vienna in June 1961, Soviet Premier Nikita Khrushchev threatened to turn Berlin over to the East German government after signing a German peace treaty. After the meeting, the president issued a statement of American determination to defend West Berlin with a buildup of American military might. In August, Khrushchev counterattacked by announcing the successful testing of a one hundred-megaton nuclear weapon, and by building the infamous Berlin Wall, which would put an end to the stream of East Germans fleeing to the West. After that, the crisis ebbed, but not before Kennedy ordered a convoy of fifteen hundred American troops down the Autobahn into West Berlin

30 Although acknowledging the existence of Operation Mongoose, Arthur Schlesinger, Jr., in 1978 denied these charges, which first surfaced in Washington in 1975 during an investigation by the Senate Select Committee on Intelligence headed by Frank Church of Idaho into plots to murder foreign leaders. Conceding that in 1960 (before Kennedy's election), the CIA had "set in motion the plot to kill Castro," Schlesinger remarked that "there was no evidence that any [CIA] officials ever mentioned it to any President." The Church Committee had already reached the same conclusion, and there has been no evidence to prove otherwise, although Paterson has commented that after the Bay of Pigs, "intensified economic coercion joined assassination and sabotage as methods to undermine the Castro government" and Reeves has underscored Kennedy's secret meeting with Mafia boss Sam Giancana. Schlesinger, *Robert Kennedy and His Times* (Boston, 1978), 494–517; Paterson, "Fixation with Cuba," 138; Reeves, *A Question of Character*, 277–79. See also Brown, *J.F.K.: History of an Image*, 72–74; and Burner, *John F. Kennedy and a New Generation*, 68. On U.S. involvement in Laos during this period see Usha Mahajani, "President Kennedy and United States policy in Laos, 1961–63," *Journal of Southeast Asian Studies* 2 (September 1971): 87–99. Stephen E. Pelz points out that the Joint Chiefs of Staff opposed sending troops into Laos, warning the president that there were insufficient forces to meet potential Communist threats in Berlin, the Caribbean, Vietnam, and the Congo. Pelz, "'When Do I Have Time to Think?' John F. Kennedy, Roger Hilsman, and the Laotian Crisis of 1962," *Diplomatic History* 3 (Spring 1979): 215–29. See also Kenneth L. Hill, "President Kennedy and the Neutralization of Laos," *Review of Politics* 31 (July 1969): 353–69.

and sent Vice President Johnson to the city in order to demonstrate his determination to keep Berlin open to the West.

Kennedy apologists maintain that the president conducted himself responsibly and courageously; early revisionists that he acted provocatively and dangerously.[31] Both sides have ample evidence to support their views. In *The Berlin Crisis* (1973), Robert Slusser, a Soviet historian, has argued that Soviet politics had more to do with the crisis than any action taken by the president. In Moscow, a power struggle was taking place between Khrushchev and his hard-line opponents in the Presidium, and both attempted to choreograph the crisis to their own advantage. According to Slusser, Khrushchev provoked the crisis in order to force a treaty over Germany by the end of 1961. He hoped such a treaty would be the prelude to improved relations with Washington. Khrushchev's opponents escalated the crisis by forcing him to cease demobilization and resume atmospheric testing of nuclear weapons. It was this political tug-of-war taking place inside the Kremlin, not anything Kennedy said or did, that in Slusser's view made the Berlin crisis so dangerous. "Several attempts have recently been made to depict John F. Kennedy as a dogmatic anti-Communist whose actions helped create the very crises with which his administration tried to cope," Slusser has written. "What emerges from intensive study of the Soviet side in the Berlin crisis of 1961, however, is the recognition that the Soviet threat to vital interests was in actuality even more direct and dangerous than anyone in Washington at the time realized."[32]

In his recent study of the Kennedy-Khrushchev relationship, however, Michael Beschloss throws most of the responsibility for the Berlin crisis back into Kennedy's court. He does not deny the considerable domestic political pressures Khrushchev faced in his dealings with the American president. On the contrary, he criticizes the president for not understanding these pressures, particularly in the wake of the recent Sino-Soviet split and the Soviet leader's

31 Schlesinger, *A Thousand Days*, 288–339; Sorensen, *Kennedy*, 583–601; McGeorge Bundy, *Danger and Survival: Choices about the Bomb in the First Fifty Years* (New York, 1988), 358–85; Walton, *Cold War and Counter-Revolution*, 80–93; Fitzsimons, *The Kennedy Doctrine*, 97–125; Miroff, *Pragmatic Illusions*, 65–82.

32 Robert M. Slusser, *The Berlin Crisis of 1961: Soviet-American Relations and the Struggle for Power in the Kremlin, June–November 1961* (Baltimore, 1973), x–xi, 157–70.

agreement with Kennedy on Laos. "Taking a hard line on Berlin," Beschloss writes, "would help avoid charges that he was soft on Washington and impress his Soviet critics, the Chinese and the Third World with his assertion of Soviet power." Although Beschloss is also highly critical of Khrushchev for his inflammatory rhetoric and his bullying of the president in Vienna, he blames Kennedy for most of his problems with the Soviet Union. In fact, he maintains that the Soviet leader's determination to seek a final settlement of the Berlin question was not unreasonable. "Khrushchev would have been hard pressed," he writes, "to ignore Berlin in 1961, even if he had wished. For two and a half years, he had insisted on the fundamental importance of resolving the problem of Berlin and Germany."[33]

Beschloss's portrayal of the president, however, is not one-dimensional. Although Kennedy acted most often like a conventional Cold Warrior, at times he appeared inexperienced, irresolute, and "vulnerable to intimidation." These fluctuations in Kennedy's style and behavior confused and confounded Soviet leaders. "During his first five months in office," Beschloss states, "the President had given Khrushchev the dangerous impression that he was at once more passive and more militant than Eisenhower." Because Kennedy appeared particularly vulnerable following the Bay of Pigs, Khrushchev decided to press ahead "with removing the Berlin 'cancer' from Eastern Europe and codifying the permanent division of Germany."[34]

Other books on the Berlin crisis and the building of the Berlin Wall also refer to Kennedy's vacillation and indecisiveness during the crisis. In addition, they make it clear that the construction of the wall was a blessing in disguise for the White House, enabling Kennedy to extricate the United States from a confrontation with the Soviet Union by stopping the mass exodus out of East Berlin without denying the West its access rights to the city. As early as 1971, Jack M. Schick in *The Berlin Crisis, 1958–1962* criticized Kennedy for a lack of clarity about American objectives in Berlin and for his policy of seeking negotiations through intimidation, the same policy that Khrushchev pursued.[35] The next year Eleanor

33 Beschloss, *The Crisis Years*, 232.
34 Ibid.
35 Jack M. Schick, *The Berlin Crisis, 1958–1962* (Philadelphia, 1971), 137–241.

Lansing Dulles argued that a show of Western fortitude could have prevented the construction of the Berlin Wall. Curtis Cate makes the same point in *The Ides of August: The Berlin Wall Crisis, 1961* (1978), an angry anecdotal account of the crisis in which Cate contrasts the courage of Berliners with what he sees as the pusillanimity of Kennedy and his advisers.[36]

In 1980, Honore Catudal took an entirely different approach to the Berlin crisis, applying to Kennedy's conduct the various models of policy formulation so popular among political scientists. Placing the president's response to Khrushchev's threats on Berlin within the context of an ongoing struggle inside his administration between the hawks who favored a military response and the doves who preferred quiet diplomacy, he takes issue with revisionist historians who have argued that Kennedy's call in July for a buildup of American military forces was a surrender to the militants. "Although some revisionist historians would call his [decisions on Berlin] a capitulation to the hard line," he writes, "they actually represented somewhat of a compromise between the 'hawks' and 'doves.'" Kennedy did not declare a national emergency or ask for an immediate mobilization of forces, he notes. Furthermore, he slashed additional military budget requests from $4.3 billion to $3.2 billion, and in his 25 July speech to the American people on Berlin, he coupled his stress on firmness with a willingness to negotiate.[37]

The literature on the Berlin crisis, therefore, suggests that Kennedy was neither the decisive and courageous statesman that Kennedy apologists have maintained nor the irresponsible and dogmatic Cold Warrior that early revisionists have claimed. Instead, it portrays a leader who was determined to maintain Western access to Berlin even if that meant military conflict with the Soviet Union but, without appearing overly concerned about the people whose lives were most affected by its construction,

36 Eleanor Lansing Dulles, *The Berlin Wall: A Crisis in Three Stages* (Columbia, SC, 1972); Curtis Cate, *The Ides of August: The Berlin Wall Crisis, 1961* (New York, 1978). Other accounts of the Berlin crisis include Norman Gelb, *The Berlin Wall: Kennedy, Khrushchev, and a Showdown in the Heart of Europe* (New York, 1986); Jean Edward Smith, *The Defense of Berlin* (Baltimore, 1963), 228–341; and Eric Morris, *Blockade: Berlin and the Cold War* (New York, 1973), 195–249.

37 Honore Marc Catudal, *Kennedy and the Berlin Wall Crisis: A Case Study in U.S. Decision Making* (Berlin, 1980), 180–81.

quietly accepted the Berlin Wall as a way of resolving the crisis. As Kennedy's national security adviser, McGeorge Bundy, later put it, the president believed the freedom of two million West Berliners was worth fighting for, while "freedom of circulation in an already divided city was not."[38] At the same time, Slusser and Catudal indicate the need to consider the bureaucratic dynamic within which both Khrushchev and Kennedy operated.

The literature on the Cuban missile crisis, the most dangerous crisis of the Kennedy presidency and, arguably, of the entire Cold War era, profiles the president in much the same fashion. The issue most heatedly debated by students of the crisis is that of Kennedy's conduct as crisis manager. Did he perform as brilliantly as Kennedy apologists and many other historians have said? Or did he unnecessarily bring the world to the brink of nuclear war without first giving quiet diplomacy a chance, as early revisionists claimed? A second, related, question, concerns Khrushchev's motives for sending medium- and intermediate-range ballistic missiles to Cuba. Did he take this action to defend Cuba from a possible American invasion, or to redress the strategic imbalance in favor of the United States, or to engage in a form of nuclear blackmail in hopes of compelling the United States to agree to a Berlin settlement? These are the explanations most often given regarding Khrushchev's actions.

Although the literature on the crisis is massive and continues to grow, a consensus seems to be emerging on a number of these issues, fostered in part by the memoirs of numerous participants in the crisis and by a conference at Harvard University in 1987 that brought together many of these participants and scholars from both the United States and the Soviet Union.[39] There seems to be no question that Kennedy was prepared to use military force to take the missiles out. As Raymond Garthoff, a staff-level

38 Bundy, *Danger and Survival*, 367–69.

39 The literature on the missile crisis merits separate treatment, but an excellent introduction to some of the issues involved can be found in Giglio, *The Presidency of John F. Kennedy*, 190–215. See also William J. Medland, *The Cuban Missile Crisis of 1962: Needless or Necessary?* (New York, 1988); and David L. Larson, ed., *The Cuban Crisis of 1962: Selected Documents, Chronology, and Bibliography* (Lanham, MD, 1986). For Soviet perspectives consult Ronald R. Pope, ed., *Soviet Views on the Cuban Missile Crisis: Myth and Reality in Foreign Policy Analysis* (Lanham, MD, 1982). A good survey of the recent literature is Robert A. Divine, "Alive and Well: The Continuing Cuban Missile Crisis," *Diplomatic History* 18 (Fall 1994): 551–60.

adviser in the State Department during the missile crisis, has remarked, "from the first day [of the crisis] the president never wavered from one basic decision: the Soviet missiles must be removed."[40] In fact, the president may have been planning a military operation to overthrow Castro even before learning of the missiles in October. According to James G. Hershberg, "the Pentagon, acting at the direction of the president and the secretary of defense, dramatically accelerated contingency planning for military action against Cuba in late September and early October 1962, just as the president was ordering a sharp increase in anti-Castro covert operations." There is still insufficient evidence to conclude – as Paterson and Barton Bernstein, but not Hershberg, do – that Khrushchev was probably telling the truth when he said that he sent the missiles to Cuba to protect the island against an American invasion or that Kennedy actually intended to invade Cuba before the missile crisis.[41]

Nevertheless, Soviet participants at the 1987 conference on the missile crisis have made clear Khrushchev's near obsession with an American invasion of Cuba as a result of Kennedy's rhetoric and activities associated with Operation Mongoose. They have also acknowledged Khrushchev's desire to redress the strategic imbalance in missiles, which the White House had made public soon after Kennedy took office. But as Paterson has pointed out, these two explanations for Khrushchev's actions are not incompatible. "The Soviets hoped to enhance their much weaker deterrent power in the Cold War and [at the same time] save a threatened ally."[42]

40 Raymond L. Garthoff, *Reflections on the Cuban Missile Crisis* (Washington, 1989), 44. See also Robert F. Kennedy, *Thirteen Days: A Memoir of the Cuban Missile Crisis* (New York, 1971); Bundy, *Danger and Survival*, 392–456; Dean Rusk with Richard Rusk and Daniel S. Papp, *As I Saw It* (New York, 1990), 229–45: Maxwell D. Taylor, *Swords and Plowshares* (New York, 1972), 261–81: George W. Ball, *The Past Has Another Pattern: Memoirs* (New York, 1982), 158–73; and Charles E. Bohlen, *Witness to History, 1929–1969* (New York, 1973), 489–98.

41 James G. Hershberg, "Before the Missiles of October: Did Kennedy Plan a Military Strike against Cuba?" *Diplomatic History* 14 (Spring 1990): 163–98; Paterson, "Fixation with Cuba," 141–42; Barton Bernstein, "Commentary: Reconsidering Khrushchev's Gambit – Defending the Soviet Union and Cuba," *Diplomatic History* 14 (Spring 1990): 231–39.

42 James G. Blight and David A. Welch, *On the Brink: Americans and Soviets Reexamine the Cuban Missile Crisis* (New York, 1989), 238–52 and 293–302; Paterson, "Commentary: The Defense-of-Cuba Theme and the Missile Crisis," *Diplomatic History* 14 (Spring 1990): 205–6. See also Beschloss, *The Crisis Years*, 377–87; and Herbert S. Dinerstein, *The Making of a Missile Crisis, October 1962* (Baltimore, 1976).

Not only was Kennedy set on forcing Moscow to dismantle the missiles and take them back to the Soviet Union, he was also determined not to negotiate over the matter. The issue of whether the president should have tried the path of quiet diplomacy before raising the possibility of nuclear war in a televised address on 22 October has elicited considerable controversy. Those who argue that he should have tried diplomacy maintain that he might have been able to persuade Moscow to remove its missile from Cuba in exchange for his agreement to remove America's obsolete Jupiter missiles from Turkey.[43]

Interestingly, though, one of those most strongly challenging that claim is Sergo Mikoyan, son of the former first deputy premier of the Soviet Union, Anastas I. Mikoyan, and secretary to his father at the time of the missile crisis. According to Mikoyan, Khrushchev and the Presidium were not interested in negotiations but in seeing how far they could push Kennedy before he responded. They were taken completely by surprise when the president announced on television that the Soviets had placed missiles in Cuba and warned that any nuclear missile fired from Cuba against a nation in the Western Hemisphere would be regarded as an attack by Moscow against the United States and would require a full retaliatory response.[44]

At the same time, participants at the Harvard conference seemed to agree that President Kennedy would have stopped short of war with the Soviet Union. One of the most dangerous moments of the crisis occurred following Kennedy's receipt on 26 and 27 October of two letters from Khrushchev, the first agreeing to remove the missiles from Cuba in return for a promise from the United States not to invade Cuba, the second insisting that the United States would first have to remove American missiles from Turkey. Instead of responding to the second letter, whose terms were unacceptable, the president responded to the first letter, accepting its conditions. In response, Khrushchev, who had been

43 Walton, *Cold War and Counter-Revolution*, 134–42; Miroff, *Pragmatic Illusions*, 96–97; Wills, *The Kennedy Imprisonment*, 278–79.

44 Bernd Greiner, "The Soviet View: An Interview with Sergo Mikoyan," *Diplomatic History* 14 (Spring 1990): 205–22. See also Arnold J. Horelick, "The Cuban Missile Crisis," *World Politics* 16 (April 1964): 378–83; Blight and Welch, *On the Brink*, 299–301, 303–4; and Garthoff, *Reflections on the Cuban Missile Crisis*, 42–45.

assured secretly by Bobby Kennedy that his brother would remove the Jupiter missiles from Turkey, agreed to withdraw the Soviet missiles from Cuba.

Until recently, most writers have maintained that had Khrushchev rejected the president's response to his first letter, war would have followed. At the Harvard conference, however, McGeorge Bundy read a letter from Dean Rusk, the former secretary of state, that revealed that Kennedy was willing to allow the United Nations to act as an intermediary should Khrushchev still insist on a quid pro quo for removal of the Cuban missiles. According to a plan worked out at the White House, Secretary General U Thant would ask both parties to withdraw their missiles from Cuba and Turkey, and Kennedy would consent to the UN request. The plan rested on the assumption that a request from the United Nations would be more palatable to the American people than unilateral action by the president. Robert McNamara, secretary of defense under Kennedy, also indicated that such a ploy was under serious consideration even though word of it never surfaced. "It's possible," he remarked, "that the President would have settled on something like the missile trade. . . . To my mind [an invasion of Cuba] was highly unlikely."[45]

None of this undermines the point made by revisionists concerning Kennedy's responsibility for the Cuban missile crisis. Paterson may have been overly simplistic when he commented that "the origins of the crisis . . . derived largely from the concerted American campaign to squash the Cuban revolution." But there can be no denying Kennedy's almost irrational attitude toward Castro and his determination to undermine his regime.[46] At the same time, though, the point made by Schlesinger and Sorensen a quarter of a century ago – that, throughout the thirteen-day crisis, Kennedy resisted military action – remains valid. As even the Soviet participants at the Harvard conference acknowledged, moreover, Khrushchev, who was profoundly ignorant of the United States, not only badly misjudged the president but

45 Blight and Welch, *On the Brink*, 82–84, 263; Garthoff, *Reflections on the Cuban Missile Crisis*, 94–96.

46 Paterson, "Defense-of-Cuba Theme," 256. See also Garthoff, *Reflections on the Cuban Missile Crisis*, 188–89.

ignored the advice of his own experts in thinking that he could get away with placing nuclear missiles within the Western Hemisphere and so close to the Florida coast.[47] Finally, it now seems clear that while Kennedy was determined that the missiles had to be removed even if that meant some form of military action, he was willing to accept as a quid pro quo the removal of America's missiles from Turkey.

Two other matters having to do with the Cuban missile crisis shed additional light on Kennedy's conduct of the crisis. The first concerns the decision-making process. In his landmark work, *The Essence of Decision: Explaining the Cuban Missile Crisis* (1971), Graham Allison argued the need to look at the Cuban missile crisis – and, by extension, any major crisis – in terms of bureaucratic politics rather than any particular rationale. More specifically, he strongly suggested that the playing out of the crisis had to do as much with the tug of personalities and bureaucratic interests within the ExCom (the executive committee Kennedy established to advise him on the crisis) as with any single decision Kennedy made.[48]

Almost certainly Allison exaggerated the role of bureaucratic politics in the development and outcome of the missile crisis. As Ronald Steel has pointed out, Kennedy's first and in many respects most important decision – to forgo diplomacy in favor of force to get the missiles out of Cuba – was made without resort to the ExCom.[49] Throughout the crisis, moreover, the president relied far more on his brother and his own judgment in making his decisions than on the ExCom, which had difficulty reaching agreement on anything.[50] Nevertheless, the debate that took place in the ExCom provided him with a menu of options and a sense of the risks each one involved. In their meetings at the White House, ExCom members consulted outside experts like former Secretary of State Dean Acheson, looked at various proposals

47 Blight and Welch, *On the Brink*, 301–2. See also Greiner, "The Soviet View: An Interview with Sergo Mikoyan," 207.

48 Graham T. Allison, *Essence of Decision: Explaining the Cuban Missile Crisis* (Boston, 1971), esp. v–viii, 1–9.

49 Ronald Steel, "Cooling It," *New York Review of Books* 19 (19 October 1972): 43–46.

50 On this point see especially Robert McNamara's comments at the Harvard conference. Blight and Welch, *On the Brink*, 51. See also ibid., 123–24.

from a number of different angles, and discussed and rejected simplistic stereotypes. Bobby Kennedy and Ted Sorensen played devil's advocate. In a sense, the ExCom acted as a brake on precipitate action, although the sheer exhaustion of the men serving the president, as described at the Harvard conference, may in fact have been one of the great dangers of the crisis.[51]

The second matter concerning the missile crisis has to do with the role of domestic politics. Early revisionists argued that Kennedy played politics with or even manufactured the crisis in an effort to gain Democratic seats in Congress in the November elections.[52] In 1986, Paterson and William J. Brophy challenged that view, maintaining that Kennedy did not have to create a crisis for the Democrats to do well in November because the polls already showed that the Democrats would win impressively in the midterm elections.[53]

More recently, however, Richard Ned Lebow has argued the need for a more sophisticated assessment of Kennedy's political motives than either earlier revisionists or Paterson and Brophy have presented. In contrast to Paterson and Brophy, Lebow maintains that Kennedy was very concerned about the domestic political consequences of the Soviet missiles in Cuba. But what bothered him as much as the political cost of not confronting the Soviets over the missiles, was the cost of challenging Moscow, for he was worried that if he invaded Cuba or launched an air strike, even prominent Democrats like Senators Richard Russell of Georgia and J. William Fulbright of Arkansas would turn against him. Instead of causing the president to manufacture a crisis, therefore, political concerns made him shy away from military action. According to Lebow, the action that Kennedy

51 Ibid., 47, 72–73, 95–96, 123, 128–29. See also Janis, *Victims of Groupthink*, 138–66. Janis regards the Cuban missile crisis, in contrast to other situations, including the Bay of Pigs, as one instance in which groupthinking was successful.

52 James A. Nathan, "The Missile Crisis: His Finest Hour Now," *World Politics* 27 (January 1975): 262–65; Barton J. Bernstein, "The Cuban Missile Crisis," in *Reflections on the Cold War: A Quarter Century of American Foreign Policy*, ed. Lynn H. Miller and Ronald Preussen (Philadelphia, 1974), 131–33; Ronald Steel, "Endgame," *New York Review of Books* 12 (16 March 1969): 15; Wills, *The Kennedy Imprisonment*, 282–83.

53 Thomas G. Paterson and William J. Brophy, "October Missiles and November Elections: The Cuban Missile Crisis and American Politics, 1962," *Journal of American History* 73 (June 1986): 87–119.

finally decided upon, a quarantine, "represented a tradeoff between the imperatives for action . . . and the risk of a confrontation."[54]

In sum, the literature on the Cuban missile crisis suggests that while the world was a more dangerous place as a result of the missiles in Cuba, it did not quite reach the brink of nuclear disaster as both early revisionists and Kennedy apologists maintained. It also shows that Khrushchev has to bear a good share of the responsibility for the crisis; that in any evaluation of Kennedy as crisis manager, bureaucratic and domestic political considerations have to be factored in; and that, finally, the president was far more judicious in his conduct of the crisis than early revisionists have allowed. In other words, where Kennedy's conduct as world statesman is concerned, the literature on the Cuban missile crisis parallels that on the Bay of Pigs and Berlin crises.

According to most accounts of the Kennedy administration, the Cuban missile crisis had a sobering effect on the president, leading him to tone down his rhetoric and to seek an accommodation with the Soviet Union. At American University on 10 June, he called for improved relations with Moscow and advocated a nuclear test ban treaty. Although he failed to achieve the comprehensive agreement he wanted, in July the United States and the Soviet Union signed a limited agreement prohibiting the atmospheric testing of nuclear weapons.[55] As a result, even so ardent a critic of Kennedy as Thomas Reeves has commented on the beneficial impact of the Cuban missile crisis on the president. After the crisis, he notes, "it seemed imperative to limit the possibilities of mutual destruction."[56]

Not all historians share this view, however. Paterson points to Kennedy's continued efforts to destroy the Castro regime and

54 Richard Ned Lebow, "Domestic Politics and the Cuban Missile Crisis: The Traditional and the Revisionist Interpretations Reevaluated," *Diplomatic History* 14 (Fall 1990): 471–92.

55 According to Glenn T. Seaborg, the chairman of the Atomic Energy Commission during Kennedy's administration, however, "the situation was to get worse [after the Cuban missile crisis] before it got better." See his *Kennedy, Khrushchev, and the Test Ban* (Berkeley, 1981), esp. 172–85. See also Bernard J. Firestone, *The Quest for Nuclear Stability: John F. Kennedy and the Soviet Union* (Westport, 1982).

56 Reeves, *A Question of Character*, 397. See also Giglio, *The Presidency of John F. Kennedy*, 215–17.

concludes that he learned very little from the missile crisis.[57] In a fascinating and incisive essay, Gordon Chang maintains that Kennedy and his closest advisers even pursued the possibility of a joint Soviet-American attack on China in order to prevent it from developing its own nuclear capability.[58] Similarly, Desmond Ball shows that, despite the president's sincere efforts on behalf of a nuclear test ban treaty, he supported a strategic missile program providing for the production of one thousand Minuteman missiles, even though the so-called missile gap of the 1960 election had been debunked. He argues, furthermore, that Kennedy made that decision largely in response to domestic political pressures with little regard for existing military needs.[59]

More likely, the impact of the missile crisis on Kennedy was real but modest. His foreign policy continued to be unpredictable. As a result, it remains uncertain what he would have done had he lived about the conflict in Vietnam, which became the most significant legacy of his abbreviated administration. Like the Cuban missile crisis, the Vietnam War has spawned a virtual cottage industry of books and commentary, much of it touching upon Kennedy's responsibility for America's growing involvement in the conflict.[60] Although former Kennedy aides like Kenneth

57 Paterson, "Introduction: John F. Kennedy's Quest for Victory and Global Crisis," in Paterson, ed., *Kennedy's Quest for Victory*, 4–23. See also idem, "Fixation with Cuba," 153–55; and idem, "Bearing the Burden: A Critical Look at JFK's Foreign Policy," *Virginia Quarterly Review* 54 (Spring 1976): 210–12.

58 Gordon H. Chang, "JFK, China, and the Bomb," *Journal of American History* 74 (March 1988): 1287–1310. The article also appears as a chapter in idem, *Friends and Enemies: The United States, China, and the Soviet Union* (Stanford, 1990), 228–52. For a critical view of Kennedy's policy with respect to China see also James Fetzer, "Clinging to Containment: China Policy," in Paterson, ed., *Kennedy's Quest for Victory*, 178–97; and Warren I. Cohen, "The United States and China since 1945," in *New Frontiers in American-East Asian Relations: Essays Presented to Dorothy Borg*, ed. Warren I. Cohen (New York, 1983), 159–63. Cohen writes that there was "little in Kennedy's attitude toward the People's Republic on the policies he pursued to suggest that he was interested in . . . seeking accommodation with Beijing." Ibid., 160.

59 Desmond Ball, *Politics and Force Levels: The Strategic Missile Program of the Kennedy Administration* (Berkeley, 1980). For the administration's war plan against the Soviet Union, based on "an inflexible overwhelming nuclear offensive to destroy . . . the full range of Sino-Soviet bloc targets," see Scott D. Sagan, "SIOP-62: The Nuclear War Plan Briefing for President Kennedy," *International Security* 12 (Summer 1981): 22–51.

60 An indispensable reference work to the literature prior to 1982 is Richard Dean Burns and Milton Leitenberg, eds., *The Wars in Vietnam, Cambodia, and Laos* (Santa Barbara, 1985). This should be supplemented with the bibliographical essay

O'Donnell, Pierre Salinger, and Arthur Schlesinger, Jr., have persistently maintained that at the time of his assassination Kennedy was considering withdrawal or had already decided to withdraw from Vietnam after the 1964 presidential election, former Secretary of State Dean Rusk maintains that at no time did "Kennedy ever say or hint or suggest to me that he was planning to withdraw from Vietnam in 1965."[61] Even Schlesinger has acknowledged that "Kennedy's legacy [on Vietnam] was dual and contradictory" and that "he had left on the public record the impression of a major national stake in the defense of South Vietnam."[62]

Three writers who have dealt recently with the question of Kennedy's role in the Vietnam War also disagree as to what course he would have followed. In *An International History of the Vietnam War: The Kennedy Strategy* (1986), R. B. Smith argues the need to understand Kennedy's strategy of counterinsurgency on "its own terms, and not as a prelude to intervention." Nevertheless, he also believes that Kennedy would probably have continued the war in Vietnam because of his view of the mounting importance of the Third World.[63] In contrast, William J. Rust, a correspondent for *U.S. News and World Report*, maintains that Kennedy most likely would have gotten out of Vietnam although he acknowledges "the absence of a clear direction to Kennedy's policy and the contradictory speculation of his former advisers."[64] In the most recent study of Kennedy's Vietnam policy, *JFK and Vietnam: Deception, Intrigue, and the Struggle for Power*

in George Herring, *America's Longest War: The United States and Vietnam, 1950–1975* (New York, 1986), 283–302. See also Herring's review article, "America and Vietnam: The Debate Continues," *American Historical Review* 92 (April 1987): 350–62; Warren I. Cohen's review essay, "Vietnam: New Light on the Nature of War?" *International History Review* 9 (February 1987): 108–16; and John Mirsky's review essay, "Reconsidering Vietnam," *New York Review of Books* 38 (10 October 1991): 44–51.

61 Kenneth B. O'Donnell and David F. Powers, *Johnny, We Hardly Knew Ye: Memories of John Fitzgerald Kennedy* (Boston, 1970), 16–18; Pierre Salinger, *Je Suis un Americain* [I am an American] (Paris, 1975), 239; Schlesinger, *Robert Kennedy and His Times*, 755–58. Rusk's comment is in Giglio, *The Presidency of John F. Kennedy*, 254.

62 Schlesinger, *Robert Kennedy and His Times*, 758.

63 R. B. Smith, *An International History of the Vietnam War: The Kennedy Strategy* (New York, 1986), 2–16.

64 William J. Rust, *Kennedy in Vietnam* (New York, 1985), xi–xvi, 179.

(1992), John M. Newman declares that by the time of his assassination, Kennedy had realized his Vietnam policy was a failure and that "had he lived, he still would have had time to take his case truthfully to the American people in 1964, and he might have done so."[65]

Thus, there remains no clear answer as to whether America's role in Vietnam would have been substantially different had Kennedy lived and won reelection in 1964. That may be because the president was unclear himself about what course to pursue. Certainly Newman and Rust indicate this was the case. What is particularly fascinating about Newman's book, in fact, is the author's characterization of Kennedy as a leader who was not in command of his own policy. Newman spins a tale of suspense and conspiracy, suggesting, for example, the existence of a secret arrangement between President Ngo Dinh Diem of South Vietnam and Vice President Lyndon Johnson, whom Kennedy sent to Saigon in May 1961 to reassure Diem of American support. According to Newman, Johnson, acting without the knowledge of the president, encouraged Diem to ask Kennedy for American combat troops, something the Joint Chiefs of Staff, but not the president, supported. "Unfortunately, this important episode has thus far been lost in the dustbin of history," Newman writes.[66] Because much of *JFK and Vietnam* is filled with such gossipy tidbits of history based largely on circumstantial evidence, Newman's argument has to be treated with considerable caution and even skepticism. But his portrayal of the president as tragic hero is not inconsistent with other portrayals of Kennedy described elsewhere in this essay.

Rust's characterization of Kennedy is very similar to Newman's. Like Eisenhower, Rust says, Kennedy had major reservations about committing American forces to Vietnam, and he was disgusted with the repressive Diem regime. But because he feared the

65 John M. Newman, *JFK and Vietnam: Deception, Intrigue, and the Struggle for Power* (New York, 1992), 458–59.

66 Ibid., 67–78. Kennedy's ambassador to Vietnam, Frederick Nolting, also strongly suggests that Kennedy had lost control of his Vietnam policy, in part because State Department officials and military leaders often acted at cross purposes from one another. Nolting, *From Trust to Tragedy: The Political Memoirs of Frederick Nolting, Kennedy's Ambassador to Diem's Vietnam* (New York, 1988).

international and domestic political consequences of a withdrawal from Vietnam, his administration "could never credibly threaten [Diem] with the ultimate sanction – abandoning the country to the Communists." As a result, even though the president told CBS News anchorman Walter Cronkite in September 1963 that "in the final analysis," it was up to the Saigon government to win or lose the war, he sent sixteen thousand combat troops to Vietnam. Even worse, despite intense debate within the administration over whether to support a coup to overthrow the Diem government (which, of course, the White House did), the president and his senior advisers failed to pay adequate attention to the possibility raised in Cronkite's interview with Kennedy that "with or without Diem, the war might be a loser."[67] In sum, Kennedy's policy toward Vietnam, according to Rust, was prompted by fear and resulted in frustration, futility, and failure.[68]

Although the historiographical debate over Kennedy's foreign policy has naturally concentrated on the president's conduct of the major crises facing his administration, it has also touched upon a number of other issues, including his overall policy toward the Third World; his grand design for Europe; his foreign economic policy; his efforts on behalf of nuclear disarmament; and those programs closely associated with his administration, such as the Alliance for Progress and the Peace Corps. Space precludes an extended discussion of these issues. But the literature on these matters confirms that Kennedy was both more complex and more ambiguous than either the Kennedy apologists or the early revisionists have allowed.

For example, his policy toward the Third World suggests a statesman very much aware of and sympathetic to Third World

67 Rust, *Kennedy in Vietnam*, 50–59, 128–30, 137–38, 179.

68 See also the fine essay by Lawrence J. Bassett and Stephen E. Pelz, "The Failed Search for Victory: Vietnam and Politics of War," in Paterson, ed., *Kennedy's Quest for Victory*, 223–52. Among the factors influencing Kennedy's Vietnam policy, Bassett and Pelz note issues of credibility, Kennedy's personal reputation, Khrushchev's bluster, domestic politics (fear of losing southern and northern white ethnics in the 1964 election should Vietnam fall to the Communists), and Kennedy's personal and ideological commitment to containment in South Vietnam. Ibid., 245–46. In addition, consult Ellen J. Hammer, *A Death in November: America in Vietnam, 1963* (New York, 1987), an account of the Kennedy administration's involvement in the coup against Diem. Hammer writes about the "mirage that American policy makers had pursued in Vietnam" prior to the coup (p. 312).

nationalism. Yet it also suggests an inveterate Cold Warrior whose dogmatic anticommunism often blinded him to the very forces he championed, a leader who often seemed imaginative, innovative, and daring but whose foreign policy, hindered by a torpid bureaucracy and the president's own orthodoxies, was traditional, cautious, and not particularly effective. Writing on the Alliance for Progress and Latin America, for instance, Stephen Rabe declares that New Frontiersmen exaggerated their ability to promote change and "underestimated the daunting nature of Latin America's socioeconomic problems."[69] More than that, Rabe asserts, "through its recognition policy, internal security initiatives, and military and economic programs, the Administration demonstrably bolstered regimes and groups that were undemocratic, conservative, and frequently repressive."[70]

As for the Middle East, Kennedy was the first American

69 The Alliance for Progress has itself elicited a considerable literature. Its impact on Latin America is an issue that scholars have debated with considerable passion. According to Schlesinger, the alliance was, indeed, a major accomplishment, "channeling the energies of both public and private agencies as never before." See *A Thousand Days*, 660. Sorensen is more ambivalent, conceding that "reality did not match the rhetoric which flowed about the Alliance on both sides of the Rio Grande" but emphasizing its contribution to Latin America's economic growth. See *Kennedy*, 535–36. Similar views can be found in Lincoln Gordon, *A New Deal for Latin America: The Alliance for Progress* (Cambridge, MA, 1963); Herbert K. May, *Problems and Prospects for the Alliance for Progress: A Critical Examination* (New York, 1968); and Harvey S. Perloff, *Alliance for Progress: A Social Invention in the Making* (Baltimore, 1969). For the opposite view see Victor Alba, *Alliance without Allies: The Mythology of Progress in Latin America* (New York, 1965). For a more balanced view consult Jerome Levinson and Juan de Onis, *The Alliance that Lost Its Way: A Critical Report on the Alliance for Progress* (Chicago, 1970); and Abraham F. Lowenthal, "United States Policy toward Latin America: 'Liberal,' 'Radical,' and 'Bureaucratic' Perspectives," *Latin American Research Review* 35 (1973): 3–26. Even Schlesinger later criticized the alliance for its cumbersome bureaucracy. See Schlesinger, "The Alliance for Progress: A Retrospective," in *Latin America: The Search for a New International Role*, ed. Ronald G. Hellman and H. Jon Rosenbaum (New York, 1975), 57–92.

70 Stephen G. Rabe, "Controlling Revolutions: Latin America, the Alliance for Progress, and Cold War Anti-Communism," in Paterson, ed., *Kennedy's Quest for Victory*, 109–22. On many of these same points see also Paul J. Dosal, "Accelerating Dependent Development and Revolution: Nicaragua and the Alliance for Progress," *Inter-American Economic Affairs* 38 (Spring 1985): 75–96; and Joseph S. Tulchin, "The United States and Latin America in the 1960s," *Journal of Interamerican Studies and World Affairs* 30 (Spring 1988): 1–36. Tulchin also adds that "as in all matters," style was so important to Kennedy "that a clear argument elegantly presented impressed him more than mountains of data and evidence presented in an indiscriminate fashion" (p. 14).

president to recognize Arab nationalism as a force independent of the Cold War. For a period of time he even engaged in a friendly correspondence with the foremost leader of the Arab world, President Gamal Abdel Nasser of Egypt. But as Douglas Little has pointed out, traditional American support for Israel, the strength of the American Jewish community, ongoing concern about Soviet influence in the Middle East, and divisions within the Arab world itself, particularly following a coup in Yemen believed to have been instigated by Nasser, undermined Kennedy's efforts at an "even-handed policy" and pushed Nasser closer to the Soviet Union.[71]

Kennedy also championed the cause of black nationalism in Africa. But according to Richard Mahoney, who gives him high marks for his African policy, the president did so at least in part to win and maintain the support of blacks in the United States. Africa became a "surrogate for the explosive subject of civil rights." Moreover, Kennedy's African policy was erratic; he was unwilling, for example, to oppose Portugal over its colony of Angola for fear of losing the American lease to the military complex in the Portuguese Azores. Mahoney acknowledges that as a result "the expectations [of Africans] proved far greater than the achievements" of Kennedy's African policy.[72]

Kennedy's concern for the Third World was one reason why he endorsed the establishment of the Peace Corps, the concept of which originated with Hubert Humphrey and Congressman Henry Reuss of Wisconsin. But in a highly favorable account of the

71 Douglas Little, "The New Frontier on the Nile: JFK, Nasser, and Arab Nationalism," *Journal of American History* 75 (September 1988): 501–27; Mordechai Gazit, *President Kennedy's Policy toward the Arab States and Israel: Analysis and Documents* (Tel Aviv, 1983), esp. 14–16, 22–30; William J. Burns, *Economic Aid and American Policy toward Egypt* (Albany, 1985), 121–49. See also Little, "From Even-Handed to Empty-Handed: Seeking Order in the Middle East," in Paterson, ed., *Kennedy's Quest for Victory*, 156–77; and James Goode, "Reforming Iran during the Kennedy Years," *Diplomatic History* 15 (Winter 1991): 13–29. For Kennedy's policy toward other parts of the Third World consult Ronald J. Nurse, "Critic of Colonialism: JFK and Algerian Independence," *Historian* 39 (February 1977): 307–26; B. J. Jain, "The Kennedy Administration's Policy towards Colonialism: A Case Study of GOA, 1961 in the Indian Context," *Indian Journal of American Studies* 14 (July 1984): 145–54; B. J. B. Krupadanam, "US Food Aid to India and Its Implications," ibid., 169–83; and Giglio, *The Presidency of John F. Kennedy*, 221–54.

72 Richard Mahoney, *JFK: Ordeal in Africa* (New York, 1984), 24–33, 203–22, 248. See also Thomas J. Noer, "New Frontiers and Old Priorities in Africa," in Paterson, ed., *Kennedy's Quest for Victory*, 253–83; and F. Usgboaja Ohaesbulam, "Containment in Africa: From Truman to Reagan," *TransAfrica Forum* 6 (Fall 1988): 7–33.

Peace Corps, which he terms Kennedy's "bold experiment," Gerard T. Rice points out that the Democratic candidate for president also supported its establishment because he needed an attractive campaign issue as the 1960 election drew to a close. Furthermore, the White House regarded the Peace Corps as an instrument of American foreign policy in the Cold War struggle with the Soviet Union as much as an agency for economic development.[73]

In addition to promising to reach out to the Third World more than his predecessor, Kennedy also talked about a "grand design" for Europe, by which he meant a greater sense of partnership between the United States and a united Western Europe. But by all accounts, the grand design was never achieved. In part, this was due to the obstructionism of President Charles de Gaulle of France. But according to Frank Costigliola, it was also due to Kennedy's unwillingness to engage fully in the type of partnership with Europe that he professed to want. What he really wanted, Costigliola maintains, was to turn Western Europe into a "unified, faithful helpmate" of the United States. While former Undersecretary of State George Ball, one of the administration's strongest proponents of the grand design, does not take such a harsh, revisionist view of Kennedy, he makes clear his own regret that Kennedy never really embraced the Atlantic partnership he advocated.[74]

Closely tied to Kennedy's grand design was his foreign economic policy, predicated on trade expansion and a resolution of the nation's balance-of-payments problem. As William Borden has written, the president hoped that increased exports would "be the key to domestic growth, curing the balance of payments deficit, and cementing the alliance with Western Europe." The president's efforts to liberalize world trade soon ran into the wall of European agricultural protectionism. But according to Borden, an even more fundamental flaw in Kennedy's foreign economic

73 Gerard T. Rice, *The Bold Experiment: JFK's Peace Corps* (Notre Dame, 1985); Gary May, "Passing the Torch and Lighting Fires: The Peace Corps," in Paterson, ed., *Kennedy's Quest for Victory*, 284–316; and Harris Wofford, *Of Kennedy and Kings: Making Sense of the Sixties* (New York, 1980). Wofford helped organize the Peace Corps and served for two years as Kennedy's special assistant for civil rights.

74 Frank Costigliola, "The Pursuit of Atlantic Community: Nuclear Arms, Dollars, and Berlin," in Paterson, ed., *Kennedy's Quest for Victory*, 24–56; Ball, *The Past Has Another Pattern.*

policy was his failure to adjust the nation's international financial and monetary policy to reflect the weakened state of the American dollar. Instead, he pressured the nation's European trading partners and allies to defend the reserve status of the dollar, not only angering and embarrassing them, but also binding "his successors to this defensive strategy, and [bringing] the entire [international monetary] system down with the dollar in 1971 and 1972." In sum, what Kennedy did, according to Borden, was to "launch an aggressive but ultimately futile defense of American economic hegemony."[75]

In Eastern Europe, Kennedy promised an activist policy that, in contrast to Eisenhower's policy, would try to weaken Soviet influence in the region through cultural agreements and flexible aid and trade policies. As a result, Eastern Europeans greeted his election with great enthusiasm. But A. Paul Kubricht shows that reality outran promise. In Czechoslovakia, for example, "Kennedy's willingness to use aid and trade policy to create leverage for the United States . . . was non-existent." What applied to Czechoslovakia also applied to most of the other Eastern European nations. Notwithstanding his campaign promises, the president was simply unwilling to challenge Congress on such a sensitive issue as trade and aid to Eastern bloc countries. Because of the escalation in "the ideological confrontation between East and West" that took place during his administration, the president's own interest in strengthening economic and cultural ties with Eastern Europe also diminished considerably.[76]

75 William S. Borden, "Defending Hegemony: American Foreign Economic Policy," in Paterson, ed., *Kennedy's Quest for Victory*, 57–85. On Kennedy's trade policy see also Thomas W. Zeiler, "Free Trade Politics and Diplomacy: John F. Kennedy and Textiles," *Diplomatic History* 11 (Spring 1987): 127–42; Alan P. Dobson, "The Kennedy Administration and Economic Warfare against Communism," *International Affairs* 64 (Autumn 1988): 599–616; and John W. Evans, *The Kennedy Round in American Trade Policy: The Twilight of the GATT?* (Cambridge, MA, 1971), 11–16.

76 A. Paul Kubricht, "United States-Czechoslovak Relations during the Kennedy Administration," *East European Quarterly* 22 (September 1989): 355–64; idem, "Politics and Foreign Policy: A Brief Look at the Kennedy Administration's Eastern European Diplomacy," *Diplomatic History* 11 (Winter 1987): 55–65. See also Joseph F. Harrington, "Rumanian-American Relations during the Kennedy Administration," *East European Quarterly* 18 (Summer 1984): 215–36; idem, "American-Romanian Relations in the 1960's," *New England Social Studies Bulletin* 43 (1985–86): 18–56; and Stephen S. Kaplan, "United States Aid to Poland, 1957–1964: Concerns, Objectives and Obstacles," *Western Political Quarterly* 28 (March 1975): 147–66.

In summary, then, Kennedy's role as world leader defies easy description or analysis. The literature on his foreign policy has suggested a person with two very different sides, torn by contradictory impulses. On the one hand, there was the Kennedy of Camelot, a worldly, perceptive, strong, and judicious leader exuding confidence and charisma, deeply affected by the early crises of his administration, recognizing the rapid changes taking place in the world, and responding with a New Frontier of foreign policy initiatives. Then there was the darker Kennedy, a shallow, cynical, passionless, and vainglorious politician, a traditional Cold Warrior, a weak and vulnerable president not always in control of his own foreign policy, and for all these reasons, an extremely dangerous man to have in the Oval Office. If the first image is the one of Kennedy apologists and the second of the early revisionists, the most recent literature suggests a more complex figure whose personality embraced elements of both images, but more of the latter than the former.

13

The Unending Debate: Historians and the Vietnam War

GARY R. HESS

The burgeoning literature on the Vietnam War testifies to its status as a defining event in American history. The early availability of a considerable body of documentation on U.S. policy-making in Washington and warmaking in Vietnam, together with the intensity of controversies stirred by the war, help to account for this extensive writing. The duration of the war and its antecedents – a thirty-year process between Ho Chi Minh's 1945 assertion of independence in the name of the Democratic Republic of Vietnam and the Ho Chi Minh campaign of 1975 that reunified the country – make this a lengthy story and one being told more in fragments than in its entirety. Hence, while much early scholarship was devoted to American policy and actions in World War II and the early Cold War, the more recent focus has moved to subsequent developments, with considerable attention to the administrations of Dwight D. Eisenhower and Lyndon B. Johnson. Most scholarship has been devoted to the American side, but the emerging literature includes a number of important efforts to see the conflict from Vietnamese perspectives and to set it in an international context. This essay explores the development of the principal interpretive issues in an emerging Vietnam War historiography with a focus on the literature that has appeared in the last dozen years.[1]

1 There are numerous assessments of the literature on Vietnam. Among the more recent are: David L. Anderson, "Why Vietnam? Postrevisionist Answers and a Neorealist Suggestion," *Diplomatic History* 13 (Summer 1989): 419–29; Warren I. Cohen, "Vietnam: New Light on the Nature of the War?" *International History Review* 9 (February 1987): 108–16; Robert A. Divine, "Vietnam Reconsidered," *Diplomatic*

At one time, the Vietnam War seemed easily understandable. While it was being waged, the predominant (orthodox) interpretation saw the United States, driven by a mindless anticommunism and with disregard for Vietnamese politics and culture, being drawn into a conflict that it could not win. The titles of representative orthodox books convey the sense of misguided, if not arrogant, idealism leading to a tragic military intervention: *The Making of a Quagmire*; *Washington Plans an Aggressive War*; *The Abuse of Power*; *The Arrogance of Power*; *The Bitter Heritage*; *The Lost Crusade*.[2]

Just as the administration of Richard M. Nixon was ending U.S. involvement in 1972, the orthodox critique was given its fullest expression in two influential and highly praised books: David Halberstam's *The Best and the Brightest* and Frances FitzGerald's *Fire in the Lake*. Together these works explained the tragedy that Vietnam had by then come to symbolize: Halberstam's devastating portraits of the men brought to power by John F. Kennedy, who embodied the "historical sense of inevitable victory"; and FitzGerald's contention that the war they waged was

History 12 (Winter 1988): 79–93; John M. Gates, "Vietnam: The Debate Goes On," *Parameters* 14 (Spring 1984): 15–24; George C. Herring, "America and Vietnam: The Debate Continues," *American Historical Review* 92 (April 1987): 350–62; idem, "Vietnam Remembered," *Journal of American History* 73 (June 1986): 152–64; Gary R. Hess, "The Military Perspective on Strategy in Vietnam [Review of Harry G. Summers's *On Strategy* and Bruce Palmer's *The 25-Year War*]," *Diplomatic History* 10 (Winter 1986): 91–106; Thomas G. Paterson, "Historical Memory and Illusive Victories: Vietnam and Central America," ibid. 12 (Winter 1988): 1–18; and Geoffrey S. Smith, "Light at the End of the Tunnel? New Perspectives on the Vietnam War," *Canadian Journal of History* 26 (April 1991): 67–86.

2 David Halberstam, *The Making of a Quagmire: America and Vietnam during the Kennedy Era* (New York, 1964); Ralph L. Stavins, Richard J. Barnet, and Marcus G. Raskin, *Washington Plans an Aggressive War* (New York, 1971); Theodore Draper, *The Abuse of Power* (New York, 1966); Chester Cooper, *The Lost Crusade: America in Vietnam* (Fawcett, CT, 1970); J. William Fulbright, *The Arrogance of Power* (New York, 1966); and Arthur M. Schlesinger, Jr., *The Bitter Heritage: Vietnam and American Democracy*, rev. ed. (Greenwich, CT, 1968). The most scholarly of the orthodox works was George McT. Kahin and John W. Lewis, *The United States in Vietnam* (New York, 1967).

Other early works stressed an imperialist imperative leading to the war in Vietnam; these included: Richard J. Barnet, *Roots of War: The Men and Institutions behind U.S. Foreign Policy* (New York, 1972); and Gabriel Kolko, *The Roots of American Foreign Policy* (Boston, 1969). For contemporary apologies of U.S. policy see Chester A. Bain, *Vietnam: The Roots of Conflict* (Englewood Cliffs, 1967); and Robert Scigliano, *South Vietnam, Nation under Stress* (Boston, 1963).

irrelevant given the forces of Vietnamese history, which assured the triumph of the Communist revolution.[3]

As Halberstam and FitzGerald were providing what seemed to be definitive explanations of the war, the scholarly impact of what quickly became known as the Pentagon Papers was changing the terms of thinking about Vietnam. The controversial publication in 1971 of the massive Department of Defense study of policymaking from 1945 to 1967 gave Americans an unprecedented opportunity to read classified documents about a war while it was still being waged. But it also challenged orthodox assumptions and provided the opening scholarly wedge of revisionism. In early interpretations of the Pentagon Papers, the project's documents and narrative were seen as stripping the veneer of innocence from U.S. policymaking by showing that officials recognized the likelihood that escalatory steps would fail as well as the deceit they engaged in by publicly promising "progress." To Daniel Ellsberg, who had helped to compile the study and then to leak it to the press, the story of the Pentagon Papers was simple: Each president had done the minimum necessary to avoid defeat in Vietnam.[4]

After publication of the Pentagon Papers, a spate of revisionist-oriented works quickly appeared, principal among them four books published in 1978 and 1979 – *The Irony of Vietnam* by Leslie Gelb with Richard Betts; *Summons of the Trumpet* by David Richard Palmer; *Strategy for Defeat* by U. S. Grant Sharp; and *America in Vietnam* by Guenter Lewy.

In *The Irony of Vietnam: The System Worked*, Gelb, who had directed the Pentagon Papers project, collaborated with Betts in countering the conventional view that America had blundered into Vietnam. The bureaucratic system "worked" in that policymakers: (1) were consistently aware of the obstacles to U.S. objectives; (2) did the minimum necessary to avoid defeat at each escalatory step; and (3) were successful until losing "the essential domino" – American public support. The Gelb and Betts emphasis

3 David Halberstam, *The Best and the Brightest* (New York, 1972), 123; Frances FitzGerald, *Fire in the Lake: The Vietnamese and the Americans in Vietnam* (Boston, 1972).

4 Daniel Ellsberg, *Papers On the War* (New York, 1972).

on a designed stalemate reinforced the wave of military revisionism that began in earnest with Sharp's *Strategy for Defeat* and Palmer's *Summons of the Trumpet*. These works, and several that followed, reflect the military leadership's long-standing resentment of civilian direction of the war. Sharp, a retired admiral who was Commander in Chief Pacific from 1964 to 1968, and Palmer, a general who served in various command positions in Vietnam, were the first of several high-ranking officers to write revisionist accounts of the war in which they served.

Finally, Lewy's *America in Vietnam*, based in large part on special access to classified documents, offers a scholarly apology for the U.S. effort, stressing the morality of the objective of defending South Vietnam and of the military means employed toward that end. The United States, Lewy asserts, failed to do enough: It should have taken direct control of the South Vietnamese government, incorporated the Army of the Republic of Vietnam (ARVN) into the U.S. command structure, and enforced the reforms necessary to win peasant support.[5]

In the years following this initial wave of revisionist literature, three main groups of revisionists have emerged: the Clausewitzians, the "hearts-and-minders," and the "legitimacists." Although there are elements of "if only" history in all of these works, it is a central tool for the Clausewitzians, who promise a retrospective prescription for victory. The hearts-and-minders and the legitimacists tend to be more scholarly and less certain that the American effort could have attained its objectives.

The most explicit and best known Clausewitzian statement is provided by Harry Summers's *On Strategy*, which cleverly contrasts U.S. conduct of the war with the classic strategic doctrines set forth in Karl von Clausewitz's *On War*. Summers contends that American political leaders were principally responsible for a strategy that was deficient on every count. Other officers of the Vietnam War have argued along similar lines; their works include

5 Leslie Gelb, with Richard K. Betts, *The Irony of Vietnam: The System Worked* (Washington, 1978); Dave Richard Palmer, *Summons Of the Trumpet: U.S.-Vietnam in Perspective* (Novato, CA, 1978); U. S. Grant Sharp, *Strategy for Defeat: Vietnam in Retrospect* (San Rafael, CA, 1978); Guenter Lewy, *America in Vietnam* (New York, 1978).

The 25-Year War: America's Military Role in Vietnam, by Bruce Palmer; *The Rise and Fall of an American Army: U.S. Ground Forces in Vietnam, 1965–1973*, by Shelby Stanton; and two works by Phillip B. Davidson, *Vietnam at War: The History, 1946–1975*, and *Secrets of the Vietnam War*.[6]

With varying degrees of intensity and emphasis, Clausewitzian revisionists argue that civilian leaders misunderstood the Vietnam conflict and sent the military off to wage the wrong kind of war. Had Washington recognized Vietnam as a war of aggression from the North and not as an insurgency supported by the North, had U.S. power been used fully against the North, and had Johnson enlisted popular support and a national commitment, the war could have been won quickly and decisively. Instead, a protracted war played into the hands of the enemy and contributed to disillusionment at home, a factor aggravated by the antiwar protest and biased reporting in the media. Even in the mistaken war of search-and-destroy, the United States had its opportunities to win, but the military was restrained by civilian leaders: It could not bomb vital targets in the North; it could not pursue the enemy into Cambodian and Laotian "sanctuaries"; it could not exploit its "victory" in the Tet Offensive. When Nixon removed many restrictions, some revisionists argue, U.S. air power demonstrated its ability to force concessions. Generally, Vietnamization succeeded, but the South Vietnamese were let down by a spineless Congress and were overwhelmed by the North's 1975 invasion.

Although the Clausewitzian revisionists focus their criticism on civilian leadership, they are mindful of many shortcomings in

6 Harry G. Summers, *On Strategy: A Critical Analysis of the Vietnam War* (Novato, CA, 1982); Bruce Palmer, Jr., *The 25-Year War: America's Military Role in Vietnam* (Lexington, KY, 1984); Phillip B. Davidson, *Vietnam at War: The History, 1946–1975* (Novato, CA, 1988); idem, *Secrets of the Vietnam War* (Novato, CA, 1990); Shelby Stanton, *The Rise and Fall of an American Army: U.S. Ground Forces in Vietnam, 1965–1973* (New York, 1985).

Among other expressions are William C. Westmoreland, *A Soldier Reports* (Garden City, NY, 1976); Richard M. Nixon, *No More Vietnams* (New York, 1985); General William E. DePuy, "What We Might Have Done and Why We Didn't Do It," *Army* 36 (February 1986): 23–40; and Robert F. Turner, "Myths and Realities in the Vietnam Debate," *World Politics* 149 (Summer 1986): 35–47.

For the thinking of military officers who opposed the war on political, strategic, and moral grounds see Bob Buzzanco, "The American Military's Rationale against the Vietnam War," *Political Science Quarterly* 101:4 (1986): 559–76.

the military's command structure and in its conduct of the war. Some accounts are critical of Westmoreland's leadership, while others see him as forced by circumstances into a futile war of attrition.

Such revisionism has a familiar tone. Just as revisionist writings on American intervention in the two world wars found America victimized by conspirators or, at the least, by incompetent civilian leaders, so too do Clausewitzians see fools and knaves undermining the Vietnam War effort. Beyond criticism of Johnson's conduct of the war, revisionists maintain that the media and the antiwar protest movement misled and divided the country. Elevating Vietnam into the mythology of a lost cause, some revisionist writing thus explains defeat implicitly in "stab-in-the-back" terms.[7]

While the Clausewitzians criticize Johnson and other civilian leaders for misinterpreting the conflict and restraining the military, the hearts-and-minds revisionists argue that too much attention was devoted to conventional warfare to the detriment of effective pacification. While the Clausewitzians blame civilian officials for failure, the hearts-and-minders fault the army leadership for both resisting and misapplying counterinsurgency doctrine. The search-and-destroy campaign was actually waged in far too conventional a manner, resulting in insufficient attention to pacification.

To many participants in the war, this issue still stirs deep emotions. For instance, in *About Face*, David Hackworth, renowned for his battlefield achievements in Vietnam, indicts the search-and-destroy strategy, the shortcomings of which were evident to the American command early in the war. General William Westmoreland had "enough troops and charts and graphs and formulas to do everything but win and solve the conflict," Hackworth writes. But he failed to understand guerrilla warfare – "an almost criminal shortcoming."[8]

Andrew Krepinevich and Larry Cable share Hackworth's

7 Jeffrey P. Kimball, "The Stab-in-the-Back Legend and the Vietnam War," *Armed Forces and Society* 14 (Spring 1988): 433–58.

8 Colonel David H. Hackworth and Julie Sherman, *About Face* (New York, 1989), 556, 613–14.

assessment of the U.S. military leadership but offer more measured and fuller expressions of the hearts-and-minds argument. In *The Army and Vietnam*, Krepinevich criticizes the army's dismissal of counterinsurgency as a "fad" of the New Frontier and its insistence on waging it "American-style" through an air mobile "high-cost low-payoff strategy" that minimized the "other war" of pacification. Securing the countryside would have been difficult, but according to Krepinevich, who served as an army officer in Vietnam, it would have been less costly in human and financial terms and "would have placed the Army in a position to sustain its efforts in a conflict environment certain to produce a protracted war."[9]

In both *Conflict of Myths* and *Unholy Grail*, Cable faults the army's misapplication of counterinsurgency doctrine. In fact, he turns the Clausewitzian argument on its head and says that the United States actually (but incorrectly) fought a conventional war against the North. Insisting that the Vietcong insurgency exemplified partisan warfare in which a guerrilla movement depended on external support, the army incorrectly saw North Vietnam as the enemy and fought a conventional war with Clausewitzian emphasis on massive destruction. Only the Marines, with their experience in the Banana Wars of the early twentieth century, understood and dealt with the indigenous origins of insurgency. American military strategy consistently played into the hands of North Vietnam, giving it greater influence in the South: Rolling Thunder provided the impetus for increased infiltration of the South; and the mindless ground war disrupted Southern society and undermined the Vietcong. "In an attempt to solve a problem that did not exist," Cable writes, "[the United States] created a problem that could not be solved."[10]

Complementing the Clausewitzians and the hearts-and-minders are the legitimacists, who emphasize the moral and political necessity of U.S. involvement in terms of national security and the viability and progress of the South Vietnamese government. Also

9 Andrew F. Krepinevich, *The Army and Vietnam* (Baltimore, 1986), 233.

10 Larry E. Cable, *Conflict of Myths: The Development of Counterinsurgency Doctrine and the Vietnam War* (New York, 1988), 225; idem, *Unholy Grail: The U.S. and the Wars in Vietnam, 1965–1968* (London, 1991).

emphasizing the "aggression" of North Vietnam, the legitimacists help reinforce the Clausewitzian contention of a conventional war. Legitimacists see the United States as headed in the right direction in the late 1950s and argue that it should have stood by Ngo Dinh Diem, who, as subsequent events would demonstrate, was the South's most effective leader. His overthrow led only to the political instability that eventually necessitated U.S. military intervention. In an early expression of this viewpoint, Norman Podhoretz's strident *Why We Were in Vietnam* stresses the moral and political imperatives of U.S. policy, the strength of anticommunism in the South, and the shallowness of the war's critics.[11]

The legitimacist argument is being presented most fully in R. B. Smith's multivolume *An International History of the Vietnam War*. In his first two volumes – *Revolution versus Containment* and *The Kennedy Strategy* – Smith advances a view of the emerging conflict that emphasizes the Chinese and Soviet interest in Vietnam. As the Soviet Union pursued coexistence with the West in the late 1950s, Hanoi feared isolation and dependence on China. But by taking advantage of Southern insurgent demands for support, Ho Chi Minh forced the Chinese and the Soviets into backing the nationalist cause. By the time that John F. Kennedy became president, Vietnam had become a major problem "for reasons more to do with the global strategies of the Soviet Union and China, and with American vulnerability, than with the exercise of options on the part of the United States." The symbolic value was real: "In both the American and the Marxist-Leninist context, South Vietnam – an agrarian country of fewer than fifteen million people – thus acquired an international significance out of all proportion to its size." The demise of Ngo Dinh Diem played into the hands of the North Vietnamese, who exploited and infiltrated a Buddhist protest movement that attracted widespread notoriety in the reports of gullible Western journalists. Contrary to the conventional view that the political deterioration of South Vietnam began in the summer of 1963, Smith believes that "there can be little doubt that the principal factor in the deterioration (which certainly occurred by

11 Norman Podhoretz, *Why We Were in Vietnam* (New York, 1982).

ecember) was the coup itself and its political consequences." d by the weaknesses of the South and the assurances of al support, Hanoi forced the military showdown with the icans in February 1965. To the Americans and the Chinese, the ultimate prize was Indonesia. Hence, U.S. intervention "bought time" for "democracy" in the region.[12]

Ellen Hammer and Patrick Hatcher concur with Smith that the "crisis" leading to Diem's overthrow was more of American than Vietnamese origin and that the United States erred in replacing him. This judgment essentially restates the Defense Department's 1963 position as it opposed State Department and Central Intelligence Agency (CIA) maneuvering against Diem. To his contemporary and retrospective supporters, Diem's strong-willed nationalism was the best hope for South Vietnam. In *A Death in November*, Hammer suggests that Diem, despite his considerable faults, had a better sense of South Vietnam's interests than other indigenous leaders and certainly than the Americans. Resentful of American manipulation, Diem refused to play the puppet and was prepared to lessen his dependence on Washington by pursuing a neutral course. As a result, the CIA engaged in intrigue with South Vietnamese dissidents that led to Diem's assassination. In their frustrations with a situation that defied American expectations, correspondents Neil Sheehan, Malcolm Browns, David Halberstam, and others found a scapegoat in Diem and blithely assumed that his overthrow would bring stability and progress.

In *The Suicide of an Elite: American Internationalists and Vietnam*, Hatcher cites evidence of rural and urban economic growth during the Diem era. He contends that the failure to stand by Diem deprived the South of the only leader capable of upholding Vietnamese pride in the face of the technical superiority of the growing American presence, which "denied authenticity to the Vietnamese character of Saigon's intervention."[13]

12 R. B. Smith, *An International History of the Vietnam War*, vol. 1, *Revolution versus Containment, 1955–1961* (New York, 1983), 261; vol. 2, *The Kennedy Strategy* (New York, 1985), 1, 190.

13 Ellen Hammer, *A Death in November: America in Vietnam, 1963* (New York, 1987); Patrick Lloyd Hatcher, *The Suicide of an Elite: American Internationalists and Vietnam* (Stanford, 1990).

The conviction that Diem was America's best hope was shared by the legendary hard-nosed CIA operative Edward Lansdale and is implicitly embraced by Cecil B. Currey in his admiring biography, *Edward Lansdale: The Unquiet American.* Convinced that lessons from his renowned work in the Philippines could be applied in Vietnam, Lansdale pressed Americans and Diem to recognize the centrality of pacification and preparation for counterinsurgency. Despite their close friendship, Lansdale could not persuade Diem to pursue rural reform or to broaden his political base. Yet he strongly criticized the coup, believing that only Diem could bring orderly constitutional development to South Vietnam.[14]

The subsequent Americanization of the war is treated in R. B. Smith's third volume, *The Making of a Limited War, 1965–66*, where he argues that the international challenge posed by the situation in Vietnam justified Johnson's decision for war. Given the Soviet and Chinese support of Hanoi, the instability of Southeast Asia, and "a very real Chinese campaign to eliminate United States power and influence not just from South Vietnam but from the East and Southeast Asian region," Vietnam was by 1965 "part of a global power struggle which President Johnson could not easily have ignored." By the end of 1966, however, Johnson was forced by circumstances to accept Secretary of Defense Robert S. McNamara's prescription for "stabilization," which meant to gird for a longer war. "Limiting the scope of the war was now more vital to the interests of the United States," Smith writes, "than going all out to win it."[15]

In *The War Everyone Lost – And Won*, Timothy J. Lomperis carries the legitimacy argument to the end of the war, contending that the United States "lost while winning" and betrayed South Vietnam in the process. Lomperis characterizes the struggle between the North and the South as one to attain legitimacy. The Communists failed to demonstrate the legitimacy of people's war and, after defeat in the Tet Offensive, they resorted to conventional warfare. By 1973, the Saigon government "found the

14 Cecil B. Currey, *Edward Lansdale: The Unquiet American* (Boston, 1988).
15 R. B. Smith, *An International History of the Vietnam War*, vol. 3, *The Making of a Limited War, 1965–66* (New York, 1991), 3, 18, 417.

tide . . . decidedly in its favor," but it had gained only a "passive legitimacy" and never had the opportunity to build an "active legitimacy." When the critical test came in the North Vietnamese attack of 1975, the United States abandoned South Vietnam. In the end, Hanoi may have unified the country, but the lack of revolutionary legitimacy has plagued its governance.[16]

Paralleling the wave of revisionism has been refinement of the orthodox criticism of U.S. involvement, with most of this neo-orthodox scholarship focusing on the 1954–1968 period.[17] As revisionism was taking hold, George Herring's very influential *America's Longest War* and Paul Kattenburg's *The Vietnam Trauma in American Foreign Policy*, published in 1979 and 1980, respectively, cast the war in the context of a Cold War-driven quarter century's effort to assure the establishment of a non-Communist state in Vietnam. Suggesting a more complex policy-making than that described by Gelb and Betts, Herring and Kattenburg contend that a misreading of U.S. interests and Vietnamese realities led to a doomed effort to build an independent South Vietnam and ultimately to an unwinnable military

16 Timothy J. Lomperis, *The War Everyone Lost – And Won: America's Intervention in Viet Nam's Twin Struggles* (Baton Rouge, 1984), 173.

17 On the earlier involvement dating from World War II, much work has been done that is being augmented by recent notable efforts that promise to recast developments in Vietnam in World War II and the early Cold War within an international history context. These include at least two dissertations in progress – Mark Bradley, Harvard University, "Making Cold War: Vietnam and the United States, 1941–1955," and Patricia Lane, University of Hawaii, "U.S.-Vietnam-France Relations, 1940–1945: The View from the Field." Already completed is Stein Tonnesson, *The Vietnamese Revolution of 1945: Roosevelt, Ho Chi Minh, and de Gaulle in a World at War* (Oslo, 1991), which stresses the importance of the Japanese coup of March 1945 in the Vietminh's bid for power. Tonnesson argues that the United States fostered the coup. Roosevelt, clinging to his objective of eliminating the French administration as essential to realization of his trusteeship plan, deceived the Japanese into anticipating a U.S. attack and thus encouraged the coup.

The geopolitical interests behind the U.S. reconsideration of its Southeast Asian policy in 1949–50 that led to the initial diplomatic and material support of the French has been explored in a number of works, including William S. Borden, *The Pacific Alliance: United States Foreign Economic Policy and Japanese Trade Recovery, 1947–1955* (Madison, 1984); Gary R. Hess, *The United States' Emergence as a Southeast Asian Power, 1940–1950* (New York, 1987); Andrew J. Rotter, *The Path to Vietnam: Origins of the American Commitment in Southeast Asia* (Ithaca, 1987); and Michael Schaller, *The American Occupation of Japan: The Origins of the Cold War in Asia* (New York, 1985). For a useful survey of the literature see Robert J. McMahon, "The Cold War in Asia: The Elusive Synthesis," in this volume.

intervention.[18] This "flawed containment" interpretation is central to much subsequent neo-orthodox scholarship. These works have moved beyond analysis of decision making in Washington to examine the impact of the war protests and media on the home front and the conduct of the war itself. Although most of the recent writing has an American emphasis, some scholars have tried to understand the various Vietnamese "sides" of the story, including the struggle for control of the South Vietnamese countryside and the strategies of the North Vietnamese and Vietcong. In the process, these works help to join the debate with revisionism, for their findings provide insight into the viability of certain revisionist arguments and "if only" scenarios.

A few scholars endeavor to relate the war to cultural imperatives. To Loren Baritz and James William Gibson, American involvement reflected a technological culture run amuck. Both Baritz, a social historian, and Gibson, a sociologist, stress an expansionist and militarist technology. Their works are assuredly not dispassionate, and perhaps ought to be dismissed as more polemic than scholarship. Yet each of their books offers certain insights. In *Backfire: A History of How American Culture Led Us into Vietnam and Made Us Fight the Way We Did*, Baritz contends that a "national myth showed us that we were good, [that] our technology made us strong, and [that] our bureaucracy gave us standard operating procedures. It was not a winning combination." Ethnocentric American leaders "invented" South Vietnam and relied on a technologically based capacity to kill to achieve a vision of Pax Americana.[19]

18 George C. Herring, *America's Longest War: The United States and Vietnam, 1950–1975* (New York, 1979); Paul M. Kattenburg, *The Vietnam Trauma in American Foreign Policy, 1945–1975* (New Brunswick, 1980).

There have been several recent general studies of U.S. involvement in Vietnam. Reflective of the "flawed containment" approach are Gary R. Hess, *Vietnam and the United States: Origins and Legacy of War* (Boston, 1990); and William S. Turley, *The Second Indochina War: A Short Political and Military History, 1954–1975* (Boulder, CO, 1986). The most determinedly even-handed account is George Donelson Moss, *Vietnam: An American Ordeal*, 2d ed. (Englewood Cliffs, 1992). Stressing an economic imperative behind U.S. involvement is Patrick J. Hearden, *The Tragedy of Vietnam* (New York, 1991). The sharpest indictment of U.S. intervention is Marilyn B. Young, *The Vietnam Wars, 1945–1990* (New York, 1991), which blends American domestic developments with the warfare in Vietnam and provides considerable attention to the human dimensions of the various aspects of the U.S.-Vietnamese interaction.

19 Loren Baritz, *Backfire: How American Culture Led Us into the Vietnam War and Made Us Fight the Way We Did* (New York, 1985), 27, 40.

In a similar argument, Gibson, in *The Perfect War: The War We Couldn't Lose and How We Did*, characterizes American society as enthralled by the "logic of Technowar," which rendered unthinkable any outcome other than that the "largest, fastest, most technologically advanced system [would] win." Although filled with abstraction and jargon, *The Perfect War* nonetheless includes useful information on how war managers' obliviousness to Vietnamese political realities and faith in quantitative data led to consistent miscalculations and an inept military strategy.[20]

With the opening of British and American archives as well as the personal papers of key figures, scholars have reexamined the 1954 crisis that began with the siege of Dienbienphu and continued through the Geneva and Manila conferences partitioning Vietnam and establishing the Southeast Asia Treaty Organization (SEATO), respectively. In a careful study of Eisenhower's leadership, *Decision against War*, Melanie Billings-Yun follows the Eisenhower revisionist interpretation of a decisive leader shrewdly and indirectly achieving his goal of keeping the United States out of war. As Billings-Yun demonstrates, the conventional view of a president restrained by British and congressional opposition to intervention was an astute misrepresentation designed by Eisenhower, who had decided early in the crisis that the use of U.S. force was not worth the resultant damage to American stature and, above all, the risk of a war. Restating a more conventional view is James Arnold's *The First Domino*. Arnold contends that only political considerations held back a hawkish Eisenhower in 1954, but that his critical decisions in the "watershed year" 1955 forged inexorable links to the subsequent Americanization of the struggle.[21]

In *Approaching Vietnam*, Lloyd Gardner casts U.S. policy within the context of the "liberal empire's" post-World War II objective of "liberation," which by 1954 centered on freeing Indochina from French mistakes. Gardner stresses the role of the peripatetic John Foster Dulles in forging a British-French-American commitment

20 James William Gibson, *The Perfect War: The War We Couldn't Lose and How We Did* (Boston, 1986), 16–17, 23.

21 Melanie Billings-Yun, *Decision against War: Eisenhower and Dien Bien Phu, 1954* (New York, 1988); James R. Arnold, *The First Domino: Eisenhower, the Military, and America's Intervention in Vietnam* (New York, 1991).

to the partition of Vietnam at Geneva and the subsequent reaffirmation of that outcome through SEATO. The resultant support of a "liberated" Vietnam ultimately revealed the "contradictions in nation building . . . [derived from] the conviction, shared before [Dulles] by people all the way back to Roosevelt with his plan for a trusteeship, that America had a special talent for liberating colonized peoples."[22]

Like Gardner, Anthony Short criticizes U.S. policy in 1954 as being shortsighted and leading to warfare a decade later. In Short's judgment, however, the U.S. failure was not so much in misguided nation-building, but in missing what was in its grasp: international commitment to permanent partition. The principal contribution of Short's *The Origins of the Vietnam War*, a work notable for its even-handed criticism of all of the governments involved in leading Vietnam to war in 1965, is a detailed reexamination of the 1954 crisis. Short questions whether America's determined effort to be "in but not of" the Geneva settlement served its interests. The failure of the United States to approve the Geneva Accords, Short argues, undermined its very interest in partition. "By refusing to join in any guarantees with the communist states," Short contends, "one has to ask whether Dulles rejected a finite end to the first Vietnam War and, in so doing, doomed the United States to participate in the second."[23]

Scholars are also reexamining America's relationship with the government headed by Ngo Dinh Diem. Chief among them is David L. Anderson, whose *Trapped by Success* describes U.S. support for Diem during the Eisenhower administration as "buying

22 Lloyd C. Gardner, *Approaching Vietnam: From World War II through Dienbienphu, 1941–1954* (New York, 1988), 354.

23 Anthony Short, *The Origins of the Vietnam War* (London, 1989), 328–29. In addition to the monographs regarding the United States and the 1954 crisis, a number of articles – notably the work of Richard H. Immerman – add significantly to the story: George C. Herring and Richard H. Immerman, "Eisenhower, Dulles, and Dienbienphu: 'The Day We Didn't Go to War' Revisited," *Journal of American History* 71 (September 1984): 343–63; Immerman, "Between the Unattainable and the Unacceptable: Eisenhower and Dienbienphu," in *Reevaluating Eisenhower: American Foreign Policy in the Fifties*, ed. Richard A. Melanson and David Mayers (Urbana, 1987), 120–54; and idem, "The United States and the Geneva Conference of 1954: A New Look," *Diplomatic History* 14 (Winter 1990): 43–66. Immerman finds Eisenhower's diplomacy to be reasonably effective in responding to the Dien Bien Phu crisis but questions the soundness of the U.S. approach to the Geneva settlement.

time but also buying trouble." American policy was the "creator and [the] captive of an illusion in Vietnam." Dismissing any idea of a "stalemate" thesis, Anderson shows how officials believed that time was in their favor, that progress was occurring, and that North Vietnam was not a serious threat. The mission of J. Lawton Collins in 1955 constituted the "point of no return," for Collins alone among high officials recognized Diem's shortcomings. Nevertheless, spurred by Dulles's enthusiasm for Diem, American policy embraced a partnership with his government. Ignorance and indifference resulted in a "commitment to the survival of [America's] own counterfeit creation."[24]

The analyses of Ronald Spector on the early military assistance program and of D. Michael Shafer's on pacification reinforce Anderson's conclusions. In *Advice and Support*, Spector describes the first flawed effort at Vietnamization. Trained by Americans to resist Korea-type aggression from the North, ARVN was ill prepared for counterinsurgency. More important, it suffered from the moral, structural, and political problems that were endemic to the Diem regime.

In his *Deadly Paradigms: The Failure of U.S. Counterinsurgency Policy*, Shafer challenges the retrospective "might have beens" about "winning" the countryside through pacification by pointing out the flaws in American thinking and programs. He faults American doctrine for linking insurgency to external sources, based in part on inappropriate "lessons" of Greece and Turkey. In both cases, U.S. efforts were irrelevant as leaders of threatened regimes used aid to reinforce their strength but without confronting the basis of the insurgency. Hence, contrary to the thinking of people like Edward Lansdale, the United States had no useful experience to bring to the Vietnam conflict. Focusing on counterinsurgency during the Diem regime, Shafer finds an uncoordinated U.S. program compounded by Diem's resistance to U.S. suggestions and Washington's reluctance to employ its leverage.[25]

24 David L. Anderson, *Trapped by Success: The Eisenhower Administration and Vietnam, 1953–1961* (New York, 1991), 227, 304, 409.

25 Ronald H. Spector, *Advice and Support: The Early Years of the U.S. Army in Vietnam, 1941–1960* (New York, 1985); D. Michael Shafer, *Deadly Paradigms: The Failure of U.S. Counterinsurgency Policy* (Princeton, 1988).

There are two books on Kennedy's Vietnam policy: William J. Rust, *Kennedy in*

The opening of documentation on Johnson's decisions to Americanize the war in 1965 has led to several notable studies, with the president's role a point of historiographical debate. Whether writing critically or sympathetically of Johnson's situation, scholars generally stress the influence of "guns-and-butter" thinking on his 1965 decisions and see a flaw in his penchant for compromise.

Larry Berman's *Planning a Tragedy* characterizes Johnson as driven by a domestic political agenda that would "merit nothing less than Mount Rushmore" and therefore as determined to resolve the Vietnam problem quickly and quietly. Fearful that the loss of Vietnam would trigger the kind of partisan debate that followed the Chinese civil war, Johnson used the decision-making process from February through July 1965 in ways that ignored any examination of the assumptions about the commitment to South Vietnam and that placed the burden of proof on dovish, not hawkish, advisers. With scant regard for the magnitude of his decisions, Johnson went to war out of fear that "losing Vietnam in the summer of 1965 would wreck his plans for a truly Great Society."[26]

The inadequacy of decision making in the Johnson White House is also stressed in *How Presidents Test Reality: Decisions on Vietnam 1945 and 1965* by John P. Burke and Fred I. Greenstein (with the assistance of Berman and Richard H. Immerman). Comparing Johnson's decision-making process with that of Eisenhower, Burke

Vietnam: American Foreign Policy, 1960–1963 (New York, 1985); and John M. Newman, *JFK and Vietnam: Deception, Intrigue, and the Struggle for Power* (New York, 1992). Newman's book, which accompanied the release of Oliver Stone's motion picture *JFK*, pieces together documents that purportedly demonstrate a conspiracy against a Kennedy commitment to withdraw from Vietnam; immediately after Kennedy's assassination, Johnson, duped into thinking he was carrying on Kennedy's policy, actually reversed it and took the measures that led to U.S. military involvement. The Rust work summarizes Kennedy's involvement and, like Newman's (although without any hint of conspiracies) sees Kennedy disengaging from Vietnam. For more critical appraisals of Kennedy's policy see Lawrence Bassett and Stephen Pelz, "The Failed Search for Victory: Vietnam and the Politics of War," *Kennedy's Quest for Victory: American Foreign Policy, 1961–1963*, ed. Thomas G. Paterson (New York, 1989), 223–52; and Gary R. Hess, "Commitment in the Age of Counter-Insurgency: Kennedy and Vietnam," *Shadow on the White House: Presidents and the Vietnam War*, ed. David L. Anderson (Lawrence, 1993).

26 Larry Berman, *Planning a Tragedy: The Americanization of the War in Vietnam* (New York, 1982), 147.

and Greenstein suggest that Johnson could have learned something from Eisenhower's more formal, open advocacy advisory system. In the incoherent policy review leading to the 28 July 1965 troop commitment, it seemed that "a great swirl of policy recommendations and analyses . . . simply floated past the President."[27]

In Brian Van De Mark's *Into the Quagmire*, Johnson and his advisers are seen as more reluctant warriors. "Like figures in a Greek tragedy," Van De Mark writes, "pride compelled these supremely confident men further into disaster." In this largely sympathetic appraisal of a president confronting intractable problems, Johnson emerges as soliciting advice from dovish as well as hawkish advisers. While Van De Mark portrays a more open minded Johnson than Berman and Burke and Greenstein, his work also underlines the fact that debate was limited by the failure to examine basic assumptions of U.S. interest in Southeast Asia and the fears of right-wing backlash if Johnson appeared irresolute.[28]

According to Yuen Foong Khong, these conventional accounts of the decision for war minimize the significance of historical analogies – in this case, the lessons of the Korean War – on the reasoning of policymakers. In *Analogies of War: Korea, Munich, Dien Bien Phu, and the Vietnam Decisions of 1965*, Khong offers a provocative interpretation of the mindset that both exaggerated Vietnam's importance and minimized the obstacles to American objectives. Employing cognitive psychology research and techniques, he examines policymakers' reasoning through historical analogies. Earlier scholars have acknowledged the references to "lessons of the past" in policy debates and in public justifications for intervention, but often this has been to show how poorly history is used and without substantive analysis of the extent to which lessons actually influenced decisions or provided rationales for choices made on other grounds. Khong contends that schemas and analogies are fundamental to apprehending reality, interpreting problems, and determining policy options. After analyzing

27 John P. Burke and Fred I. Greenstein, *How Presidents Test Reality: Decisions on Vietnam 1954 and 1965* (New York, 1991), 261.

28 Brian Van De Mark, *Into the Quagmire: Lyndon Johnson and the Escalation of the Vietnam War* (New York, 1991), 219.

how policymakers used the Munich, Korean, and Dien Bien Phu analogies, Khong concludes that the lessons of the Korean War (a successful limited war in which the only major mistake was the provocation of China) defined the terms of intervention in Vietnam.[29]

In contrast to the centrality of Washington in most accounts of the 1965 decisions, the culmination of George Kahin's notable binational study, *Intervention*, is both the decision for war and its effects on the Vietnamese. American indifference toward Vietnamese history and politics is central to Kahin's careful analysis of U.S.-Vietnamese interaction beginning in 1946. In the South, American actions after 1954 blunted the emergence of a viable "third force" centering around the Buddhist leadership. By 1964–65, Johnson weighed his options in a deteriorating situation. Recognizing that the Saigon government would likely seek negotiations with the National Liberation Front (NLF), that the Chinese had a strong interest in Vietnam, and that America's allies did not support escalation, Johnson searched for answers to an intractable problem. A negotiated settlement risked South Vietnam's survival and hence political support for his Great Society. When Johnson intervened, it was done cautiously, rejecting calls for an invasion or all-out bombing of the North. Intervention, however, had a devastating effect on South Vietnam as it buttressed U.S. support of the government headed by Generals Nguyen Cao Ky and Nguyen Van Thieu and thus destroyed whatever prospects existed for the Buddhist third force between the NLF and the Saigon military. The "rigid polarization" left the South Vietnamese without the option of compromise, "permitting only two active choices – supporting the NLF or a Saigon regime shaped by and dependent upon the United States." Hence, U.S. intervention meant an ever-widening divergence of American objectives from indigenous political forces.[30]

Johnson's determined consensus building, which hindered effective decision making in 1965, continued, in the judgment of

29 Yuen Foong Khong, *Analogies of War: Korea, Munich, Dien Bien Phu, and the Vietnam Decisions of 1965* (Princeton, 1992).

30 George McT. Kahin, *Invention: How America Became Involved in Vietnam* (New York, 1986), 432.

most scholars, to limit his effectiveness as a wartime president. In *When Governments Collide*, Wallace Thies finds that Johnson's determination to control the conduct of the war actually led to a loss of control. Thies's focus is the futile search for a means of negotiation. The doctrine that orchestrating diplomacy with fine-tuned military coercion could bring the North Vietnamese to the negotiating table failed in practice. Johnson was largely to blame: His consistent search for consensus within his administration, rather than control of the U.S. war, "provides an almost perfect lesson in how *not* to engage in coercion." As Johnson compromised between the advice of the hawks and the doves, which always meant increased warfare, he left leaders in Hanoi seeing only hypocrisy and deceit. Whether the two sides could have reached an agreement on the issue of South Vietnam's political status is problematic, but mismanagement of U.S. diplomacy and warfare meant that "errors and misunderstandings *did* exist, and their effect was to make an already difficult problem virtually insoluble."[31]

Johnson's leadership at home, according to Kathleen J. Turner and Larry Berman, suffered from similar flaws. Turner, in *Lyndon Johnson's Dual War: Vietnam and the Press*, analyzes the public dimension of the futile effort to appease both hawks and doves by demonstrating that the United States was doing "enough" but not "too much." Turner examines in detail the Johns Hopkins University address of April 1965 – in which Johnson blended a strident defense of the American position with a proposal for American-financed cooperative development of the Mekong Delta – as an early illustration of Johnson's frustrations in rationalizing Southeast Asian policy.[32]

In *Lyndon Johnson's War*, Berman extends such analysis into

31 Wallace J. Thies, *When Governments Collide: Coercion and Diplomacy in the Vietnam Conflict, 1964–1968* (Berkeley, 1980), 373–74 (emphasis in original).

Although now somewhat dated, Robert L. Gallucci, *Neither Peace Nor Honor: The Politics of American Military Policy in Viet-Nam* (Baltimore, 1975), provides a still useful comparative analysis of Kennedy and Johnson policymaking within a bureaucratic politics framework. As the war escalated from 1965 to 1967, a pattern of compromise continued, but without benefit of sufficient non-military input – a conclusion that challenges revisionist contentions about a lack of military influence.

32 Kathleen Turner, *Lyndon Johnson's Dual War: Vietnam and the Press* (Chicago, 1985).

a portrayal of Johnson as becoming a tragic figure whose ultimate demise resulted from flaws of leadership. The "tragedy in the making" in Berman's earlier book thus gained national and personal dimensions. Berman writes of a president who took the country to war without calling for national commitment and who publicly embraced a strategy that he privately questioned. Unable to resolve the dilemma of maintaining the independence of South Vietnam without destroying North Vietnam, Johnson by 1967 faced the imperfect alternatives of sending another three hundred thousand troops or stabilizing the commitment at five hundred thousand. With a presidential campaign on the horizon, Johnson avoided difficult choices and indulged in wishful thinking that the war was actually being won. He thus orchestrated the "big sell" of "progress" in Vietnam and unwittingly contributed to the popular disillusionment that came with the Tet Offensive.[33]

Besides paying considerable attention to Johnson's leadership, historians have also been reassessing the roles of other key figures in Vietnam policymaking. As the war went sour, the reputations of the "best and the brightest" were tarnished and "doves" moved into the ascendancy. Scholarship thus far completed suggests that the war left mostly "losers."

Dean Rusk may be doing as well as any. In retrospect, Rusk looks much as he did in the 1960s: the uncomplicated Cold Warrior unswervingly loyal to Kennedy and Johnson and committed to U.S. objectives. In Warren I. Cohen's close analysis of Rusk's years as secretary of state and in Thomas Schoenbam's biography of Rusk – both sympathetic accounts – and in Rusk's own quasi-memoir, told largely in response to his son's questions, Rusk emerges as skeptical of U.S. military strategy and Saigon's viability and perplexed by the dedication of the enemy and the war weariness of the American public. Only domestic political necessity forced his acceptance of negotiations and deescalation.[34]

Rusk's self-effacing style contrasts sharply with that of the

33 Larry Berman, *Lyndon Johnson's War: The Road to Stalemate* (New York, 1989).
34 Warren I. Cohen, *Dean Rusk* (Totawa, NJ, 1980); Thomas J. Schoenbam, *Waging Peace and War: Dean Rusk in the Truman, Kennedy, and Johnson Years* (New York, 1988); Dean Rusk, as told to Richard Rusk, *As I Saw It*, ed. Daniel S. Papp (New York, 1990).

visible and energetic Robert McNamara, the subject of Deborah Shapley's insightful and unflattering biography. *Promise and Power: The Life and Times of Robert McNamara* is strongest in its effort to come to terms with McNamara's mind and character. Shapley describes an arrogant, number-crunching, emotionally and intellectually flawed Cold Warrior who believed that "applied intelligence, organization, and resources could mold reality to suit his will." McNamara's quantitative measures in Vietnam led to arbitrary decisions and premature evaluations of success. Moreover, as the good manager, McNamara determined what superiors wanted and acted accordingly. Yet he was unable to accept a flawed outcome. The emotional strain of his growing realization that the war was unwinnable brought him nearly to the breaking point, and going to the World Bank in 1967 provided an opportunity to atone for the suffering that he helped to inflict on Vietnam. McNamara agreed to be interviewed by Shapley, who finds his recollections on Vietnam to be self-serving and disingenuous. Yet Shapley gives McNamara a hearing, allowing him to emphasize that as early as 1965 he doubted whether the military could achieve U.S. objectives and that he thus sought to keep open the negotiating channels even as intervention went forward. Had his calls for extended bombing pauses been accepted, he argues, the war could have ended earlier.[35]

Among the Kennedy advisers on Vietnam none carried greater initial prestige than Maxwell Taylor. Yet as Douglas Kinnard illustrates in *The Certain Trumpet*, Taylor – as Kennedy adviser, chairman of the Joint Chiefs of Staff, ambassador to South Vietnam, and consultant to Johnson – underestimated the problems facing the United States and exhibited a lack of character. The Taylor-Rostow report, Kinnard correctly notes, is often remembered for the eight thousand troop recommendation that Kennedy rejected, but more important was the open-ended increase of advisers and resources it portended. In 1963 Taylor declined to "stand up and be counted when in the minority," putting aside his reservations about U.S. complicity in the plotting against Diem

35 Deborah Shapley, *Promise and Power: The Life and Times of Robert McNamara* (Boston, 1993), 559.

and about promises that American personnel could be withdrawn within two years. As ambassador in 1965, Taylor supported the bombing of North Vietnam and just as strongly opposed the introduction of ground forces. After losing on that issue, however, he characteristically stated that ground forces should have been committed earlier. In sum, Taylor's shortcoming in Vietnam policy "was not in what he did, but what he failed to do."[36]

Critics of the war were not necessarily more knowledgeable about Vietnam nor more honorable under pressure. The renowned dissent of resident dove Undersecretary of State George Ball is analyzed fully by David L. DiLeo in *George Ball, Vietnam, and the Rethinking of Containment*. Ball emerges as a complex, ambitious man whose opposition to escalation and advocacy of negotiation reflected a Europe-centered worldview. Disdain, with a trace of racism, characterized his thinking on the Third World. Ball's refusal to make his December 1966 resignation a matter of principle reflected more than loyalty to those he served. It also stemmed from Ball's reluctance to sabotage whatever prospects there were of Johnson turning to him to replace Rusk as secretary of state. According to DiLeo, Ball was too concerned with preserving his stature to vigorously criticize American conduct of the war.[37]

Then there was John Paul Vann, who was never modest about "understanding" the Vietnamese and who Neil Sheehan calls "the one compelling figure [in the] war without heroes." Sheehan was part of the small Saigon press corps in the early 1960s that Vann transformed "into a band of reporters propounding the John Vann view of the war." In *A Bright Shining Lie: John Paul Vann and America in Vietnam*, he argues that Vann's "accumulated expertise and aptitude for this war made him the one irreplaceable American." Yet the subsequent analysis of Vann's military and advisory career in Vietnam sustains Vann as more "compelling" than "irreplaceable." Losing his life in a helicopter accident in 1972, Vann "died believing he had won this war." The "lie"

36 Douglas Kinnard, *The Certain Trumpet: Maxwell Taylor and the American Experience in Vietnam* (Washington, 1991), 16, 219.
37 David L. DiLeo, *George Ball, Vietnam, and the Rethinking of Containment* (Chapel Hill, 1991).

in all of this was Vann's non-heroic side. He was an amoral, selfish, deceitful, compulsive man whose duality of character exemplified the American role in Vietnam. Vann emerges as a tragic figure in a doomed enterprise: "He was much that was wrong about the war . . . but he could never bring himself to conclude that the war itself was wrong and unwinnable." In the end, Americans were betrayed by Vann and the U.S. government, for both became a "bright shining lie." Whether the career of Vann or any figure can be a metaphor for the American experience, Sheehan's work yields insight into the remarkable arrogance of the American intervention.[38]

The paucity of documents on the administration of Richard M. Nixon has limited research on its Vietnam policy. The fullest account is Arnold R. Isaacs's *Without Honor*. Isaacs acknowledges the problems and accomplishments of the approach taken by Nixon and Henry Kissinger. They came to power recognizing that the war could not be won and seeking an exit that would be tolerable to the American public and that would preserve American credibility. The 1973 agreement they brokered was more favorable to American and South Vietnamese interests than what could have been negotiated at the beginning of Nixon's term. Yet the flaw in the Nixon-Kissinger approach was that the two realists failed to focus on the objective of an honorable exit. They could not understand that the North's suspicion of negotiations derived from frustrating experiences in 1946 and 1954. In "the single act by which the Nixon administration closed the trap on itself," they senselessly expanded the fighting into Cambodia with devastating consequences for both that country and the United States. Before and especially after the 1973 agreement, they allowed the South Vietnamese government to expect long-term American aid and thus "nourished [Thieu's] fantasies of support in pursuit of an unattainable victory." And they shamelessly blamed Congress and antiwar protesters for undermining their efforts and South Vietnam's capacity to survive.[39]

38 Neil Sheehan, *A Bright Shining Lie: John Paul Vann and America in Vietnam* (New York, 1988).

39 Arnold R. Isaacs, *Without Honor: Defeat in Vietnam and Cambodia* (Baltimore, 1983), 493, 505.

Two early appraisals of the Paris agreement – Gareth Porter, *Peace Denied: The United States, Vietnam, and the Paris Agreement* (Bloomington, 1975); and Allan E.

Finger pointing accompanied the end of the war, as Kissinger and President Gerald Ford blamed Congress for the U.S. defeat. P. Edward Haley's *Congress and the Fall of South Vietnam and Cambodia* sees this criticism as disingenuous and contradictory. The White House kept secret its promises to save the Thieu government because it knew Congress would disapprove, and then in 1975 acted as if Congress should approve. Despite the realization that the commitments were meaningless and that the war was lost, congressional inaction brought Kissinger's "frustrations out, and he dressed them in cataclysm and the decline of the West."[40]

As Gelb and Betts write, the home front was "the last domino," and recent scholarship suggests a more complex domestic scene than that depicted by revisionists, who emphasize biased media coverage of the war and unpatriotic antiwar protesters as undermining public support and contributing to defeat. Two complementary studies – *An American Ordeal* by Charles DeBenedetti and Charles Chatfield and *The Debate over Vietnam* by David Levy – yield insight into the controversies generated by the war. DeBenedetti and Chatfield examine the many and shifting expressions of the antiwar "movement of movements" and capture the spontaneity and disjointed nature of protest. They contend that the major role of the antiwar movement was in "keeping open the prospect of defeat as a national option. Never a popular position, disengagement – and even policy failure – was discussed in public from the start." The public always mistrusted the protesters even as it gravitated toward the antiwar contention that Vietnam was not related to U.S. security.[41]

Goodman, *The Lost Peace: America's Search for a Negotiated Settlement of the Vietnam War* (Stanford, 1978) – stress the futility of negotiating where fundamental issues defied compromise. Porter is the more critical of the American negotiating position, seeing the commitment to the preservation of an independent South Vietnam as delaying a settlement, precluding its implementation, and preventing adaptation to political-military changes in 1973–1975. Goodman is more apologetic for the American position, faulting Johnson's strategy of escalation mixed with conciliatory gestures for sending the wrong message to Hanoi. Yet Goodman is also skeptical of the viability of the Saigon government and concurs with Porter that the Paris Agreement was fundamentally flawed.

40 P. Edward Haley, *Congress and the Fall of South Vietnam and Cambodia* (Rutherford, NJ, 1982), 154.

41 Charles DeBenedetti, assisted by Charles Chatfield, *An American Ordeal: The Antiwar Movement of the Vietnam Era* (Syracuse, 1990), 407.

Levy's work looks at the arguments dividing hawks and doves and at the way the war affected various subcommunities, including minorities, intellectuals, religious groups, organized labor, political parties, and higher education. Unlike DeBenedetti and Chatfield, Levy largely eschews judgments on the meaning of the debate that he chronicles, but he does observe, as have scholars of public opinion, that war weariness augmented by the surprise of the Tet Offensive, rather than the force of argumentation, led to popular disaffection.[42]

In *Johnson, Nixon, and the Doves*, Melvin Small undertakes the difficult task of tracing the antiwar movement's influence on two presidents, each of whom professed indifference to protest. Small's cautious conclusions are plausible, as he finds a largely indirect but significant impact. Together with the force of events, protest informed the thinking of the intellectual and opinion-making communities, whose support is vital to any president, and thus helped to force Johnson and Nixon into deescalatory steps. Moreover, both presidents shaped policy partly on the calculation that Hanoi considered popular opposition in America as a factor in its favor.[43]

The role of J. William Fulbright (D-AR) who, as chairman of the Senate Foreign Relations Committee emerged as the leading congressional critic of the war, has been most fully analyzed by William C. Berman. Presenting Fulbright's opposition within the framework of his realist approach to foreign policy, Berman details his tireless role, both through his writings and the Foreign Relations Committee, to educate Americans about the folly of the war and, more generally, about mindless militant anticommunism. It took longer than Fulbright and other doves had anticipated to reassert congressional prerogatives, but in 1973 the curtailment of the Cambodian campaign and the passage of the War Powers Resolution constituted important victories.[44]

42 David W. Levy, *The Debate over Vietnam* (Baltimore, 1991).

43 Melvin Small, *Johnson, Nixon, and the Doves* (New Brunswick, 1988).

44 Preceding Berman's work were studies by Eugene Brown, who also integrates Fulbright's ideas and actions and reaches similar conclusions, and by Lee Riley Powell, who highlights the contents of the Fulbright committee's hearings on Asian policy. William C. Berman, *William Fulbright and the Vietnam War: The Dissent of a Political Realist* (Kent, OH, 1988); Eugene Brown, *J. William Fulbright: Advice*

The conclusions reached by Daniel Hallin in *The "Uncensored War"* and by William Hammond in *The Military and the Media* refute revisionist claims regarding biased reporting. Hallin's analysis of selected newspaper and television coverage finds that the media as an establishment institution represented, rather than determined, public opinion. Coverage of the war in the *New York Times* and on network news supported the U.S. effort through 1967; afterward, stories became more skeptical, but by that time the war was a topic of legitimate controversy. Hammond's study, a volume in the army's history of the war that stresses the dilemmas facing the military's information officers, criticizes coverage for a lack of depth but also emphasizes the accuracy of the media, especially when contrasted with the Johnson administration's record of concealments and circumlocutions. Most television coverage was banal and stylized, and Hammond questions its impact on public opinion.[45]

Besides the attention to events in the United States, scholars have also focused on Vietnam – the nature of warfare, the struggle for the South Vietnamese countryside, and the conflict from the "other side." Perhaps the best account of a single battle is Harold Moore and Joseph Galloway's *We Were Soldiers Once . . . and Young*, which recounts the Ia Drang Valley campaign of November 1965 in which American and North Vietnamese regular units met for the first time and from which both sides drew "lessons" that guided subsequent warfare. Moore and Galloway base their compelling narrative on interviews with American and North Vietnamese veterans. They conclude their account of the brutal combat in a final chapter outlining the lessons each side

and Dissent (Iowa City, 1985); Lee Riley Powell, *J. William Fulbright and America's Lost Crusade: Fulbright's Opposition to the Vietnam War* (Little Rock, 1984).

Congress and the war has received little attention. The role of Republicans, especially their congressional leaders, in the debate over Vietnam policy has been studied by Terry Dietz. The war strained the party's commitment to bipartisanship and caused divisions within its ranks, thus preventing it from playing an effective opposition role. As House minority leader, Gerald Ford was an exception; his probing of Johnson's policy contrasted sharply to the deference shown Johnson by his friend, Senate minority leader Everett Dirksen. Terry Dietz, *Republicans and Vietnam, 1961–1968* (Westport, 1986).

45 Daniel C. Hallin, *The "Uncensored War": The Media and Vietnam* (New York, 1986); William M. Hammond, *Public Affairs: The Military and the Media, 1962–1968* (Washington, 1988).

took from the encounter. While the North Vietnamese learned that they could withstand mobile airpower, the American command read the twelve-to-one casualty ratio and incorrectly deduced that "they could bleed the enemy to death over the long haul, with a war of attrition." Alone among civilian officials, McNamara recognized that the war had changed as the stalemate at Ia Drang signaled a long and costly war.[46]

A number of notable studies have analyzed the ensuing air and ground war. In *The Limits of Air Power: The American Bombing of North Vietnam*, Mark Clodfelter challenges the air force's central historical lesson that "airpower can be strategically decisive if its application is intense, continuous, and focused on the enemy's vital systems." Clodfelter's argument rests on two main points: (1) The ineffectiveness of Operation Rolling Thunder reflected inherent limitations on strategic bombing and the ineptitude of military, as much as civilian, leaders; (2) The Linebacker campaign is an inappropriate model of what air power could have achieved earlier, since it "worked" because Nixon had the limited objective of facilitating U.S. withdrawal and because the North Vietnamese had shifted to conventional warfare. On the politics of the bombing, Clodfelter's work complements James Clay Thompson's earlier study, *Rolling Thunder*, which employs organizational theory to explain the air force's resistance to evidence of the bombing campaign's failure.[47]

The air war in the South has been analyzed in John Schlight's *Years of the Offensive*, a volume in the air force history, and in Donald J. Mrozek's *Air Power and the Ground War in Vietnam*. Both find that the air force handled its tactical mission effectively and innovatively. But Mrozek, in the more critical analysis, concludes that although the air war enabled the United States to wage the ground conflict with fewer troops, at most it helped to

46 Harold G. Moore and Joseph L. Galloway, *We Were Soldiers Once . . . and Young: Ia Drang – The Battle That Changed the War in Vietnam* (New York, 1992), 339. Moore does not limit his criticism to Westmoreland. Instead, like almost all other commanders in Vietnam, he questions the limitations placed on military operations that allowed the retreating North Vietnamese to take sanctuary in Cambodia.

47 Mark Clodfelter, *The Limits of Air Power: The American Bombing of North Vietnam* (New York, 1989), 209; James Clay Thompson, *Rolling Thunder: Understanding Policy and Program Failure* (Chapel Hill, 1980).

avoid defeat rather than to bring victory. An especially controversial aspect of the air war was Operation Ranch Hand, which between 1962 and 1971 sprayed some eighteen million gallons of chemicals in the South. William Buckingham's *Operation Ranch Hand*, another volume in the air force history, explains the expansion of the defoliation campaign as a function of escalation as well as the controversy surrounding the political, military, and ecological effects of the defoliants themselves. Richard L. Stevens is outspoken on the ecological issue and the futility of bombing. His study, *The Trail: A History of the Ho Chi Minh Trail and the Role of Nature in the War in Vietnam*, asserts that bombing was doomed to fail for the North Vietnamese had the advantage of nature and were able to change the trail to meet their needs. The Americans gained only a tragic "victory" over nature through the bombing's massive ecological damage.[48]

Ronald Spector's *After Tet* offers analysis not only of the neglected bloodshed of the year after the Tet Offensive but of the entire nature of the ground war. In many ways, this book is the most comprehensive integration of the conflict's political and military dimensions. Nineteen sixty-eight began and ended in stalemate, suggesting a repetition on the battlefield and in military thinking more akin to World War I than other modern wars. Each side was convinced that the other was about to capitulate and that victory would result from maintaining the offensive. Hence, the North Vietnamese undertook three subsequent offensives in the year after Tet and suffered enormous losses. Meanwhile, the United States continued inconclusive operations that reflected "the lack of any systematic attempt to pass on lessons or develop doctrine." Moreover, the South Vietnamese army had learned "how to rule, but not how to fight." In Spector's assessment, the "battles of 1968 were decisive . . . because they were so indecisive," for the stalemate benefited North Vietnam. Hence, the American position steadily eroded, as military morale declined

48 John Schlight, *The United States Air Force in Southeast Asia: The War in Vietnam: The Years of the Offensive, 1965–1968* (Washington, 1988); Donald J. Mrozek, *Air Power and the Ground War in Vietnam: Ideas and Actions* (Washington, 1989); William Buckingham, *Operation Ranch Hand: The Air Force and Herbicides in Southeast Asia, 1961–1971* (Washington, 1981); Richard L. Stevens, *The Trail: A History of the Ho Chi Minh Trail and the Role of Nature in the War in Viet Nam* (New York, 1993).

in a morass of drug abuse and racial tensions and as the Communists rebuilt their forces and shadow governments in the countryside.[49]

Jeffrey Clarke's study of Vietnamization, a volume in the Department of the Army's history, reinforces Spector's findings. Clarke's study of the army's advisory role sees Vietnamization as clarifying U.S. objectives for ARVN and fostering American-ARVN operational cooperation. Evidence of military progress, however, was offset by ARVN's continuing lack of mobility and by its dependence on U.S. air and sea power. The ultimate failure was that no one believed ARVN could withstand an assault from the North on its own. Thus, Vietnamization, like earlier advisory phases, reflected an effort that may have been "hopeless from the start . . . [for] it was beyond the capacity of one power to reform and reshape the society of another." Vietnamization could equip ARVN, but it could not buy a will to fight.[50]

All sides in the conflict believed that what was happening in South Vietnam's villages was vital to the war's outcome. Several efforts have been made to examine political developments in rural areas, but the body of such work, by definition, remains fragmented and limited by the scant availability of documentation. The few studies thus far completed suggest that the NLF had greater strength than the Saigon government and that American-South Vietnamese pacification programs, often flawed in their basic assumptions, had little effect. Vietnamization, it also seems, may have weakened the insurgency, but it did not necessarily bring attendant gains for the Saigon government.

In *The Endless War*, James Harrison traces the resiliency of Vietnamese communism and attributes its ultimate success to a program of determined organization in the South during the 1950s and 1960s. Examining village level work in three Mekong Delta provinces, Harrison argues that the entrenched Communists managed to survive Diem's anti-Communist campaign.[51] Among

49 Ronald H. Spector, *After Tet: The Bloodiest Year in Vietnam* (New York, 1993), 116, 313.

50 Jeffrey J. Clarke, *United States Army in Vietnam. Advice and Support: The Final Years, 1965–1973* (Washington, 1988), 521.

51 James P. Harrison, *The Endless War: Fifty Years of Struggle for Independence in Vietnam* (New York, 1989).

the provinces included in Harrison's study is Long An, and, for that part of his work, Harrison draws on Jeffrey Race's pioneering 1972 study, *War Comes to Long An*, which documents the insurgency's success in virtually eliminating the South Vietnamese government's presence by 1965 and how subsequent American and South Vietnamese military operations and reform efforts only further alienated the peasantry.[52]

Race completed his work in 1968, just as pacification was gaining renewed emphasis, and subsequent studies suggest that such efforts had negligible impact. Adjacent to Long An was the province of Hau Nghia, the locale Eric Bergerud studies in *The Dynamics of Defeat*. Detailing the various efforts of Americans and South Vietnamese in Hau Nghia from 1963 to 1973, Bergerud finds that the "difficulties [the Americans] faced were virtually beyond solution." Nothing could overcome the Saigon government's lack of legitimacy, which meant that while the NLF was weakened by the Phoenix campaign of 1969–1973, the Saigon government could not replace it. The rural population generally, and especially the "best and the brightest" among young people, supported the NLF, which derived its strength from its legacy of struggle and its promise of a better future. Finally, the Americans and the South Vietnamese were caught in the contradictions of the use of military force; it was the only means of attacking NLF strongholds, but it caused great suffering and destructions which the NLF turned to its advantage.[53]

James Trullinger's *Village at War*, based on research in a different part of South Vietnam and at a later time, yields similar findings. Conducting interviews in a village near Hue from 1974 until overwhelmed by events in 1975, Trullinger stresses Communist resiliency. My Thuy Phuong was atypical in that the U.S. Army in 1968 had established an airmobile base there that brought ten thousand Americans into a village normally populated by seventy-six hundred Vietnamese. Reconstructing the history of the struggle in this village, Trullinger finds that most of the village's

52 Jeffrey Race, *War Comes to Long An: Revolutionary Conflict in a Vietnamese Province* (Berkeley, 1972).

53 Eric M. Bergerud, *The Dynamics of Defeat: The Vietnam War in Hau Nghia Province* (Boulder, 1991), 3.

inhabitants were disdainful of ARVN, sympathized with the activities of the insurgents, identified with their bold strikes in the Tet Offensive, and saw during the 1972 Easter offensive ARVN's continued dependency on the United States.[54]

The pacification efforts of the Marine Corps, which had a tradition of such operations, have been cited by some of the hearts-and-minds revisionists as a model that should have been applied widely in Vietnam. Michael E. Peterson concurs, but with reservations. In *The Combined Action Platoons: U.S. Marines' Other War in Vietnam*, Peterson, a veteran of such operations in Vietnam, asserts that Westmoreland's application of the traditional army emphasis on warfare against "partisans" who are seen as dependent on an external country misinterpreted Vietnamese insurgency. The search-and-destroy strategy "declared war against peasant society [and] . . . the United States irretrievably lost that war." Peterson goes on to criticize the Marine Corps leadership for failing to devote greater manpower to the pacification and to document a record of success disproportionate to the limited commitment. Yet he also concludes that a nationwide program would not have been successful; at best, firepower "with an eye to protecting – rather than disrupting the hamlets [meant that] we would not have lost the war so terribly as we did."[55]

Robert Chandler's study of U.S. propaganda programs, *War of Ideas*, likewise suggests the enormity, if not the impossibility, of the American challenge in the countryside. In 1965 the Joint United States Public Affairs Office (JUSPAO) effectively became the information agency of the Saigon government and managed a prodigious outpouring of printed communications (at the rate of fifteen hundred for every Vietnamese) as well as radio and television programming to all parts of the country. Most JUSPAO propaganda was directed toward enlisting Southern support for the Saigon government and undermining the morale and credibility of the Vietcong. The results were disappointing, in part because JUSPAO's personnel were poorly trained and culturally insensitive,

54 James Walker Trullinger, *Village at War: An Account of Revolution in Vietnam* (New York, 1980).

55 Michael E. Peterson, *The Combined Action Platoons: The U.S. Marines' Other War in Vietnam* (Westport, 1989), 9, 125.

and, in part because its propaganda was not targeted to specific groups. In a larger sense, the propaganda campaign failed precisely because it was an American, not a Vietnamese, program.[56]

The most systematic, and controversial, pacification effort was the Phoenix program, which became a cornerstone of Vietnamization. Criticized as amounting to a program of political assassination and defended by officials led by William Colby and Robert Kommer as a model that ought to have been employed earlier, the program has received reasonably balanced appraisals from Stuart Herrington and Dale Andrade. Both see it as making significant inroads against the Vietcong but also as limited by the longstanding hostility between the South Vietnamese government and the rural population. In *Silence Was a Weapon*, Herrington, who served in 1971–72 as a Phoenix program officer in Hau Nghia Province west of Saigon, contends that the Phoenix operation was generally discriminating and successful in terms of eliminating the Vietcong infrastructure, but it was undermined by the resistance and corruption of South Vietnamese officials and the resultant cynicism of the peasantry toward the Saigon government. Andrade's *Ashes to Ashes* details several Phoenix operations between 1968 and 1971 and finds that they decimated the Vietcong infrastructure at the village level, only to be limited by the hostility of South Vietnamese provincial officials and by the shift toward conventional warfare, which made pacification less relevant.[57]

56 Robert W. Chandler, *War of Ideas: The U.S. Propaganda Campaign in Vietnam* (Boulder, 1981).

57 Stuart A. Herrington, *Silence Was a Weapon: The Vietnam War in the Villages, A Personal Perspective* (Novato, CA, 1982); Dale Andrade, *Ashes to Ashes: The Phoenix Program and the Vietnam War* (Lexington, MA, 1990). For recent criticisms of the Phoenix program see Zolin Grant, *Facing the Phoenix: The CIA and the Political Defeat of the United States in Vietnam* (New York, 1991); and Douglas Valentine, *The Phoenix Program* (New York, 1990).

In *Lost Victory* and *The Bureaucracy at Work*, Colby and Komer, respectively, argue that the Phoenix program illustrated how the war could have been won earlier and at greatly reduced costs. Had the United States given priority to pacification during the 1955–1963 period and had it not betrayed the South's most effective leader, Ngo Dinh Diem, the Vietcong would not have been able to build its considerable strength in the rural areas. Defending the Phoenix program that he directed against charges that it amounted to little more than a campaign of terrorism and political assassination, Colby sees the ends justifying the means. The CIA and the South Vietnamese accomplished what the Army's search-and-destroy ignored: the

The Land-to-the-Tiller program constituted another belated effort at securing Saigon's rural base of support. Charles Callison's field-research-based study of the program from 1971 to 1974 in relatively secure, pro-government Mekong Delta villages concludes that it brought social and economic changes that enhanced political stability.[58]

If there is one thing on which virtually all accounts agree it is that the United States faced a determined enemy. Although documentation is limited, several works have made use of existing materials to examine Hanoi's strategy and its implementation. In compiling *Portrait of the Enemy*, David Chanoff and Doan Van Toai interviewed Vietnamese refugees, including Vietcong and North Vietnamese army veterans, and drew upon recorded interrogations of prisoners. In a book in which participants in the war do most of the talking, Chanoff and Toai conclude that although the Communist leadership engaged in "utter ruthlessness and massive social manipulation," it succeeded because of "the nature of the human material it had to work with" and its compelling patriotic vision. Hundreds of thousands displayed a "quixotic disregard for the impossible, . . . throw[ing] themselves into the perils, accepting the terrible risks in exchange for a very distant glimpse of something better."[59] Drawing principally upon RAND Corporation interviews with prisoners of war and defectors, Michael Lanning and Dan Cragg, in *Inside the VC and the NVA*, similarly underscore the effectiveness of North Vietnam's tactics, logistics, recruitment, and organization. Attention to the military basics resulted in a mobile, committed, disciplined, and well-equipped fighting force.[60]

Several works trace the reason for the Communist success to an effective integration of political and military strategy that built

need to confront the Communist insurgents on their own terms. Robert W. Komer, *Bureaucracy at War: U.S. Performance in the Vietnam Conflict* (Boulder, 1986); William E. Colby, *Lost Victory: A First Hand Account of America's Sixteen Year Involvement in Vietnam* (Chicago, 1989).

58 Charles Stuart Callison, *Land-to-the-Tiller in the Mekong Delta: Economic, Social, and Political Effects of Land Reform in Four Villages of South Vietnam* (Lanham, MD, 1983).

59 David Chanoff and Doan Van Toai, *Portrait of the Enemy* (New York, 1986), 209.

60 Michael Lee Lanning and Dan Cragg, *Inside the VC and the NVA: The Real Story of North Vietnam's Armed Forces* (New York, 1992).

on a nationalist tradition. The principal contribution of Gabriel Kolko's massive *Anatomy of a War: Vietnam, the United States, and the Modern Historical Experience* is its analysis of "the Revolution's" political-military strategy against an American intervention that was driven by the need to control revolutionary regimes in the Third World. Kolko contrasts America's imprecise objectives and mindless warfare and the attendant shallowness of the South Vietnamese regime with the North's dedicated and disciplined cadres and the mass mobilization that characterized Northern society. If the North's victory was inevitable, it was facilitated by the limits placed on the use of American power, a fact plainly evident in how the war's devastating effect on the U.S. economy forced deescalation. The Tet Offensive, while costing the Communist forces heavily, guaranteed that they would not be defeated.[61]

William Duiker's *The Communist Road to Power in Vietnam* offers a similar, but more even handed, appraisal of Hanoi's response to American warfare and ultimate victory. The groundwork was laid by the Communist party's ability to organize and direct an insurgency that exploited "the pervasive sense of malaise through[out] South Vietnamese society, the legacy of a generation of failure by successive governments to build the foundations of a viable non-Communist state." The ultimate success of the Communist party resulted from its commitment to a comprehensive strategy of people's war that linked nationalism with social reform and built on the leadership of Ho Chi Minh – "an unusual composite of moral leader and organizational genius, half Gandhi, half Lenin."[62]

Douglas Pike, although decidedly not sympathetic to the Communists, also writes respectfully of their success in unconventional warfare, which he attributes to a capacity to exploit the enemy's weakness and to integrate political-military strategy. The latter, labeled Dau Tranh, a "strategy for which there is no known counterstrategy," eliminated distinctions between combatants and

61 Gabriel Kolko, *Anatomy of a War: Vietnam, the United States, and the Modern Historical Experience* (New York, 1985).
62 William J. Duiker, *The Communist Road to Power in Vietnam* (Boulder, 1981), 319, 323.

civilians and prolonged the struggle to dishearten the enemy. But despite the cogency of the strategy, Pike, unlike Kolko, rejects any suggestion that it assured victory. He embraces instead a revisionist perspective, similar to that of Lomperis in *The War Everyone Lost – And Won*, that the war was more "lost" by Americans than "won" by the North Vietnamese. The Americans and South Vietnamese, he argues, won the armed struggle because ARVN was still intact by 1975, but the "political dau tranh gauntlet was never actually picked up; no comprehensive counterstrategy was ever developed, and the effort that was made failed."[63]

Dismissing Pike's work as a "not very promising venture into Vietnamese metaphysics" and contending that Western scholars generally have paid insufficient attention to the People's Army, Greg Lockhart, in *Nation in Arms*, traces the simultaneous evolution of the political and military arms of Vietnamese nationalism from 1940 to 1954. In a situation where struggle was the only way to attain nationhood, the army played a central role in defining the power of the state. Detailing the history of the army from its origins in the World War II guerrilla bases and the August revolution to its integrative role in the subsequent struggle against the French culminating at Dienbienphu, Lockhart finds that not only did the People's Army "[grow] as a manifestation as well as an instrument of the legitimate power of the Vietnamese nation-state" but that it was also "the central reason for the outcome of the Vietnam War."[64]

Ken Post's multivolume *Revolution, Socialism and Nationalism in Viet Nam*, although written with certain acknowledged biases, offers a remarkably comprehensive overview of the revolution, which was a struggle for both liberation and social transformation and which the United States sought to contain. Offering what he describes as "an independent Marxist viewpoint," Post criticizes most other Western analyses of Vietnamese nationalism for being unsympathetic toward communism and contends that R. B. Smith's international history minimizes the internal forces

63 Douglas Pike, *PAVN: People's Army of Vietnam* (Novato, CA, 1986), 55, 127, 251.
64 Greg Lockhart, *Nation in Arms: The Origins of the People's Army of Vietnam* (Wellington, Australia, 1991), 1, 11 (emphasis in original).

that led to conflict. While stressing the development of the Vietnamese Communist party, Post also emphasizes its relationship to China and the Soviet Union, which provided political and material support and, equally important, ideological guidance. Indeed, the ideological connection is central to Post's view of the Vietnamese revolution's significance. "The Hanoi leaders['] . . . skill in combining Marxist-Leninist internationalism with . . . Vietnamese patriotism," he argues, "made theirs the quintessential national liberation movement of the twentieth century."[65]

Post's fourth volume, *The Failure of Counter-Insurgency in the South, 1961–1965*, is the only one devoted principally to U.S. involvement. Predictably, Post foresees U.S. efforts as effectively futile. Like some revisionists, Post faults the American military leadership's emphasis on the military, and not on the economic, component of counterinsurgency and argues that the overthrow of the Diem regime was a major mistake in terms of U.S. interests. Yet the American ability to influence the situation was limited, for historical developments were working to the advantage of the Communist revolution. Despite his bias and Marxist fondness for an endless sequence of "contradictions," Post offers a substantial analysis of Hanoi's worldview and its response to changes inside and beyond Vietnam.[66]

With the opening of more documents and the coming of more reflective scholarship, the literature on the Vietnam War will refine some of the contentions dividing the neo-orthodox and revisionist views, and eventually a fuller synthesis will emerge. The more conspiratorial and "if only" aspects of revisionism traditionally are relegated to the fringes of scholarship, and that will likely be true in the case of the writing on the Vietnam War. The Clausewitzians' prescription for retrospective victory has been criticized for minimizing the Vietnamese and international politics of the war, but their attention to a variety of command, logistical, and bureaucratic problems is likely to remain a part of

65 Ken Post, *Revolution, Socialism and Nationalism in Viet Nam*, vol. 1, *An Interrupted Revolution* (Aldershot, England, 1989), xiii; vol. 4, *The Failure of Counter-Insurgency in the South* (Aldershot, England, 1990), 324.

66 Ken Post, *Revolution, Socialism and Nationalism in Viet Nam*, vol. 2, *Viet Nam Divided* (Aldershot, England, 1989); vol. 3, *Socialism in Half a Country* (Aldershot, England, 1989).

the military histories. Likely also to have a lasting impact is the hearts-and-minders' indictment of the military leadership's approach to the war and of the flawed approach to pacification. The legitimacists should force fuller attention to the range of competing international interests at stake in Vietnam (which rarely receives much attention in neoorthodox accounts) and to the "better side" of the Diem government, but whether they will convince future scholars to embrace the conclusions that the international situation demanded U.S. military intervention or that Diem deserved unswerving U.S. support is more problematic. The useful work done thus far on the Vietnamese "sides" speaks to the need for more research on the wide range of social, political, economic, and military issues that helped to define and shape the struggle. Such scholarship will underscore that the conflict was a "long war . . . a trauma . . . an ordeal . . . a tragedy" even more for Vietnamese than for Americans. Only then can historians approach a genuine synthesis that addresses one of the major events of the twentieth century in its Vietnamese, American, and international dimensions.

14

Complaints, Self-Justifications, and Analysis: The Historiography of American Foreign Relations since 1969

ROBERT D. SCHULZINGER

In 1990, at the end of a long doctoral oral exam, I tried to lighten the load of the Ph.D. candidate. "Of the hundreds of books you read in preparation what are the worst and the best," I asked. He groped about for the worst: he could think of many contenders, but his award for the best came swiftly: Raymond Garthoff's *Détente and Confrontation.*[1] I gulped, thinking the student was trying some transparent flattery. I customarily spend a couple of weeks in a graduate reading seminar analyzing *Détente and Confrontation.* "Not the heaviest, but the best," I said.

The student then explained what makes Garthoff's book so good: Its reflections by a participant who is refreshingly modest, not a know-it-all; its vast command of available U.S. and Soviet sources; its masterful grasp of the interplay between domestic and foreign policy considerations; its demonstration that Soviet policy, like American, resulted from a complicated mixture of internal and external forces. I probed deeper. "Don't you believe it is really three books, one on the Nixon-Ford period, one on the Carter administration, and one on Reagan? The first section, down to 1976, is splendid, but the analysis in the last six hundred pages may not stand the test of time. Wouldn't many historians resist the predictions in the last section decrying the Reagan administration's anti-Soviet bluster?" Alright, he agreed, maybe

1 Raymond L. Garthoff, *Détente and Confrontation: American-Soviet Relations from Nixon to Reagan*, rev. ed. (Washington, 1994).

the sections on the Nixon-Ford period were so richly detailed that the discussion of the Carter years suffered by comparison, and the account of the Reagan administration's early belligerence toward Moscow did not completely predict the future. But who could have anticipated the dramatic end of the Cold War? He explained that the first five hundred pages were a masterpiece and the concluding remarks about the Reagan years did more than anything else written at the time to demonstrate that, despite their mutual recriminations, the United States and the Soviet Union had positioned themselves to resume work on arms control.

The student was right. *Détente and Confrontation* is the major work on U.S. foreign relations of the period after 1968 and is exemplary because it both represents and transcends its genre. In this paper, I include *Détente and Confrontation* in a discussion of the writings on recent American foreign relations that are of most interest to two separate but often overlapping groups of readers of this volume on the historiography of U.S. foreign relations: scholars who will draw on these works in their research and instructors who will borrow from these writings in their teaching. *Détente and Confrontation* is unusual both in its range – its mastery of Soviet as well as American affairs – and in the superior quality of its analysis. The latter is all the more surprising in that the research and writing took place in the early 1980s, before the explosion in records about the Nixon administration led to several publications by historians in 1989 and 1990.[2]

Garthoff does not fit in one major category of writers on recent foreign affairs subjects – journalists. The growth in the amount of serious work on foreign affairs by journalists derives from the collapse of the Cold War consensus caused by controversy over Vietnam and from the availability of some written records sooner than they might otherwise reach researchers. During the war in

2 An excellent review of *Détente and Confrontation*, which summarizes much of its detailed contents, is Stephen E. Ambrose, "Between Two Poles: The Last Two Decades of the Cold War," *Diplomatic History* 11 (Fall 1987): 371–79. For the recent works on the foreign policy of the Nixon administration see idem, *Nixon: The Triumph of a Politician* (New York, 1989) and *Nixon: Ruin and Recovery* (New York, 1991); Walter Isaacson, *Kissinger: A Biography* (New York, 1992); Robert D. Schulzinger, *Henry Kissinger: Doctor of Diplomacy* (New York, 1989); Herbert Parmet, *Richard Nixon and His America* (Boston, 1990); and Joan Hoff, *Nixon Reconsidered* (New York, 1994).

Vietnam, the intensity of domestic debate over foreign relations was louder than at any point since the late 1930s. By the late 1960s, bitter division over the war had fractured the broad but temporary consensus existing among politicians, opinion makers, and researchers over the aims and conduct of U.S. foreign policy. As Thomas G. Paterson has recently noted, "The Vietnam War experience fractured the Cold War consensus, raised concern about violation of cherished values, exposed flaws in the nation's checks and balance system of decision making, and revealed limits to American power."[3] Observers offered a rich array of alternatives to realism in international affairs, the prevailing view from the late 1940s until the mid-1960s, when they questioned the basic premises of U.S. foreign relations. Critics of realism often wrote with passion as they presented alternatives for continuing U.S. involvement in world affairs.

Even as Vietnam declined as an issue, some of the anger produced by that war remained when journalists wrote about current issues after 1968: the end of the Vietnam War, the rise and fall of détente, arms control, the Middle East, Central America, and the Iran-contra affair all provoked intense public passions. The result was an enormous body of literature, informed by the breakdown of the Cold War consensus and rooted in a larger amount of documentary evidence than had been available at similar times to earlier writers. The lack of consensus over current foreign policy also produced an unexpected result: Because so much of the good contemporary writing on foreign relations came from journalists, it made few explicit references to the theories of international relations or politics that informed the 1960s critiques of American behavior in the early days of the Cold War or in Vietnam. Most contemporary accounts of American foreign relations rest on conventional, quotidian assumptions about how the American system should operate: Officials should be responsible to a populace able to exercise judgment based on accurate information. Leaders should be competent, honest, and informed. When officials or citizens did not meet these standards, as often happened,

3 Michael J. Hogan and Thomas G. Paterson, "Introduction," *Explaining the History of American Foreign Relations*, ed. Hogan and Paterson (New York, 1991), 6.

their missteps formed the subject matter of much of the journalism on recent American foreign relations.

Although the end of the Cold War consensus represented a distinct period in the conduct of and reflection on U.S. foreign relations, diplomacy after 1968 clearly followed themes articulated since the Second World War: U.S.-Soviet conflict, American globalism, the importance of the military, and suspicion of excessive public interference in the conduct of foreign affairs. As policymakers tried to adapt to the post-Vietnam environment, they operated within the framework of containment. Not surprisingly, therefore, some of the most useful discussions of recent American foreign policy appear in works by historians dealing with a longer time frame. John Lewis Gaddis, a neorealist with a broad grasp of contemporary international relations theory, wrote that the Nixon administration's efforts to reduce the prominence of Vietnam and to recast the U.S.-Soviet relationship represented a variation on earlier strategies of containment. In *The American Style of Foreign Policy*, Robert Dallek described the psychological makeup of people involved in foreign affairs in the seventies as reflecting enduring tensions between sophisticated practitioners and a xenophobic public. Thomas J. McCormick adopts perhaps the broadest of all the general explanations of recent American foreign policy in *America's Half-Century.* McCormick employs a world-systems model in which states at the center of the international system attempt to exercise control over regions on the periphery that sometimes cooperate and sometimes resist. In this view, American foreign policy after 1968 represented efforts by a declining power to assert itself.[4] By explicitly using theory and placing recent events in a longer context, these valuable works depart from the pattern set by most of studies of the recent past. Insights and chronological range represented the strengths of these works. But as broad, integrative

4 John Lewis Gaddis, *Strategies of Containment: A Critical Appraisal of Postwar American National Security Policy* (New York, 1982). See also idem, *The Long Peace: Inquiries into the History of the Cold War* (New York, 1989) and *The United States and the End of the Cold War: Implications, Reconsiderations, Provocations* (New York, 1992); Robert Dallek, *The American Style of Foreign Policy: Cultural Politics and Foreign Affairs* (New York, 1983); and Thomas J. McCormick, *America's Half-Century: United States Foreign Policy in the Cold War* (Baltimore, 1989).

accounts, they did not have the rich detail characteristic of the best of the other studies of recent American foreign relations.

Such broad, interpretive works are less common when dealing with the recent past than are studies that present and attempt to assimilate the mass of information available regarding current affairs. As indicated earlier, Raymond Garthoff's *Détente and Confrontation* is the outstanding account of American foreign relations after 1968, combining extraordinary factual detail with theoretical insights into great-power relations.[5] Written by a participant, *Détente and Confrontation* takes issue with other studies by managers of U.S.-Soviet relations. Garthoff believes that the two superpowers were doomed to coexist after the qualitative changes in armaments in the mid-1960s: Coexistence did not imply cooperation, however. Garthoff presents an insightful, and ultimately devastating, portrait of Kissinger's negotiating style with the Soviet Union. For years, Kissinger had believed that the danger of outright war between the United States and the Soviet Union was slight. The exact details of agreements with the Soviets thus mattered less than the fact that any agreement at all hastened the process of détente.[6] The intended consequence was public excitement, verging on euphoria. The unintended consequence was public disillusionment, abetted by members of Congress led by Senator Henry Jackson (D-WA), who highlighted the sloppiness of the agreements Kissinger and Nixon had negotiated at the first summit with Brezhnev in May 1972.

Garthoff was not the only writer to note the hastiness and technical flaws of the 1972 pacts – SALT I and the ABM treaty – and the subsequent arms negotiations in 1973 and 1974. Gerard Smith, Garthoff's superior at ACDA, made the same point in his memoir of the arms control negotiations, the aptly titled *Doubletalk*. In another work, *Cold Dawn: The Inside Story of SALT*, written in the midst of the euphoria over Kissinger's triumphant

5 An early but stimulating study of the implications of détente for international relations is Robert Litwak, *Détente and the Nixon Doctrine* (Cambridge, England, 1984). Two works by British authors also put détente into a broader context of great-power relations, without the richness of detail of Garthoff's *Détente and Confrontation*. See Richard W. Stevenson, *The Rise and Fall of Détente* (Champaign, 1985); and Mike Bowker and Phil Williams, *Superpower Détente: A Reappraisal* (London, 1988).

6 On this point see also Schulzinger, *Henry Kissinger*, 52–74.

diplomacy, journalist John Newhouse, not a member of the official SALT team, favored Kissinger's approach. For Newhouse, the technical details of SALT I mattered less than the signing of an agreement.[7] For Smith, Kissinger had expropriated his staff's territory, so the product necessarily was flawed. Garthoff's account superseded both because of what made the first half of his book so good – the richness of the detail, the understanding of bureaucratic rivalries within both the United States and the Soviet Union, and Garthoff's consistent ability to place the criticism of U.S. conduct in a context larger than that of personal pique. Kissinger's diplomatic efforts with the Soviets were flawed, Garthoff argued, not because they rendered his own work superfluous but because serious issues of arms control required meticulous attention to detail. If the foundations of détente were not firm, the breezes of fickle public opinion could blow down the structure of peace promised in Nixon's first term.

Kissinger never seemed to understand this – in office or in his memoirs. Much of Kissinger's massive account of the Nixon administration, *White House Years* and *Years of Upheaval*, consists of criticism of Senator Jackson and other politicians who opposed détente for their own gain. Although their criticism often resulted from political motives, Kissinger and Nixon had started the political bidding.[8] When the Nixon Papers opened in 1986, we had the evidence of what most people knew all along: Nixon and Kissinger conducted negotiations with a view to the 1972 election. As Nixon told Kissinger before sending him to Moscow to lay the groundwork for the May 1972 summit, "what I am concerned about is . . . that when we do make the formal agreements there will be no real news value to them."[9] He ordered Kissinger to make certain that the SALT I agreement was not finished until Nixon arrived to conduct the final bargaining with Brezhnev in May. To be sure, this produced excellent theater, but

7 Gerard Smith, *Doubletalk: The Story of the First Strategic Arms Limitation Talks* (Garden City, NY, 1980); John Newhouse, *Cold Dawn: The Inside Story of SALT* (New York, 1973).

8 Henry Kissinger, *White House Years* (Boston, 1979); idem, *Years of Upheaval* (Boston, 1982).

9 Nixon to Kissinger, 11 March 1972, White House Staff Files, Staff Members' Office Files, Haldeman Files, box 45, Nixon Papers, National Archives, Washington, DC.

the product was so flawed that Jackson and other skeptics of détente pounced on the ambiguities of the agreement. Détente reached its high point in the summer of 1972, and support for it never recovered from the complaints Jackson and others made that summer. Critics had such a wide opening because of the way in which Kissinger mishandled the negotiations. No book presents those negotiations and what they meant for the future of U.S.-Soviet relations as well as Garthoff's.

The title of Gerard Smith's memoir, *Doubletalk*, is a pun, referring both to Kissinger's preference for backchannel negotiations and the Nixon administration's Orwellian use of language. The former led to some of the breathtaking drama of the period from 1969 to 1973 – détente with the Soviet Union, the efforts to end the war in Vietnam, the opening to China, and American mediation of the Arab-Israeli conflict. The latter helped to produce the widespread public sense that Nixon's foreign policy was deceitful, based on sleight of hand, producing only the illusion of peace. The drama and the sense of betrayal produced an enormous interest in Nixon's foreign policy, at the time and for the next sixteen years. Watergate fed the public's eagerness to read about the Nixon administration and provided researchers with a vast array of source material that otherwise would not have become available as soon as it did. Taken together, the abrupt changes of direction in Nixon's foreign policy, the sense that Kissinger was more a stuntman than a miracle worker, and the revelations of Watergate produced more memoirs and journalistic accounts than had appeared earlier. The federal government's seizure of Nixon's White House papers led to the release of hundreds of thousands of pages beginning in 1986 and continuing to the present. Although the National Security Files remain classified, what has been made public has led to a substantial body of works by historians able to offer a more complete picture than might be expected of the recent past. In 1994, one of the richest sources of original documents useful for studying the Nixon administration was published as *The Haldeman Diaries*.[10]

Regarding the memoirs, Kissinger's stand in a category by

10 H. R. Haldeman, *The Haldeman Diaries: Inside the Nixon White House* (New York, 1994).

themselves. Over twenty-four hundred pages in length, they are the fullest account by a national security adviser or secretary of state we are ever likely to get, simply because of the economics of the publishing industry. Not since Winston Churchill had there been a public official with a following wide enough to make it feasible to print such a massive memoir. Kissinger had a special standing with the press and public from 1969 until at least his defense of the Chinese government after the suppression of the movement for democracy in Tianamen Square in June 1989. For those twenty years, Kissinger maintained a reputation as a bridge between the tough guys and law breakers of the Nixon White House and the academic establishment he had grown up in. From 1969 to 1972, reporters felt the need to show that they were not prejudiced against the entire Nixon administration, so they built up Kissinger as the resident intellectual, strategist, even link to the stylish Kennedys. The categorization of Kissinger as part Otto von Bismarck and part Warren Beatty continued for years afterward with editors at *Time* and the producers of ABC's "Nightline." *White House Years* and *Years of Upheaval* remain valuable for two reasons: Kissinger's portraits of others – Nixon, Brezhnev, Le Duc Tho, Golda Meir, Zhou Enlai, and Henry Jackson, to name a few – and his recollection of what he felt at the time. Despite their length, the memoirs are less useful in determining what Kissinger actually did. Their very bulk gets in the way, with often maudlin digressions about, for example, student protesters or the difficulties of conducting foreign affairs with an assertive Congress getting in the way. The memoirs are also defensive, blaming others for failures, taking credit for successes, omitting or downplaying embarrassing incidents – for example, Chile, the wiretaps of subordinates, the Iranian connection, the bombing of Cambodia, and the Christmas bombing of North Vietnam in 1972 and 1973.[11]

Whatever their shortcomings, Kissinger's memoirs tower above those of the other Nixon officials involved in foreign affairs. Nixon's memoirs and his *In the Arena* have little value for his-

11 Kissinger went over much of the same ground, but in a shortened form, in his book *Diplomacy* (New York, 1994).

torians seeking a factual account of events.[12] They have far fewer documents or direct quotations than do Kissinger's, so using them to reconstruct the details of what went on is dangerous. They are notable mostly for their reiteration of Nixon's self-pity.

Like Nixon's stream of books since 1974, the memoirs of his staff members originated with Watergate. Four of them are useful for understanding the suspicious atmosphere surrounding Nixon and his courtiers: John Ehrlichman's *Witness to Power*, H. R. Haldeman's *The Ends of Power*, Raymond Price's *With Nixon*, and William Safire's *Before the Fall.*[13] Like the other memoirs, they cast little light on who did what on a specific date. (*The Haldeman Diaries* [1994] do contain an excellent day-by-day account.) Kissinger's subordinate Roger Morris's *Uncertain Greatness* has the same strengths and weaknesses – good on presenting the dark, suspicious atmosphere of the NSC staff, but less successful in describing the details of what went on. A work by Anthony Lake, another NSC staff member who left in disgust after the Cambodian invasion, *The "Tar Baby" Option*, is a special case in that it uses the documents available at the time to analyze and criticize U.S. indifference to southern Africa.[14]

Journalistic accounts of the Nixon administration's foreign policy provide much more raw factual information than the memoirs. Tad Szulc's *The Illusion of Peace* appeared five years after Nixon's resignation.[15] Szulc put that time to good use interviewing everyone he could find who had participated in the events of the Nixon years, many of whom possessed documents that Szulc could use. He names names, gives dates, and provides a good picture of what happened. He does not, however, cite either

12 Richard Nixon, *RN: The Memoirs of Richard Nixon* (New York, 1978); idem, *In the Arena* (New York, 1990).

13 John Ehrlichman, *Witness to Power* (New York, 1982); idem, with Joseph DiMona, *The Ends of Power* (New York, 1978); Raymond Price, *With Nixon* (New York, 1977); William Safire, *Before the Fall: An Inside Look at the Pre-Watergate Nixon White House* (Garden City, 1975).

14 Roger Morris, *Uncertain Greatness: Henry Kissinger and American Foreign Policy* (New York, 1976); Anthony Lake, *The "Tar Baby" Option: American Policy toward Southern Rhodesia* (New York, 1976). Melvin Laird, Nixon's first secretary of defense, did not write a full memoir. See, however, Laird, "A Strong Start in a Difficult Decade: Defense Policy in the Nixon-Ford Years," *International Security* 10 (Fall 1985): 10–15.

15 Tad Szulc, *The Illusion of Peace: Foreign Policy in the Nixon Years* (New York, 1979).

the people he interviewed or the documents themselves. The results are both useful and frustrating for historians, who welcome the detail but wonder about verification or probing the documents more deeply.

Eight years after Szulc convicted Nixon of duplicity and manipulation, another journalist who defended Nixon at the time tried to rehabilitate his foreign policy in retrospect. C. L. Sulzberger's *New York Times* columns were a constant source of comfort to Nixon and Kissinger in the early seventies. In 1987 Sulzberger published *The World and Richard Nixon*, which elevated the former president to the highest level.[16] Sulzberger's account was more reminiscence than narrative or analysis, but it has one important value for researchers: Sulzberger had close ties to the Nixon White House, and he includes much of his correspondence with the president and Kissinger.

Kissingerology has been a sizable industry since the early seventies. Among the accounts by journalists, the most enduring is Walter Isaacson, *Kissinger: A Biography*.[17] Like Szulc, Isaacson interviewed widely, including many discussions with Kissinger himself. Isaacson was also able to use the material in the Nixon Papers at the National Archives. Isaacson praises Kissinger's diplomatic skills but faults him for his egoism, personal insecurities, and manifold deceits, as well as for his personal shortcomings and his dependence on the approval of Richard Nixon.[18]

16 C. L. Sulzberger, *The World and Richard Nixon* (New York, 1987).

17 Walter Isaacson, *Kissinger: A Biography* (New York, 1992). Isaacson's book has supplanted Seymour Hersh, *The Price of Power: Kissinger in the Nixon White House* (New York, 1983), as the standard full-length account of Kissinger activities in the White House. Isaacson had access to the material in the Nixon Papers and was able to interview Kissinger.

18 Isaacson's and Hersh's books are far superior to an earlier journalists' account, Marvin Kalb and Bernard Kalb, *Kissinger* (Boston, 1974). The other contemporary discussions of Kissinger have largely been supplanted by later work. Among the earlier works are Stephen Graubard, *Kissinger: Portrait of a Mind* (New York, 1973); David Landau, *Kissinger: The Uses of Power* (Boston, 1973); and John Stoessinger, *Henry Kissinger: The Anguish of Power* (New York, 1976). Peter Dickson, *Kissinger and the Meaning of History* (New York, 1979), is still useful for understanding the interplay between Kissinger's academic writings and his performance in office.

Besides *The Price of Power*, the best book on Kissinger to appear before the opening of the Nixon Papers was Harvey Starr, *Henry Kissinger: Perceptions of World Politics* (Lexington, KY, 1983). Starr, a professor of political science, made extensive use of Kissinger's memoirs to argue that Kissinger tried unsuccessfully to lay an essentially static, old-world view of international relations onto contemporary problems.

There have also been good special studies of Nixon administration foreign policy by participants, journalists, and scholars. Despite its name, Garthoff's *Détente and Confrontation* covers more than U.S.-Soviet relations. It is also a superior resource for studying Vietnam, China, and the Middle East. In general, however, coverage of Vietnam after 1968 is not as good as discussions of events before Nixon's election. The reason is simple – sources. The publication of the *Pentagon Papers* in 1971 provided a river of information on events before 1968.

Nevertheless, studies making good use of uneven documentation do exist. William Shawcross, a journalist, mined congressional sources and used the Freedom of Information Act to produce *Sideshow*, the story of the secret bombing of Cambodia. Historian George Herring's *America's Longest War* makes good use of the available primary sources in the last chapters, although they are, necessarily, less densely packed than the earlier discussions. One controversial book on the end of the war in Vietnam in the Nixon and Ford administrations is Nguyen Tien Hung and Jerrold Schechter's *The Palace File*. Hung, a former South Vietnamese government official, and Schechter, *Time*'s diplomatic correspondent during the Nixon years, base their account of the American betrayal of Saigon on documents. But the breathless quality of their writing implies the discovery of more new information than actually is presented in the book.[19]

With the exception of Herring's last chapters, the best works on Vietnam during the Nixon years discuss outsiders, critics, and opponents of the war. Because primary sources are more quickly made available for domestic than foreign affairs, good scholarship by academics exists on the interplay between the executive

19 William Shawcross, *Sideshow: Nixon, Kissinger, and the Destruction of Cambodia* (New York, 1979); George Herring, *America's Longest War: The United States and Vietnam, 1950–1975*, 2d ed. (New York, 1986); Nguyen Tien Hung and Jerrold Schechter, *The Palace File* (New York, 1986).

Two accounts written by political scientists who take diametrically contrary positions on the negotiations ending the war are Alan E. Goodman, *The Lost Peace: America's Search for a Negotiated Settlement of the Vietnam War* (Stanford, 1978); and Gareth Porter, *A Peace Denied: The United States, Vietnam, and the Paris Agreements* (Bloomington, 1975). Goodman is highly supportive of Kissinger, Porter extremely critical. Both interviewed participants and used the documents available at the time of writing. Both are now somewhat dated.

and Congress and between the presidents and antiwar critics. Two political scientists, Edward Franck and Thomas Wiesband, interviewed the major figures involved in creating the congressional foreign policy revolution of 1973–1977. Their *Foreign Policy by Congress*, probably overly critical of Congress, is still a superior monograph.[20] Even richer detail can be found in the later chapters of Melvin Small's *Johnson, Nixon, and the Doves*, Tom Wells, *The War Within: America's Battle over Vietnam* and Charles DeBenedetti's (with the assistance of Charles Chatfield), *An American Ordeal: The Antiwar Movement of the Vietnam Era*. Ole Holsti and James Rosenau investigated the impact of Vietnam on the articulate public and opinion makers with a questionnaire distributed to thousands of them. Their findings, presented in *American Leadership in World Affairs: Vietnam and the Breakdown of Consensus*, explained the complicated divisions of opinion and emotions regarding overseas involvement, the use of force, and the credibility of American political leaders.[21]

Good special studies of U.S. Middle East policy by participants and scholars also make use of newly available documents and in-depth interviews with participants. As is the case of several of the books on Vietnam, some of the studies of the Middle East discuss a long period of time, so readers almost naturally compare coverage of different eras. Not surprisingly, earlier periods, for which there is an abundance of data, receive deeper treatment than the later years. Setting aside such comparisons across time, however, Steven L. Spiegel's *The Other Arab-Israeli Conflict* and James Bill's *The Eagle and the Lion: The Tragedy of American-Iranian Relations* show how American policy toward the Middle East was created and then go on to analyze and criticize it. William Quandt's *Decade of Decisions* and *Peace Process* are two other

20 Published a few years after Alton Frye, *A Responsible Congress: The Politics of National Security* (New York, 1975), Thomas Franck and Edward Wiesband, *Foreign Policy by Congress* (New York, 1979), covers similar ground more thoroughly. A good recent study of a single member, Senator J. William Fulbright (D-AR), is William C. Berman, *William Fulbright and Vietnam: The Dissent of a Political Realist* (Kent, OH, 1988).

21 Melvin Small, *Johnson, Nixon, and the Doves* (New Brunswick, 1988); Tom Wells, *The War Within: America's Battle over Vietnam* (Berkeley, 1993); Charles DeBenedetti, with the assistance of Charles Chatfield, *An American Ordeal: The Antiwar Movement of the Vietnam Era* (Syracuse, 1990); Ole Holsti and James Rosenau, *American Leadership in World Affairs: Vietnam and the Breakdown of Consensus* (Boston, 1984).

accounts by a participant-turned-scholar. The latter made use of previously classified documents. (Quandt served as a Middle East expert on the NSC staff for some of this time.)[22]

The most recent accounts of Nixon's foreign policy have appeared after the opening of his Presidential Materials Project in 1986. Several of the new works by historians make use of these documents to present more details of the years from 1969 to 1974, although all acknowledge an enormous debt to Garthoff's *Détente and Confrontation.* They are Stephen Ambrose, *Nixon: The Triumph of a Politician* and *Nixon: Ruin and Recovery*, which carries the story from 1962 to 1990; Herbert Parmet, *Richard Nixon and His America*, a biography covering Nixon's entire career, with a few chapters on the foreign policy of his presidency; Joan Hoff, *Nixon Reconsidered*, which praises his domestic acheivements and condemns his foreign policy as a failure; Walter Isaacson, *Kissinger: A Biography*, which presented a detailed and balanced view of Kissinger; and Robert Schulzinger, *Henry Kissinger: Doctor of Diplomacy*, which discusses Kissinger's role in the Nixon and Ford administrations.[23]

There is, of course, less literature devoted to events during the Ford administration. Several of the accounts of the Nixon years also bring the story down to 1976.[24] Generally, the same kinds

22 Steven L. Spiegel, *The Other Arab-Israeli Conflict: Making America's Middle East Policy from Truman to Reagan* (Chicago, 1985); James Bill, *The Eagle and the Lion: The Tragedy of American-Iranian Relations* (New Haven, 1988); William Quandt, *Decade of Decisions: American Policy toward the Arab-Israeli Conflict, 1967–1976* (Berkeley, 1977) and *Peace Process: American Diplomacy and the Arab Israeli Conflict since 1967* (Berkeley and Washington, 1993). See also Alan Dowty, *Middle East Crisis: U.S. Decisionmaking in 1958, 1970, and 1973* (Berkeley, 1983). Dowty, a political scientist, makes good use of existing documentation to lay out a typology of decision styles in three crises. Ishaq I. Ghanayen and Alden Voth, *The Kissinger Legacy: American Middle East Policy* (New York, 1984), had less original source material to use than other accounts.

23 Ambrose, *Nixon*; Parmet, *Richard Nixon and His America*; Schulzinger, *Henry Kissinger*; Isaacson, *Kissinger*; Hoff, *Nixon Reconsidered.* See also Franz Schurmann, *The Foreign Politics of Richard Nixon: The Grand Design* (Berkeley, 1987). This book appeared after the first flood of works on Nixon and Kissinger but before the opening of the archives. As such, it tended to fall between stools, too late to contribute to the policy debate, too early to benefit from the unpublished documents.

24 Garthoff's *Détente and Confrontation* is just as good on U.S.-Soviet relations from 1974 to 1976 as it is in its coverage of the earlier period. Schulzinger, *Henry Kissinger*, covers the period after August 1974, as does Isaacson, *Kissinger*. Bill, *The Eagle and the Lion*, Quandt, *Peace Process* and *Decade of Decision*, and Speigel, *The Other Arab-Israeli Conflict*, all have good material on U.S. Middle East policy in these years. Franck and Wiesband, *Foreign Policy by Congress*, is very good on the Ford period.

of writers have addressed events in the middle of the seventies – former officials, journalists, and a few academics. Among the memoirs, one stands out – William G. Hyland's *Mortal Rivals*.[25] Hyland covers much of the same ground that Garthoff did in *Détente and Confrontation*, and Hyland explicitly offers a rebuttal. The core of *Mortal Rivals*, however, covers the Ford period, when Hyland was Kissinger's deputy on Soviet relations. He presents a full defense of the secretary of state's negotiations surrounding the 1974 Vladivostok framework and its aftermath. More sympathetic to Kissinger than Garthoff, Hyland also gives greater credit to the constraints of domestic politics as forcing the Ford administration to back away from arms control agreements.

Ford's own memoirs, *A Time to Heal*, also contain considerable raw material regarding foreign affairs.[26] They are as different from Nixon's *RN* as Ford is from Nixon. Ford does not whine, blame others, or think the world is against him. Like the earlier memoirs, however, Ford's are not especially useful for determining precisely what happened. Rather, they offer the president's reminiscences of how he felt during key episodes – for instance, during the decision to keep Kissinger, the cabinet shakeup of 1975, and the Ronald Reagan-Henry Jackson-Jimmy Carter challenge to détente during the campaign of 1975–76.

Two important foreign policy turning points of the Ford years have attracted the most attention from historians – the end of the war in Vietnam and the congressional investigation of abuses by the CIA. The end of Herring's *America's Longest War* has good material on the fall of Saigon. Again, limitations of available documents make this account less detailed than earlier parts of the book.[27] Fuller documentation about the end of the war comes from the congressional side, so scholarly analysis of the role of Congress in ending the war has been easier. Franck and Wiesband's *Foreign Policy by Congress* is the most useful source. P. Edward Haley, who served on the staff of the House Foreign Affairs

25 William G. Hyland, *Mortal Rivals: Superpower Relations from Nixon to Reagan* (New York, 1987).

26 Gerald R. Ford, *A Time to Heal: The Autobiography of Gerald R. Ford* (Garden City, 1979).

27 Hung and Schechter's *The Palace File* also discusses Washington's 1975 policy toward Vietnam. Journalist Arnold Isaacs, *Without Honor: Defeat in Vietnam and Cambodia* (Baltimore, 1983), concentrates on the end of the war in Vietnam.

Committee at the time of the decision to restrict aid to South Vietnam and Cambodia and later became a professor of political science, explained congressional actions in *Congress and the Fall of South Vietnam and Cambodia.*[28]

After the congressional revolution in foreign policy of 1973–74, newly assertive senators and representatives tried to control the CIA. They left an enormous record as they tried to create legislation preventing the abuses they had discovered. This documentation has helped historians to present a good picture of Congress's investigation, although the records of the executive branch's own investigation, conducted by Vice President Nelson Rockefeller, have not been released by the Ford Library. The best scholarly account of how Congress sought to control the CIA appears in Rhodri Jeffreys-Jones, *The CIA and American Democracy.*[29]

The election of 1976 represented in part a referendum on Kissinger, détente, and Washington's practice of realpolitik. Therefore, accounts of the campaign discuss the interplay between public attitudes and the conduct of foreign affairs. If the prize for the best title of a book about the Nixon years goes to Gerard Smith for *Doubletalk*, then historian Peter Carrol's *It Seemed Like Nothing Happened* wins hands down for the period 1969–1980.[30] Writing so quickly after the events, Carroll had little documentation, but he was a shrewd and sophisticated reader of newspapers and news magazines. His is the best account of the foreign affairs aspect of the 1976 election. Betty Glad's *Jimmy Carter: In Search of the Great White House* is a splendid psychological portrait of the 1976 winner. It is deeper, however, on his personality and his conduct in office than it is on the role foreign affairs played in the 1976 election.[31]

It appears on the surface that writing on events after 1976

28 P. Edward Haley, *Congress and the Fall of South Vietnam and Cambodia* (East Brunswick, 1982).

29 Rhodri Jeffreys-Jones, *The CIA and American Democracy* (New Haven, 1989). There is also relevant journalism and memoir literature on Congress and the CIA in 1974 and 1975. Like nearly all the literature on intelligence, it is longer on reminiscence than specific detail. See the memoir by William Colby with Peter Forbath, *Honorable Men: My Life in the CIA* (New York, 1978); journalist Thomas Powers, *The Man Who Kept the Secrets: Richard Helms and the CIA* (New York, 1981); and a memoir by a journalist, Daniel Schorr, *Clearing the Air* (Boston, 1978).

30 Peter N. Carroll, *It Seemed Like Nothing Happened: The Tragedy and Promise of America in the 1970s* (New York, 1982).

31 Betty Glad, *Jimmy Carter: In Search of the Great White House* (New York, 1980).

differs from the earlier period by having benefit of fewer *systematic* archival sources. A deeper look, however, offers another, more complex picture. Public interest in foreign affairs remained at a high level throughout the period – so many unexpected and often unwelcome things happened in both the Carter and Reagan years. A result of having the spotlight focused on the diplomacy of Carter and Reagan has been a substantial body of journalism, memoirs, and useful scholarship.

The best overview of the Carter administration's foreign policy comes from a historian, Gaddis Smith. His *Morality, Reason, and Power* has three advantages:[32] (1) The writing is clear and economical. (Students especially like it because it makes complicated stories comprehensible.) (2) It neatly summarizes the memoirs of the participants at the highest level.[33] (3) It places Carter in a long Wilsonian tradition, although the president himself seemed unaware of the historical roots of his actions.[34] Although it is

32 Gaddis Smith, *Morality, Reason, and Power: American Diplomacy in the Carter Years* (New York, 1986). See also Jerel A. Rosati, *The Carter Administration's Quest for Global Community: Beliefs and Their Impact on Behavior* (Columbia, SC, 1987), which contains very good accounts of the ideas of foreign relations held by officials in the Carter administration.

33 The memoirs of the president, secretary of state, national security adviser, presidential press secretary, and White House chief of staff are, respectively, Jimmy Carter, *Keeping Faith* (New York, 1982); Cyrus Vance, *Hard Choices: Critical Years in American Foreign Policy* (New York, 1983); Zbigniew Brzezinski, *Power and Principle: Memoirs of the National Security Adviser, 1977–1981* (New York, 1983); Jody Powell, *The Other Side of the Story* (New York, 1984); and Hamilton Jordan, *Crisis: The Last Year of the Carter Presidency* (New York, 1982). These books are uneven in their detail. The richest are Brzezinski's and Jordan's. Carter's is good on following the day-by-day negotiations at Camp David. All, of course, are good on explaining how the protagonist felt at a given moment.

34 For another historian's sophisticated reflections of the Wilsonian legacy and its impact on American foreign relations after 1965 see Lloyd Ambrosius, *Woodrow Wilson and the American Diplomatic Tradition: The Treaty Fight in Perspective* (New York, 1987), 290–98.

Although Carter may not have known a lot about the roots of his moralism, subordinates in his administration had read and thought a great deal about the background of recent American foreign policy. One of the most intriguing scholarly studies of the Carter administration is Richard A. Melanson, *Writing History and Making Policy: The Cold War, Vietnam, and Revisionism* (Lanham, MD, 1983). Melanson interviewed scores of Carter administration officials to discover if they had read the historical literature on the origins of the Cold War. Many had, and they told Melanson that they favored the moderate revisionism presented by Daniel Yergin in *Shattered Peace: The Origins of the Cold War and the National Security State*, 2d ed. (Boston, 1990). Somewhat discouraging for historians was that Melanson's informants told him that historical knowledge had little direct influence on their day-to-day actions. For policymakers, history was last week, not thirty years ago.

dangerous to predict the future, it may be safe to say that Smith's explanation of why Carter failed is likely to stand the test of time. The president used his status as an outsider to win the White House, but his lack of connections proved his undoing. He could not end the warfare between Secretary of State Cyrus Vance and national security adviser Zbigniew Brzezinski, and neither of them acquired the standing with the press that Kissinger did. Smith argues that "only a President with deep experience in foreign affairs and a grasp of issues equal or superior to that of such contending advisers could have prevented such crippling contradictions. Carter lacked such experience and grasp."[35]

Carter's administration began in hope and ended in public disillusionment – a good recipe for producing polemics explaining the change. The issues attracting the most attention from journalists, participants, and scholars were human rights, Central America, relations with the Soviets, and the Middle East (Camp David and Iran). Discussions of Carter's human rights policies often were more contentious than analytical. Neoconservative writers and political figures, led by Jeane Kirkpatrick, set the tone. Her 1979 *Commentary* article, "Dictators and Double Standards," set the tone for the Reagan challenge to Carter in 1980. Later, Kirkpatrick wrote the preface for a biased, scholarly study attacking Carter's human rights record, Joshua Muravchik's *The Uncertain Crusade*. Muravchik interviewed officials of the Carter administration extensively and made some use of the large congressional literature on human rights. He did not like what he found. On nearly every page he blasted the administration for naiveté and the supposed harm it did to old friends of the United States in authoritarian countries. There was one exception to the generally acrimonious accounts of Carter's human rights policy. Jerel Rosati's *The Carter Administration's Quest for Global Community* was generally sympathetic to the administration.[36]

Neoconservatives did not have the field to themselves, however. Lars Schoultz produced *Human Rights and United States Policy toward Latin America*, written at the very end of the Carter

35 Smith, *Morality, Reason, and Power*, 245–46.

36 Joshua Muravchik, *The Uncertain Crusade: Jimmy Carter and Dilemma of Human Rights Policy* (Washington, 1986); Jerel A. Rosati, *The Carter Administration's Quest for Global Community: Beliefs and Their Impact on Behavior* (Columbia, SC, 1987).

years. Although noting inconsistencies in Carter's human rights record, Schoultz, unlike the neoconservatives, believed that the promotion of human rights in generally friendly countries had merit. Finally, A. Glenn Mowrer compared Carter's and Reagan's human rights records in *Human Rights and American Foreign Policy*. His conclusion directly challenged the neoconservative polemics of the Reagan years: "in Carter there was a stronger commitment to human rights than in his successor."[37]

Carter's diplomacy left its most enduring legacy in Central America, especially in Panama, Nicaragua, and, to a lesser extent, El Salvador. Studies of events in these three countries provide some of the best accounts of the Carter years. The Panama Canal treaties provided a particularly rich field, primarily because of the deep congressional involvement. Congress customarily leaves more records more quickly than does the White House or State Department. The result has been several good studies by historians of the fate of the treaties: J. Michael Hogan, *The Panama Canal in American Politics*; Walter LaFeber, *The Panama Canal*; and, for the treaties' reception at home, George Moffett III, *The Limits of Victory: The Ratification of the Panama Canal Treaties*.[38]

The literature on Nicaragua includes a fine recent study by a historian, Gaddis Smith, *The Last Years of the Monroe Doctrine, 1945–1993*.[39] There are two excellent accounts by participants who became academics after leaving the Carter White House or the State Department. Robert A. Pastor served as a Central American specialist on Brzezinski's National Security Council staff and then became a professor of political science at Emory University. His *Condemned to Repetition: The United States and Nicaragua* covered events throughout the twentieth century but concentrated on the period from 1978 to 1984.[40] His discussion

37 Lars Schoultz, *Human Rights and United States Policy toward Latin America* (Princeton, 1981); A. Glenn Mowrer, *Human Rights and American Foreign Policy: The Carter and Reagan Experiences* (Washington, 1987), 154.

38 J. Michael Hogan, *The Panama Canal in American Politics* (Carbondale, IL, 1986); Walter LaFeber, *The Panama Canal: The Issue in Historical Perspective*, 3d ed. (New York, 1990); George Moffett III, *The Limits of Victory: The Ratification of the Panama Canal Treaties* (Ithaca, 1985).

39 Gaddis Smith, *The Last Years of the Monroe Doctrine, 1945–1993* (New York, 1994).

40 Robert A. Pastor, *Condemned to Repetition: The United States and Nicaragua* (Princeton, 1987).

of the last years of the Carter administration blends a fast paced day-by-day account of Washington's reaction to the fall of Somoza and the victory of the Sandinistas with analysis of how Brzezinski made decisions and prescriptions of how the U.S. government should react to revolutions. *Condemned to Repetition* is a model of the best sort of practitioner's scholarship. Its scope is smaller than Garthoff's *Détente and Confrontation*, but in its own way it is just as successful. Anthony Lake, disappointed veteran of the Kissinger NSC, returned to the State Department as director of the Policy Planning Staff in the Carter years. Now a political science professor at the University of Massachusetts, he provided his own memoir cum analysis of Washington's actions in the last days of the Nicaraguan dictatorship in *Somoza Falling*. A more modest book than Pastor's, *Somoza Falling* is well written and succeeds as few of the memoirs do in letting readers know how officials in the State Department relate to one another and to the White House.[41] El Salvador did not attract as much attention, because the issue did not penetrate until the end of the Carter administration. *New York Times* correspondent Raymond Bonner provided the best coverage, linking Washington's behavior from 1979 to 1980 to past actions in *Weakness and Deceit*.[42]

Carter came to office as both critic and defender of Kissinger's policy of détente with the Soviet Union. He opposed the Republicans' indifference to human rights abuses in the Soviet Union and accused them of not going far enough toward reducing nuclear armaments. On the other hand, he stressed that the general idea of reducing superpower tensions and the likelihood of nuclear war was good. The general accounts of the Carter administration and the memoirs of the top officials all devote considerable attention to the management of U.S.-Soviet relations. So does Garthoff in *Détente and Confrontation*. As I indicated

41 Anthony Lake, *Somoza Falling: The Nicaraguan Dilemma* (Boston, 1989). Another good work by a Carter State Department staff member, combining personal reminiscence and scholarly analysis, is David Newsom, *The Soviet Brigade in Cuba: A Study in Political Diplomacy* (Bloomington, 1987). Newsom details how the contrived issue of a Soviet brigade in Cuba undermined Carter's political standing in 1979. Carter could hardly afford it, as the SALT II treaty was under attack and the public resented the gasoline lines created by the Iranian Revolution.

42 Raymond A. Bonner, *Weakness and Deceit: U.S. Policy and El Salvador* (New York, 1984).

earlier, Garthoff's discussion of events after 1976 is not the masterpiece that his treatment of the preceding seven years is. But it is still extremely good. It weaves together domestic politics, relations with the Soviets, relations with China, and events in Afghanistan to present a compelling picture of an administration out of its depths in dealing with the complexity of modern global politics.

Carter's difficulties with arms control also became the subject of the first of a superb series of accounts by a journalist writing on U.S.-Soviet relations after 1976. Strobe Talbott, *Time*'s Moscow correspondent, had excellent sources among the U.S. delegation, and he put them to good use in *Endgame: The Inside Story of SALT II*. Here was a case where the ad writer's cliché "inside story" told the truth. Ten years later, Talbott wrote *The Master of the Game: Paul Nitze and the Nuclear Peace*, a biography of one of the bitterest critics of SALT II. *The Master of the Game* concentrates on Nitze's work in government in the Truman, Nixon, and, especially, Reagan administrations, but Talbott's brief discussion of Nitze's opposition to SALT II is the best account of the way old arms controllers split over Carter's conduct of détente with the Soviets.[43]

Carter's greatest success and his ultimate failure came in two parts of the Middle East: his efforts at arranging peace between Israel and Egypt and the catastrophe of the Iranian hostage crisis. One of the happiest moments in Carter's life after his defeat for reelection in 1980 was the release of a *New York Times*-CBS News poll in April 1985 showing that the American public considered Carter's handling of the 1978 Camp David negotiations and his brokering of the 1979 Egyptian-Israeli treaty to be the greatest foreign policy successes of the previous ten years.[44] The general studies of the Carter administration and the memoirs of the top officials all treat Camp David in detail.The best account is another of the hybrid memoir-analyses by an important technical

43 Strobe Talbott, *Master of the Game: Paul Nitze and the Nuclear Peace* (New York, 1989), 145–61. Another richly detailed but more critical work on Nitze is David Callahan, *Dangerous Capabilities: Paul Nitze and the Cold War* (New York, 1990), 350–411.

44 *New York Times*, 23 April 1985.

expert on the U.S. side. William Quandt's *Camp David* has all the strengths of Robert Pastor's similar study of the Carter administration's less successful diplomacy regarding Nicaragua, *Condemned to Repetition.*[45] Quandt's *Camp David* is a more richly detailed study than his earlier *Decade of Decision.* The focus of *Camp David* is two, not ten years. Also, the nature of Middle East diplomacy in the Carter administration differed from that of the Nixon years when Kissinger operated independently of and often at odds with the State Department. When it came to the Arab-Israeli dispute (although not other important aspects of U.S. foreign policy), the president kept control. From Quandt's vantage point in the Carter NSC, he could see more precisely what went on than was possible in writing about the Johnson, Nixon, and Ford administrations' handling of the Arab-Israeli conflict.

The Iranian hostage crisis drove Carter from office and did more than anything else to turn American public opinion toward the crude chauvinism of the first years of the Reagan administration. Naturally, more has been written on Iranian-American relations and the hostage crisis than on anything else in late 1970s. The quality of the discussion covers the widest spectrum, from excellent to dreadful. The very best are two books written by men at odds with each other, Gary Sick *All Fall Down: America's Tragic Encounter with Iran*, and James Bill, *The Eagle and the Lion.*[46]

Sick, a naval officer, served as the Iran expert on the National Security Council during the revolution and hostage crisis. His defense of the White House's actions during the hostage crisis is dramatic, gripping, critical of others, but calm. The best parts of *All Fall Down* trace NSC-State Department rivalry from 1978 to the summer of 1979 and explain in detail the negotiations from October 1980 to January 1981 leading to the hostages' release.[47] Bill, an academic Iran specialist long critical of the shah, had good contacts among the opposition. As things fell apart in 1979 and 1980, the State Department occasionally asked Bill's advice, but, as he makes clear, policymakers did not understand what he

45 William Quandt, *Camp David: Peacemaking and Politics* (Washington, 1988).
46 Gary Sick, *All Fall Down: America's Tragic Encounter with Iran* (New York, 1986).
47 Ibid., 50–204.

had to say and paid little attention to him when they did. Bill's book is a history of American-Iranian relations from 1941 to the unfolding of the Reagan administration's arms for hostages deal in 1986 and 1987. It does not deal with the hostage crisis in depth, but its discussion of the earlier American response to the revolution in 1977 and 1978 is superb. Bill also includes a fascinating portrait of the Iranian connection in America, including Henry Kissinger, David Rockefeller, Jacob Javits (D-NY), and about a dozen lesser journalists, military officers, and politicians.[48] Only someone personally familiar with these personalities could have written this portrait. Bill's analysis violates the general rule that distance and availability of documents improve the writing of foreign policy studies. Someone writing later, lacking Bill's familiarity with the culture of the Iran lobby, probably could not have written this valuable and enduring account.[49]

The foreign policy of the Reagan administration will produce an abundance of literature as time offers perspective and the documents open. A rich flow of memoirs and journalists' accounts has already been supplemented by some important scholarship. There are several reasons why historians are bound to devote considerable attention to the Reagan period: It lasted eight years, which has not happened since the 1950s. The world in 1989 was radically different from the one of 1980. Reagan changed his mind on the Soviets in ways that no one could have predicted. The

48 Bill, *The Eagle and the Lion*, 319–78.

49 Those looking for tight monographs to assign undergraduates probably will receive a more favorable response from Sick's *All Fall Down*, which students consider sprightly and engaging, than from Bill's *The Eagle and the Lion*, which they consider confusing and impenetrable. A pity, as Bill's analysis actually provides illuminating insights for understanding American behavior toward revolutions in Asia and Latin America, as well as Iran, in the entire post-World War II period. Students also like another of the good studies of Iran, Barry Rubin, *Paved with Good Intentions: The American Experience and Iran* (New York, 1980).

The least successful study of the hostage crisis is Michael Ledeen and William Lewis, *Debacle: The American Failure in Iran* (New York, 1981). *Debacle* is a neoconservative tract designed to show that the Carter administration's naiveté led to jettisoning the shah and the humiliation of the hostage crisis. Ledeen later became an important go-between in the Reagan administration's effort to sell arms to Iran.

Sick's *All Fall Down* is only one of the scholarly studies by participants. He joined six other Carter officials, led by Deputy Secretary of State Warren Christopher, who wrote chapters in a good, detailed account of the hostage crisis and the efforts to win their release: Warren Christopher et al., *American Hostages in Iran: The Conduct of a Crisis* (New Haven, 1985).

Iran-contra affair, "a neat idea" in Oliver North's words, astonished everyone and infuriated most people. The squabbling within the administration surpassed anything that happened in the preceding fifteen years.

These factors already have combined to produce a lode of memoirs and journalism that can be mined for years. The memoirs of the Reagan period contain marvelous nuggets showing how deeply divided the president's advisers were and how little he seemed to care about what went on. Casper Weinberger, secretary of defense for the first seven years of the Reagan administration, continued his bureaucratic battles in his memoir *Fighting for Peace*. George Shultz, Reagan's secretary of state from 1982 until the end of the administration, wrote a magisterial and elaborately detailed memoir, *Turmoil and Triumph*. It lacked the drama and personal vignettes that enlivened Kissinger's earlier memoirs, but it provided an almost day by day reckoning of the turn away from confrontation toward the end of the Cold War.[50]

Sensational stories in memoirs had been the norm since Watergate, and the Reagan people maintain the tradition. Reagan's first secretary of state, Alexander Haig, published *Caveat: Realism, Reagan, and Foreign Policy* in 1984, at nearly the height of the president's popularity.[51] Haig's account of how Reagan really did not seem interested in governing and was insulated from reality by a palace guard of California smoothies made little impact. This, after all, was Al "I am in control" Haig complaining. Later, when the Iran-contra scandal broke, Haig's criticism became the standard view of the Reagan approach to foreign affairs.

That view was strengthened in a memoir by Constantine Menges, *Inside the National Security Council*.[52] Menges held a position in the Reagan NSC similar to the ones occupied in the

50 Casper Weinberger, *Fighting for Peace: Seven Critical Years in the Pentagon* (New York, 1990, 1991); George P. Shultz, *Turmoil and Triumph: My Years as Secretary of State* (New York, 1993).

51 Alexander Haig, *Caveat: Realism, Reagan and Foreign Policy* (New York, 1984). A highly critical study of Haig by Roger Morris, *Haig: The General's Progress* (New York, 1981), was completed just as Haig took office as secretary of state and concentrates on his career in the Nixon administration as Kissinger's deputy at the National Security Council and later as White House chief of staff.

52 Constantine Menges, *Inside the National Security Council: The True Story of the Making and Unmaking of Reagan's Foreign Policy* (New York, 1988).

Carter administration by Robert Pastor and Gary Sick. But he is much more of a polemicist than the two Carter officials; indeed, the difference in style between *Inside the National Security Council* and *Condemned to Repetition* or *All Fall Down* is emblematic of the differences between the Carter and Reagan administrations. The former are quiet, moderate, maybe boring; the latter strident, combative, apparently naive. Menges announces his point at the beginning of the preface: "I encountered a small but influential group of foreign policy officials who believed they knew better than the president. . . . The officials constituted what I came to view as a subculture of manipulation and deception within the foreign policy institutions of the executive branch."[53]

Why Menges should have been so surprised to have found a snakepit of whispering conspiracy in the White House basement is not clear. He probably believed Reagan's 1980 campaign pledge to make American foreign policy "speak with a single voice." As a foreign affairs specialist, he should have known that such unanimity has not occurred for over fifty years, and is impossible, given the kind of global foreign policy the United States has conducted since the Second World War. As a Reagan partisan, however, he thought that simple truths should play as well in Washington as they did with the electorate in 1980 and 1984. Whatever the reason for Menges's expectations of harmonious consistency among the president's men and women, the result is a book seething with contempt for and filled with unfavorable anecdotes about Robert McFarlane, Oliver North, George Shultz, and Casper Weinberger.

Internal bickering within the Reagan administration's foreign policy apparatus is also the theme of the best of the journalism about its foreign policy. Don Oberdorfer, the diplomatic correspondent for the *Washington Post*, chronicled the vast changes in U.S.-Soviet relations at the end of the Cold War in *The Turn*. Strobe Talbott continued his series of good books with *Deadly Gambits*. In this account, Talbott, like Garthoff writing at approximately the same time, faulted the Reagan administration's arms control efforts as a hodgepodge of contradictory, even silly, proposals, designed to score debaters' points, not reduce tensions.

53 Ibid., 11.

He stressed the same point in *The Russians and Reagan*. The world changed abruptly after Reagan decided to run for reelection as a man who could calm fears and the rise of Mikhail Gorbachev in 1985. Talbott's later books, *The Master of the Game* and *Reagan and Gorbachev*, explain the shift.[54]

Iran-contra nearly undid Reagan. It probably would have, had it not been for the improvement in U.S.-Soviet relations and congressional resistance to bringing down another president. Reagan would have been the fifth in a row to leave office murdered or disgraced, and many thoughtful politicians believed that would have been too much for the public to bear. Iran-contra also opened a window into the intrigues of the National Security Council and the CIA. The report of the Tower Commission shed some light and the joint House-Senate Committee provided more. The historian Gaddis Smith surveys the entire Reagan policy toward Central America in *The Last Years of the Monroe Doctrine*.[55]

This wealth of documentation and testimony regarding Iran-contra provided major sources for two of the most illuminating journalistic accounts of the tensions within the Reagan White House: Jane Mayer and Doyle McManus, *Landslide*; and Bob Schieffer and Gary Paul Gates, *The Acting President*.[56] In addition to being the two best summaries of the Iran-contra affair, both

54 Callahan, *Dangerous Capabilities*, 415–504; Don Oberdorfer, *The Turn: From the Cold War to a New Era, the United States and the Soviet Union, 1983–1990* (New York, 1990); Strobe Talbott, *Deadly Gambits: The Reagan Administration and the Stalemate of Nuclear Arms Control* (New York, 1984); idem, *The Russians and Reagan* (New York, 1984); idem, *Reagan and Gorbachev* (New York, 1987).

55 *The Tower Commission Report: The Full Text of the President's Special Review Board* (New York, 1987). U.S. House of Representatives, Select Committee to Investigate Covert Arms Transactions with Iran, and U.S. Senate, Select Committee on Secret Military Assistance to Iran and the Nicaraguan Opposition, *Report of the Congressional Committees Investigating the Iran-Contra Affair*. House Report No. 100–433, Senate Report No. 100–216. 100th Cong., 1st sess. 1987. Smith, *The Last Years of the Monroe Doctrine*.

Serious questions remain about the depth of the congressional investigation of Iran-contra. Seymour Hersh is currently writing about Congress's inquiry into Iran-contra and argues that the leadership of the committees purposely resisted aggressive pursuit of evidence that might tie Reagan too closely to the illegal diversion of profits from the arms sales to the contras. To have done so, Hersh argues, would have raised the specter of impeachment. That, they feared, would have devastated the public's recovering, but still fragile, faith in governmental institutions. See also National Security Archive, *Iran-Contra: The Complete Chronology* (Washington, 1988).

56 Jane Mayer and Doyle McManus, *Landslide: The Unmaking of the President, 1984 1988* (Boston, 1988); Bob Schieffer and Gary Paul Gates, *The Acting President* (New York, 1989).

books appeared after memoirs by such important Reagan administration officials as Michael Deaver, Larry Speakes, and Donald Regan.[57] Both use them extensively; *Landslide* is footnoted, *The Acting President* is not.

The first scholarly account of the Reagan administration's foreign policy has now appeared. To no one's surpise, it was written by the indefatigable Raymond Garthoff. In *The Great Transition: American-Soviet Relations and the End of the Cold War*, Garthoff interviews the key players on the Soviet and American sides and makes use of the memoirs and journalistic accounts to present a compelling account of the end of the Cold War. Garthoff credits Gorbachev more than Reagan with recognizing the vast changes in international relations from the mid-sixties to the mid-eighties. In that sense, Gorbachev is the main player and Reagan the reactor in Garthoff's account. Garthoff quarrels with advocates of the Reagan defense buildup who claim that it bankrupted the Soviet Union. Rather, he argues that the true accomplishment of the Reagan administration was its ability to grasp how profoundly Gorbachev had changed the Soviet Union.[58]

The end of the Cold War is bound to become a central research area of analysts over the next generation. Several analytical and journalistic accounts have already appeared on the events from 1989 to 1992. Twenty-two prominent historians and political scientists from the United States and Europe offered a preliminary assessment of the meaning and implications of the end of the Cold War in a volume entitled *The End of the Cold War*

57 Michael Deaver, *Behind the Scenes* (New York, 1987); Donald Regan, *For the Record* (San Diego, 1988); Larry Speakes, *Speaking Out* (New York, 1988). These memoirs follow the familiar pattern, going back to the Nixon administration. They are sharp, contentious, and point up differences of opinion. They do not present day-by-day accounts, but they are very good on offering the feelings of participants. The other memoir regarding foreign affairs to have appeared so far from a Reagan administration official in Casper Weinberger, *Fighting for Peace: Seven Critical Years at the Pentagon* (New York, 1990). Weinberger follows the discreet approach of Cyrus Vance, so his memoir lacks the bite of the others.

Landslide also makes use of two good journalists' accounts of covert operations, Bob Woodward, *Veil: The Secret Wars of the CIA* (New York, 1987); and David Martin and John Walcott, *Best Laid Plans* (New York, 1988). Like many books about espionage and counterterrorism, the sources for *Veil* and *Best Laid Plans* combine press reports and interviews. They often ring true; they almost always are difficult to verify.

58 Raymond L. Garthoff, *The Great Transition: American-Soviet Relations and the End of the Cold War* (Washington, 1994).

edited by Michael J. Hogan.[59] In addition to the works by Garthoff and Oberdorfer mentioned above, Michael Beschloss and Strobe Talbott have written *At the Highest Levels*, an inside account based on interviews with many participants of the foreign policy apparatus of the administration of George Bush.[60]

The flood of memoirs and first cuts at assessing the Bush administration's foreign policy is bound to appear in the next few years. While Bush was president it appeared as if the brief war between a U.S.-led alliance and Iraq stood as the centerpiece of his foreign policy. As time goes on, the Persian Gulf War may recede in importance. Since that short engagement riveted public attention for months, it became the subject of two worthwhile accounts: the editors of *U.S. News and World Report*, *Triumph without Victory*; and Lawrence Freedman and Efraim Karsh, *The Gulf Conflict, 1990–1991*.[61] Both books outline the issues involved in the war with Iraq and are filled with vignettes of the internal dynamics of policymaking within the Bush administration.

As future historians continue to write about the foreign policy of recent administrations, they probably will find the minutiae of the rivalries of the president's men of secondary interest to some of the deeper changes in the U.S. global economic position that were hastened during the 1980s. A serious debate began in the late 1980s and continues to the present among historians and other academic foreign affairs specialists about whether the United States had entered a period of relative decline after 1960. Advocates of the relative decline school of thought include historian Paul Kennedy and political economist David Calleo. Kennedy argues in the best selling *Rise and Fall of the Great Powers* that the United States approached the sort of insolvency anticipated with unhappiness by Walter Lippmann in the 1940s.[62]

59 Michael J. Hogan, ed., *The End of the Cold War: Its Meaning and Implications* (New York, 1992).

60 Michael Beschloss and Strobe Talbott, *At the Highest levels: The Inside Story of the End of the Cold War* (Boston, 1993).

61 The editors of *U.S. News and World Report*, *Triumph without Victory* (New York, 1992); Lawrence Freedman and Efraim Karsh, *The Gulf Conflict, 1990–1991* (New York, 1992).

62 Paul Kennedy, *The Rise and Fall of the Great Powers: Economic Change and Military Conflict from 1500 to 2000* (New York, 1987); David P. Calleo, *Beyond American Hegemony* (New York, 1987); Walter Lippmann, *American Foreign Policy: Shield of the Republic* (Boston, 1943), 9.

Kennedy believes that an appropriate adjustment of the United States's commitments to its resources might reverse the trend, but Calleo appears less sanguine.[63] Joseph Nye, Jr., a political scientist who served in the Carter administration, presented a rebuttal to the believers in the relative decline of the United States in *Bound to Lead*.[64] Like Kennedy and Calleo, Nye opposed the profligacy of the Reagan administration, its extraordinary military buildup, and its concentration on military competition to the exclusion of more important economic or social concerns. He believed, however, that its jingoism was transient. With the amazing changes in Eastern Europe and the end of the Cold War, he predicted that the United States could easily reduce the military burden that had led to the Lippmann gap. If it did so, its position of leadership would probably continue.

The works of Kennedy, Calleo, and Nye represented an important shift from the kind of writing that dominated the study of U.S. foreign relations from 1969 to 1987. It is impossible to predict that these grander, economic-cultural-social studies will become the model for the future, but some evidence is there. In *America in the Age of Soviet Power, 1945–1991*, the final volume of the Cambridge History of American Foreign Relations, Warren I. Cohen observes that the most lasting legacy of the Cold War is likely to be cultural, not political: "the McDonald's, Pizza Huts, and Kentucky Fried Chicken franchises found all over the world. . . . More significant will be the computers and fax machines that facilitate global interdependence."[65]

For twenty turbulent years, American writers concentrated on the personal behavior of their leaders. Writers based their work on the premise that if we could understand where leaders succeeded and where they went wrong, we could understand how foreign policy worked and failed. Historians of U.S. foreign relations

63 See also Samuel P. Huntington, "Coping with the Lippmann Gap," *Foreign Affairs* 66 (1987/88): 453–77. A good discussion of the relative decline school appears in Peter Schmeisser, "Taking Stock: Is America in Decline?" *New York Times Magazine*, 17 April 1988.

64 Joseph Nye, Jr., *Bound to Lead: The Changing Nature of American Power* (New York, 1990).

65 Warren I. Cohen, *The Cambridge History of American Foreign Relations*, vol. 4, *America in the Age of Soviet Power, 1945–1991* (New York, 1993), 259.

have recently engaged in a major reevaluation of the direction of their writing as they contemplate the apparent isolation and marginalization of their subdiscipline among professional historians. Far from an indicator that their field is moribund, their anxiety over the significance and theoretical potency of their writings have been signs of a healthy lack of complacency and desire to make their work speak to other historians' concerns. In one of the fifteen articles appearing in symposiums on the current state of work on the history of American foreign relations, Robert J. McMahon called upon diplomatic historians to join with others to "provide a fresh synthesis for American history." McMahon urged the integration of the diplomatic historians' study of the ways in which power is exercised into the larger story of American history.[66] Certainly, interpretive works like Kennedy's, Calleo's, Nye's, and Cohen's fit this category.

It is also likely, however, that diplomatic historians will heed Richard H. Immerman's "plea for pluralism" in which he calls on them to refrain from the "obsessive introspection and self-flagellation" that has characterized their recent concerns over the state of their subdiscipline.[67] There is so much more to learn about the recent past as new documentary evidence becomes available and the outlines of the end of the Cold War era become clearer. Time will permit the creation of histories that assess the entire twenty-five-year period from 1969 to 1994. Did earlier events presage the extraordinary changes of the period 1989–1991?[68] Nineteen eighty-nine is likely to be recorded as one of the most significant turning points in modern history. Virtually no one predicted the changes in Europe and China. How the world arrived at that point is an obvious task for future research. Now may also be the time to step back and look for deeper economic and cultural trends that set the boundaries in which officials make their decisions and the long-term effects of such actions.

66 Robert J. McMahon, "The Study of American Foreign Relations: National History or International History?" in Hogan and Paterson, eds., *Explaining the History of American Foreign Relations*, 23.

67 Richard H. Immerman, "The History of U.S. Foreign Policy: A Plea for Pluralism," *Diplomatic History* 14 (Fall 1990): 575, 582.

68 Garthoff's *The Great Transition* and Oberdorfer's *The Turn* begin this search for discovering the antecedents of the momentous changes of 1989–1991.

15

An Emerging Synthesis? U.S.–Latin American Relations since the Second World War

MARK T. GILDERHUS

Though often overshadowed by other topics in the course of the Cold War, the subject of U.S. relations with Latin America since the Second World War has retained a compelling interest. Since the publication in 1981 of Richard V. Salisbury's historiographical essay, "Good Neighbors? The United States and Latin America in the Twentieth Century," a wide assortment of studies have advanced the thresholds of knowledge and understanding in this field. This body of scholarship to an extent still manifests one of the attributes identified by Salisbury as a characteristic – that is, an eclecticism of approach and interpretation.[1] Dominated by the monograph, narrowly focused, and largely dependent upon the records of the United States, the literature shows the effects of fragmentation. No commonly conceived synthesis is presently in ascendance. Nevertheless, the persistent influence of scholarly investigations characterized by Salisbury as revisionist suggests the possibility of constructing integrative accounts on the basis of radical perspectives. At the same time, countervailing impulses also exist, especially in those works seeking to appraise current trends and circumstances, emphasizing the growth of democratization and free enterprise practices.

This essay assesses the principal historiographical tendencies in the study of U.S.-Latin American relations in recent times. Though admittedly selective, my choice of titles includes studies in English by historians and some by social scientists, journalists, and

1 Richard V. Salisbury, "Good Neighbors? The United States and Latin America in the Twentieth Century," in *American Foreign Relations: A Historiographical Review,* ed. Gerald K. Haines and J. Samuel Walker (Westport, 1981), 311–34.

diplomats. When confronted with the outpouring of books and articles on Central America in the 1980s, I decided to exclude most commentaries on contemporary events in order to focus on publications of more enduring consequence by and for historians.

Scholars incessantly dispute the means by which historians can best understand the goals and ambitions of the United States vis-à-vis Latin America. Over the years, the definitions of national purpose have retained a remarkable consistency. They include affirmations of support for republicanism and independence, the animation of capitalist enterprise, and the constriction of European presences. Nevertheless, the ambiguity of relationships among these aims has resulted in interpretive complexities and profound differences over the roles of ideology, economics, and security as determinants in the formulation of foreign policy. An article published by Abraham F. Lowenthal in 1973 illustrates the range of discussion in this field. Lowenthal created a useful typology of U.S.-Latin American relations, which he applied to the Alliance for Progress, but which is applicable also to other issues. He presented three conceptual approaches – the "liberal," the "radical," and the "bureaucratic" – and demonstrated that each entailed very different forms of understanding and evaluation.[2]

2 Abraham F. Lowenthal, "United States Policy toward Latin America: 'Liberal,' 'Radical,' and 'Bureaucratic' Perspectives," *Latin American Research Review* 8 (Fall 1973): 3–25. For additional historiographical commentary see Jorge I. Domínguez, "Consensus and Divergence: The State of the Literature of Inter-American Relations in the 1970s," *Latin American Research Review* 13:1 (1978): 87–126; Jules R. Benjamin, "The Framework of U.S. Relations with Latin America in the Twentieth Century: An Interpretive Essay," *Diplomatic History* ll (Spring 1987): 91–112; Stephen G. Rabe, "Marching Ahead (Slowly): The Historiography of Inter-American Relations," ibid. 13 (Summer 1989): 297–316; Louis A. Pérez, Jr., "Intervention, Hegemony, and Dependency: The United States in the circum-Caribbean, 1898–1980," *Pacific Historical Review* 51 (May 1982): 165–94; and David M. Pletcher, "Caribbean 'Empire,' Planned and Improvised," *Diplomatic History* 14 (Summer 1990): 447–59. Two new survey texts by political scientists address the subject: Michael J. Kryzanek, *U.S.-Latin American Relations* (New York, 1985); and Harold Molineu, *U.S. Policy toward Latin America: From Regionalism to Globalism* (Boulder, 1986). Frank Niess, a German Marxist, offers an unsophisticated, lop-sided economic interpretation in *A Hemisphere to Itself: A History of US-Latin American Relations,* trans. Harry Drost (London, 1990). Editors Ronald H. Chilcote and Joel C. Edelstein have provided a useful introduction to "dependency theory" in *Latin America: Capitalist and Socialist Perspectives of Development and Underdevelopment* (Boulder, 1986). See also Louis A. Pérez, "Dependency," *Journal of American History* 77 (June 1990): 133–42. Lester D. Langley's *America and the Americas: The United States in the Western Hemisphere*

For proponents of the liberal perspective, the distinguishing feature of U.S. relations with Latin America has been "an essential compatibility of interest" among the nations involved. This conception held special allure for historians of an earlier generation. Arthur P. Whitaker described it as "the western hemisphere idea" and asserted that the nations of North and South America comprised a unique community fashioned from the shared experience of republican rebellions in the New World against the decadent monarchies of the Old. Perhaps the most influential example of this liberal perspective, Samuel Flagg Bemis's *The Latin American Policy of the United States, An Historical Analysis,* appeaed in print in 1943 in the middle of the Second World War. Bemis saw the Axis threat as "the supreme test of the Latin American policy of the United States" and rejoiced in "the solidarity of the American republics" against the enemy. The wartime accord between North and South America, Bemis believed, brought about the culmination of years of effort; it was "built upon the basis of continental security, independence, and republican solidarity" and was made possible by the wisdom of the Good Neighbor Policy in the 1930s. Viewed by Bemis as a correction of historical errors in dealings with Latin America, for example, the various interventions and the protectorates established

(Athens, GA, 1989) employs a new version of the idealist/realist distinction in the inaugural volume of a new series from the University of Georgia Press.

According to editorial design, the books in this series will go beyond conventional diplomatic history and incorporate cultural dimensions. Other volumes now in print include: William F. Sater, *Chile and the United States: Empires in Conflict* (1990); Louis A. Pérez, Jr., *Cuba and the United States: Ties of Singular Intimacy* (1990); Thomas J. Leonard, *Central America and the United States, The Search for Stability* (1991); Stephen J. Randall, *Colombia and the United States: Hegemony and Interdependence* (1992); W. Dirk Raat, *Mexico and the United States: Ambivalent Vistas* (1992); Brenda Gayle Plummer, *Haiti and the United States: The Psychological Moment* (1992); and John Herd Thompson and Stephen J. Randall, *Canada and the United States: Ambivalent Allies* (1994). Other useful, general works include F. Parkinson, *Latin America, The Cold War and the World Powers, 1945–1973* (Beverly Hills, 1974), now somewhat dated; Josefina Zoraida Vázquez and Lorenzo Meyer, *The United States and Mexico* (Chicago, 1985), a view by two distinguished Mexican scholars; amd the volumes making up Twayne Publishers International History Series, edited by Akira Iriye. They include Joseph S. Tulchin, *Argentina and the United States: A Conflicted Relationship* (Boston, 1990); Lester D. Langley, *Mexico and the United States: The Fragile Relationship* (Boston, 1991); John H. Coatsworth, *Central America and the United States: The Clients and the Colossus* (New York, 1994); and Robert Freeman Smith, *The Caribbean World and the United States: Mixing Rum and Coca-Cola* (New York, 1994).

in and around the Caribbean after the war with Spain, the innovations under Franklin D. Roosevelt mitigated the effects of past "imperialism," which in any case Bemis described as "comparatively mild . . . [and] essentially . . . protective" of Latin America. Bemis discounted economic explanations of overseas expansion and in fact entitled one of his chapters "The Myth of Economic Imperialism." For such reasons he became a special target for revisionist historians.[3]

For proponents of the radical perspective, the distinguishing feature of U.S. relations with Latin America has been the prevalence of conflict and exploitation, viewed in Lowenthal's words as the consequence of "the expansive interests of North American capitalism." Often described as insatiable and aggressive in the quest for markets and materials, the United States in this analysis has functioned as an ambitious hegemon with imperial aims, seeking not so much fraternity and cooperation with Latin American nations as dominion and advantage over them. As set forth by William Appleman Williams and others associated with the so-called Wisconsin school, notably Walter LaFeber and Lloyd C. Gardner, the essential themes emphasize the informality of the U.S. empire and the importance of the Open Door policy in accounting for it. Though perhaps more formal in the Western Hemisphere than elsewhere, the result of the proximity and overwhelming power of the United States, the North American imperial system nevertheless aspired not so much to exercise direct political control over Latin American territory as to assure easy access for purposes of trade and investment.[4]

For proponents of the bureaucratic perspective, the distinguishing feature of U.S. relations with Latin America has been the interplay of governmental mechanisms of decision making. Presented by Lowenthal as an alternative to the other two models,

3 Lowenthal, "United States Policy," 6; Arthur P. Whitaker, *The Western Hemisphere Idea: Its Rise and Decline* (Ithaca, 1954); Samuel F. Bemis, *The Latin American Policy of the United States* (New York, 1943), 368, 372, 385, chap. 20. Gordon Connell-Smith, *The United States and Latin America, An Historical Analysis of Inter-American Relations* (New York, 1975), is an extended criticism of Bemis.

4 Lowenthal, "United States Policy," 10; William Appleman Williams, *The Tragedy of American Diplomacy*, 2d rev. ed. (New York, 1972); Lloyd C. Gardner, *Economic Aspects of New Deal Diplomacy* (Madison, 1964); and Walter LaFeber, *The New Empire: An Interpretation of American Expansion, 1860–1898* (Ithaca, 1963).

this analytical approach has appeared in books by R. Harrison Wagner, Graham T. Allison, Morton Halperin, and Howard J. Wiarda. These books focus on the behavior of bureaucrats in the United States and explain foreign policy "not as a choice of a single, rational actor" but as "the product of overlapping and interlocking bargaining processes" among "both intragovernmental and extra-governmental actors." Such works concentrate upon the impact of "events and procedures internal to governmental organization . . . often minimized (or overlooked) by liberal and radical observers." As Lowenthal explained in his book on the Dominican intervention in 1965, "Foreign policy actions are often best understood as the outputs of established organizational procedures" and as reflections of "the distinct perspectives of different government agencies."[5]

The bureaucratic model, a source of captivation for many social scientists and government officials, has appealed less to historians, especially those with a radical perspective. For them, the wrangling between government agencies has little meaning because it occurs within the context of prevailing capitalist assumptions and addresses merely tactical concerns. Gabriel Kolko has declared his disbelief in the notion "that bureaucratic politics . . . really alters the substance of basic national policies," because they are rooted not in "capricious or arbitrary bureaucratic processes" but in "the fundamental issues of power, interests, and purposes that underlay all U.S. government decisions."[6]

For historians, these issues of power, interests, and purposes have weighed heavily upon the study of U.S. relations with Latin America since the Second World War. Much of the historiography of this period has elucidated the legacies of the Good Neighbor

5 Lowenthal, "United States Policy," 14–15; idem, *The Dominican Intervention* (Cambridge, MA, 1972), 147; R. Harrison Wagner, *United States Policy toward Latin America: A Study in Domestic and International Politics* (Stanford, 1970); Graham T. Allison, *The Essence of Decision: Explaining the Cuban Missile Crisis* (Boston, 1971); and Morton Halperin, *Bureaucratic Politics and Foreign Policy* (Washington, 1974). Using the bureaucratic perspective, Howard J. Wiarda, a political scientist, presents an insider's point of view from the American Enterprise Institute in *American Foreign Policy toward Latin America in the 80s and 90s: Issues and Controversies from Reagan to Bush* (New York, 1992).

6 Gabriel Kolko, *Confronting the Third World: United States Foreign Policy, 1945–1980* (New York, 1988), xii.

Policy and the intrusions of the Cold War. On the whole, the bureaucratic perspective has had only a selective impact upon this scholarship. The liberal approach, though still in evidence, commands diminishing influence, mainly because of the difficulty in showing that compatible interests have encouraged cooperation between nations north and south. In contrast, radical critiques have established a basis for a revisionist synthesis. They emphasize the disparities and divergences of purpose and capability among the countries of the Western Hemisphere and point to the significance of asymmetries in the distribution of wealth, power, and prestige. Moreover, they usually assume a critical stance toward the United States. As suggested by this body of literature under review, the central themes devolve upon questions of economic development; political reform and revolution in Latin America; the responses of the United States to events in Latin America; and the connections between U.S. actions and the Cold War.

The impact and meaning of the Good Neighbor Policy has retained an essential importance in postwar historiography. When the Roosevelt administration advanced a measure of accommodation with Latin Americans in the 1930s by giving up the Caribbean protectorates and the self-proclaimed right of intervention, the leaders dissipated much of the ill will accumulated in earlier times and facilitated a high level of hemispheric solidarity during the Second World War. For Bemis, this change emanated from a well-meaning desire to liquidate the remnants of past imperialism and to embrace the Latin American nations as juridical equals. Bemis portrayed the wartime partnership as a manifestation of common interest. Indeed, the near unanimity among the nations – in Bemis's words, "One for All and Almost All for One" – marked a principal Pan American achievement.[7]

More recent investigations of the economic ramifications of this change have compelled a modification of Bemis's view. Following Lloyd C. Gardner's lead, various scholars have scrutinized

7 Bemis, *The Latin American Policy*, chap. 22. Other books emphasizing the political and ideological bases of policy include Bryce Wood, *The Making of the Good Neighbor Policy* (New York, 1961); and Irwin F. Gellman, *Good Neighbor Diplomacy: United States Policies in Latin America, 1933–1945* (Baltimore, 1979).

the Good Neighbor Policy as a subtle vehicle of economic self-interest. In their view, by endorsing the principle of nonintervention, the United States paid the political price for attaining more favorable terms of trade and investment. Conceived primarily as a means of fighting the Great Depression at home, the various programs of the Good Neighbor Policy, such as the reciprocal trade agreements and the Export-Import Bank, encouraged economic expansion in Latin America and precipitated intense competition with British and German interests, especially in the countries of the southern cone. *The Limits of Hegemony,* by Michael L. Francis, a political scientist, and *Struggle for Hegemony in South America,* by Gary Frank, a historian, describe U.S. relations with Argentina, Brazil, and Chile during the Second World War as case studies in the pursuit of hegemony. Though limited in capability, as indicated by Francis's title, the Roosevelt policy nevertheless contained powerful economic components and compelled some measure of compliance on the part of Latin American nations.[8]

Michael Grow's *The Good Neighbor Policy and Authoritarianism in Paraguay* explores similar themes in U.S. relations with Paraguay and explicitly evaluates the utility of the liberal and radical approaches. While characterizing the leaders of the Roosevelt administration as the "heirs of Woodrow Wilson's 'liberal internationalist' world vision," Grow also explains the bases of their foreign policy convictions. They believed in the viability of a "world order of capitalist democracies," led by the United States and "linked interdependently through mutually profitable free trade." They also presumed that such an approach would constitute "the surest path to international peace and prosperity." When assessed within the context of the liberal critique, this view might suggest that the ensuing "expansion of United States power and influence in the Western Hemisphere" came about

8 Gardner, *Economic Aspects*; David Green, *The Containment of Latin America: A History of the Myths and Realities of the Good Neighbor Policy* (Chicago, 1971); Dick Stewart, *Trade and Hemisphere: The Good Neighbor Policy and Reciprocal Trade* (Columbia, MO, 1975); Frederick C. Adams, *Economic Diplomacy: The Export-Import Bank and American Foreign Policy, 1934–1939* (Columbia, MO, 1976); Michael J. Francis, *The Limits of Hegemony: United States Relations with Argentina and Chile during World War II* (Notre Dame, 1977); Gary Frank, *Struggle for Hegemony in South America: Argentina, Brazil, and the United States during the Second World War* (Coral Gables, 1979).

both as "an altruistic and pragmatic campaign to construct a prosperous, stable new hemispheric order mutually beneficial to the United States and the nations of Latin America." But Grow rejects any such claim, arguing instead a more radical proposition that President Franklin D. Roosevelt's Latin American policy was "less . . . an example of 'liberal internationalism' than of 'liberal imperialism' – a concerted drive to achieve informal United States hegemony," motivated "consistently by considerations of national economic self-interest."[9]

For Latin American ruling elites, such forms of economic expansion heightened the prospect of unwanted dependency upon the United States. As producers of raw materials and unfinished goods, Latin American leaders understood their reliance upon the outside world for markets, capital, and products. They knew too their singular vulnerability to calamities such as the Great Depression. Yet in explaining the economic relationship between the United States and Latin American nations, as Thomas J. McCormick observes, radical analysts such as dependency theorists sometimes exaggerate the impact of "the metropole" upon "the periphery" by suggesting mechanistically that Third World countries have only two alternatives at their disposal – either "radical revolution" to escape the confines of the capitalist system or "abject surrender" to it. McCormick maintains that the capacity of outlying regions "to resist external exploitation has been considerably more varied and extensive" than often perceived. Historians need to acknowledge the complexity of bilateral relationships by paying greater heed to economic causes and effects in both the United States and Latin America.[10]

9 Michael Grow, *The Good Neighbor Policy and Authoritarianism in Paraguay: United States Economic Expansion and Great-Power Rivalry in Latin America during World War II* (Lawrence, 1981), 113–15. Studies of espionage have shown how the competition between Germany and the United States persisted in Latin America during the war and also warn against blowing the magnitude of the threat out of proportion. See Stanley E. Hilton, *Hitler's Secret War in South America, 1939–1945: German Military Espionage and Allied Counterespionage in Brazil* (Baton Rouge, 1981); Leslie B. Rout, Jr., and John F. Bratzel, *The Shadow War: German Espionage and United States Counterespionage in Latin America during World War II* (Frederick MD, 1986); and Ronald C. Newton, *The "Nazi Menace" in Argentina, 1931–1947* (Stanford, 1992).

10 Thomas J. McCormick, "Something Old, Something New: John Lewis Gaddis's 'New Conceptual Approaches,'" *Diplomatic History* 14 (Summer 1990): 427. See also idem, "World Systems," *Journal of American History* 77 (June 1990): 125–32.

The books by Francis, Frank, and Grow mentioned above are good examples of works that consider the ramifications for both partners in economic relationships. In addition, significant studies by Stanley E. Hilton and Frank D. McCann provide abundant detail on political and economic dealings between Brazil and other nations. Their works are based on extensive research in Brazilian archives. Hilton's *Brazil and the Great Powers, 1930–1939* describes the complex stratagems of the late 1930s by which the Getulio Vargas regime sought advantages while playing off Germany against the United States. McCann's *The Brazilian-American Alliance, 1937–1945* similarly shows the central importance of trade considerations in Brazil's international behavior.[11] In another essay, McCann develops a similar point, arguing that "the history of the prewar maneuvering of the great powers is too easily cast in ideological terms – totalitarianism versus democracy." He prefers "to study it as a struggle for raw materials and markets." Moreover, rather than describing the power contests among policymakers in countries such as Brazil as cases of "democrats versus the pro-Nazis," he depicts the contenders "as representatives of different, conflicting elements of the national elite who perceived their interests as best served by ties with one or another of the major powers."[12]

The Brazilians played the international economic game with special skill. Nevertheless, when the onset of war sealed off Europe and later brought in the United States as a belligerent, Brazil and the other states of Latin America had little choice but to

11 Frank D. McCann, *The Brazilian-American Alliance, 1937–1945* (Princeton, 1973); Stanley E. Hilton, *Brazil and the Great Powers, 1930–1939: The Politics of Trade Rivalry* (Austin, 1975). See also Stanley E. Hilton, "Brazilian Diplomacy and the Washington-Rio de Janeiro 'Axis' during the World War II Era," *Hispanic American Historical Review* 59 (May 1979): 201–31; idem, "The United States, Brazil, and the Cold War, 1945–1960: End of the Special Relationship," *Journal of American History* 68 (December 1981): 599–624; idem, "The Argentine Factor in Twentieth-Century Brazilian Foreign Policy Strategy," *Political Science Quarterly* 100 (Spring 1985): 27–51; idem, "Brazil's International Economic Strategy, 1945–1960: Revival of the German Option," *Hispanic American Historical Review* 66 (May 1986): 287–318; idem, "The Overthrow of Getulio Vargas in 1945: Diplomatic Intervention, Defense of Democracy, or Political Retribution?" ibid. 67 (February 1987): 1–39; and idem, *Brazil and the Soviet Challenge, 1917–1947* (Austin, 1991).

12 Frank D. McCann, "Brazil, the United States, and World War II: A Commentary," *Diplomatic History* 3 (Winter 1979): 63.

become even more dependent upon "the Colossus of the North." The fighting transformed international relations in the Western Hemisphere and altered the purpose, function, and structure of the inter-American system. What previously had operated as a voluntary association of nations, in which the members consulted with one other on an occasional basis, now became an agency of wartime cooperation and later a formal means of collective security. Before Pearl Harbor, at meetings in Lima, Panama, and Havana, the American republics established mechanisms for maintaining solidarity against the Axis powers. Later, in San Francisco, Mexico City, Rio de Janeiro, and Bogotá, they gave formal structure to a regional system.

In the meantime, all but two of the twenty republics in Latin America either severed relations with the Axis nations or declared war upon them. The exceptions, Chile and Argentina, remained neutral until nearly the end of the war. According to most historins, they did so more for particularistic reasons than out of any overtly pro-Axis orientation. Nevertheless, their stance angered American officials such as Secretary of State Cordell Hull, who attributed pro-Fascist sympathies to Chilean and Argentine leaders and demanded unanimity in the Western Hemisphere. Randall Bennett Woods has conducted a thorough study of U.S. efforts to force Argentina into line in *The Roosevelt Foreign Policy Establishment and the "Good Neighbor."* Woods traces the evolution of policy in the United States by utilizing the bureaucratic perspective on decision making. In this case, according to his analysis, a Latin Americanist contingent in the State Department consisted of regional specialists who favored accommodation with Argentina. In the bureaucratic struggle, they battled against an internationalist group around Secretary Hull that insisted upon Argentine subordination to the needs of total war.[13]

During the war the United States vastly expanded its role within the Western Hemisphere. To obtain strategic materials and to underwrite the isolated Latin American economies, the United States bought the products of Latin America on a large scale. The

13 Randall Bennett Woods, *The Roosevelt Foreign-Policy Establishment and the "Good Neighbor": The United States and Argentina, 1941–1945* (Lawrence, 1979).

United States also became Latin America's main supplier of finished goods, obtaining thereby a strong position for after the war. In addition, the Roosevelt administration bestowed loans, grants, and technical aid upon public works projects and other such activities to support economic development and diversification and also managed through the distribution of such incentives, enticements, and bribes to mobilize support and cooperation against pro-Fascists. Meanwhile, the Office of the Coordinator of Inter-American Affairs under Nelson Rockefeller built morale, mutual understanding, and common purpose through propaganda and cultural outreach, all the while emphasizing, according to Gerald K. Haines, "the mythical ideological unity of the nations of the New World." Finally, the administration also instituted programs centered on Latin American military establishments and provided equipment and training to strengthen relations with the officer corps of the various nations. During the ensuing Cold War, these programs brought about new kinds of dependency upon U.S. weapons and expertise.[14]

The best overview of the relationships between the Great Powers and Latin America during the war years is *Latin America and the Second World War, 1938–1945*, a two-volume study by the British historian R. A. Humphreys. Based upon the records of the British Foreign Office and to an extent a reflection of British views, this impressive work deftly combines analyses of politics and economics by examining the situation in each of the Latin American countries and showing the principal considerations governing the development of foreign policy in each nation. One of Humphreys's central themes focuses on the means by which the United States advanced the cause of hemispheric solidarity during the war and then undermined it in the early days of the Cold War. Preoccupied with the Soviet Union, the United States established priorities in other regions and thus violated Latin

14 R. A. Humphreys, *Latin America and the Second World War, 1938–1945*, 2 vols. (London, 1981–82); Fitzroy Andre Baptiste, *War, Cooperation, and Conflict: The European Possessions in the Caribbean, 1939–1945* (New York, 1988); Gerald K. Haines, "Under the Eagle's Wing: The Franklin Roosevelt Administration Forges an American Hemisphere," *Diplomatic History* 1 (Fall 1977): 373–88, quote, 373; Claude C. Erb, "Prelude to Point Four: The Institute of Inter-American Affairs," ibid. 9 (Summer 1985): 249–69; Graham D. Taylor, "The Axis Replacement Program: Economic Warfare and the Chemical Industry in Latin America, 1942–44," ibid. 8 (Spring 1984): 145–64.

American expectations of large-scale economic aid and assistance. No Marshall Plan came about to repay Latin American nations for their wartime support, and disenchantment soon set in. Brazil, for example, which (along with Mexico) had sent armed forces to fight side by side with the Allies, allowed its relations with the United States to cool and moved away from "the unwritten alliance." Other states similarly became estranged from their neighbor to the north.[15]

Questions of political change, economic development, and Cold War have dominated the historical record of the postwar years. Recent relations with Latin America, as opposed to Europe or Asia, have inspired comparatively small amounts of writing by historians. Perhaps that in itself is a reflection of policy priorities. The fullest account of U.S.-Latin American relations in this era appeared in 1971. David Green's notable book, *The Containment of Latin America*, incorporates the essential elements of the radical critique in assessing the legacies of the Good Neighbor Policy and ascribing significant unresolved contradictions to it. According to Green, Roosevelt's innovations did indeed create an unprecedented degree of cooperation between the United States and Latin America during the war years, but they also failed to come to terms with the reality of economic nationalism. This shortcoming produced another difficulty. When after the war Latin American reformers and modernizers sought to bring about economic development and diversification through the techniques of state planning and intervention, the United States characteristically threw up obstacles in their path while extolling the preferred route of free enterprise and private investment. Green argues that the Truman administration cleverly tried to shut off the Western Hemisphere from the remainder of the world by establishing U.S. economic dominance. At the same time, U.S. officials sought to obtain in other regions unrestricted economic access and to constrain the expansion of anti-capitalist movements. What the Truman administration aimed for, in Green's phrase, was "a closed hemisphere in an open world."[16]

Green's interpretation hinges upon his understanding of U.S.

15 See Humphreys, *Latin America and the Second World War,* esp. vol. 2; and the articles by Hilton cited in footnote 11.

16 Green, *Containment of Latin America,* esp. chap. 11 and "Epilogue."

purposes in creating international and regional organizations, specifically the United Nations (UN) and the Organization of American States (OAS). In the Roosevelt administration, the planners concentrated upon the creation of a strong international body based on centralized authority. During the Truman presidency, they shifted ground, moving toward a more eager acceptance of a regional bloc in the New World. Consequently, when the UN conference took place in San Francisco during the spring of 1945, the delegates permitted regional organizations under the terms of Article 51 of the charter, a provision that later sanctioned other moves toward regional autonomy at meetings in Mexico City, Rio de Janeiro, and Bogotá. The results established formal systems of military alliance and political consultation within the Western Hemisphere through the Act of Chapultepec, the Rio Pact, and the OAS.[17]

To forestall unilateral actions by the United States, the Latin Americans insisted upon adherence to the principle of nonintervention and wrote it into the OAS charter. Undeterred by this provision, the Truman administration viewed the organization as a means of manipulation by which to work its will in the Western Hemisphere. Though disguised with the language of anticommunism and hemispheric defense, the OAS actually enabled the United States to police its traditional sphere of influence against the combined threats of economic nationalism and political revolution while operating outside the purview of the UN. In this way, according to Green, the United States brought about "the containment of Latin America."[18]

Roger R. Trask's more recent essay, "The Impact of the Cold War on United States-Latin American Relations, 1945–1949," sets forth an alternative explanation of events in the postwar period. While Green incorporates aspects of Marxist thought into his analysis, emphasizing in particular the requirements of capitalist enterprise, Trask's approach recalls the methods of Leopold von Ranke by depicting foreign policy as a reaction to the actions

17 Ibid., esp. chaps. 9–11.

18 Ibid. For another view see J. Tillapaugh, "Closed Hemisphere and Open World? The Dispute over Regional Security at the U.N. Conference, 1945," *Diplomatic History* 2 (Winter 1978): 25–42.

of other states, in this case the Soviet Union, which appeared to pose a threat in the Western Hemisphere. According to Trask, the emergent Cold War "must be considered a new and progressively more important influence" upon U.S. policy and the formalization of the inter-American system. As evidence, he points to the Truman administration's shift "from opposition to strong regional organization . . . to enthusiasm about the Organization of American States." He characterizes the change as a defensive response to Communist moves, noting further that the Rio Pact and the OAS later functioned as models for Cold War agreements in other parts of the world.[19]

The few existing studies of U.S.-Latin American relations during the Truman years suggest that significant issues in this period remain for examination. While urging additional inquiry, Leslie Bethell and Ian Roxborough have affirmed the importance of what they called "the 1945–48 Conjuncture" in Latin America, a time during which conservative U.S. policies allowed traditional oligarchs to regain influence after wartime losses to reformers, liberals, and leftists. This thesis, fully spelled out in a collection of essays in the book, *Latin America Between the Second World War and the Cold War, 1944–1948*, holds that for most of Latin America the immediate postwar period fell into two phases. During the first, "democratization, a shift to the Left, and labor militancy" became primary political characteristics. During the second, when the onset of the Cold War preoccupied the United States, "organized labor was disciplined . . . Communist parties . . . suffered proscription and severe repression; reformist parties moved to the Right, and the democratic advance was for the most part contained, and in some cases reversed." The editors maintain, "just as the United States *indirectly* promoted political and social change in Latin America at the end of the Second World War, it *indirectly* imposed limits on change in the postwar years." Bethell and Roxborough believe, therefore, that "an opportunity, however limited, for significant political and social change was lost."

19 Roger R. Trask, "The Impact of the Cold War on United States-Latin American Relations, 1945–1949," *Diplomatic History* 1 (Summer 1977): 282–83; Rabe, "Marching Ahead (Slowly)," 307; David F. Trask, "Past and Future of National Security History," SHAFR *Newsletter* 19 (March 1988): 12–13.

Similarly, Stephen G. Rabe has shown the extent of the damage inflicted upon Latin America when the United States assigned low priority to the region and repeatedly postponed a proposed inter-American economic and technical conference. According to Chester J. Pach, even military aid to Latin America declined because of U.S. commitments elsewhere. Robert Freeman Smith also emphasizes the impact of Cold War crises in other parts of the world, resulting in confusion and indirection as Truman tried to maintain essential parts of the Good Neighbor Policy as he understood them. Clearly historians concerned with this period in the Western Hemisphere need to define very carefully the effects of crosspurposes and rival designs.[20]

As the Cold War deepened for the United States, an urgent debate got under way in Latin America over the proper way to foster economic growth and development. It also became a source of North-South friction. At a time when economic nationalism and state-directed activity generated enthusiasm among Latin American modernizers, the Truman and Eisenhower administrations resisted such alternatives, denied appeals for aid and assistance, and celebrated the virtues of capitalist enterprise. This important subject also calls for additional investigation. A groundbreaking book by Samuel L. Baily, *The United States and the Development of South America, 1945–1975*, suggests some of the requisites for work in this area. Proceeding from the premise that the United States historically has functioned as an external obstacle to modernization in Latin America, Baily attempts to explain why and to illustrate how diffusionist and dependency models have affected thinking in the course of debate over economic development in the United States and Latin America.

Baily's two models recall Lowenthal's distinction between liberal

20 Leslie Bethell and Ian Roxborough, "Latin America between the Second World War and the Cold War: Some Reflections on the 1945–8 Conjuncture," *Journal of Latin American Studies* 20 (May 1988): 167–89; Bethell and Roxborough, eds., *Latin America between the Second World War and the Cold War, 1944–1948* (New York, 1992) 2, 23; Stephen G. Rabe, "The Elusive Conference: United States Economic Relations with Latin America, 1945–1952," *Diplomatic History* 2 (Summer 1978): 279–94; Chester J. Pach, Jr., "The Containment of U.S. Military Aid to Latin America, 1944–49," ibid. 6 (Summer 1982): 225–44; Robert Freeman Smith, "United States Policy-Making for Latin America during the Truman Administration," *Continuity* 16 (Fall 1992): 87–111.

and radical perspectives but offer refined variations of these approaches. According to Baily, U.S. officials typically favored the diffusionist model as a strategy of development because it conformed with their understanding of their own country's experience and that of Great Britain. Based on the precepts of free enterprise, this model affirms "the belief that development comes about as a result of the diffusion of technology, capital, trade, political institutions, and culture from the 'advanced' to the 'backward' countries of the world." Moreover, it establishes the modern capitalist countries as "the agents of development." Working in alliance with the growing local middle class in the developing country, the influence of the former supposedly would edge latecomers along, helping them to move "step by step up the ladder from their own backward condition toward that of the advanced countries." According to diffusionist principles, developing countries must shun state action and adhere to proven capitalist practices in order to promote growth and progress.[21]

The dependency model appealed more to Latin American modernizers and in fact emerged from the attempts of Latin American intellectuals to account for conditions of economic stagnation in their own countries. Traditional explanations pointed to the negative impact of colonial legacies, especially feudal and noncapitalist practices. In contrast, the proponents of *dependencia* developed another analysis, emphasizing the injurious effects of an inequitable system of world capitalism. Dependency theorists rejected the fundamental assumption of the diffusionists, arguing instead that modernity and development would never spread into the Third World through capitalist mechanisms. On the contrary, they said, "the diffusion of capital and ideas" would actually result in adverse consequences because it would make "the receiving country dependent on the giving country, slow down potential growth, and widen the gap between the standards of living of the countries involved." Paradoxically, the conditions of development and underdevelopment had come about over the long term as part of "the same historical process" in the course

21 Samuel L. Baily, *The United States and the Development of South America, 1945–1975* (New York, 1976), 9.

of which "Western Europe and the United States developed by exploiting the resources of the underdeveloped world and thus contributed to its underdevelopment." Accordingly, for dependency theorists, the central question focused on the rectification of "a structural relationship of inequality among different countries and areas of the world." Latin American advocates affirmed that only state action would enable them to break out of this predicament.[22]

Baily acknowledges the methodological shortcomings of both theoretical constructs. The diffusionist model, for example, took shape in the course of unique national histories and may not provide much guidance in other settings. Similarly, dependency theory is "vague, difficult to apply," and in need of "more precise definition." In a recent, highly critical work, Robert A. Packenham has depicted "the dependency movement" more as an affirmation of the socialist faith than as a verifiable critique of capitalist functions. Such problems have deterred widespread applications of the model. Not many diplomatic historians in the United States have tried to work explicitly within the context of dependency theory. Nevertheless, Baily concludes on the basis of his study of Brazil and Chile that "a high degree of continuity in United States policy toward South America" has perpetuated "the dependency relationship and the external obstacles to the development of South America."[23]

Though less formally reliant upon the apparatus of dependency theory than Baily, Gerald K. Haines in *The Americanization of Brazil: A Study of U.S. Cold War Diplomacy in the Third World, 1945–1954*, arrives at a similar judgment. This book argues that the United States after the Second World War "assumed, out of self-interest, responsibility for the welfare of the world capitalist system" upon which its prosperity and well-being rested. Perceiving the Soviet Union as "a major threat," the Truman administration

22 Steve J. Stern, "Feudalism, Capitalism, and the World-System in the Perspective of Latin America and the Caribbean," *American Historical Review* 93 (October 1988): 829–72; Baily, *The United States and Development*, 10–12. See also Chilcote and Edelstein, *Latin America*.

23 Baily, *The United States and Development*, 211–12; Robert A. Packenham, *The Dependency Movement: Scholarship and Politics in Development Studies* (Cambridge, MA, 1992). This devastating attack seeks to disenroll dependency theory as a means toward real knowledge and understanding.

sought not only "to contain Communist expansion" but also to "preserve as much of the world as possible for capitalist development." This strategy had important ramifications in Latin America. In Brazil it meant a series of efforts by the United States to sustain free enterprise while opposing economic nationalism and state control. Though Haines perhaps overstates the point, his conclusion asserts compellingly that "the United States in Brazil during the late 1940s and early 1950s had great power and influence, both formally and informally" and that, moreover, "the intensity of the American efforts" to promote capitalism in Brazil resulted in an "overall success." This view varies somewhat from Thomas E. Skidmore's careful assessment in *Politics in Brazil, 1930–1964*, which suggests in contrast that Brazil possessed some greater capacity to resist, thus anticipating Thomas J. McCormick's warning against exaggerating the effects of "the metropole" upon "the periphery." Two fine additional works further amplify understanding of relations with Brazil after the Second World War. W. Michael Weis's *Cold Warriors and Coups D'Etat: Brazilian-American Relations, 1945–1964*, shows "why Brazilian-American relations deteriorated between 1945 and 1964, and why the United States aided in the overthrow of the João Goulart regime." Commendably this work draws extensively on primary Brazilian sources. In addition, Elizabeth A. Cobbs's *The Rich Neighbor Policy: Rockefeller and Kaiser in Brazil*, describes the activities of Nelson A. Rockefeller and Henry J. Kaiser in efforts to put diffusionist theory into action by enhancing private economic development. Cobbs's work displays a number of intriguing, interpretive twists.[24]

Although a few leaders in Washington displayed sporadic interest in Latin America during the early stages of the Cold War, the region for the most part was *terra incognita* to top officials. As Gerald K. Haines shows, they understood little and misunderstood much about their southern neighbors. A set of observations

24 Gerald K. Haines, *The Americanization of Brazil: A Study of U.S. Cold War Diplomacy in the Third World, 1945–1954* (Wilmington, DE, 1989), ix, 191; Thomas E. Skidmore, *Politics in Brazil, 1930–1964: An Experiment in Democracy* (New York, 1967); W. Michael Weis, *Cold Warriors and Coups d'Etat: Brazilian-American Relations, 1945–1964* (Albuquerque, 1993); and Elizabeth A. Cobbs, *The Rich Neighbor: Rockefeller and Kaiser in Brazil* (New Haven, 1992).

drawn by George F. Kennan, a high-level State Department official and the father of containment toward the Soviet Union, bears out the observation. Early in 1950 a first trip to Latin America unnerved Kennan. He later claimed that in this part of the world an inhospitable natural environment in combination with a miscegenated population had produced an "unhappy and hopeless background for the conduct of human life." In Mexico City "the sounds of . . . nocturnal activity" struck him as "disturbed, sultry, and menacing." He disliked Caracas, "debauched by oil money," and in Rio de Janeiro the "noisy, wildly competitive traffic and [the] unbelievable contrasts between luxury and poverty" repulsed him. In Lima he became depressed upon reflecting "that it had not rained . . . for twenty-nine years." Such views ran remarkably parallel with the stereotypes examined by Frederick B. Pike in *The United States and Latin America.* On the whole, Kennan judged such places as unimportant to the United States. Except for Cuba, Panama, and portions of Central America, he declared, "we have really no vital interests in that part of the world. Let us be generous in small things . . . but not greatly concerned for their opinion of us, and happy enough not to be an active factor in their affairs." Nevertheless, Kennan developed apprehensions over the allure of communism in Latin America and put no faith in the capability of Latin Americans to resist. In what Gaddis Smith has called "the Kennan Corollary" to the Monroe Doctrine, Kennan advised that:

> where the concepts and traditions of popular government are too weak to absorb successfully the intensity of the communist attack, then we must concede that harsh governmental measures of repression may be the only answer; that these measures may have to proceed from regimes whose origins and methods would not stand the test of American concepts of democratic procedures; and that such regimes and such methods may be preferable alternatives, and indeed the only alternatives, to further communist success.

Smith charitably allows that Kennan's position on this matter "is inconsistent with much of his subsequent thought." Smith's highly critical survey of U.S.-Latin American relations in recent times, *The Last Years of the Monroe Doctrine, 1945–1993*, also attributes to high American officials a "pervasive lack of knowledge about or concern . . . for Latin America on its own terms." Instead, they saw it as a Cold War arena.[25]

In the 1950s the character of relations between the United States and Latin America shifted markedly away from the friendly feelings of FDR's time. As Bryce Wood argues in *The Dismantling of the Good Neighbor Policy*, the process culminated in 1954 when, after a period of gradual deterioration in U.S.-Latin American relations, the United States intervened in Guatemala. This volume proceeds in much the same methodological fashion as Wood's previous book, *The Making of the Good Neighbor Policy*, analyzing the intellectualized deliberations of high officials in the State Department in largely ideological and political terms. Wood scarcely talks about economics. As he explains, "The Good Neighbor policy was a policy; it was not simply rhetoric." Essentially it consisted of "principled action" in support of "nonintervention" and "noninterference" in Latin America and rested on the expectation of "reciprocity" and "favorable responses" from Latin Americans. During the war years and immediately after, intense strains jeopardized the policy's coherence, especially in the controversies over Argentine neutrality and the presidential ambitions of Colonel Juan Domingo Perón. Regarded by critics in the United States as unduly nationalistic and perhaps pro-Fascist, Perón, in a much-studied episode, won election in spite of the publicly voiced opposition of Assistant Secretary of State Spruille Braden. Perón's election inflicted a diplomatic setback upon the United States, but Wood believes nevertheless that the Good Neighbor Policy survived until the Eisenhower administration's intervention in Guatemala.[26]

25 Roger R. Trask, "George F. Kennan's Report on Latin America (1950)," *Diplomatic History* 2 (Summer 1978): 308, 311; Frederick B. Pike, *The United States and Latin America: Myths and Stereotypes of Civilization and Nature* (Austin, 1992), a fascinating work, drawn perhaps somewhat loosely from the "new" cultural history; Gaddis Smith, *The Last Years of the Monroe Doctrine, 1945–1993* (New York, 1994), 6, 70–71, a signficant work, highly critical of the arrogance and condescension so typical of U.S. policy in Latin America.

26 Bryce Wood, *The Dismantling of the Good Neighbor Policy* (Austin, 1985), ix. Other studies of the Argentine issue include Gary Frank, *Juan Perón vs. Spruille Braden: The Story behind the Blue Book* (Lanham, MD, 1980); Roger R. Trask, "Spruille, Braden versus George Messersmith: World War II, the Cold War, and Argentine Policy, 1945–1947," *Journal of Inter-American Studies and World Affairs* 26 (February 1984): 69–95; and Jesse H. Stiller, *George S. Messersmith: Diplomat of Democracy* (Chapel Hill, 1987). See also Raanan Rein, *The Franco-Perón Alliance: Relations between Spain and Argentina, 1946–1955*, trans. Martha Grenzeback (Pittsburgh, 1993).

The Guatemala undertaking receives close scrutiny in books by Blanche Wiesen Cook, Stephen Schlesinger and Stephen Kinzer, Richard H. Immerman, and Piero Gleijeses. Somewhat similar in approach, these studies draw upon newly released materials at the Eisenhower Library and raise difficult questions about the wisdom and necessity of employing covert means to overthrow the reform-minded, left-leaning, but non-Communist government of Jacobo Arbenz Guzmán. Immerman in particular won plaudits for obtaining access to otherwise classified documents through the Freedom of Information Act. These accounts, really exposés, severely criticize the Eisenhower administration, the State Department, and the Central Intelligence Agency for acting out of an exaggerated anticommunism and a narrowly conceived sense of economic self-interest in defense of private property, in this case the holdings of the United Fruit Company. Such actions typified an emergent and pervasive Cold War mentality and entailed damaging consequences for both the United States and Latin America. They shattered the remnants of the Good Neighbor Policy in Latin America, reestablished the interventionist tradition in practice, and introduced a reign of right-wing political terror in Guatemala under Carlos Castillo Armas and his successors until the present day. Although not all historians concur in this grim assessment (Frederick W. Marks III is one notable exception), most agree that the short-term success of the clandestine operation in Guatemala, itself a result of Eisenhower's wartime infatuation with covert activity, later encouraged similar undertakings elsewhere and led inexorably to the debacle at the Bay of Pigs.[27]

27 Blanche Wiesen Cook, *The Declassified Eisenhower: A Divided Legacy* (Garden City, NY, 1981); Stephen C. Schlesinger and Stephen Kinzer, *Bitter Fruit: The Untold Story of the American Coup in Guatemala* (Garden City, NY, 1982); Richard H. Immerman, *The CIA in Guatemala: The Foreign Policy of Intervention* (Austin, 1982). The most recent account of the intervention, Piero Gleijeses's *Shattered Hope: The Guatemalan Revolution and the United States, 1944–1954* (Princeton, 1991), also presents a critical assessment of Eisenhower's policies. A view more sympathetic to Castillo Armas and to the administration's concern over Communist subversion appears in Frederick W. Marks III, "The CIA and Castillo Armas in Guatemala, 1954: New Clues to an Old Puzzle," *Diplomatic History* 14 (Winter 1990): 67–86; see Stephen G. Rabe's rejoinder in the same issue. Marks's *Power and Peace: The Diplomacy of John Foster Dulles* (Westport, 1993), also places a positive construction on the episode. Significant histories of intelligence, espionage, and clandestine operations are presented in Stephen E. Ambrose and Richard H. Immerman, *Ike's*

The appearance of Eisenhower revisionism in recent years has stimulated a great deal of discussion about his foreign policies. Eisenhower revisionists claim that 1950s liberals and their descendants in more recent times profoundly misunderstood the president and his methods. Rather than depict Eisenhower as aimless, ineffective, and overshadowed by assertive subordinates such as John Foster Dulles, revisionist authors portray the president truly as the man in charge. He was both competent and energetic. Books by Fred I. Greenstein, Stephen E. Ambrose, and Robert A. Divine suggest that Eisenhower was a clever politician and a strong but subtle leader who knew the appropriate levels of restraint in the nuclear age and presided effectively over the nation's diplomacy. For many students of Latin American relations, in contrast, the larger assertions of Eisenhower revisionism have proven unconvincing.[28]

In the early 1950s, questions of political change and economic development became ever more pressing in Latin America. The United States persisted in defending the status quo by supporting Latin American dictators and promoting anticommunism. President Eisenhower knew little of the region and depended for advice upon his younger brother Milton, who warned of impending trouble. During the president's first term, Milton Eisenhower unsuccessfully urged the implementation of public programs of aid and assistance by which to mitigate the effects of poverty in Latin America. During his second term the president became more flexible. In an important revisionist work, Burton I. Kaufman bestows high marks upon Eisenhower for bringing about a

Spies: Eisenhower and the Espionage Establishment (Garden City, 1981); John Prados, *Presidents' Secret Wars: CIA and Pentagon Covert Operations since World War II* (New York, 1986); Rhodri Jeffreys-Jones, *The CIA and American Democracy* (New Haven, 1989); and Charles D. Ameringer, *U.S. Foreign Intelligence: The Secret Side of American History* (Lexington, MA, 1990). All of these studies bear on Latin America and the legacies of the Guatemalan operation.

28 Fred I. Greenstein, *The Hidden-Hand Presidency: Eisenhower as Leader* (New York, 1982); Stephen E. Ambrose, *Eisenhower*, vol. 2, *The President* (New York, 1984); Robert A. Divine, *Eisenhower and the Cold War* (New York, 1981). See also Richard A. Melanson and David Mayers, eds., *Reevaluating Eisenhower: American Foreign Policy in the 1950s* (Urbana, 1987); Mary S. McAulliffe, "Commentary: Eisenhower, the President," *Journal of American History* 68 (December 1981): 625–32; and Robert J. McMahon, "Eisenhower and Third World Nationalism: A Critique of the Revisionists," *Political Science Quarterly* 101:3 (1986): 453–73.

fundamental change in policy and attitude. Kaufman claims that "under Eisenhower's leadership, the United States became more attentive to the problems of Third World countries and assumed greater responsibility for meeting their economic needs." Indeed, he writes that "the economic development of the Third World became one of the administration's highest priorities." Unpersuaded by such claims in the case of Latin America, Thomas Zoumaras insists to the contrary that "innovations in United States' foreign policy came slowly, haphazardly, even reluctantly, and that changes were inadequate responses to cold-war challenges rather than a reasoned and comprehensive plan to overcome structural underdevelopment in Latin America."[29]

In the fullest treatment of the subject, *Eisenhower and Latin America: The Foreign Policy of Anticommunism*, Stephen G. Rabe arrives at a similar assessment. Presented as a kind of test case of Eisenhower revisionism, this book critically appraises the administration's foreign policy and concludes that anticommunism became a virtual obsession, resulting in misperceptions and mistakes, among them, the intervention in Guatemala. Rabe concedes that the Eisenhower administration's Latin American strategy was at least "coherent" and "consistent." Administration officials "wanted Latin Americans to support the United States in the Cold War, adopt free trade and investment principles, and oppose communism." Nevertheless, the strategy failed to generate Latin American support during the Korean War, to blunt the Soviet economic offensive in the middle 1950s, and to provide an adequate response to the problems in U.S.-Latin American relations, all of which was dramatically highlighted by Vice President Richard M. Nixon's disastrous visit to South America in 1958.[30]

29 H. W. Brands, Jr., "Milton Eisenhower and the Coming Revolution in Latin America," chap. 2 in *Cold Warriors: Eisenhower's Generation and American Foreign Policy* (New York, 1988); Burton I. Kaufman, *Trade and Aid: Eisenhower's Foreign Economic Policy, 1953–1961* (Baltimore, 1982), 6–7; Thomas Zoumaras, "Eisenhower's Foreign Economic Policy, The Case of Latin America," in Melanson and Mayers, eds., *Reevaluating Eisenhower*, 156. Paul Coe Clark, Jr., presents a provocative view of relations with one of the dictators in *The United States and Somoza, 1933–1956, A Revisionist Look* (Westport, 1992). It rejects the view that Somoza functioned as a surrogate created by the United States to serve larger policy purposes. Instead, it argues that Somoza created a myth of special intimacy with the United States for his own political reasons.

30 Stephen G. Rabe, *Eisenhower and Latin America: The Foreign Policy of Anticommunism* (Chapel Hill, 1988), 174.

In his second term, Eisenhower moved away from dictators and tyrants and expended public monies in support of development in Latin America. "Trade and aid" became the policy aims, but still in Rabe's view the administration "never wavered from its goals of exercising and preserving U.S. leadership in the Western Hemisphere." Essentially cosmetic, the changes in the second half of Eisenhower's presidency were more tactical than strategic in importance. Rabe also has trouble reconciling revisionist claims for Eisenhower with interventionist measures in Guatemala, Cuba, and the Dominican Republic, to say nothing of efforts to oust and perhaps to assassinate Fidel Castro and Rafael Trujillo. Those actions recall Robert J. McMahon's observation that officials in the Eisenhower administration "grievously misunderstood and underestimated the most significant historical development of the mid-twentieth century – the force of Third World Nationalism."[31]

Misconceptions about Third World nationalism especially influenced U.S. responses to Fidel Castro and the Cuban Revolution, the consequences of which have dominated relations with Latin America more than any other issue since 1959. The events leading to the Bay of Pigs, the Alliance for Progress, and the Cuban missile crisis have produced an impressive body of writing, much of it critical of the United States. Other U.S. undertakings, such as the intervention in the Dominican Republic, the destabilization of Chile, and the support of the contras, have elicited writings from other scholars. Many of them draw upon radical critiques by depicting the foremost characteristic of recent relations as a determination by the United States to contain the Cuban Revolution. This view underscores again the disparity between U.S. and Latin American aims and ambitions. As political scientist John D. Marty notes, "controversy and complexity have grown exponentially" within the Western Hemisphere in the years since Castro, and "the emergence of revolutionary Cuba has left an indelible mark" upon all of the principal diplomatic participants.[32]

31 Ibid. See Rabe's *The Road to OPEC: United States Relations with Venezuela, 1919–1976* (Austin, 1982), for consideration of oil diplomacy in recent times. McMahon, "Eisenhower and Third World Nationalism," 457.

32 John D. Martz, ed., *United States Policy in Latin America: A Quarter Century of Crisis and Challenge, 1961–1986* (Lincoln, NE, 1988), ix. See also the collection of essays mainly by political scientists in John D. Martz and Lars Schoultz, eds., *Latin America, the United States, and the Inter-American System* (Boulder, 1980).

Recent studies of Castro and Cuba have illuminated many issues and have cleared away various myths about the Cuban Revolution. For example, historians have demonstrated that Castro in all probability came to power as a non-Communist revolutionary when most of the Cuban people turned against the Fulgencio Batista regime. For Castro, the revolution in all likelihood meant the reduction of U.S. influence in Cuba. Moreover, his turn toward the Soviet Union probably came about less for reasons of Marxist conviction than out of a pragmatic need to secure help in consolidating his regime and defending it against the United States. Such views appear prominently in Thomas G. Paterson's *Contesting Castro: The United States and the Triumph of the Cuban Revolution*. Paterson effectively makes the point with these words:

> For the *fidelistas* who ultimately dominated Cuban politics, the proposition that "the friend [the United States] of my enemy [Batista], is my enemy" became prominent. They held responsible for Cuba's plight both *batistianos* and *norteamericanos*, which they grouped as the "selfish interests" and the "international oligarchy." To oppose one was to oppose both, so integrated had they become. And the daily stories about the activities of U.S. customs agents, military advisers, businesses, CIA and FBI operatives, and notables like the casino boss Meyer Lansky ensured that a revolution to oust the Batista dictatorship also became a revolution to expel the United States from the island.

In addition, scholars have largely abandoned the claim that unresponsiveness by the Eisenhower administration drove Castro into Soviet arms. Because of the extent to which Castro defined his goals in opposition to the United States, he probably would not have reacted with gratitude and thanksgiving to small favors. At the same time, some greater measure of forbearance by the United States – instead of covert operations and attempted assassinations – might have retarded the deterioration in relations between the two countries.[33]

33 Recent writing about Castro and the diplomatic implications of the Cuban Revolution includes Alan H. Luxenberg, "Did Eisenhower Push Castro into the Arms of the Soviets?" *Journal of Inter-American Studies and World Affairs* 30 (Spring 1988): 37–71, an extended historiographical appraisal pointing to the difficulty of holding Eisenhower responsible for Cuba; Jorge I. Domínguez, *To Make a World Safe for*

The most recently published studies of the conduct of U.S. diplomacy have contributed significantly to our understanding of U.S.-Cuban relations. The late Richard E. Welch, Jr., looked at the unfolding of governmental and public responses to Fidel Castro and the process of radicalizing the Cuban Revolution. His account attributed U.S. antipathy to exaggerated assumptions about the evils of communism, the presumed righteousness of the United States, and the supposed benevolence of traditional policies toward Cuba. The North Americans, he concluded, perceived in the Cuban repudiation of the United States a kind of betrayal after years of tutelage and support.[34] Jules R. Benjamin, who is also concerned with the effects of national ethnocentrism, explores "the nature of hegemony" in the Cuban setting in *The United States and the Origins of the Cuban Revolution.* Characterized by the author as something other than "a traditional diplomatic history," this study proposes to uncover "what deeper elements in North American institutions and culture directed the use of [United States] power" in dealings with Cuba. Benjamin points to a fundamental problem. Overcome by habitual forms of self-deception, the inhabitants of the United States refused to see themselves and their international practices for what they were and therefore could not comprehend the consequences of their own conduct. In Benjamin's words, "by defining its role in the

Revolution: Cuba's Foreign Policy (Cambridge, MA, 1989), an explication of the Cuban view showing the importance of politics and ideology in U.S.-Cuban relations that demonstrates that Cuba had a degree of autonomy in its dealings with other nations and was not completely subject to Moscow; Thomas C. Wright, *Latin America in the Era of the Cuban Revolution* (Westport, 1991), an investigation of the effects of Castroism in other regions; Wayne S. Smith, *The Closest of Enemies: A Personal and Diplomatic Account of U.S.-Cuban Relations since 1957* (New York, 1987), an account critical of the United States by a former Foreign Service officer; idem, "Critical Junctures in U.S.-Cuban Relations: The Diplomatic Record," *Diplomatic History* 12 (Fall 1988): 463–81; Thomas Zoumaras, "Containing Castro: Promoting Homeownership in Peru, 1956–61," ibid. 10 (Spring 1986): 161–81, a depiction of the consequences of U.S. antipathy to Cuba at the local level; Warren Hinckle and William W. Turner, *The Fish is Red: The Story of the Secret War against Castro* (New York, 1981), a disconcerting account by journalists of conspiracies and assassination attempts against Castro with possible linkages to the death of John F. Kennedy; and Thomas G. Paterson, *Contesting Castro: The United States and the Triumph of the Cuban Revolution* (New York, 1994), the most recent scholarly treatment of the subject.

34 Richard E. Welch, Jr., *Response to Revolution: The United States and the Cuban Revolution, 1959–1961* (Chapel Hill, 1985), chap. 10.

world as anti-imperialist, the United States has made difficult any self-understanding of its acts of domination." Therefore, "North American scholars need to begin their study of U.S. expansion from a position outside the sway of this aspect of their culture." As expressed by Benjamin's thesis, "the relationship between the United States and Cuba broke down under its own weight: it could no longer bear the burden placed upon it by the antagonism between the U.S. desire to influence Cuba and the Cuban desire to fulfill the dream of independence."[35]

In one of the most ambitious and controversial of the recent publications, *Imperial State and Revolution: The United States and Cuba, 1952–1986*, Morris H. Morley, a political sociologist, combines extensive research in the available documents with a sophisticated and uncompromising Marxist model of analysis. Morley seeks "to explicate the involvement and effectiveness of the United States as an imperial state in prerevolutionary Cuba" and to show "how the United States responded to the fundamental challenge to capitalist accumulation embodied in the Cuban Revolution." One of his major premises holds that "the mechanisms of capitalist development are tightly interwoven with the activities of the state" and that the U.S. government, "conceived of as an imperial state," normally functioned "as the engine of a worldwide system of capital accumulation." Morley also insists that the imperialist actions of a capitalist nation "are deliberate and pragmatic; they reflect and rationalize the interests of the capitalist class as a whole." For such reasons he emphatically rejects the bureaucratic perspective, arguing that it merely affirms different approaches in defense of essential capitalist interests.[36]

Radical appraisals such as Morley's have flourished in part as a result of Vietnam. This dragged-out struggle, America's longest war, overshadowed the foreign policies of Presidents John F. Kennedy, Lyndon B. Johnson, and Richard M. Nixon. It also instigated a search for parallels in U.S. policy toward Southeast Asia, Latin America, and other Third World regions and encouraged

35 Jules R. Benjamin, *The United States and the Origins of the Cuban Revolution: An Empire of Liberty in an Age of National Liberation* (Princeton, 1990), 1–4.

36 Morris H. Morley, *Imperial State and Revolution: The United States and Cuba, 1952–1986* (Cambridge, England, 1987), 1, 3.

unconventional, radical scholarly reassessments, according to which dominating Cold War imperatives in U.S. diplomacy obscured distinctions between Soviet-inspired Communist subversion and indigenous revolutionary nationalism. The problem in Cuba became perplexing, indeed maddening, because of the Bay of Pigs invasion and later the missile crisis. The late Trumbull Higgins, a self-proclaimed "specialist in military fiasco," examined the 1961 Bay of Pigs debacle in his book, *The Perfect Failure*. It stressed the magnititue of ineptitude, miscalculation, self-delusion, and error among the planners of the operation. It also pointed out the importance of the 1954 Guatemalan intervention as a model, in the Cuban case, for disaster.[37]

Similar appraisals of the U.S.-Cuban conflict appear in *Kennedy's Quest for Victory*, edited by Thomas G. Paterson. This volume is a compilation of recent research on the Kennedy presidency by ranking scholars. Like Eisenhower scholarship, work on the Kennedy period has entered a revisionist stage, which among other things emphasizes the distinction between substance and style. Seeking to demythologize the president, the essays in this volume underscore "the disparity between image and reality" in Kennedy's case. Resulting in part from the availability of new documentation at the Kennedy Library, the reinterpretation of the Kennedy administration has projected a large measure of ambiguity into the Kennedy legend. In Paterson's words, Kennedy now appears "as both confrontationist and conciliator, hawk and dove, decisive leader and hesitant improviser, hyperbolic politician and prudent diplomat, idealist and pragmatist, glorious hero and flawed man of dubious character."[38]

In a concise essay on the Alliance for Progress, Stephen G. Rabe shows how a kind of Marshall Plan at last came into existence for Latin America. Conceived as an alternative to communism and Castro, this ambitious project to advance development and modernity within the context of democratic capitalism promised

37 Trumbull Higgins, *The Perfect Failure: Kennedy, Eisenhower, and the CIA at the Bay of Pigs* (New York, 1987).

38 Thomas G. Paterson, ed., *Kennedy's Quest for Victory: American Foreign Policy, 1961–63* (New York, 1989), 4–5. Some similar themes appeared in Herbert S. Parmet, *JFK*, vol. 2, *The Presidency of John F. Kennedy* (New York, 1983).

much, delivered less, and eventually "lost its way." To an extent a victim of misplaced European analogies, the undertaking stumbled over bureaucratic impediments, faulty planning, and Latin American obstruction. Among other things, the experience showed the difficulty of seeking to promote change while working through vested elites essentially opposed to it. Unlike the leaders in the United States, the traditional oligarchy in Latin America saw reform as an invitation to revolution, not as a deterrent against it.[39]

Thomas G. Paterson's essay presents an adroit summary of the missile crisis and its preliminaries in the "covert war against Castro." Paterson explains Kennedy's "obsession" with Cuba as an outgrowth of "a major phenomenon in twentieth-century world history: the steady erosion of the authority of imperial powers" over "dependent, client, and colonial governments." Because "the Cuban Revolution exemplified the process of breaking up and breaking away," it led Kennedy administration officials to fear that a spreading contagion would "further diminish United States hegemony in the Western Hemisphere." The missile crisis was thus a product of "Kennedy's unvarnished hostility toward Cuba" and "Castro's understandable apprehension that United States invasion was inevitable." Except for the existence of such regional tensions, Paterson claims, Nikita Khrushchev "would never have had the opportunity to begin his dangerous missile game."[40]

39 Stephen G. Rabe, "Controlling Revolutions: Latin America, the Alliance for Progress, and Cold War Anti-Communism," chap. 4 in Paterson, ed., *Kennedy's Quest for Victory*. See also Jerome Levinson and Juan de Onís, *The Alliance That Lost Its Way: A Critical Report on the Alliance for Progress* (Chicago, 1970); and Joseph S. Tulchin, "The United States and Latin America in the 1960s," *Journal of Inter-American Studies and World Affairs* 30 (Spring 1988): 1–36.

40 Thomas G. Paterson, "Fixation with Cuba: The Bay of Pigs, Missile Crisis, and Covert War against Fidel Castro," chap. 5 in Paterson, ed., *Kennedy's Quest for Victory*. Other essential writings include Raymond L. Garthoff, *Reflections on the Cuban Missile Crisis* (Washington, 1987), an exhortation by a participant and a scholar to understand the behavior of the Soviets from their own point of view; Barton J. Bernstein, "Pig in a Poke, Why did Kennedy Buy the Bay of Pigs Invasion?" *Foreign Service Journal* 62 (March 1985): 28–33; Thomas G. Paterson and William J. Brophy, "October Missiles and November Elections: The Cuban Missile Crisis and American Politics, 1962," *Journal of American History* 73 (June 1986): 87–119; James G. Hershberg, "Before 'The Missiles of October': Did Kennedy Plan a Military Strike against Cuba?" *Diplomatic History* 14 (Spring 1990): 163–98; and Bruce J. Allen, James G. Blight, and David A. Welch, "Essence of Revision: Moscow, Havana and the Cuban Missile Crisis," *International Security* 14 (Winter 1989–90): 136–72.

Diplomatic historians have not written extensively about the years after the Kennedy administration, in part because of classification restrictions. Much of the work on the Johnson presidency has focused on the drift away from the Alliance for Progress toward more conservative, traditional, and interventionist policies. In accounts critical of the Johnson administration, Phyllis R. Parker, Ruth Leacock, and W. Michael Weis have raised questions about the propriety of U.S. actions in Brazil in 1964 during the ouster of President João Goulart. Perceived by conservative Brazilian military leaders as a Communist sympathizer, Goulart also distressed officials in the Johnson administration who supported the dissident generals in removing him from power. Emphasizing indigenous politics more than external influences, Thomas E. Skidmore's carefully nuanced study downplays the U.S. role. In the case of the 1965 U.S. intervention in the Dominican Republic, General Bruce Palmer, Jr., a military participant, has published an operational history reflecting official views. Like leaders in the Johnson administration, Palmer's book endorses the need to ward off Communist threats in the Western Hemisphere. In contrast, academic studies more typically raise dubious questions about Johnson's statements of purpose and rationale.

The last piece reviews Soviet and Cuban perceptions and motives, based on recent memoirs, and cautions that historians have only limited access to Soviet and Cuban documents.

For an elaboration of the current status of the missile crisis controversy see "The Cuban Missile Crisis Reconsidered" in *Diplomatic History* 14 (Spring 1990): 205–56, featuring "The Soviet View: An Interview with Sergo Mikoyan" by Bernd Greiner and "Commentaries" by Raymond L. Garthoff, Barton J. Bernstein, Marc Tractenberg, and Thomas G. Paterson. Another update incorporating recently declassified materials appears in Robert A. Divine's review essay, "Alive and Well: The Continuing Cuban Missile Crisis Controversy," *Diplomatic History* 18 (Fall 1994): 551–60, in which seven books come under review: Mary S. McAuliffe, ed., *CIA Documents and the Cuban Missile Crisis, 1962* (Washington, 1992); Laurence Chang and Peter Kornbluh, eds., *The Cuban Missile Crisis, 1962: A National Security Archive Documents Reader* (Washington, 1992); James G. Blight and David A. Welch, *On the Brink: Americans and Soviets Reexamine the Cuban Missile Crisis* (New York, 1989); Dino A. Brugioni, *Eyeball to Eyeball: The Inside Story of the Cuban Missile Crisis* (New York, 1991); Robert Smith Thompson, *The Missiles of October: The Declassified Story of John F. Kennedy and the Cuban Missile Crisis* (New York, 1991); Michael R. Beschloss, *The Crisis Years: Kennedy and Khrushchev, 1960–1963* (New York, 1991); and James A. Nathan, ed., *The Cuban Missile Crisis Revisited* (New York, 1992). Contrary to the received wisdom, these books show that the missile crisis did not bring the world to the brink of nuclear war and that the principal players performed with considerable responsibility.

As noted by Piero Gleijeses in his study of the Dominican intervention, no matter what the U.S. government said, "the Americans wanted anti-Communist stability more than democracy in the Dominican Republic as well as in the rest of the hemisphere."[41]

Latin America diminished in importance during the Richard M. Nixon presidency, in large measure because of preoccupations with Vietnam, détente, and Watergate and also because of indifference toward the region. The geopolitician Henry Kissinger preferred to concentrate his attention upon the activities of the Great Powers. In a disdainful remark, he once disparaged Chile as "a pistol pointed at the heart of Antarctica." Nevertheless, he paid attention when Salvador Allende's Marxist Socialist government came to power in Chile, conjuring up for the Nixon administration frightening images of falling dominoes and revolutionary tides in South America. Kissinger attributed Allende's election to the irresponsibility of Chilean voters, and subsequently the Nixon administration stood in opposition. With the support of multinational corporations threatened by nationalization, Nixon and Kissinger employed overt and covert means to isolate Allende and shake his regime. The consequences of these actions have divided scholars. A conservative commentator, Mark Falcoff, has argued that Allende's government, characterized as incompetent and maladroit, fell under the weight of its own shortcomings. This happy conclusion absolves the United States of responsibility for the subsequent excesses of General Augustín Pinochet. Others have judged more harshly. In *The Price of Power,* a lurid account of egotism, vanity, arrogance, and double-dealing in the Nixon administration, the journalist Seymour Hersh attributes

41 Walter LaFeber, "Latin American Policy," chap. 2 in *Exploring the Johnson Years,* ed. Robert A. Divine (Austin, 1981); E. V. Niemeyer, Jr., "Personal Diplomacy: Lyndon B. Johnson and Mexico, 1963–1968," *Southwestern Historical Quarterly* 90 (October 1986): 159–86; Phyllis R. Parker, *Brazil and the Quiet Intervention, 1964* (Austin, 1979); Ruth Leacock, *Requiem for Revolution: The United States and Brazil, 1961–1969* (Kent, OH, 1990); Skidmore, *Politics in Brazil, 1930–1964;* idem, *The Politics of Military Rule in Brazil, 1964–85* (New York, 1988); Weis, *Cold Warriors and Coups D'Etat*; Cobbs, *The Rich Neighbor Policy*; Bruce Palmer, Jr., *Intervention in the Caribbean: The Dominican Crisis of 1965* (Lexington, KY, 1989); more critical accounts appear in Jerome Slater, *Intervention and Negotiation: The United States and the Dominican Revolution* (New York, 1970); Lowenthal, *The Dominican Intervention;* and Piero Gleijeses, *The Dominican Crisis: The 1965 Constitutionalist Revolt and American Intervention* (Baltimore, 1978), 284.

Allende's fall directly to the clandestine activities of the United States. In a concise, judicious narrative, Robert D. Schulzinger's *Henry Kissinger: The Doctor of Diplomacy*, surveys the events leading to Allende's overthrow and his ensuing death, either by suicide or murder, and concludes with biting understatement that "the United States-inspired campaign of destabilization had worked."[42]

Public perceptions of incompetence and failure in foreign policy ruined the credibility of James Earl Carter's presidency and limited it to one term. Carter's attempts to find new purpose and inspiration for the United States through the advocacy of human rights as an alternative to the geopolitics of Nixon and Kissinger elicited mixed responses. So did the Panama Canal treaties and the successful Sandinista revolution against Anastasio Somoza in Nicaragua. In each case, various critics assailed Carter on the grounds that his policies actually had advanced the interests of enemies of the United States. Though historians' judgments have not sustained such drastic conclusions, they do show the devastating effects of Carter's incapacity to persuade the public to support his foreign policy. As Gaddis Smith observes, "Judged by the scoreboard of Presidential elections, the Carter administration was a failure." Indeed, the president became the first incumbent since Herbert Hoover to lose the office after one term. Smith shows how Carter's efforts to "grapple with and relieve the terrible insecurity of the nuclear age" through a more "effective combination of morality, reason, and power" fell short of winning public endorsement and how the alleged deficiencies of his policies in Latin America, a region to which Carter attached importance, contributed to the undoing of his administration.[43]

42 Robert D. Schulzinger, *Henry Kissinger: The Doctor of Diplomacy* (New York, 1989, 132, 138–39. A thorough, balanced account of the Nixon presidency appears in Stephen E. Ambrose's three-volume biography, *Nixon* (New York, 1987–91). See also Mark Falcoff, *Modern Chile, 1970–1989: A Critical History* (New Brunswick, 1989); Seymour Hersh, *The Price of Power: Kissinger in the Nixon White House* (New York, 1983), chaps. 21, 22; and Schulzinger's "Complaints, Self-justifications, and Analysis: The Historiography of American Foreign Relations since 1969," in this volume.

43 Gaddis Smith, *Morality, Reason, and Power: American Diplomacy in the Carter Years* (New York, 1986), 3–4, chap 5. Smith's is the basic work on the Carter years. See also Donald S. Spencer, *The Carter Implosion: Jimmy Carter and the Amateur Style of Diplomacy* (New York, 1988), a strong criticism based on the idealist/realist

The Reagan administration capitalized on Carter's weaknesses by focusing public attention on revolutionary violence in Central America, specifically in Nicaragua and El Salvador, and linking it to alleged threats from the Soviet Union and Cuba. Unlike Carter administration officials who understood the problem as a North-South issue – that is, an attempt by less-developed countries to throw off the inequities of the past – the leaders in the Reagan administration depicted the turmoil as an East-West issue. Indeed, they presented it as a Cold War confrontation conducted by surrogates. According to this view, the Communists supposedly sought strategic advantage by destabilizing countries on the southern flank of the United States, aiming ultimately at Mexico and the border regions. In melodramatic language, Thomas O. Enders, the assistant secretary of inter-American affairs, proclaimed: "There can be no mistaking that our national security interests are being challenged. . . . Cuba is systematically expanding its capacity to project military power beyond its own shores. Nicaragua is being exploited as a base for the export of subversion and armed intervention throughout Central America. . . . The decisive battle for Central America is under way in El

critique, emphasizing the view that Carter placed undue reliance on meaningless rhetoric and symbols; Joshua Muravchik, *The Uncertain Crusade: Jimmy Carter and the Dilemmas of Human Rights Policy* (Lanham, MD, 1986), which is critical of contradictions, inconsistencies, and flawed implementation of policy during the Carter years; Lars Schoultz, *Human Rights and United States Policy toward Latin America* (Princeton, 1981), a more sympathetic treatment of Carter; George D. Moffett III, *The Limits of Victory: The Ratification of the Panama Canal Treaties* (Ithaca, 1985); J. Michael Hogan, *The Panama Canal in American Politics: Domestic Advocacy and the Evolution of Policy* (Carbondale, IL, 1986); Walter LaFeber, *The Panama Canal: The Crisis in Historical Perspective* (New York, 1979); and John Major, *Prize Possession: The United States and the Panama Canal, 1903–1979* (New York, 1993).

Carter's critics include scholar/practitioners with links to the Reagan administration, such as Michael Ledeen and Jeane J. Kirkpatrick. See Ledeen, *Grave New World* (New York, 1985), a thoughtful conservative critique; and Kirkpatrick, *Dictatorships and Double Standards: Rationalism and Reason in Politics* (New York, 1982, 23–90, which attacks Carter's Nicaraguan and Iranian policies for failing to distinguished between friendly authoritarians and hostile totalitarians. For an assessment of Kirkpatrick's views see Judith Ewell, "Barely in the Inner Circle: Jeane Kirkpatrick," in *Women and American Foreign Policy, Lobbyists, Critics, and Insiders,* ed. Edward P. Crapol (New York, 1987), 153–71. For a kinder appraisal of Nicaraguan policy consult Robert A. Pastor, *Condemned to Repetition: The United States and Nicaragua* (Princeton, 1987), by a scholar/practitioner with links to the Carter administration.

Salvador."[44] For such reasons the Reagan administration sanctioned clandestine war against the Sandinistas and aid for the contras.

The Central American question elicited a torrent of publications, polemical and otherwise. Books by Timothy Ashby, Mark Falcoff, and Howard J. Wiarda gave credence to President Reagan's apprehensions by affirming the existence of mounting Soviet ambitions in the Western Hemisphere. Less alarmist and more balanced works by Nicola Miller and Cole Blasier placed claims about Soviet aspirations in context by pointing out the limited nature of Soviet capabilities.[45] On the whole, historians have displayed difficulty in accepting the validity of the Reagan position. Characteristically, they tend to interpret the revolutionary instability in Central America more as an outgrowth of historical experience than as a consequence of Communist designs. In addition, as scholars, they have shown greater willingness to examine the traditional role of the United States in the region and to assess its responsibility for condoning and contributing to conditions of inequality, oppression, and want. Among the many publications devoted to such inquiries, John E. Findling's *Close Neighbors, Distant Friends,* is a balanced, judicious survey in which the author tries "to tell, in as straightforward a manner as possible, the story of the United States's relationship with Central America." Thomas E. Leonard has examined the attitudes and perceptions of policymakers and diplomats toward change in Latin America in the 1940s and also has contributed a fine, even-handed volume in the Langley series. Walter LaFeber presents his analysis within the framework of "neodependency," arguing that the violence in Central America came about when indigenous radicalism challenged the fundamentals of the political-economic

44 Ender's Statement, U.S. Dept. of State, Bureau of Public Affairs, *Current Policy No. 364,* "Democracy and the Security of the Caribbean Basin," February 1982.

45 Timothy Ashby, *The Bear in the Back Yard: Moscow's Caribbean Strategy* (Lexington, MA, 1987); Howard J. Wiarda and Mark Falcoff, eds., *The Communist Challenge in the Caribbean and Central America* (Washington, 1987); Wiarda, *American Foreign Policy toward Latin America in the 80s and 90s*; Nicola Miller, *Soviet Relations with Latin America, 1959–1987* (New York, 1989); Cole Blasier, *The Giant's Rival: The USSR and Latin America* (Pittsburgh, 1983); Aldo César Vacs, *Discreet Partners: Argentina and the USSR since 1917,* trans. Michael Joyce (Pittsburgh, 1984); and Lars Schoultz, *National Security and United States Policy toward Latin America* (Princeton, 1987).

system supported by the United States. Similarly, employing a Marxist frame of reference, Morris H. Morley in *Washington, Somoza and the Sandinistas* argues that U.S. policymakers attached special importance to the maintenance of friendly and receptive state institutions in Latin America, and Robert H. Holden, in his article, "The Real Diplomacy of Violence: United States Military Power in Central America, 1950–1990," explains the role of military aid as one of the means toward that end. John H. Coatsworth's superb work, *Central America and the United States: The Clients and the Colossus*, summarizes "patterns of foreign policy activity or behavior" since 1945, "assesses the success or failure of U.S. policy on its own terms," and "tries to come to grips with the impact of such policy on the six isthmian countries." Coatsworth attributes much of the Central American tumult in recent times to political and economic dependencies upon the United States. Also critical in tone, E. Bradford Burns's devastating account of Reagan policy as the misguided product of arrogance, ignorance, and wrong-headedness was denounced by the White House as disinformation.[46]

46 John E. Findling, *Close Neighbors, Distant Friends: United States-Central American Relations* (New York, 1987); Thomas E. Leonard, *The United States and Central America, 1944–1949: Perceptions of Political Change* (University, AL, 1984); idem, *Central America and the United States*; Walter LaFeber, *Inevitable Revolutions: The United States and Central America* (New York, 1983); idem, "The Reagan Administration and Revolutions in Central America," *Political Science Quarterly* 99 (Spring 1984): 1–25; Morris H. Morley, *Washington, Somoza and the Sandinistas: State and Regime in U.S. Policy toward Nicaragua, 1969–1981* (Cambridge, 1994); Robert H. Holden, "The Real Diplomacy of Violence: United States Military Power in Central America, 1950–1990," *International History Review* 15 (May 1993): 283–322; Coatsworth, *Central America and the United States*, xi; and E. Bradford Burns, *At War in Nicaragua: The Reagan Doctrine and the Politics of Nostalgia* (New York, 1987).

Other examples drawn from the vast number of publications on Central America include a fine survey by a Costa Rican, Hector Pérez-Brignoli, *A Brief History of Central America,* trans. Ricardo B. Sawrey A. and Susan Stettri de Sawrey (Berkeley, 1989); Donald C. Hodges, *Intellectual Foundations of the Nicaraguan Revolution* (Austin, 1986); Kenneth M. Coleman and George C. Herring, eds., *The Central American Crisis, Sources of Conflict and the Failure of U.S. Policy* (Wilmington, DE, 1985); Robert A. Pastor, "The Centrality of Central America," in *Looking Back on the Reagan Presidency,* ed. Larry Berman (Baltimore, 1990), 33–49; Lester D. Langley, "Latin America from Cuba to El Salvador," in *Modern American Diplomacy,* ed. John M. Carroll and George C. Herring (Wilmington, DE, 1986), 183–200; idem, "Fire Down Below: A Review Essay on the Central American Crisis," *Diplomatic History* 9 (Spring 1985): 161–67; Susanne Jonas, "Reagan Administration Policy in Central America," in *Reagan and the World,* ed. David E. Kyvig (New York, 1990),

Recent publications bearing on the recent past ponder the implications of big issues, such as the end of the Cold War, the move toward democratization in Latin America, and the tendency away from state intervention in the economy. Some imply a quiet optimism, suggesting that in the immediate future, vital U.S. and Latin American interest will run along a more parallel course. *The United States and Latin America in the 1980s,* edited by two political scientists, Kevin J. Middlebrook and Carlos Rico, presents a comprehensive set of essays surveying such concerns. Other significant publications include *The Democratic Revolution in Latin America* by Howard J. Wiarda and *Democracy in the Americas* edited by Robert A. Pastor, both of which discuss the eclipse of military and authoritarian governments in Latin America; and *Limits to Friendship: The United States and Mexico* by Robert A. Pastor and Jorge G. Castañeda, a wonderfully revealing series of dialogues from both the Mexican and U.S. points of view. Pastor's recent *Whirlpool: U.S. Foreign Policy toward Latin America and the Caribbean*, a survey of affairs under Carter, Reagan, and Bush, argues that "the end of the Cold War changed inter-American relations in important ways, but it did not liberate us from the whirlpool" – his term for the process "that draws the United States into its center, where it spins us in perilous eddies and then, just as suddenly, releases us to drift to the rim, where we forget the region and deal with other matters." The

97–118; Roy Gutman, *Banana Diplomacy: The Making of American Policy in Nicaragua, 1981–1987* (New York, 1988), a journalist's account emphasizing personalities and bureaucratic politics; and George Black, *The Good Neighbor: How the United States Wrote the History of Central America and the Caribbean* (New York, 1988), another journalist's account depicting U.S. policy as the product of arrogance, self-delusion, and ignorance.

For consideration of related matters consult Cheryl A. Rubenberg, "U.S. Policy toward Nicaragua and Iran and the Iran-Contra Affair: Reflections on the Continuity of American Foreign Policy," *Third World Quarterly* 10 (October 1988): 1467–1504; David Lewis Feldman, "The United States Role in the Malvinas Crisis, 1982: Misguidance and Misperception in Argentina's Decision to Go to War," *Journal of Inter-American Studies and World Affairs* 27 (Summer 1985): 1–22; and Joseph S. Tulchin, "The Malvinas War of 1982: An Inevitable Conflict that Never Should Have Occurred," *Latin American Research Review* 22:3 (1987): 123–41. Other significant matters come under discussion in William O. Walker III, *Drug Control in the Americas,* rev. ed. (Albuquerque, 1989); Donald J. Mabry, ed., *The Latin American Narcotics Trade and U.S. National Security* (New York, 1989); James W. Van West, "The U.S. State Department's Narcotics Control Policy in the Americas," *Journal of Inter-American Studies and World Affairs* 30 (Summer/Fall 1988).

end of the Cold War has not solved the recurring problems of the hemisphere. "What the end of the Cold War does offer is time to learn from past mistakes and to use new opportunities presented by the more important trends of democracy and freer trade." Similarly, Jorge G. Castañeda in *Utopia Unarmed: The Latin American Left after the Cold War* sees an opportunity to transform political groups critical of the status quo into a genuinely democratic force. This volume also discusses thoroughly the history of radical movements in Latin America during the era of the Cold War and the debilitating effects of identification with the Soviet Union. A compilation of essays by political scientists edited by Jonathan Hartlyn, Lars Schoultz, and Augusto Varas, *The United States and Latin America in the 1990s: Beyond the Cold War*, surveys current political and economic tendencies and arrives at some moderatively hopeful projections into the future. Progress and change in some measure seem on the move in Latin America. Finally, two works by Abraham F. Lowenthal establish concluding perspectives. In *Partners in Conflict: The United States and Latin America,* Lowenthal examines the principal issues affecting U.S.-Latin American relations and depicts the widespread changes that have occurred in Latin America during the past twenty-five years. As he explains, Latin American countries have become more urban, industrial, and middle class and less subject to U.S. coercion. He hopes for the inauguration of a new era of friendship, featuring new policies in the United States based upon higher levels of cooperation and *confianza*. Similarly in an edited work, *Exporting Democracy: The United States and Latin America*, Lowenthal and other scholars applaud the retreat of Latin American authoritarianism, evaluate earlier U.S. efforts to promote democracy, and set forth "a cautionary tale." According to Lowenthal, "Past U.S. attempts to promote Latin American democracy have met with little enduring success." As he remarks, "Although the idea that the United States knows how to export democracy is widely accepted today, the historical record strongly suggests reasons for skepticism."[47]

47 Kevin J. Middlebrook and Carlos Rico, eds., *The United States and Latin America in the 1980s: Contending Perspectives on a Decade of Crisis* (Pittsburgh, 1986); Howard J. Wiarda, *The Democratic Revolution in Latin America: History, Politics, and U.S. Policy* (New York, 1990); Robert A. Pastor, ed., *Democracy in the Americas:*

Some of the recent writing suggests a renewed appreciation for mutualities and compatibilities of interest between the United States and the countries of Latin America. Nevertheless, the main body of historical literature reviewed here emphasizes the disparities and divergences of national aims and aspirations. The United States and Latin America have had much less in common than Pan-American mythologies have claimed. In addition, historians and other students of inter-American relations have confirmed the point. Though not fully formed, the contours of an evolving synthesis have appeared around elaborations and refinements of the radical point of view. Although the scholarship on U.S.-Latin American relations is by no means monolithic, historians for the most part have criticized U.S. policies toward Latin America since the Second World War, alleging oftentimes the practice of imperious if indeed not imperialistic behavior. Historians generally have embraced sets of assumptions different from those of the policymakers and also have displayed a measure of discomfort with official views. Whether a fully articulated synthesis will ever come into existence is problematic. One conceivable approach might amalgamate radical thinking with aspects of the world-system analysis recently advocated by Thomas J. McCormick and thereby place the study of U.S. relations with Latin America more securely in a global political and economic context.[48] Meanwhile, the dialectical nature of historical investigation and debate should enliven the field and amplify our understanding of diplomatic relationships between the United States and the diverse countries of Latin America.

Stopping the Pendulum (New York, 1989); idem and Jorge G. Castañeda, *Limits to Friendship: The United States and Mexico* (New York, 1988), 1–18; Pastor, *Whirlpool, U.S. Foreign Policy toward Latin America and the Caribbean* (Princeton, 1992), xi; Castañeda, *Utopia Unarmed, The Latin American Left after the Cold War* (New York, 1993); Jonathan Hartlyn, Lars Schoultz, and Augusto Varas, *The United States and Latin America in the 1990s: Beyond the Cold War* (Chapel Hill, 1992); Abraham F. Lowenthal, *Partners in Conflict: The United States and Latin America* (Baltimore, 1987), chap. 7; idem, ed., *Exporting Democracy, The United States and Latin America* (Baltimore, 1991), x. For a full-scale study, also somewhat skeptical, see Tony Smith, *America's Mission, The United States and the Worldwide Struggle for Democracy in the Twentieth Century.*

48 Thomas J. McCormick, *America's Half-Century: United States Foreign Policy in the Cold War* (Baltimore, 1989). W. Dirk Raat attempted a "world-systems analysis" in *Mexico and the United States: Ambivalent Vistas.*

16

Gideon's Band: America and the Middle East since 1945

DOUGLAS LITTLE

> The people stared at us every where, and we stared at them. We generally made them feel rather small, too, before we got done with them, because we bore down on them with America's greatness until we crushed them. . . .
>
> If ever those children of Israel in Palestine forget when Gideon's Band went through there from America, they ought to be cursed once more and finished. It was the rarest spectacle that ever astounded mortal eyes, perhaps.
>
> Mark Twain, *The Innocents Abroad*

On a rainy Saturday in June 1867, Mark Twain scurried down Wall Street and boarded the *S.S. Quaker City*, a first-class steamer bound for the Holy Land, where he would witness one of America's earliest and best publicized encounters with the Middle East. Expecting to find a blend of Old World splendor and Christian asceticism in a setting as familiar as the nearest bible, Twain's fellow travelers – self-styled pilgrims who hailed from Boston, St. Louis, and points west – stumbled instead into terra incognita. Appalled by scenes of oriental squalor, harried by constant demands for baksheesh, and astonished by how little nineteenth-century Arabs and Jews resembled idealized biblical figures, Twain's innocents abroad scrambled back aboard the *Quaker City* and steamed home, leaving the Middle East to the handful of American missionaries and merchants for whom the exotic region remained a life's work.

Just a century after Twain's calamitous 1867 excursion to the Holy Land, the United States would emerge as the preeminent power in the Middle East. Two wars – one hot and one cold –

transformed modest religious and commercial interests into a compelling stake in the political stability of a region whose economic and strategic importance is now unparalleled. Having ridden a wave of oil to military triumph in 1945 and to postwar prosperity thereafter, U.S. officials quickly came to regard secure access to Persian Gulf petroleum as their central objective in the Middle East. Achieving that objective, however, would not be easy. The erosion of British and French influence and the growth of Soviet interest in the region frequently produced diplomatic schizophrenia as American policymakers struggled to strike a delicate balance between anticolonialism and anticommunism. America's emerging special relationship with Israel was increasingly difficult to square with its rhetorical support for Arab self-determination. And America's burgeoning global responsibilities often diverted attention away from the Middle East to more acute problems in Europe or Asia.

From the very start, scholars and statesmen alike found it almost impossible to reconcile these seemingly irreconcilable interests. Despite repeated efforts to clarify U.S. priorities in the region during the quarter century after the Second World War, more often than not U.S. policies appeared confusing and self-contradictory. Gradually, however, the rough outlines of a distinctly American approach toward the Middle East did begin to emerge. By the early 1970s, America had lined up three pillars – Israel, Iran, and Saudi Arabia – with whose help it hoped to fill the vacuum created by Britain's departure and keep the region's oil out of the hands of the Arab radicals and their friends in the Kremlin. Thanks to the rich array of American, European, and Israeli archival material that has become available during the past decade, historians have been able to chart with greater and greater precision how Gideon's Band has fared since beginning its long-running return engagement in the Middle East in 1945.[1]

On the eve of the Second World War, the Middle East remained for most Americans what it had been for the pilgrims aboard the *Quaker City* seventy years earlier – terra incognita. In

1 For an up-to-date compendium of the recent scholarship on American policy toward the Middle East see Sanford R. Silverburg and Bernard Reich, *U.S. Foreign Relations with the Middle East and North Africa: A Bibliography* (Metuchen, NJ, 1994).

his classic account of the prewar era, John DeNovo argued that before 1939, the U.S. presence in the region was still mainly cultural and religious – "economic aspiration bulked larger than economic reality; political ambition and strategic concern were virtually absent." To be sure, DeNovo acknowledged that the discovery of oil in the Persian Gulf and the collapse of the Ottoman Empire tempted Woodrow Wilson and his successors to expand America's role.[2] Recent accounts have shown that U.S. officials were somewhat more sympathetic toward Arab nationalism and far more deeply involved in Iraqi petroleum during the 1920s than many Americans realized.[3] Down through 1939, however, Washington regarded the Middle East as a European sphere of influence where U.S. interests were better served by private investment in the region's oil than by public involvement in regional affairs.[4]

The Second World War changed all that. Rapidly expanding wartime energy requirements dictated a greater government role in securing American access to the rich oil fields that rimmed the Persian Gulf.[5] The anticolonial rhetoric of the Atlantic Charter helped spark nationalist challenges to British and French rule from Baghdad to Beirut and forced the United States to pay closer attention to Arab aspirations for self-determination.[6] Hitler's

2 John DeNovo, *American Interests and Policies in the Middle East, 1900–1939* (Minneapolis, 1963). The quote is on pp. vii–viii.

3 See William Stivers, *Supremacy and Oil: Iraq, Turkey, and the Anglo-American World Order, 1918–1930* (Ithaca, 1982); F. W. Brecher, "Charles R. Crane's Crusade for the Arabs, 1919–1939," *Middle Eastern Studies* 24 (January 1988): 42–55; and David Fromkin, *A Peace to End All Peace: The Fall of the Ottoman Empire and the Creation of the Modern Middle East* (New York, 1989), 389–402.

4 See especially John A. DeNovo, "On the Sidelines: The United States and the Middle East between the Wars, 1919–1939," and Barry Rubin, "America as Junior Partner: Anglo-American Relations in the Middle East, 1919–1939," both in *The Great Powers in the Middle East, 1919–1939*, ed. Uriel Dann (New York, 1988). On America and the Arabs during the interwar years see Hisham H. Ahmed, "From the Balfour Declaration to World War II: The U.S. Stand on Palestinian Self-Determination," *Arab Studies Quarterly* 12 (Winter/Spring 1990): 9–41.

5 Michael Stoff, *Oil, War, and American Security: The Search for a National Policy on Foreign Oil* (New Haven, 1980); Daniel Yergin, *The Prize: The Epic Quest for Oil, Money, and Power* (New York, 1991), 391–408.

6 Aviel Roshwald, *Estranged Bedfellows: Britain and France in the Middle East during the Second World War* (New York, 1990); Thomas A. Bryson, *Seeds of Mideast Crisis: The United States Diplomatic Role in the Middle East during World War II* (Jefferson, NC, 1981).

slaughter of European Jewry prompted American Zionists to redouble their efforts to win U.S. support for the creation of a Jewish homeland in Palestine first outlined a quarter century earlier in the Balfour Declaration.[7] And fears of a postwar depression led some in Washington to try to loosen Europe's grip on the markets of the Middle East in order to open the door for American exports.[8] Phillip Baram has woven all these themes – the quest for oil, the specter of Arab nationalism, the Zionist dream, the economic and diplomatic rivalry with Britain and France – into a comprehensive study that unfolds against the backdrop of America's emerging confrontation with the Soviet Union. Although Baram's depiction of key U.S. officials as anti-Semitic seems too harsh, his analysis of the State Department's wartime strategy – neutralize the French and the British, ignore the Zionists, outmaneuver the Soviets, and "encourage individual Arab states to be free, sovereign, and pro-American" – provides an excellent blueprint for America's earliest efforts to cope with new challenges in the Middle East after V-J Day.[9]

The economic and strategic imperatives of the Cold War quickly made the words "Middle East" synonymous with national security in Harry Truman's Washington. In the beginning, there was oil. Much of the Truman administration's attention was focused on Saudi Arabia, where the Arabian-American Oil Company (ARAMCO), a wholly-owned subsidiary of Texaco and Standard Oil of California, held an exclusive concession. Rejecting earlier exposés of a sinister "brotherhood of oil"[10] as too simplistic, recent scholarship has revealed an increasingly symbiotic relationship between ARAMCO executives eager to shore up sagging

7 Michael J. Cohen, *Palestine: Retreat from the Mandate – The Making of British Policy, 1936–45* (New York, 1978), 125–39; David S. Wyman, *The Abandonment of the Jews: America and the Holocaust, 1941–1945* (New York, 1984), 157–92.

8 John DeNovo, "The Culbertson Economic Mission and Anglo-American Tensions in the Middle East, 1944–1945," *Journal of American History* 63 (March 1977): 913–36; Nathan Godfried, *Bridging the Gap between Rich and Poor: American Development Policy toward the Arab East, 1942–1949* (Westport, 1987); idem, "Economic Development and Regionalism: United States Foreign Relations in the Middle East, 1942–5," *Journal of Contemporary History* 22 (July 1987): 481–500.

9 Phillip Baram, *The Department of State in the Middle East, 1919–1945* (Philadelphia, 1978). The quote in on pp. 56–57.

10 Robert Engler, *The Brotherhood of Oil: Energy Policy and the Public Interest* (Chicago, 1977).

profits and fend off foreign competitors and American policymakers eager to use Saudi crude to fuel the postwar economic recovery of Western Europe. Relying heavily on corporate archives and interviews with oil company officials, Irvine Anderson has argued persuasively that America's deepening involvement in Persian Gulf petroleum during the 1940s resulted less from ARAMCO's aggressive lobbying than from shrewd State and Commerce department planning that converted the firm into an informal instrument of U.S. diplomacy.[11] In his masterful account of Saudi-American relations under Roosevelt and Truman, Aaron Miller confirms the confluence of corporate and government interests regarding Middle East oil and highlights the crucial role played by a newly emerging national security bureaucracy preoccupied with broad economic and strategic concerns rather than narrow balance-sheet calculations.[12]

Having defined secure access to Persian Gulf oil as central to American national security, the Truman administration took a series of steps designed to facilitate its informal partnership with ARAMCO and other petroleum giants. To forestall British encroachments in Saudi Arabia, the United States wooed King Ibn Saud with military assistance. To ensure that Saudi oil flowed west to fuel the Marshall Plan, the State Department helped ARAMCO steer through a thicket of inter-Arab rivalries to complete a new Trans-Arabian Pipeline (TAPLINE) stretching from Dhahran to Sidon in Lebanon. And to encourage U.S. oil firms to coordinate their operations in the Middle East, Harry Truman himself very reluctantly halted criminal antitrust proceedings against ARAMCO and its parents.[13] David Painter has employed a corporatist framework to place these Middle Eastern developments into a global context in his superb overview of American

11 Irvine Anderson, *ARAMCO, the United States, and Saudi Arabia: A Study of the Dynamics of Foreign Oil Policy 1933–1950* (Princeton, 1981).

12 Aaron David Miller, *Search for Security: Saudi Arabian Oil and American Foreign Policy, 1939–1948* (Chapel Hill, 1980).

13 James L. Gormly, "Keeping the Door Open in Saudi Arabia: The United States and the Dhahran Airfield, 1945–46," *Diplomatic History* 4 (Spring 1980): 189–205; Douglas Little, "Pipeline Politics: America, TAPLINE, and the Arabs," *Business History Review* 64 (Summer 1990): 255–85; Burton I. Kaufman, "Mideast Multinational Oil, U.S. Foreign Policy, and Antitrust: The 1950s," *Journal of American History* 63 (March 1977): 937–59.

oil policy during the first decade of the Cold War. From Mexico to Venezuela and from Saudi Arabia to Iran, he traces the evolution of a mutually beneficial strategy in which private enterprise oversaw day-to-day operations in the oil fields while public officials combatted Third World nationalism and British imperialism. Although he is the first to admit that what was best for ARAMCO was not always what was best for America, Painter argues that a business-government partnership was probably the best option available in the Middle East as the Truman administration geared up for its struggle for supremacy with the Kremlin.[14]

Soviet strong-arm tactics in Eastern Europe and Soviet encouragement for nationalist revolutions in East Asia had led many in Washington to prophesy as early as 1945 that Moscow would soon resort to military intervention or political subversion to undermine Western influence in the Middle East. The possibility of a Communist victory in the Greek civil war, the Kremlin's persistent diplomatic pressure on Turkey, and the presence of thousands of Russian troops in Iran eventually prompted the Truman administration to embrace containment as the best antidote against potential Soviet inroads from the Persian Gulf to the Suez Canal. The nature of Russia's intentions in the Middle East during the late 1940s and the appropriateness of America's response have sparked much scholarly controversy. Some observers have argued that the Soviet threat to U.S. strategic and economic interests in the region was all too real.[15] In the view of Bruce Kuniholm, for example, Truman was able to thwart Russian designs on the Middle East only by mixing liberal doses of American military aid with large amounts of diplomatic bluster.[16]

14 David S. Painter, *Oil and the American Century: The Political Economy of U.S. Foreign Oil Policy, 1941–1954* (Baltimore, 1986). In his *United States Foreign Oil Policy, 1919–1948: For Profits and Security* (Montreal, 1985), Stephen J. Randall traces many of these themes back through the interwar years and includes material on Canada and the Netherlands East Indies but does not employ Painter's corporatist framework.

15 See Barry M. Rubin, *Great Powers in the Middle East, 1941–1947: The Road to Cold War* (Totowa, NJ, 1980); and Galia Golan, *Soviet Policies in the Middle East: From World War II to Gorbachev* (New York, 1990), 29–43.

16 Bruce R. Kuniholm, *The Origins of the Cold War in the Near East: Great Power Conflict and Diplomacy in Iran, Turkey, and Greece* (Princeton, 1980).

Other scholars contend that U.S. policymakers overreacted to what was at best a Soviet spoiling operation.[17] In his magisterial study of Truman's national security policy, Melvyn Leffler makes a strong case that American officials exaggerated the Russian menace, escalating local problems into global ones and legitimating their own quest for strategic bases in the Middle East.[18] This debate over the Kremlin's motives is not likely to be settled until we have access to Soviet archives.

Most scholars agree, however, that during the tense months between the fall of China and the outbreak of the Korean War, the threat of Russian expansion in the Middle East, whether real or imagined, haunted top American officials, who reluctantly sought British help in shoring up regional defense.[19] Wm. Roger Louis has reconstructed the complex story of America's ambivalent relationship with Britain in the Middle East from 1945 to 1951 in a panoramic masterwork that remains, a decade after its publication, the definitive account.[20] Louis provides a brilliant portrait of Foreign Secretary Ernest Bevin, who struggled for six years to preserve British influence in the Middle East by converting a formal empire into an informal one. Relying on American military muscle to prevent Soviet encroachments along the "northern tier" that stretched from Greece to Iran, the British would be free to consolidate their own influence in the Arab world by pursuing an accommodation with "moderate nationalists" in Iraq and Egypt. Ingenious as it was in theory, Bevin's scheme was in practice plagued by a series of Anglo-American squabbles during the late 1940s that embittered policymakers on both sides of the Atlantic. U.S. officials accused the British of poaching on ARAMCO's oil concession in Saudi Arabia, U.K. officials charged that the Americans were playing politics with

17 Bruce D. Porter, *The USSR in Third World Conflicts: Soviet Arms and Diplomacy in Local Wars, 1945–1980* (New York, 1984), 14–15; Hashim S. H. Behbehani, *The Soviet Union and Arab Nationalism, 1917–1966* (New York, 1986), 56–68.

18 Melvyn P. Leffler, *A Preponderance of Power: National Security, the Truman Administration, and the Cold War* (Stanford, 1992), 77–81, 121–25, 237–46.

19 Bruce R. Kuniholm, "U.S. Policy in the Near East: The Triumphs and Tribulations of the Truman Administration," in *The Truman Presidency*, ed. Michael J. Lacey (New York, 1989); Leffler, *Preponderance of Power*, 351–53.

20 Wm. Roger Louis, *The British Empire in the Middle East, 1945–1951: Arab Nationalism, the United States, and Postwar Imperialism* (New York, 1984).

Palestine, and each side blamed the other for fueling the revolution of rising expectations among Muslim nationalists hellbent on achieving self-determination as soon as possible.

Determined that the Middle East must not go the way of East Asia, Washington and London tried to set aside their differences in the early 1950s in order to promote a system of regional security some likened to NATO. As a first step, in May 1950 U.S. and U.K. diplomats brokered the Tripartite Declaration, under which America, Britain, and France embraced the principles of arms limitation and territorial integrity in the Middle East.[21] Later that year, British and American officials unveiled plans for a new Middle East Command (MEC) based at Suez and charged with building an anti-Soviet strategic consensus throughout the region. The proposed MEC, however, foundered on the shoals of revolutionary nationalism, as did the Middle East Defense Organization (MEDO) that was supposed to succeed it.[22] Not for the last time, American officials had deluded themselves that Egyptian and Iranian nationalists would regard Soviet expansion as a greater threat than British imperialism. And not for the last time, Washington was caught off guard by anti-British outbursts in Cairo and Tehran. Unwilling to be tarred with the brush of colonialism, the Truman administration distanced itself from Whitehall in 1951, undermining Britain's bargaining position in Egypt and opposing British plans for military intervention in Iran.[23] By the time Truman left office, the United States was poised to supplant Great Britain as the most influential power in Iran and elsewhere in the Middle East.[24]

There is no shortage of books and articles on American relations with Iran after the Second World War, nor is there any

21 Shlomo Slonim, "Origins of the 1950 Tripartite Declaration on the Middle East," *Middle Eastern Studies* 23 (April 1987): 135–49.

22 Peter L. Hahn, "Containment and Egyptian Nationalism: The Unsuccessful Effort to Establish the Middle East Command, 1950–53," *Diplomatic History* 11 (Winter 1987): 23–40.

23 H. W. Brands, "The Cairo-Tehran Connection in Anglo-American Rivalry in the Middle East, 1951–1953," *International History Review* 11 (August 1989): 432–56.

24 For an account that employs a more theoretical framework to analyze Anglo-American rivalry not only in the Middle East but also in Africa down through 1960 see Wm. Roger Louis and Ronald Robinson, "The Imperialism of Decolonization," *Journal of Imperial and Commonwealth History* 22 (September 1994): 462–509.

shortage of historical controversy. Among the first to explore the documentary record of Washington's deepening postwar ties with Tehran was Richard Pfau, who contended in 1977 that Truman's "get tough" approach toward Stalin reflected an accurate assessment of the Soviet threat to Iran.[25] Writing three years later at the height of Khomeini's anti-American revolution, Barry Rubin argued that U.S. policy toward the shah's Iran was "paved with good intentions" – saving the country from Russian aggression in 1946, shielding it from British imperialism in 1951, then saving it again from Mohammed Mossadegh's reckless left-wing nationalism in 1953.[26] Echoing Pfau and Rubin, Bruce Kuniholm interpreted American policy in Iran as a legitimate response to Soviet adventurism, which gradually forced Truman to embrace the shah.[27]

Other scholars, however, believe Washington overreacted to Moscow's initiatives and misunderstood the complex political situation in Tehran. Amin Saikal, for example, has questioned America's good intentions, highlighting instead the growing U.S. interest in Iranian oil and depicting the shah as something of a Frankenstein's monster, created by but not controllable from Washington.[28] Mark H. Lytle has likewise documented how knee-jerk anticommunism, American exceptionalism, and petrodiplomacy drew the Truman adminstration into an alliance with an increasingly autocratic regime in Tehran during the late 1940s.[29] Relying on an impressive array of Farsi sources, Stephen McFarland has argued that the United States blundered into a trap laid by Iran, whose leaders had actively been seeking outside help for more than a century in resolving their nagging boundary disputes with Russia.[30] James F. Goode's critique goes even further, showing how the ideological short-sightedness and the fiscal

25 Richard Pfau, "Containment in Iran, 1946: The Shift to an Active Policy," *Diplomatic History* 1 (Fall 1977): 359–72.
26 Barry Rubin, *Paved with Good Intentions: The American Experience and Iran* (New York, 1980).
27 Kuniholm, *Origins of the Cold War in the Near East*, 304–50.
28 Amin Saikal, *The Rise and Fall of the Shah* (Princeton, 1980).
29 Mark H. Lytle, *The Origins of the Iranian-American Alliance, 1941–1953* (New York, 1987).
30 Stephen L. McFarland, "A Peripheral View of the Origins of the Cold War: The Crises in Iran, 1941–1947," *Diplomatic History* 4 (Fall 1980): 333–51.

tight-fistedness of top U.S. officials played into the hands of the shah, who persuaded Washington that the Communist threat was too great and his economic resources too limited to risk establishing the constitutional monarchy that Iranian nationalists regarded as the only hope for long-term stability in Tehran.[31]

In the end, it was nationalist attacks against Britain's monopoly over Iranian oil, not Communist machinations against the Pahlavi dynasty, that triggered the crisis that cemented American ties with the shah. Ervand Abrahamian and Richard Cottam have confirmed how bitterly firebrands like Mohammed Mossadegh resented the power and wealth of the Anglo-Iranian Oil Company (AIOC) and how central the struggle over petroleum was to the rise of nationalism in postwar Iran.[32] Wm. Roger Louis and Mary Ann Heiss have traced how AIOC's refusal to accept Prime Minister Mossadegh's demands for higher royalties set off a chain reaction leading first to Iranian expropriation, then to reluctant American support for Britain's boycott of Iran's oil, and eventually to energetic U.K. and U.S. covert action in Tehran.[33] And James Bill has shown how such covert meddling set in motion a self-fulfilling prophecy, driving Mossadegh leftward and fanning the fires of Iranian anti-Americanism.[34]

Few CIA projects have been as well publicized or as widely debated as Operation Ajax, the code-name for the American-backed coup that deposed Mossadegh in August 1953. Although the British and American masterminds of the plot confirmed the story in memoirs published more than a decade ago, key documents

31 James F. Goode, *The United States and Iran, 1946–1951: The Diplomacy of Neglect* (New York, 1989). See also idem, "The United States and the Shah: The Metamorphosis of a Relationship, 1941–1976" (Paper presented at the 1993 OAH Convention in Anaheim, California).

32 Ervand Abrahamiam, *Iran between Two Revolutions* (Princeton, 1982), 261–80; Richard Cottam, *Nationalism in Iran: Updated through 1978* (Pittsburgh, 1979), 259–85.

33 Louis, *British Empire in the Middle East*, 632–89; Mary Ann Heiss, "The United States, Great Britain, and Iranian Oil, 1951–1954" (Ph.D. diss., Ohio State University, 1991). For a discussion of how U.S. covert action in 1953 opened the way for U.S. penetration of the U.K. oil monopoly in Iran a year later see Mary Ann Heiss, "The United States, Great Britain, and the Creation of the Iranian Oil Consortium, 1953–1954," *International History Review* 16 (August 1994): 511–35.

34 James Bill, *The Eagle and the Lion: The Tragedy of American-Iranian Relations* (New Haven, 1988).

remain classified.[35] But thanks to the sleuthing of Mark Gasiorowski, who tracked down and interviewed over twenty CIA veterans of the Iranian caper, we have as detailed a picture of the 1953 coup as we are likely to get. Proposed by Whitehall, rejected by Truman, and resurrected by Eisenhower, Operation Ajax enlisted right-wing officers and clerics to save the shah's throne.[36] While early accounts interpreted the coup as economically motivated,[37] more recently a consensus has emerged that Mossadegh's challenge to multinational oil was less worrisome for Washington than his apparent flirtation with Moscow.[38]

There is no consensus, however, regarding the larger question of whether Mossadegh would have fallen without CIA covert action. Citing the old man's increasingly erratic and autocratic behavior, some scholars wonder, in the words of Moyara de Moraes Ruehsen, "how long Mussadiq could have survived on his own had the coup not taken place."[39] Others, most notably Gasiorowski and Bill, insist that without CIA help, Mossadegh's foes would, like the shah himself, have cut and run.[40] What mattered most in the long run, as Richard Cottam has recently

35 On the CIA role see Kermit Roosevelt, *Countercoup* (New York, 1979). On the MI6 role see Christopher Montague Woodhouse, *Something Ventured* (London, 1982). As late as 1989, the CIA succeeded in preventing the publication of any material relating to Operation Ajax. See U.S. Department of State, *Foreign Relations of the United States 1952–1954* (Washington, 1989), 10 (hereafter *FRUS* with appropriate year and volume). For a discussion of the problems surrounding the declassification of materials relating to CIA operations elsewhere in the Middle East see Peter L. Hahn, "*Glasnost* in America: *Foreign Relations of the United States* and the Middle East, 1955–1960," *Diplomatic History* 16 (Fall 1992): 631–42.

36 Mark J. Gasiorowski, "The 1953 Coup d'Etat in Iran," *International Journal of Middle East Studies* 19 (May 1987): 261–86.

37 David Horowitz, *The Free World Colossus: A Critique of American Foreign Policy in the Cold War* (New York, 1965), 187–88; Richard J. Barnet, *Intervention and Revolution: America's Confrontation with Insurgent Movements Around the World* (New York, 1971), 225–29; Joyce and Gabriel Kolko, *The Limits of Power: The World and United States Foreign Policy, 1945–1954* (New York, 1971), 413–20.

38 See John Prados, *President's Secret Wars: CIA and Pentagon Covert Operations from World War II through Iranscam* (New York, 1986), 91–98; John Ranelagh, *The Agency: The Rise and Decline of the CIA* (New York, 1986), 260–64; and Kuross A. Samii, *Involvement by Invitation: American Strategies of Containment in Iran* (University Park, PA, 1987), 113–45.

39 Moyara de Moraes Ruehsen, "Operation 'Ajax' Revisited: Iran, 1953," *Middle Eastern Studies* 29 (July 1993): 482.

40 Mark J. Gasiorowski, *U.S. Foreign Policy and the Shah: Building a Client State in Iran* (Ithaca, 1991), 72–84; Bill, *Eagle and Lion*, 86–97. See also Stephen E. Ambrose, *Ike's Spies: Eisenhower and the Espionage Establishment* (Garden City, 1981), 189–214.

pointed out, was that the Iranian people saw the CIA as the guiding hand behind America's special relationship with the shah, something that would not escape the Ayatollah Khomeini's notice a quarter century later.[41]

Meanwhile, a rather different special relationship was emerging between the United States and Israel during the two decades after 1945. America's role in the creation of the Jewish state has received more scholarly attention than almost any other diplomatic issue in the immediate postwar period. Few would disagree with Peter Grose's verdict that Harry Truman received an ambiguous and ambivalent legacy from Franklin Roosevelt, who publicly supported a Jewish homeland in Palestine but privately counseled Zionist leaders to go slow while permitting the State Department bureaucracy to undermine their efforts to spirit Jews out of Hitler's Europe to safety in the Holy Land. Truman's approach proved far more straightforward, pressing Britain to lift its restrictions on Jewish immigration to Palestine in 1946, backing Zionist efforts to win United Nations support for partition instead of trusteeship in 1947, and, after thwarting a last-minute flip-flop engineered at Foggy Bottom, recognizing the new state of Israel in May 1948.[42]

Secretary of State George Marshall privately accused Truman of playing politics, a charge echoed in the initial scholarly accounts of the episode despite subsequent denials by White House counsel Clark Clifford.[43] As early as 1949, Frank Manuel hinted that Truman's speedy recognition of Israel was calculated to sew up the Jewish vote in the 1948 presidential election, an argument John Snetsinger made explicit twenty-five years later.[44] The

41 Richard Cottam, *Iran & the United States: A Cold War Case Study* (Pittsburgh, 1988), 189–207.

42 Peter Grose, *Israel in the Mind of America* (New York, 1983), 137–58, 277–98; idem, "The President versus the Diplomats," in *The End of the Palestine Mandate*, ed. Wm. Roger Louis and Robert W. Stookey (Austin, 1986), 32–60. For an early but still useful appraisal of Roosevelt's legacy on Palestine see Samuel Halperin and Irvin Oder, "The United States in Search of a Policy: Franklin D. Roosevelt and Palestine," *Review of Politics* 24 (July 1962): 320–41.

43 For Marshall's caustic comments see Marshall memcon, 12 May 1948, *FRUS, 1948* (Washington, 1976), 5:972–77. For Clifford's denials see Clark Clifford, "Recognizing Israel," *American Heritage* 28 (April 1977); and idem, *Counsel to the President* (New York, 1991), 3–25.

44 Frank Manuel, *The Realities of American-Palestine Relations* (Washington, 1949); John Snetsinger, *Truman, the Jewish Vote, and the Creation of Israel* (Stanford, 1974).

declassification of records at the Truman Library and the National Archives during the early 1970s enabled Kenneth Bain and Evan Wilson to document the linkage between domestic politics and Truman's diplomatic decisions in the Middle East.[45] The opening of the British archives later that decade allowed Roger Louis to show how, from Whitehall's point of view, the White House had made Palestine a political football.[46]

The calculus of geopolitics, however, seems to have been at least as important in shaping U.S. policy toward Palestine as election-year algebra. Arguing that the Zionist lobby in Washington hurt Israel's case as often as it helped, Zvi Ganin attributes Truman's support for the Jewish state to mounting frustration over Arab intransigence and to growing awareness of British weakness. Domestic political considerations, Ganin argues persuasively, affected only the timing of the American decision to recognize Israel, not the decision itself.[47] Moreover, Fred Lawson has reminded us that, domestic politics notwithstanding, after 1948 the Truman administration grew increasingly unhappy with the Israelis, who ignored U.S. efforts to resolve the explosive issue of Palestinian refugees.[48] Furthermore, Bruce Evensen has recently contended that Truman's Palestine policies were influenced less by pro-Israel public opinion than by pressure from well-placed proponents of collective security eager to demonstrate the effectiveness of the newly created United Nations in conflict resolution.[49]

The geopolitical aspects of Truman's handling of the Palestine imbroglio have been articulated most clearly in the work of Michael Cohen. Utilizing archival materials on three continents, Cohen argued a decade ago that U.S. support for the creation of Israel was largely a function of great-power jockeying for position in an arena where British vulnerability meant that the new Jewish state might in a pinch become a key strategic asset against

45 Kenneth Ray Bain, *The March to Zion: United States Policy and the Founding of Israel* (College Station, 1979); Evan M. Wilson, *Decision on Palestine: How the U.S. Came to Recognize Israel* (Stanford, 1979).
46 Louis, *British Empire in the Middle East*, 381–572.
47 Zvi Ganin, *Truman, American Jewry, and Israel, 1945–1948* (New York, 1979).
48 Fred H. Lawson, "The Truman Administration and the Palestinians," *Arab Studies Quarterly* 12 (Winter/Spring 1990): 43–65.
49 Bruce J. Evensen, "A Story of 'Ineptness': The Truman Administration's Struggle to Shape Conventional Wisdom on Palestine at the Beginning of the Cold War," *Diplomatic History* 15 (Summer 1991): 339–59.

the Soviet Union.[50] Cohen, however, goes too far in his latest book, where in his zeal to downplay Truman's domestic political motives, he paints the Missouri Democrat as an anti-Semite and a closet anti-Zionist whose attitudes were not far removed from those of Loy Henderson and like-minded folks at Foggy Bottom.[51] To be sure, one ought not to swallow entirely David McCullough's recent rather dewy-eyed portrait of faithful Harry doing God's work in the Holy Land.[52] But there is still something to be said for the more complex account of Truman's efforts to square his own political and humanitarian concerns with hard-headed State Department realpolitik that H. W. Brands has presented in his biography of Henderson.[53]

Long after 1948, the tension between political realities at home and realpolitik abroad has continued to color American relations with Israel and to shape the historical dialogue about the nature of those relations. In a pair of tendentious books, Stephen Green has depicted every postwar administration but Eisenhower's as excessively pro-Israel and dismissed most American policies in the Middle East as transparent efforts to win the support of influential American Jews.[54] According to Cheryl Rubenberg, four decades of pro-Israel lobbying in Washington left America unable to persuade the Israelis to accept the principle of Palestinian self-determination and unwilling to admit that the Jewish state had become a diplomatic liability rather than a strategic asset.[55] Edward Tivnan likewise maintains that the American Israel Public Affairs Committee (AIPAC) and other pro-Israel interest groups have weakened the United States in the Middle East while leaving the

50 Michael J. Cohen, *Palestine and the Great Powers, 1945–1948* (Princeton, 1982). For Soviet policy on Palestine see Oles M. Smolansky, "The Soviet Role in the Emergence of Israel," in Louis and Stookey, eds., *End of the Palestine Mandate*, 61–78.

51 Michael J. Cohen, *Truman and Israel* (Berkeley, 1990).

52 David McCullough, *Truman* (New York, 1992), 595–620.

53 H. W. Brands, *Inside the Cold War: A Biography of Loy Henderson* (New York, 1990), 165–92.

54 Stephen Green, *Taking Sides: America's Secret Relations with a Militant Israel* (New York, 1984); idem, *Living by the Sword: America and Israel in the Middle East, 1968–87* (Brattleboro, VT, 1988). For a provocative critique of U.S. policy toward Israel stressing regional concerns rather than domestic politics see Noam Chomsky, *The Fateful Triangle: The United States, Israel, and the Palestinians* (Boston, 1983), 9–37.

55 Cheryl A. Rubenberg, *Israel and the American National Interest: A Critical Examination* (Chicago, 1986).

Israelis dangerously dependent on U.S. economic largesse.[56] Seymour Hersh has contended that sympathetic American Jews and friendly American bureaucrats helped ensure that Israel acquired nuclear weapons sooner rather than later.[57] Most recently, George and Douglas Ball have argued that a "passionate attachment" for Israel over the past half century has repeatedly led American policymakers to practice "unilateral diplomatic disarmament" in the Middle East at great cost to the United States.[58]

Other scholars interpret things rather differently. More than a decade ago, Nadav Safran reminded us how vulnerable Israel was in the years after 1948 and how anxious its leaders were over what they took to be signs of America's dispassionate detachment.[59] Indeed, Isaac Alteras has recently attributed the frosty relationship between the United States and Israel during the mid-1950s to American policies that appeared "even-handed" in Washington but "heavy-handed" in Tel Aviv.[60] In an important but at times tedious overview published in 1985, Steven Spiegel likewise portrayed the Middle East policies of Eisenhower and his successors as far less pro-Israel than Green or Rubenberg. According to Spiegel, more often than not, global or regional considerations were more important than elections or interest group politics in shaping American relations with Israel down through the late 1960s.[61] In fact, I. L. Kenen, who helped found AIPAC in 1958, insists that his organization always operated on the assumption that what was good for Israel was good for America and that it served merely as a badly needed counterweight to the well-funded Arab lobby on Capitol Hill.[62] And

56 Edward Tivnan, *The Lobby: Jewish Political Power and American Foreign Policy* (New York, 1987).

57 Seymour M. Hersh, *The Samson Option: Israel's Nuclear Arsenal and American Foreign Policy* (New York, 1991).

58 George and Douglas Ball, *The Passionate Attachment: America's Involvement with Israel, 1947 to the Present* (New York, 1992).

59 Nadav Safran, *Israel: The Embattled Ally* (Cambridge, MA, 1981), 333–80.

60 Isaac Alteras, *Eisenhower and Israel: U.S.-Israeli Relations, 1953–1960* (Gainesville, 1993).

61 Steven L. Spiegel, *The Other Arab-Israeli Conflict: Making America's Middle East Policy from Truman to Reagan* (Chicago, 1985).

62 I. L. Kenen, *Israel's Defense Line: Her Friends and Foes in Washington* (Buffalo, 1981). For an account more skeptical of Arab influence on Capitol Hill see Nabeel A. Khoury, "The Arab Lobby: Problems and Prospects," *Middle East Journal* 41 (Summer 1987): 379–96.

despite what Seymour Hersh says, Shai Feldman and others have argued that U.S. policymakers consistently opposed Israeli acquisition of nuclear weapons.[63]

Thanks to David Schoenbaum, we finally have a beautifully written synthesis that captures America's forty-five-year relationship with Israel in all its complexity. Acknowledging that narrow political calculations as well as broader strategic and humanitarian considerations predisposed Truman and most of his successors to sympathize with Israel, Schoenbaum is nevertheless quick to point out that Washington and Tel Aviv banged heads as early as 1949 over the Jewish state's territorial ambitions. From the Eisenhower era through the Bush years, Schoenbaum sees the special relationship as a paradox, where U.S. sympathy for Israel's thriving democracy was often undermined by U.S. frustration with Israel's unilateral diplomacy. Despite all the rhetoric about Israel as a strategic asset, relations between the two nations were always fraught with tension because neither side could ever agree whether the Jewish state ought to be America's partner or merely its proxy.[64]

Because America's relations with Israel looked much less paradoxical through Arab eyes, nationalist leaders from the Fertile Crescent to the Nile Delta cast a skeptical eye toward the United States during the years after 1945. Nowhere was the skepticism greater than in Egypt, where revolutionary officers led by Gamal Abdel Nasser seized power in July 1952. One of the few scholars to look carefully at relations between Washington and Cairo prior to the revolution is Peter Hahn, who has shown how America's strategic concerns clashed with Egypt's nationalist aspirations as early as 1946. Well aware of how vital the isthmus

63 Shai Feldman, *Israeli Nuclear Deterrence: A Strategy for the 1980s* (New York, 1982), 210–14; Shlomo Aronson, *The Politics and Strategy of Nuclear Weapons in the Middle East: Opacity, Theory, and Reality, 1960–1991* (Albany, 1991), 61–111. In the chapter on Israel in his *Nuclear Proliferation Today* (New York, 1984), Leonard Spector argues that the United States worked hard to prevent Israeli acquisition of nuclear weapons until 1970, at which point the Nixon administration quietly acquiesced.

64 David Schoenbaum, *The United States and the State of Israel* (New York, 1993). For a provocative account of the ambivalent relationship between Washington and Tel Aviv down through the early 1990s that places Schoenbaum's interpretation in a theoretical framework see Abraham Ben-Zvi, *The United States and Israel: The Limits of the Special Relationship* (New York, 1993).

of Suez and the canal that bisected it were not only to Whitehall's plans for informal empire in the Middle East but also to America's efforts to contain the Soviets, the Truman administration pressed the Egyptians to accept a British proposal acknowledging Egypt's full independence while preserving Britain's military presence. But Egypt's humiliating defeat by Israel in 1948 and Britain's high-handed dealings with Mossadegh's Iran shortly thereafter persuaded Egyptian nationalists that only the overthrow of the corrupt King Farouk and the expulsion of his British patrons could guarantee their country security and independence.[65]

The American response to the 1952 revolution that toppled Farouk was mixed. Despite earlier claims that the CIA actually helped plan Nasser's coup, Joel Gordon has used Egyptian sources to argue convincingly that the military takeover caught the United States by surprise.[66] Most scholars agree that although U.S. officials were troubled by the new regime's anti-British pronouncements and its anti-Israeli rhetoric, both the Truman and Eisenhower administrations initially held out some hope that Nasser and like-minded officers could bring about a revolution from above, fostering economic development and political reform while preventing a more radical social upheaval. To this end, the CIA cultivated close ties with Nasser's inner circle, the Pentagon hinted that Egypt might soon receive U.S. military assistance, and the White House pressured Whitehall to evacuate the huge British base on the banks of the Suez canal.[67]

Scholars disagree vehemently, however, over just what short-circuited this budding Egyptian-American rapprochement during the mid-1950s. Some, like Barry Rubin, blame Nasser, whose Pan-Arab nationalism and Third World neutralism seemed to jeopardize a whole range of U.S. interests from Persian Gulf oil

65 Peter L. Hahn, *United States, Great Britain, and Egypt, 1945–1956: Strategy and Diplomacy in the Early Cold War* (Chapel Hill, 1991), 38–130.

66 Joel Gordon, *Nasser's Blessed Movement* (New York, 1991). On alleged CIA involvement see Miles Copeland, *The Game of Nations: The Amorality of Power Politics* (New York, 1969), 57–72.

67 Muhammed Abd el-Wahab Sayed-Ahmed, *Nasser and American Foreign Policy, 1952–1956* (London, 1989); Laila Amin Morsy, "The Role of the United States in the Anglo-Egyptian Agreement of 1954," *Middle Eastern Studies* 29 (July 1993): 526–58.

to containment along the northern tier.[68] Others blame the British, whose ill-fated efforts to retain the Suez base arguably helped drive Nasser into the Kremlin's orbit.[69] Still others blame the Soviet Union, which under Nikita Khrushchev evidently regarded the Arab world as a target of opportunity in the Cold War.[70] A handful even blame Israel, which apparently used the Mossad to bomb U.S. installations in Cairo in a clumsy effort to poison Egyptian-American relations in 1954.[71] Most, however, would agree with Gail Meyer and Geoffrey Aronson that a major part of the blame must go to the Eisenhower administration for overestimating American economic leverage in Egypt and for underestimating Nasser's willingness to seek help from the Soviet bloc.[72] In any event, few would deny that the breakdown of U.S. relations with Egypt triggered the 1956 Suez crisis, which cast all the contradictions in America's Middle East policy into sharp relief.

The rapidly expanding literature on Suez probably warrants a review all to itself. Although dozens of memoirs and popular exposés appeared during the twenty-odd years after 1956, the first study based on American archival sources did not appear until 1981, when Donald Neff published his controversial *Warriors at Suez*, which remains easily the most readable account of the crisis. Writing from a pro-Nasser perspective, Neff argues that Israel's bloody raid on Egyptian troops at Gaza in February 1955 propelled Cairo toward a marriage of convenience with Moscow consummated by Egypt's purchase of arms from the

68 Barry Rubin, "America and the Egyptian Revolution, 1950–1957," *Political Science Quarterly* 97 (Spring 1982): 73–90.

69 Ritchie Ovendale, "Egypt and the Suez Base Agreement," in *The Foreign Policy of Churchill's Peacetime Administration, 1951–1955*, ed. John M. Young (Worcester, England, 1988), 135–55; Wm. Roger Louis, "The Tragedy of the Anglo-Egyptian Settlement of 1954," in *Suez: The Crisis and Its Consequences*, ed. Wm. Roger Louis and Roger Owen (New York, 1989), 43–71.

70 Oles M. Smolansky, *The Soviet Union and the Arab East under Khrushchev* (Lewisburg, PA, 1974), 23–33; Jon D. Glassman, *Arms for the Arabs: The Soviet Union and War in the Middle East* (Baltimore, 1975), 7–21.

71 Avi Shlaim, "Conflicting Approaches to Israel's Relations with the Arabs: Ben Gurion and Sharett, 1953–1956," *Middle East Journal* 37 (Spring 1983): 180–201; Andrew and Leslie Cockburn, *Dangerous Liaison: The Inside Story of the U.S.-Israeli Relationship* (New York, 1991), 45–61; Green, *Taking Sides*, 94–122.

72 Gail E. Meyer, *Egypt and the United States: The Formative Years* (Cranbury, NJ, 1980), 35–65; Geoffrey Aronson, *From Sideshow to Center Stage: U.S. Policy toward Egypt, 1946–1956* (Boulder, 1986), 134–36.

Soviet bloc seven months later. This in turn produced panic in Washington and London, where U.S. and U.K. officials first enticed Nasser with a multi-million dollar aid package for the Aswan Dam in late 1955, then dithered over his increasingly strident anti-Western rhetoric before foolishly withdrawing their offer in July 1956, triggering the Egyptian seizure of the Suez Canal Company. Whitehall and the White House quickly parted company, with Prime Minister Anthony Eden secretly edging toward a Franco-Israeli plan for military intervention while the Eisenhower administration labored to resolve the crisis diplomatically through the United Nations or some other multilateral forum. After Eden used Israel's lightning attack on the Sinai in late October as a pretext to intervene, Eisenhower resorted to diplomatic hardball – censure at the United Nations, an informal oil embargo, a run on sterling – to force the British out of Egypt in December 1956, all the while taking care to keep the Labour party out of power in London.[73]

The opening of the British archives and the declassification of additional American records during the 1980s have enabled scholars on both sides of the Atlantic to refine some parts of Neff's interpretation and to refute others. Few dispute the significance of the Gaza raid, but some question whether Nasser was as blameless as Neff would have us believe and contend instead that the Israeli attack merely provided the Egyptians with a military pretext for a tilt toward the Kremlin launched mainly for ideological reasons.[74] Keith Kyle and William Burns, on the other hand, have confirmed Neff's view that the Anglo-American offer to finance the Aswan Dam was a tardy response to a Soviet-Egyptian arms deal that neither the White House nor Whitehall took very seriously until too late.[75]

73 Donald Neff, *Warriors at Suez: Eisenhower Takes America into the Middle East* (New York, 1981).

74 Spiegel, *Other Arab-Israeli Conflict*, 66–71; Schoenbaum, *United States & Israel*, 107–9. For a superb account that makes use of Israeli sources to reconstruct the bloody confrontation between the Palestinian fedayeen and the Jewish state during the 1950s in all its complexity see Benny Morris, *Israel's Border Wars: Arab Infiltration, Israeli Retaliation, and the Countdown to the Suez War* (New York, 1993).

75 Keith Kyle, "Britain and the Crisis, 1955–1956," in Louis and Owen, eds., *Suez*, 103–9; William J. Burns, *Economic Aid and American Policy toward Egypt, 1955–1981* (Albany, 1985), 36–75.

More important, scholars have recently shown that the Eisenhower administration attached strings to its aid package. In return for American economic assistance, Nasser was expected to cooperate with Project Alpha, a top-secret U.S. scheme to broker an Arab-Israeli peace settlement. Frustrated by Nasser's cold-shouldering of presidential emissary Robert Anderson, U.S. officials won U.K. support for a covert plan code-named Operation Omega to isolate and destabilize the Egyptian regime in March 1956, a full three months before Nasser's hot-blooded anti-Western policies prompted Washington ostentatiously to pull the plug on the Aswan Dam.[76] Despite subsequent British complaints about American unilateralism, the documentary record reveals that, as late as July 1956, the difference between U.S. and U.K. policies toward Egypt was, in the words of one Whitehall official, "no more than a nuance."[77]

How then to explain Washington's falling out with London just four months later? Biographers such as Robert Rhodes James, Townsend Hoopes, and Stephen Ambrose have attributed the estrangement in large measure to personality conflicts – an almost pathological mistrust separating the supercilious Eden and the self-righteous Dulles, or a hot-tempered Eisenhower lashing back at the cold-blooded British for keeping him in the dark about their plans for retaking the canal.[78] But although Whitehall's Evelyn Shuckburgh is surely right to liken Eden and Dulles to a pair of cutthroat prima donnas competing for the lead role in the Suez drama, and although anyone reading the minutes of Oval Office meetings during the autumn of 1956 will agree that likeable Ike was very angry indeed,[79] such personal quirks were

76 Shimon Shamir, "The Collapse of Project Alpha," and Robert R. Bowie, "Eisenhower, Dulles, and the Suez Crisis," both in Louis and Owen, eds., *Suez*, 73–100, 189–92; Michael B. Oren, "Secret Egypt-Israel Peace Initiatives Prior to the Suez Campaign," *Middle Eastern Studies* 26 (July 1990): 351–70; Burns, *Economic Aid & American Policy toward Egypt*, 75–100.

77 Kyle, "Britain and the Crisis," 110.

78 Robert Rhodes James, *Anthony Eden: A Biography* (New York, 1986), 469–77; Townsend Hoopes, *The Devil and John Foster Dulles* (Boston, 1973), 166–70; Stephen Ambrose, *Eisenhower*, vol. 2, *The President* (New York, 1984), 359–61.

79 Evelyn Shuckburgh, *Descent to Suez: Foreign Office Diaries, 1951–1956* (New York, 1986), 185–87. For an example of Ike's anger see the minutes of his meeting with Arthur Flemming on 30 October 1956, where he growled that the British should "boil in their own oil." (*FRUS, 1955–1957* [Washington, 1990], 16:873–74.)

actually symptoms of a far more fundamental change in Anglo-American relations. Put most simply, the Suez crisis enabled the the United States to supplant Great Britain as the senior Western partner in the Middle East, tempering Dulles's neuroses while exacerbating Eden's.

The reversal of this Anglo-American partnership in late 1956 marked the culmination of a series of increasingly bitter disputes between Washington and London over Middle East policy during the preceding three years. After the joint U.S. and U.K. effort to establish MEDO as a "Middle Eastern NATO" was short-circuited in 1952, America and Britain had embraced divergent approaches toward regional defense. Determined to prevent fresh Soviet inroads along the northern tier and eager to avoid a fresh round of anti-imperialist outbursts from Nasser, the Eisenhower administration quietly pushed for a series of bilateral security treaties during 1954 among three of the region's most important non-Arab states – Turkey, Iran, and Pakistan. Whitehall, on the other hand, maneuvered to restore its waning influence in the Muslim world by working with its client regime in Iraq to promote a broader system of regional defense that would include not merely Turks and Pakistanis but also Arabs and even the British themselves.[80] The Anglo-Iraqi promulgation of the Baghdad Pact in early 1955 and Britain's ill-advised efforts to force Jordan and other conservative Arab states to become members over the next year frustrated U.S. policymakers, who on the eve of the Suez crisis were complaining that their neurotic British partners had "hijacked" American plans for Middle East defense.[81]

Some scholars have argued that economic rivalry accelerated American efforts to wrest the senior partnership from the British in late 1956. The Eisenhower administration had long suspected that Britain harbored designs on ARAMCO's huge petroleum

80 Ayesha Jalal, "Towards the Baghdad Pact: South Asia and Middle East Defence in the Cold War, 1947–1955," *International History Review* 11 (August 1989): 409–33; Richard L. Jasse, "The Baghdad Pact: Cold War or Colonialism," *Middle Eastern Studies* 27 (January 1991): 140–56.

81 Brian Holden Reid, "The 'Northern Tier' and the Baghdad Pact," in Young, ed., *Foreign Policy of Churchill's Peacetime Administration*, 159–79; Nigel John Ashton, "The Hijacking of a Pact: The Formation of the Baghdad Pact and Anglo-American Tensions in the Middle East, 1955–1958," *Review of International Studies* 19 (Spring 1993): 123–37.

concession in Saudi Arabia. Beginning in 1953, Whitehall encouraged AIOC and other U.K. oil firms to occupy the Buraimi oasis, a "no man's land" claimed by both the pro-British Sultan of Muscat and the pro-American House of Saud. After British troops seized control of Buraimi from Saudi border guards and ARAMCO engineers in late 1955, the Eisenhower administration angrily insisted that Whitehall resolve the dispute through international arbitration. According to Tore Tingvold Petersen, these nasty skirmishes over Buraimi exacerbated Anglo-American tensions just as the Suez crisis came to a climax.[82] Indeed, Daniel Yergin has made a strong case that U.S. officials opposed U.K. intervention in Egypt in November 1956 in large measure out of fear that the Saudis and other anti-British Arabs might retaliate by embargoing Persian Gulf oil or, even worse, by expropriating Western oil firms.[83] Steven Freiberger is equally provocative but less convincing when he depicts the Anglo-American showdown over Suez as the culmination of an ingenious U.S. plan to reap commercial advantage by pushing the British out of the Arab world and opening up Middle East markets.[84] Gabriel Kolko offers a somewhat more persuasive economic interpretation by placing Suez in the broader context of America's quest for commercial hegemony in the Third World during the decade after 1945.[85]

The best recent accounts of the Suez crisis, however, suggest that strategic and ideological considerations were more important in shaping U.S. policy than economic concerns. In an essay

82 Tore Tingvold Petersen, "Anglo-American Rivalry in the Middle East: The Struggle for the Buraimi Oasis, 1952–1957," *International History Review* 14 (February 1992): 71–91.

83 Yergin, *The Prize*, 489–98. Multinational firms operating in Egypt, however, bore the brunt of the Arab nationalist backlash. During the twelve months following Egyptian seizure of the Suez Canal Company in July 1956, Nasser confiscated dozens of British and French firms, ranging from Eastern Tobacco to Barclays Bank, with assets totaling nearly $1 billion. American firms operating in Egypt, by contrast, emerged largely unscathed. Robert L. Tignor, "The Suez Crisis of 1956 and Egypt's Foreign Private Sector," *Journal of Imperial and Commonwealth History* 20 (May 1992): 274–97.

84 Steven Z. Freiberger, *Dawn Over Suez: The Rise of American Power in the Middle East, 1953–1957* (Chicago, 1992).

85 Gabriel Kolko, *Confronting the Third World: United States Foreign Policy, 1945–1980* (New York, 1988), 77–84.

that highlights growing Anglo-American diplomatic friction on the eve of Suez, Wm. Roger Louis argues that Dulles's anticolonialism, Eisenhower's commitment to the United Nations, and both men's anticommunism led them to part company with their British counterparts, whose Middle East policies seemed inadvertantly to be playing into the Kremlin's hands.[86] Geoffrey Warner discounts U.S. anticolonialism and insists that containment and other Cold War imperatives lay behind Washington's breach with London in 1956.[87] But as Peter Hahn has shown, by the mid-1950s America's grand strategy in the Middle East actually relied heavily on anticolonialism to curb radical Arab nationalism and to combat communism.[88]

Such Anglo-American strategic disagreements notwithstanding, many scholars suggest that the Suez affair might have come out differently but for monumental British tactical blunders. Scott Lucas shows how Eden's obsession with keeping his plans for military intervention secret not only from the Eisenhower administration but also from his own cabinet created a bureaucratic nightmare on both sides of the Atlantic, with Britain's MI6 and the CIA working at cross purposes and with the Foreign Office and the Ministry of War moving in opposite directions.[89] Keith Kyle argues that the ponderous transformation of Operation Musketeer from a surgical strike against Egypt in August into a D-Day-style invasion in November effectively ruled out the sort of quick and dirty move against Nasser that many British officials seem to have believed Eisenhower and Dulles would welcome.[90] And most telling of all, Diane Kunz shows that despite increasingly explicit White House warnings that Whitehall should not resort to military force, Chancellor of the Exchequer Harold Macmillan failed during September and October to take even the

86 Wm. Roger Louis, "Dulles, Suez, and the British," in *John Foster Dulles and the Diplomacy of the Cold War*, ed. Richard H. Immerman (Princeton, 1990), 133–58. See also Wm. Roger Louis, "American Anti-Colonialism and the Dissolution of the British Empire," *International Affairs* 61 (Summer 1985): 395–420.

87 Geoffrey Warner, "The United States and the Suez Crisis," *International Affairs* 67 (April 1991): 303–17.

88 Hahn, *United States, Great Britain, and Egypt*, 180–239.

89 W. Scott Lucas, *Divided We Stand: Britain, the U.S., and the Suez Crisis* (London, 1991).

90 Keith Kyle, *Suez* (New York, 1991), 233–55, 425–43.

most elementary financial precautions that might have shielded his country from the economic sanctions the United States imposed at the height of the Suez crisis.[91] After Eisenhower's dollar diplomacy forced Britain out of Egypt and Eden into retirement in December 1956 and after the threat of similar sanctions forced Israel to relinquish the Sinai and Gaza two months later, the United States stood ready to try its hand at stablizing the Middle East.[92]

Some observers speculated that U.S. policy during the Suez crisis might prefigure a bold American accommodation with Nasser and Arab nationalism, but the promulgation of the Eisenhower Doctrine in early 1957 showed that the White House was almost as willing as Whitehall to employ military force in an attempt to bring order and stability to the region. Early accounts of the doctrine gave Eisenhower high marks for seeking congressional authorization prior to armed intervention in the Middle East but low marks for confusing Arab nationalism with communism.[93] Most recent studies, however, suggest that the Eisenhower administration used Cold War rhetoric to manipulate Congress and that Ike, Dulles, and other top officials actually drew clear distinctions between Nasserism and Soviet subversion. William Stivers and Irene Gendzier, for example, have shown that although the White House was well aware by 1957 that Arab nationalism was home-grown, not imported from Moscow, U.S. policymakers nevertheless regarded Nasser and other anti-Western radicals as every bit as dangerous to American interests as the Kremlin's

91 Diane B. Kunz, *The Economic Diplomacy of the Suez Crisis* (Chapel Hill, 1991).

92 Diane B. Kunz, "The Importance of Having Money: The Economic Diplomacy of the Suez Crisis," in Louis and Owen, eds., *Suez*, 215–32; Michael Fry and Miles Hochstein, "The Forgotten Middle East Crisis of 1957: Gaza and Sharm-el-Sheikh," *International History Review* 15 (February 1993): 46–83.

93 Charles C. Alexander, *Holding the Line: The Eisenhower Era, 1952–1961* (Bloomington, 1975), 184–91; Robert Stookey, *America and the Arab States: An Uneasy Encounter* (New York, 1975), 148–57. For an excellent analysis of the Eisenhower Doctrine in the context of "conventional deterrence" see Alexander L. George and Richard Smoke, *Deterrence in American Foreign Policy: Theory and Practice* (New York, 1974), 309–62. For an interesting discussion of the cognitive and bureaucratic underpinnings of Ike's approach to the Middle East during the late 1950s see Charles A. Kupchan, "American Globalism in the Middle East: The Roots of Regional Security Policy," *Political Science Quarterly* 103 (Winter 1988/89): 587–96.

operatives.[94] H. W. Brands points out that when some in Congress objected to giving the president what Hubert Humphrey termed "a predated declaration of war," Eisenhower and Dulles resorted to "calling up the reliable bogey of Soviet-backed communism" to win votes for their anti-Nasser crusade on Capitol Hill.[95] The Eisenhower administration "did not confuse nationalism or neutralism with Communism" in the Arab world, Thomas Paterson observed in 1988, but it "loathed both for serving Soviet purposes."[96]

Eisenhower's efforts to combat Nasser's brand of revolutionary nationalism put the United States on a collision course not only with Egypt but with other Arab states as well. What little has been written on American relations with Jordan, for example, confirms that Washington worked hard to isolate pro-Nasser radicals in Amman who threatened the pro-Western regime of King Hussein. Beginning in 1956, the United States worked with Britain to funnel hundreds of millions of dollars into Jordan to promote economic development and internal security.[97] The following year, the CIA began to monitor Palestinian radicals in Jordan and may well have placed Hussein himself on the agency's payroll.[98] Increasingly determined to prop up the brave young king, the White House helped airlift British troops and supplies into Amman during the summer of 1958 and sent the Sixth Fleet into the Eastern Mediterranean five years later when a pro-Nasser

94 William Stivers, "Eisenhower and the Middle East," in *Reevaluating Eisenhower: American Foreign Policy in the 1950s*, ed. Richard A. Melanson and David Mayers (Urbana, 1987), 192–219; Irene L. Gendzier, "The United States, the USSR and the Arab World in NSC Reports of the 1950s," *American-Arab Affairs* 28 (Spring 1989): 22–29.

95 H. W. Brands, *The Specter of Neutralism: The United States and the Emergence of the Third World, 1947–1960* (New York, 1990), 282–89.

96 Thomas G. Paterson, *Meeting the Communist Threat: Truman to Reagan* (New York, 1988), 159–90. The quote is on p. 162.

97 Michael B. Oren, "A Winter of Discontent: Britain's Crisis in Jordan, December 1955–March 1956," *International Journal of Middle East Studies* 22 (1990): 171–84; Stephen S. Kaplan, "United States Aid and Regime Maintenance in Jordan, 1957–1973," *Public Policy* 23 (Spring 1975): 189–217. For an excellent discussion of Anglo-American maneuvering in Amman during the 1950s see Robert B. Satloff, *From Abdullah to Hussein: Jordan in Transition* (New York, 1994).

98 On the CIA's activities in Jordan see *Washington Post*, 18 February 1977; and Wilbur Crane Eveland, *Ropes of Sand: America's Failure in the Middle East* (New York, 1980), 183–84, 191.

coup seemed imminent in Jordan.[99] By the late 1960s, Ike's successors regarded Hussein as a "friendly tyrant" and sold him arms to ensure that Jordan would adopt a hard line against the newly created Palestine Liberation Organization (PLO).[100]

The burgeoning literature on American relations with Syria likewise highlights the unintended consequences of the Eisenhower Doctrine. In a classic account published nearly thirty years ago, Patrick Seale argued that in their zeal to prevent Moscow from making inroads in Damascus, Eisenhower and Dulles set in motion a self-fulfilling prophecy that nearly led to U.S. military intervention to prevent Syria from becoming a Soviet satellite.[101] Reading between the lines of sanitized records in Washington and London, scholars have recently been able to corroborate rumors of CIA and MI6 involvement in a series of Syrian coups dating from 1949.[102] Indeed, David Lesch has confirmed that a covert American scheme to depose the pro-Nasser regime in Damascus backfired in August 1957, prompting Syrian leaders to expel three U.S. diplomats linked to the CIA, to purge dozens of pro-Western officers from the army, and to seek help from Cairo and Moscow. Despite words of caution from the British, who feared a "Suez in reverse," the United States briefly considered sending troops to Syria and quietly encouraged Turkey to mobilize its forces along the Syrian frontier. Rallying to the side of its newfound friends in Damascus, the Kremlin threatened to retaliate against

99 Uriel Dann, *King Hussein and the Challenge of Arab Radicalism: Jordan, 1955–1967* (New York, 1989), 64–67, 88–93, 130–33; Ritchie Ovendale, "Great Britain and the Anglo-American Invasion of Jordan and Lebanon in 1958," *International History Review* 16 (May 1994): 284–303.

100 Robert Satloff, "When the Friendly Tyrants Debate Does Not Matter: Jordan under the Hashemites," in *Friendly Tyrants: An American Dilemma*, ed. Daniel Pipes and Adam Garfinkle (New York, 1991), 451–78; Douglas Little, "The United States, King Hussein, and Jordan, 1951–1970," *International History Review* (forthcoming, 1995).

101 Patrick Seale, *The Struggle for Syria: A Study of Postwar Arab Politics, 1945–1958* (New York, 1965), 247–306.

102 Anthony Gorst and W. Scott Lucas, "The Other Collusion: Operation Straggle and Anglo-American Intervention in Syria, 1955–56," *Intelligence and National Security* 4 (July 1989): 576–95; Douglas Little, "Cold War and Covert Action: The United States and Syria, 1945–1958," *Middle East Journal* 44 (Winter 1990): 51–75. See also Andrew Rathmell, "The Role of Covert Action and International Terrorism in Middle East Politics: Syria, 1949–1961" (Ph.D. diss., King's College, London, 1994).

the Turks, raising the specter of a superpower confrontation that was dispelled only after Colonel Abdel Hamid al-Sarraj and other anti-Communist Syrian officers won Nasser's reluctant approval to merge their country with Egypt to form the United Arab Republic (UAR) in early 1958.[103]

Ironically, while the formation of the UAR worked to prevent American military involvement in Syria, the new Syro-Egyptian union exacerbated inter-Arab rivalries that triggered U.S. armed intervention next door in Lebanon before the year was out. Nuri Said, the pro-Western prime minister of Iraq who had long coveted Syria as part of a "Fertile Crescent" scheme designed to tilt the balance of power in the Arab world from Cairo to Baghdad, moved swiftly during the spring of 1958 to counter Nasser's gains in Damascus by mobilizing the region's conservatives against the newly created UAR.[104] Although not much has been written about U.S. policy toward Iraq, the few accounts we do have suggest that the White House, like Whitehall, viewed Nuri's regime as a bulwark against radical Arab nationalism, welcomed Iraqi efforts to combat Nasserism, and rewarded Baghdad with modest amounts of military aid.[105] Moreover, because Iraq served as a linchpin connecting fellow Baghdad Pact members Turkey and Iran, the Eisenhower administration regarded Nuri as a key ally in American efforts to contain the Kremlin along the northern tier. When left-wing officers toppled the Iraqi monarchy on 14 July 1958, murdering Nuri and the royal family and torpedoing the Baghdad Pact, top U.S. officials concluded that only American military intervention could prevent the rapid erosion of Western interests throughout the region.[106]

The intervention would come not in Baghdad, however, but rather five hundred miles to the west in Beirut, where President Camille Chamoun, a pro-American Lebanese Christian, had been

103 David W. Lesch, *Syria and the United States: Eisenhower's Cold War in the Middle East* (Boulder, 1992).

104 Elie Podeh, "The Struggle over Arab Hegemony after the Suez Crisis," *Middle Eastern Studies* 29 (January 1993): 91–110.

105 Nicholas G. Thatcher, "Reflections on U.S. Foreign Policy towards Iraq in the 1950s," and Frederick W. Axelgard, "U.S. Support for the British Position in Pre-Revolutionary Iraq," both in *The Iraqi Revolution of 1958: The Old Social Classes Revisited*, ed. Robert A. Fernea and Wm. Roger Louis (New York, 1991), 62–94.

106 Brands, *Specter of Neutralism*, 296–303; Ambrose, *Eisenhower: The President*, 462–75.

seeking U.S. help against pro-Nasser Muslim rebels for two months. Most early accounts interpreted Eisenhower's decision to send fourteen thousand American Marines to Lebanon in the wake of a bloody Iraqi coup as his finest hour. Determined to prevent anti-Western forces based in Syria from toppling Lebanon's pro-Western government in a replay of recent events in Iraq, the White House oversaw a well-planned invasion that cost but one American life and that saw the GIs return home before Christmas. Ike's ability to restore law and order in Beirut without becoming mired down in the religious strife that pitted Christians against Muslims prompted the first wave of Eisenhower revisionists to treat his handling of limited war in Lebanon as a model for successful U.S. crisis management in the Third World.[107] Writing in 1984, Alan Dowty praised Eisenhower for wisely relying on a tightly knit and level-headed group of decision makers who shared an "operational code" that placed a high premium in July 1958 on ensuring American credibility with pro-Western regimes in the Middle East.[108]

More recent work on the Lebanese crisis, however, suggests that Ike may have been more lucky than wise. Several scholars have shown that in his zeal to build public support for military intervention, Eisenhower, with an assist from John Foster Dulles, consciously exaggerated the Communist threat and downplayed the importance of Arab nationalism in Lebanon's woes.[109] Unable to convince skeptics on Capitol Hill that Moscow was behind the trouble in Beirut, an imperial president actually relied on his power as commander-in-chief, not on the congressional authorization

107 Herbert S. Parmet, *Eisenhower and the American Crusades* (New York, 1972), 574; William Bragg Ewald, Jr., *Eisenhower the Preisdent: Crucial Days, 1951–1960* (Englewood Cliffs, 1981), 242; Robert A. Divine, *Eisenhower and the Cold War* (New York, 1981), 97–104.

108 Alan Dowty, *Middle East Crisis: U.S. Decision-Making in 1958, 1970, and 1973* (Berkeley, 1984), 23–108.

109 See Erika G. Alin, *The United States and the 1958 Lebanon Crisis: American Intervention in the Middle East* (Lanham, MD, 1994); Blanche Wiesen Cook, *The Declassified Eisenhower: A Divided Legacy of Peace and Political Warfare* (New York, 1984), 206–7; Robert McMahon, "Eisenhower and the Third World," *Political Science Quarterly* 101 (1986): 463–66; Robert Schulzinger, "The Impact of Suez on United States Middle East Policy, 1957–1958," in *The Suez-Sinai Crisis, 1956*, ed. Selwyn Ilan Troen and Moshe Shemesh (New York, 1990), 251–65; and Michael B. Bishku, "The 1958 American Intervention in Lebanon: A Historical Assessment," *American-Arab Affairs* 31 (Winter 1989/1990): 106–19.

embodied in the Eisenhower Doctrine, to justify sending in the marines.[110] Widespread praise for the limited scope of Eisenhower's intervention notwithstanding, there is evidence that the 1958 Middle East crisis nearly spiralled out of control. Michael Oren, for example, has shown that Israel stood ready to seize the strategically important West Bank should Jordan's King Hussein meet the same fate as his Iraqi cousin King Feisal.[111] And William Quandt and Michael Palmer have pointed out that Eisenhower instructed the U.S. Seventh Fleet to stand by in the Persian Gulf in the event it became necessary to repel an Iraqi move against the Kuwaiti oilfields.[112] Moreover, despite Ike's claim that the United States was not taking sides in Lebanon's confessional strife, Irene Gendzier has shown in a series of provocative essays that as early as 1952, Washington had begun to align itself with Chamoun and other Christian warlords in their struggle with the more numerous Lebanese Muslims, helping to set the stage for the bloody civil war that erupted in Beirut in 1975.[113]

Far from being Eisenhower's finest hour, the Lebanese crisis actually prompted American officials to reassess their policies during the late 1950s in an effort to avoid future American military intervention in the Middle East. Jeffrey Lefebvre has shown that Egypt and America began to edge toward a rapprochement in Northeast Africa as early as November 1958.[114] William Burns

110 U.S. Congress, Senate, Committee on Foreign Relations, 85th Cong., 2d sess., 1958, *Executive Sessions of the Senate Foreign Relations Committee (Historical Series)*, Vol. 10 (Washington, 1980): 504–13; Douglas Little, "His Finest Hour? Eisenhower, Lebanon, and the 1958 Middle East Crisis," *Diplomatic History* (forthcoming, 1996).

111 Michael B. Oren, "The Test of Suez: Israel and the Middle East Crisis of 1958," *Studies in Zionism* 12:1 (1991): 55–83.

112 William B. Quandt, "Lebanon, 1958, and Jordan, 1970," in *Force without War: U.S. Armed Forces as a Political Instrument*, ed. Barry M. Blechman and Stephen S. Kaplan (Washington, 1978), 225–57, esp. 238; Michael A. Palmer, *Guardians of the Gulf: A History of America's Expanding Role in the Persian Gulf, 1833–1992* (New York, 1992), 79–81.

113 Irene L. Gendzier, "The U.S. Perception of the Lebanese Civil War According to Declassified Documents: A Preliminary Assessment," in *Toward a Viable Lebanon*, ed. Halim Barakat (Washington, 1988), 328–44; idem, "'No Forum for the Lebanese People': US Perceptions from Lebanon, 1945–1947," *Middle East Report* (January/February 1990): 34–36; idem, "The Declassified Lebanon, 1948–1958: Elements of Continuity and Contrast in US Policy toward Lebanon," in *The Middle East and North Africa: Essays in Honor of J. C. Hurewitz*, ed. Reeva S. Simon (New York, 1990), 187–209.

114 Jeffrey A. Lefebvre, "The United States and Egypt: Confrontation and Accommodation in Northeast Africa, 1956–1960," *Middle Eastern Studies* 29 (April 1993): 321–38.

has highlighted Ike's quiet efforts to use U.S. economic aid and political influence to foster an accommodation with Nasser and Arab nationalism during 1959.[115] And as H. W. Brands pointed out nearly a decade ago, by 1960 America and Egypt were working together to contain revolutionary Iraq, which both Eisenhower and Nasser regarded as a Soviet stalking horse.[116]

When John F. Kennedy moved into the Oval Office in January 1961, he hoped to expand Eisenhower's eleventh-hour rapprochement with Nasser in order to achieve a comprehensive Arab-Israeli peace settlement. In my own work, I have tried to show how Kennedy used personal diplomacy and American wheat to channel Nasserism into "constructive channels" while simultaneously encouraging Nasser's more conservative Arab rivals to implement long overdue reforms.[117] Steven Spiegel and Mordechai Gazit have detailed JFK's efforts to signal America's deepening commitment to Israel's security by selling the Jewish state HAWK anti-aircraft missiles and by providing Israeli leaders with secret assurances of American help in the event of an Arab attack.[118] And Herbert S. Parmet has recounted Kennedy's steadfast efforts to win Arab and Israeli support for the Johnson Plan, a UN scheme to resolve the Palestinian refugee dilemma through repatriation and resettlement.[119]

Although Kennedy's self-styled "even-handed" approach to the Arab-Israeli conflict seemed to have placed the region on the road

115 Burns, *Economic Aid & American Policy toward Egypt*, 108–20. For a detailed account of Eisenhower's unsuccessful attempt to foster an even broader Arab-Israeli accommodation by offering U.S. technical and financial assistance for a proposed "Jordan Valley Authority" see Sara Regner, "Controversial Waters: Exploitation of the Jordan River, 1950–1980," *Middle Eastern Studies* 29 (January 1993): 53–90.

116 H. W. Brands, "What Eisenhower and Dulles Saw in Nasser: Personalities and Interests in U.S.-Egyptian Relations," *American-Arab Affairs* 18 (Fall 1986): 50–54.

117 Douglas Little, "The New Frontier on the Nile: JFK, Nasser, and Arab Nationalism," *Journal of American History* 75 (September 1988); idem, "From Even-Handed to Empty-Handed: Seeking Order in the Middle East," in *Kennedy's Quest for Victory: American Foreign Policy, 1961–1963*, ed. Thomas G. Paterson (New York, 1989), 156–77; idem, "A Fool's Errand: America and the Middle East, 1961–1969," in *The Crucial Decade: American Foreign Policy in the 1960s*, ed. Diane B. Kunz (New York, 1994).

118 Spiegel, *Other Arab-Israeli Conflict*, 94–117; Mordechai Gazit, *President Kennedy's Policy toward the Arab States and Israel: Analysis and Documents* (Syracuse, 1983).

119 Herbert S. Parmet, *JFK: The Presidency of John F. Kennedy* (New York, 1983), 225–35. In addition see Mohammed K. Shadid, *The United States and the Palestinians* (London, 1981), 68–72; and Zaha Bustami, "The Kennedy/Johnson Administrations and the Palestinians," *Arab Studies Quarterly* 12 (Winter/Spring 1990): 101–20.

to peace and stability by mid-1962, when JFK left for Dallas eighteen months later he realized that he had come up empty-handed in the Middle East. Part of the problem lay in Israel. Spiegel and Gazit have shown how Israeli second-guessing of Kennedy's rapprochement with Nasser eventually prompted Israeli second thoughts about the American-backed Johnson Plan, which called for resettling up to one hundred thousand Palestinians inside the Jewish state.[120] And my own reading of fragmentary declassified materials at the JFK Library suggests that Israel's decision to accelerate its nuclear research at Dimona in early 1963 seriously undermined the Kennedy administration's credibility with Egypt and other front-line Arab states.[121]

In the end, however, it was long-simmering inter-Arab rivalries between revolutionary nationalists like Nasser and pro-Western conservatives like Saudi Arabia's Crown Prince Faisal, not Israeli intransigence, that doomed Kennedy's even-handed policies. Malcolm Kerr was among the first to highlight the importance of this "Arab Cold War," which heated up considerably in late 1962 after pro-Nasser officers overthrew the Imam of Yemen and touched off a civil war in the southwest corner of the Arabian Peninsula.[122] Eager to avoid its neighbor's fate, the House of Saud funneled guns and money to Yemeni royalists just across the Saudi frontier, prompting Nasser to send seventy thousand troops to defend the new Yemen Arab Republic (YAR). Inside accounts written by John Badeau and Robert Stookey shortly afterward revealed that JFK was determined to preserve his ties with Nasser by localizing the conflict. To this end, the United States recognized the YAR in December 1962, not only over the objections of Saudi Arabia but also over those of Great Britain, which feared that the upheaval in Yemen would spill over into the British protectorate next door in Aden.[123] More recently, both

120 Spiegel, *Other Arab-Israeli Conflict*, 110–17; Gazit, *Kennedy's Policy toward the Arab States & Israel*, 39–44.

121 Douglas Little, "The Making of a Special Relationship: The United States and Israel, 1957–1968," *International Journal of Middle East Studies* 25 (November 1993): 563–85.

122 Malcolm A. Kerr, *The Arab Cold War: Gamal Abd al-Nasir and His Rivals, 1958–1970*, 3d ed. (New York, 1971).

123 John S. Badeau, *The American Approach to the Arab World* (New York, 1968), 123–51; Stookey, *America & the Arab States*, 161–89. Badeau served as Kennedy's ambassador to Egypt, while Stookey was the U.S. chargé d'affaires in Yemen.

Michael Bishku and Christopher McMullen have emphasized Kennedy's reliance on the United Nations to mediate the Yemeni conflict and defuse tensions between Cairo and Riyadh.[124] But when the Egyptian-Saudi proxy war flared up again in early 1963, JFK sent a squadron of U.S. F-100 jets to Dhahran as a symbol of America's military commitment to the House of Saud and warned Nasser not to use Yemen as a springboard for further Arabian adventures.[125]

Kennedy's tilt toward Saudi Arabia was part of a broader realignment of American policy toward the Middle East that would be completed by Lyndon B. Johnson. What little has been written about America and the House of Saud confirms that a diplomatic marriage of convenience was consummated between Washington and Riyadh during the mid-1960s. Stephen Ambrose, Thomas Paterson, and others have shown that as early as 1957, top U.S. officials considered using Saudi Arabia's King Saud as a conservative counterweight to Nasser and other Arab radicals.[126] Over the next ten years, Saudi Arabia's deepening anxiety about revolutionary nationalism and America's growing dependence on Persian Gulf oil prompted closer cooperation between the White House and the House of Saud. Whitehall's liquidation of the string of British bases stretching from the Red Sea to the Persian Gulf after 1966, outlined in elegant detail by J. B. Kelly, Karl Pieragostini, and Glen Balfour-Paul, created a dangerous vacuum that the Johnson administration sought to fill by providing Saudi Arabia with HAWK missiles, early warning radar, and other defensive weaponry.[127] David Long and Nadav Safran have argued convincingly that despite frequent Saudi complaints that U.S.

124 Christopher J. McMullen, *Resolution of the Yemen Crisis, 1963: A Case Study of Mediation* (Washington, 1980); Michael B. Bishku, "The Kennedy Administration, the U.N., and the Yemeni Civil War," *Middle East Policy* 1 (Winter 1992): 116–28.

125 Little, "New Frontier on the Nile," 519–24.

126 Ambrose, *Eisenhower: The President*, 317–18, 383–85; Paterson, *Meeting the Communist Threat*, 178–79; David W. Lesch, "The Saudi Role in the American-Syrian Crisis of 1957," *Middle East Policy* 1:3 (1992): 33–48.

127 J. B. Kelly, *Arabia, the Gulf, and the West* (New York, 1980); Karl Pieragostini, *Britain, Aden, and South Arabia: Abandoning Empire* (New York, 1991); Glen Balfour-Paul, *The End of Empire in the Middle East: Britain's Relinquishment of Power in Her Last Three Arab Dependencies* (New York, 1991). See also Frank Brenchley, *Britain and the Middle East: An Economic History, 1945–1987* (London, 1989), esp. 145–88.

foreign policy was pro-Israel and despite frequent U.S. complaints that Saudi oil policy was becoming anti-American, by 1969 an "ambivalent alliance" had emerged.[128]

If Saudi Arabia was to be the Johnson administration's first pillar in the Persian Gulf after Britain pulled out, Iran was to be the second. James Goode has reminded us that Iranian-American relations had cooled considerably during the Kennedy years, when the new frontiersmen had insisted that the shah scale back his military spending and step up his programs for economic development and social change instead.[129] Taking office shortly after the shah had grudgingly launched his "White Revolution," LBJ proved far less interested in fostering political reform than in cultivating Iran as an ally in the defense of the Persian Gulf. James Bill and Barry Rubin have described how Johnson's budding friendship with the shah and America's pressing strategic imperatives in the Middle East during the mid-1960s helped cement an Iranian-American partnership in which Washington provided the guns and Tehran provided the oil. Although the shah was loath to admit it, by the end of the decade he had become America's proxy in the Persian Gulf, undermining OPEC's efforts to play its oil card, serving as a backchannel conduit for controversial U.S. efforts to arm Arab moderates like King Hussein, and deploying Iranian troops in Oman to combat anti-Western insurgents in Southeast Arabia.[130]

The most significant feature of U.S. policy in the Middle East during the Johnson years, however, was not the cultivation of partnerships with Saudi Arabia or Iran but rather the consummation of a special relationship with Israel symbolized by Washington's tilt toward Tel Aviv in June 1967. Among the first to explore Israeli-American relations during the run-up to the Six Day War was Donald Neff, who has contended that LBJ's approach to the Middle East was dictated mainly by political considerations – securing the votes of American Jews, placating AIPAC and Israel's

128 David E. Long, *The United States and Saudi Arabia: Ambivalent Allies* (Boulder, 1985), 16–20, 40–54, 113–17; Nadav Safran, *Saudi Arabia: The Ceaseless Quest for Security* (Cambridge, MA, 1985), 180–216.

129 James Goode, "Reforming Iran in the Kennedy Years," *Diplomatic History* 15 (Winter 1991): 13–29.

130 Bill, *Eagle and Lion*, 154–82; Rubin, *Paved with Good Intentions*, 113–23.

friends in Congress, and accommodating influntial Jewish Democrats like Abe Feinberg and Arthur Krim.[131] Neff's interpretation has been echoed stridently by Cheryl Rubenberg, Stephen Green, and George Ball.[132] Edward Tivnan and Etta Zablocki Bick have confirmed that Lyndon Johnson was indeed subjected to considerable pro-Israel pressure from Main Street, Capitol Hill, and the Democratic National Committee on the eve of the Six Day War.[133] And William Quandt has recently made a convincing case that although the White House may never have flashed Tel Aviv a green light for war in June 1967, LBJ used Supreme Court Justice Abe Fortas and other friends of Israel to signal that the light was not red.[134]

Unlike Neff, Rubenberg, and the others, however, Quandt has always been careful to point out that geopolitical considerations outweighed domestic politics in shaping U.S. policy during the Six Day War.[135] Indeed, Warren Cohen has recently suggested that by 1967, LBJ's Middle East policies might be more accurately described as anti-Nasser than as pro-Israel.[136] William Burns has likewise detailed Johnson's growing frustration with Nasser, who struck the Texan as insufficiently grateful for American wheat, as incredibly naive about Soviet influence in the Arab world, and as insufferably critical of U.S. policy in Vietnam.[137] Others have emphasized that Nasser's encouragement for Syrian and Palestinian radicals left little doubt among top American officials that

131 Donald Neff, *Warriors for Jerusalem: The Six Days That Changed the Middle East* (New York, 1984).

132 Rubenberg, *Israel & the American National Interest*, 88–129; Green, *Taking Sides*, 180–211; Ball and Ball, *Passionate Attachment*, 50–66.

133 Tivnan, *The Lobby*, 59–68; Etta Zablocki Bick, "Ethnic Linkages and Foreign Policy: A Study of the Linkage Role of American Jews in Relations between the United States and Israel, 1956–1968" (Ph.D. diss., City University of New York, 1983).

134 William B. Quandt, "Lyndon Johnson and the June 1967 War: What Color Was the Light?" *Middle East Journal* 46 (Spring 1992): 214–22.

135 William B. Quandt, *Decade of Decisions: American Policy toward the Arab-Israeli Conflict, 1967–1976* (Berkeley, 1977), 37–71. For an updated account see William B. Quandt, *Peace Process: American Diplomacy and the Arab-Israeli Conflict since 1967* (Washington, 1993), 25–62.

136 Warren I. Cohen, "Balancing American Interests in the Middle East: Lyndon Baines Johnson vs. Gamal Abdul Nasser," in *Lyndon Johnson Confronts the World: American Foreign Policy, 1963–1968*, ed. Warren I. Cohen and Nancy Bernkopf Tucker (New York, 1994), 279–309.

137 Burns, *Economic Aid & American Policy toward Egypt*, 149–73.

his ultimate goal was the destruction of all Western interests in the region.[138] Highlighting Washington's growing concern with radical Arab nationalism, Spiegel, Schoenbaum, and H. W. Brands have made convincing cases that by early 1967, Johnson saw Israel more as a strategic asset in his crusade against wars of national liberation than as a political asset in what seemed inceasingly certain to be a hotly contested reelection campaign.[139]

In any event, the deepening quagmire in Southeast Asia short-circuited that campaign and prompted "Big Daddy from the Padernales" to opt for an early return to his native Lone Star State. By the time he turned the Oval Office over to Richard M. Nixon in January 1969, however, Lyndon Johnson had laid the groundwork for a "three pillars" approach that would govern American policy toward the Middle East for nearly twenty years. My own research suggests that Johnson bequeathed Nixon a set of informal partnerships with Israel, Iran, and Saudi Arabia designed to cope with growing U.S. dependence on oil imported from the Persian Gulf and to combat growing Soviet influence in the Arab world.[140] Charles Kupchan has confirmed that Washington strengthened its ties with Tel Aviv, Tehran, and Riyadh by stepping up arms sales to all three during the mid-1960s.[141] William Stivers has reminded us that it was Johnson, not Nixon, who quietly encouraged the Pentagon to establish a military base at Diego Garcia over the horizon in the Indian Ocean to provide the rapid deployment capability necessary to help America's newfound partners stabilize the oil-rich Persian Gulf.[142] And Michael Palmer

138 Ethan Nadelmann, "Setting the Stage: American Policy toward the Middle East, 1961–1966," *International Journal of Middle East Studies* 14 (1982): 435–57; L. Carl Brown, "Nasser and the June War: Plan or Improvisation," in *Quest for Understanding: Arabic and Islamic Studies in Memory of Malcolm H. Kerr*, ed. Samir Seikaly, R. Baalbaki, and Peter Dodd (Beirut, 1991); Richard B. Parker, "The June 1967 War: Some Mysteries Explored," *Middle East Journal* 46 (Spring 1992): 177–97.

139 Spiegel, *Other Arab-Israeli Conflict*, 118–65; Schoenbaum, *United States & Israel*, 139–53; H. W. Brands, *The Wages of Globalism: Lyndon Johnson and the Limits of American Power* (New York, 1995), chap. 7.

140 Douglas Little, "Choosing Sides: Lyndon Johnson and the Middle East," in *The Johnson Years*, vol. 3, *LBJ at Home and Abroad*, ed. Robert A. Divine (Lawrence, 1994), 150–97.

141 Charles Kupchan, *The Persian Gulf and the West: The Dilemmas of Security* (Boston, 1987), 25–43.

142 William Stivers, *America's Confrontation with Revolutionary Change in the Middle East, 1948–83* (New York, 1988), 38–59.

has recently confirmed that the roots of the Nixon Doctrine, which called for American reliance on regional proxies to protect the Middle East, are to be found in Lyndon Johnson's efforts to enlist Israel, Saudi Arabia, and Iran to help fill the vacuum created by Britain's liquidation of its empire east of Suez.[143]

Indeed, every administration from Nixon's to Bush's employed some variant of Johnson's three pillars approach as the foundation for its Middle East policies. Seeking to promote regional stability and to preserve Western access to Mideast oil without incurring the painful costs of military intervention, Nixon, Kissinger, and Ford relied on two proxies – Israel and Iran – to protect American interests. When the Iranian pillar crumbled in 1979, Carter scrambled unsuccessfully to find a suitable Arab substitute, first in Saudi Arabia, then in Anwar Sadat's Egypt, and finally in Saddam Hussein's Iraq. The Reagan administration preferred to focus on two pillars – Israel and Saudi Arabia – in its efforts to forge an anti-Soviet "strategic consensus" designed to safeguard the region from both international communism and Islamic fundamentalism. Strained relations between Washington and Tel Aviv during the late 1980s left the Bush administration with an inherently unstable "one pillar" policy based on a deepening Saudi-American alliance. And when Saddam Hussein took aim at that last pillar with his invasion of Kuwait, Bush flexed some high-tech military muscle, crushed the Iraqi army, and showed the world that, in the aftermath of the Cold War, America no longer required proxies to protect its interests in the Middle East.[144]

According to some, by making war on Iraq in 1991, America inaugurated a new era symbolized by Israel's stunning decision to make peace with the Palestinians in 1993. Yet while America's status as the world's sole remaining superpower seems to bode

143 Palmer, *Guardians of the Gulf*, 82–88.

144 My analysis draws heavily on the following: Seth P. Tillman, *The United States and the Middle East: Interests and Obstacles* (Bloomington, 1982); Gary Sick, *All Fall Down: America's Tragic Encounter with Iran* (New York, 1984); Thomas L. Friedman, *From Beirut to Jerusalem* (New York, 1989); Donald Neff, "Nixon's Middle East Policy: From Balance to Bias," *Arab Studies Quarterly* 12 (Winter/Spring 1990): 121–52; and Elaine Sciolino, *The Outlaw State: Saddam Hussein's Quest for Power and the Gulf Crisis* (New York, 1991).

well for regional stability, sober reflection upon America's stormy relations with the Middle East since 1945 leaves some nagging doubts. To be sure, there has been no shortage of scholarly attempts to summarize the broad sweep of those relations. Few of these surveys, however, have moved beyond the realm of diplomatic detail to offer deeper insights into America's recent close encounter with the Middle East.[145] Rare is the scholar who, like L. Carl Brown, seeks to place U.S. policy in the context of an idiosyncratic set of "rules of the game" in which Middle Easterners have for centuries manipulated external powers – first France, then Britain, and eventually the United States – to achieve their own narrow regional objectives.[146]

Rarer still are those who seek to explore the cultural assumptions that shaped America's interactions with the Middle East. It is, of course, possible to explain recent U.S. polices in terms of oil, containment, and the hard calculus of national interest.[147] Yet something more intangible seems to have been at work as well, something that might be called "American orientalism." Edward Said has demonstrated how, beginning in the late 18th century, British officials developed a self-serving view of the Muslim world as decadent, alien, and inferior, a view that Whitehall used to rationalize its own imperial ambitions in the Middle East. For British orientalists, Ottoman despotism, Islamic obscurantism, and Arab racial inferiority had supposedly combined to produce a backward culture badly in need of Anglo-Saxon tutelage.[148]

Something very like British orientalism seems subconsciously to have shaped the attitudes and guided the actions of the many Anglophilic missionaries, business people, and diplomats who have guided America's uneasy encounter with the Middle East over the

145 Dankwart A. Rustow, *Oil and Turmoil: America Faces OPEC and the Middle East* (New York, 1982); T. G. Fraser, *The USA and the Middle East since World War 2* (New York, 1989); George Lenczowski, *American Presidents and the Middle East* (Durham, 1990).

146 L. Carl Brown, *International Politics and the Middle East: Old Rules, Dangerous Game* (Princeton, 1984).

147 See, for example, James W. Harper, "The Middle East, Oil, and the Third World," in *Modern American Diplomacy*, ed. John M. Carroll and George C. Herring (Wilmington, DE, 1986), 201–19, and H. W. Brands, *Into the Labyrinth: The United States and the Middle East, 1945–1993* (New York, 1994).

148 Edward Said, *Orientalism* (New York, 1978).

past century and a half. In a pair of path-breaking books, Michael Hunt and Ralph Lauren have suggested that both the American public and American policymakers have relied on a well-developed sense of racial and cultural hierarchy in their dealings with what used to be called the Third World.[149] Although neither book deals with the Middle East, recent scholarship on the mindset of U.S. diplomats and the myths evoked by popular culture suggests that by employing the framework developed by Hunt and Lauren, historians could shed new light on American relations with the Muslim world.[150] Even more new light will be shed if diplomatic historians are willing to learn the foreign languages – Arabic, Hebrew, or Russian – necessary to make full use of the memoirs, diaries, and declassified documents currently trickling out of Cairo, Tel Aviv, and Moscow.[151]

By focusing on cultural assumptions and by mastering foreign languages, scholars might be able to provide a better understanding of how, after 1945, the United States, like Great Britain before it, came to shoulder "the White Man's Burden" in the Middle East. Taking their cues from the British orientalists whom they gradually supplanted following World War II, few American

149 Michael H. Hunt, *Ideology and U.S. Foreign Policy* (New Haven, 1987); Paul Gordon Lauren, *Power and Prejudice: The Politics and Diplomacy of Racial Discrimination* (Boulder, 1988).

150 On the attitudes of policymakers see John Solecki, "The Arabists and the Myth," *Middle East Journal* 44 (Summer 1990): 446–57; John Esposito, *The Islamic Threat* (New York, 1992), 168–212; Ghassan Salamé, "Islam and the West," *Foreign Policy* 90 (Spring 1993): 22–37; and Robert Kaplan, *The Arabists: The Romance of an American Elite* (New York, 1993). On popular culture see especially Michael W. Suleiman, *The Arabs in the Mind of America* (Brattleboro, VT, 1988); Edmund Ghareeb, *Split Vision: The Portrayal of Arabs in the American Media* (Washington, 1983); and Janice Terry, *Mistaken Identity: Arab Stereotypes in Popular Writing* (Washington, 1987).

151 Indeed, so many of these materials have surfaced during the past decade that I am seriously considering learning Arabic or Hebrew myself. The memoirs of Mahmoud Riad, Muhammad Fawzi, and other Egyptian policymakers, for example, are now available in Arabic, as are many Egyptian government documents collected by Mohamed Heikal, editor of *Al-Ahram* and confidant to Gamal Abdel Nasser and Anwar Sadat. The diaries of David Ben Gurion and Moshe Sharett are open to scholars who can read Hebrew, along with many materials in the Israeli State Archives down through the late 1950s. And the Woodrow Wilson Center's Cold War International History Project has provided translations of a few Russian documents relating to Soviet policy in the Middle East, with the promise of more to come. There is also a rich scholarly literature on Israeli-American relations in Hebrew. The scholarship available in Arabic and Russian, on the other hand, seems to be much thinner.

policymakers seem to have doubted that the people of the region were, in the words of a 1949 CIA psychological profile, "non-inventive and slow to put theories into practice," prone to "astonishing acts of treachery and dishonesty," and unable to "integrate European concepts of government, of education, and of industrialization into the traditional pattern of life."[152] And fewer still seem to have doubted their own responsibility to bring peace, progress, and prosperity American-style to the Middle East, whether the people of the region liked it or not.

Born and raised in a self-proclaimed "City Upon a Hill," top U.S. officials, like Mark Twain's innocents abroad, assumed during the decades after 1945 that what was good for America was also good for the Middle East, and vice versa. To be sure, certain aspects of America's twentieth-century encounter with the Middle East – the lure of oil and the logic of containment – would probably have struck the nineteenth-century pilgrims aboard the *Quaker City* as rather odd. But others – an irresistable impulse to remake the world in America's image and a profound American ambivalence toward the peoples to be remade – would have been as familiar as the riverboat whistles that echoed down the Mississippi. More than a century after Mark Twain witnessed the first arrival of Gideon's Band in the Holy Land, the United States still seems at times determined to bear down on the people of the Middle East with America's greatness until it crushes them.

152 CIA Report SR-13, "Arab World," 27 September 1949, 65–66, Central Intelligence Agency, Office of Privacy Coordination, Washington, DC.

17

The Cold War in Asia: The Elusive Synthesis

ROBERT J. McMAHON

The main body of the text that follows appeared in the Summer 1988 issue of *Diplomatic History*. It offers a summary and critique of the scholarly literature pertaining to the Cold War in Asia, concentrating on that work published between 1980 and 1987. A substantial number of books and articles on U.S.-Asian relations during the Cold War era has been written in the intervening eight years, of course, some of which have pushed the temporal and conceptual boundaries of the field in exciting, new directions. Consequently, I have added a postscript to the original essay, in which I examine the larger themes and issues engaged by the more recent scholarship on the Cold War in Asia. Among other matters, I seek in the postscript to reexamine my own earlier conclusions about the state of the field.

The past decade has witnessed a tremendous outpouring of scholarly books and articles dealing with the Cold War in Asia. Given the significance of the subject, this veritable avalanche of work should not be surprising. Indeed, as Akira Iriye noted in a recent essay: "America's military, political, economic, and cultural involvement in the Asia-Pacific region" over the last fifty years "has fundamentally altered Asian history, American society, and international affairs in general."[1] This essay will examine the overall direction of that historical literature. In addition to noting the characteristics that tie these works together, it will suggest significant interpretive differences that separate the newer works from each other and from previous scholarship in this field. It

1 Akira Iriye, "Contemporary History as History: American Expansion into the Pacific since 1941," *Pacific Historical Review* 53 (May 1984): 91.

will also assess how the recent scholarly contributions have added to our understanding of American foreign policy as a whole during the Cold War era and, perhaps most important, determine the extent to which they have succeeded in creating a new synthetic framework for understanding America's encounter with Asia.

The problem of synthesis has been much discussed of late. Some of the historical profession's more thoughtful observers have decried the "missing synthesis" in American history. "We have built in postwar America a discipline fragmented into a large number of separate but highly cultivated boxes," complains Thomas Bender. "Interpretation, the consideration of how the boxes relate to each other to form a whole historical experience, has proceeded slowly, if at all."[2] As Bender would almost certainly agree, the building blocks for a new synthetic exposition of America's overall national experience first will have to be erected within the discipline's numerous subfields. Foreign relations must be an integral element of that effort; any synthesis that fails to account for the projection of American power and influence abroad would be fatally flawed. Even those who applaud the seeming hegemony of social history during the past two decades would probably concede the point (at least in moments of weakness). U.S.-Asian relations during the postwar era assume considerable salience to that larger task. Not only did the United States fight its two most recent wars there, establish a permanent military presence in the region, deem Asia vital to its national security, and help reconstruct a nation that would later emerge as its most potent economic rival, but with the Vietnam debacle America also faced probably its most severe domestic crisis since the Civil War. Iriye is correct: America's encounter with Asia during this period profoundly altered U.S. society.

The remarkable proliferation within the past decade of scholarly studies on U.S.-Asian relations provides a useful point of departure.

2 Thomas Bender, "Wholes and Parts: The Need for Synthesis in American History," *Journal of American History* 73 (June 1986): 128. See also Herbert G. Gutman, "The Missing Synthesis: Whatever Happened to History?" *Nation*, 21 November 1981, 521, 553–54; Eric Foner, "History in Crisis," *Commonweal*, 18 December 1981, 723–26; Thomas Bender, "Making History Whole Again," *New York Times Book Review*, 6 October 1985, 1, 42–43; and "A Round Table: Synthesis in American History," *Journal of American History* 74 (June 1987): 107–30.

In his presidential address to SHAFR several years ago, Warren I. Cohen remarked that historians toiling in this area were "producing the most exciting, the most important, and readable work to be found in the profession in the 1980s"; their efforts, he boasted, represented the "cutting edge of the historical profession."[3] Although many scholars outside the fraternity of diplomatic history would likely dispute Cohen's bold claims, his assertions certainly have some validity. Regardless of where the profession's true "cutting edge" lies, historians of Asian-American affairs have produced an impressive body of scholarship in recent years, much of it sophisticated, innovative, and challenging, most of it based on thorough research in newly opened documentary collections. But is this work leading to a new synthesis?

At least one result of recent scholarship is clear: The traditional paradigm has been thoroughly discredited. That paradigm, which reflected the broader Cold War consensus in American society, governed a large body of scholarship produced during the 1950s and 1960s. It assessed the triumph of the Chinese Communists as a major defeat for American foreign policy and held that, following the revolution in China, virtually no opportunities existed for accommodation between Washington and Beijing. The occupation of Japan was viewed as one of America's finest hours, as Supreme Allied Commander Douglas MacArthur helped steer Japan toward peace, democracy, and free enterprise. Scholars working in this mold also argued that the United States responded appropriately and forthrightly to Communist challenges in Korea and Vietnam, sympathized with nationalist aspirations throughout the region, and supported the newly emerging areas of South and Southeast Asia with varying degrees of political, economic, and military assistance.[4]

3 Warren I. Cohen, "The History of American-East Asian Relations: Cutting Edge of the Historical Profession," *Diplomatic History* 9 (Spring 1985): 102.

4 For historiographical reviews of earlier literature on U.S.-Asian relations see Ernest R. May and James C. Thomson, Jr., ed., *American-East Asian Relations: A Survey* (Cambridge, MA, 1972); Robert J. McMahon, "United States Relations with Asia in the Twentieth Century: Retrospect and Prospect," in *American Foreign Relations: A Historiographical Review*, ed. Gerald K. Haines and J. Samuel Walker (Westport, 1981), 237–70; and Warren I. Cohen, ed., *New Frontiers in American-East Asian Relations: Essays Presented to Dorothy Borg* (New York, 1983). This essay will analyze only those works published within the past ten years.

The emergence of a revisionist school of historiography in the late 1960s offered the first significant challenge to that paradigm. Revisionists viewed the United States, rather than the Soviet Union, as the power primarily responsible for the extension of the Cold War to Asia, criticized the United States for seeking to advance its own imperial interests in the region, and scored U.S. officials for attempting to stifle legitimate nationalist aspirations throughout the continent. But that work also suffered from limitations. Most seriously, it was unduly present-minded, mirroring the contemporary concerns and biases of the late 1960s and 1970s. As Roger Dingman has pointed out: "All studies written during the 1970s reflected, to some degree, America's agony in Vietnam."[5]

The more mature scholarship that has appeared in the 1980s has begun to transcend the traditionalist-revisionist debate that dominated so much of the previous decade's work. It shares several common characteristics. First, this recent literature has been produced by scholars, primarily younger scholars, whose intellectual development has been shaped unmistakably by the central foreign policy issue of their age: the war in Vietnam. That experience has led to new perspectives and different questions about Asian-American relations and lent a sharply critical edge to their work. Second, their work has been built, for the most part, on a deep and broad empirical base. The documentary record necessary to reconstruct America's postwar record in Asia only became available within the past decade; many of the works examined in this essay have mined those new sources masterfully. Further, much of this recent literature has also utilized the diplomatic records of Great Britain and, where available, various Asian countries, producing multiarchival studies with multinational perspectives. Third, recent historical treatments of U.S.-Asian relations display a great deal more sensitivity to Asian developments and Asian perspectives. A growing number of specialists in the field function as area experts as well as diplomatic historians. Their intimate knowledge of Asian languages and cultures not only sets them apart from nearly all practitioners of

5 Roger Dingman, "Lost Chance in China," *Reviews in American History* 9 (June 1981): 253.

earlier generations but also enables them to broaden the scope of the discipline in a provocative manner. Fourth, this new literature has borrowed fruitfully from the social sciences. Historians of American-Asian relations have within the past decade proved themselves especially sensitive to the complexities of the policymaking process, often utilizing bureaucratic politics models to explicate policy decisions; few of the works under review here look at the U.S. government as a unitary actor. Recent studies in this field have also tended to analyze events within a more explicit conceptual framework, reflecting the strong influence of social science methodologies.

Finally, taken together these studies reveal a number of common conclusions that, in a very general way, might point toward a new paradigm. On a number of broad points, there now exists a virtual consensus: prior to the Korean War, the Truman administration contemplated accommodation with Beijing to a much greater extent than previously recognized; Washington's decision to intervene in the Korean conflict destroyed that possibility, while militarizing American foreign policy to a regrettable degree; the United States often misread Soviet and Chinese Communist intentions in postwar Asia; America's decision to march toward the Yalu in late 1950 had disastrous consequences for Sino-American relations and for overall U.S. interests in the region; the American occupation of Japan reversed course after 1947, becoming more concerned with integrating Japan into the American strategic and economic orbit for Cold War purposes and less concerned with effecting reforms; the origins of the American commitment to Vietnam stemmed from a misplaced effort to extend containment to Southeast Asia.

Despite these significant areas of convergence, deep interpretive differences still divide historians of Asian-American relations on a number of specific and quite broad issues. Among those, the following appear most significant: When did Cold War thinking begin to influence American policy toward Asia? When and why did the United States seek to extend the containment doctrine to Asia? What were the principal political, economic, ideological, and strategic considerations that lay behind American actions in postwar Asia? And, finally, how do we assess America's ultimate impact on Asian societies? Until scholars can reach some degree of consensus on those fundamental questions, it will be difficult to talk with assurance about new paradigms or new syntheses.

China policy has attracted the most scholarly attention in recent years and is the area in which new scholarship has most dramatically overturned the old paradigm. It is the area as well that best reflects the paradoxical results of the new historical literature. That work has fundamentally shifted the grounds of the scholarly debate about U.S. policy toward China, but it has raised almost as many questions as it has answered and has led to interpretive differences as basic as those that divided specialists at the height of the traditionalist-revisionist clash.

As noted above, there are some important points of convergence in the scholarly literature of the past decade. For one, nearly all of those studies agree that U.S. policymakers never viewed China as a vital interest during the 1940s. Instead, the Truman administration's Cold War strategy always gave precedence to Europe, where American interests were judged more critical and the Soviet threat appeared more pressing. According to Warren Cohen: "Whatever American ambitions were in East Asia – and they were considerable – the Truman Administration, like every Administration preceding it, did not consider American interests there to be vital. On the scale of American priorities, unlike the scale of American sympathies, China ranked very low indeed."[6]

This is not to suggest that they deemed China insignificant to American interests. On that point too a veritable consensus now prevails. In an important essay, Steven I. Levine contends that General George C. Marshall's mediation mission to China grew out of "mounting U.S. concern with Soviet expansionism in East Asia." He argues persuasively that Marshall was never a truly impartial arbitrator. "Washington could not contemplate with

6 Warren I. Cohen, *America's Response to China: An Interpretative History of Sino-American Relations*, rev. ed. (New York, 1980), 193. See also William Whitney Stueck, Jr., *The Road to Confrontation: American Policy toward China and Korea, 1947–1950* (Chapel Hill, 1981); Thomas G. Paterson, "If Europe, Why Not China? The Containment Doctrine, 1947–1949," *Prologue* 13 (Spring 1981): 19–38; and Fred Harvey Harrington, "'Europe First' and Its Consequences for the Far Eastern Policy of the United States," in *Redefining the Past: Essays in Diplomatic History in Honor of William Appleman Williams*, ed. Lloyd C. Gardner (Corvallis, OR, 1985), 105–20.

equanimity the prospect of a Communist victory in China," Levine writes, "because it remained convinced of the links binding Yenan to Moscow."[7] Similarly, Gary May, Thomas G. Paterson, William W. Stueck, John H. Feaver, and Russell D. Buhite see fear of the global implications of a Communist Chinese victory shaping American policy decisions throughout the turbulent civil war years. U.S. analysts, Paterson notes, believed that

> continued political and economic instability or Communist victory in the civil war might serve to invite the Soviets into China. If this occurred, it was feared, Russia could use China as a springboard to communize, through infiltration, the rest of Asia, threaten America's ally Japan, close trade routes and commercial opportunities, block Western access to such raw materials as tin and rubber, and in the event of Soviet-American war, launch military operations from the vast Chinese mainland.[8]

Despite their deep concern with the likely consequences of a Guomindang collapse, American leaders chose to support Jiang Jieshi's regime with only limited aid. Granted, that aid still totaled over $3 billion during the 1945–1949 period, hardly a modest sum. Still, the United States, for a variety of reasons, chose not to pursue containment with the same kind of vigorous, open-ended commitment that it had made in Europe. Recent scholarship, which overwhelmingly approves of that policy, cites a number of factors that help explain the seeming contradiction between interests and commitments in China. First of all, most historians of Sino-American relations now stress that the Truman administration recognized the severe limitations on U.S. financial and material resources; additional support for China would have come at the expense of Europe, a higher priority. In the aftermath of the Marshall mission, moreover, American analysts viewed Jiang as a weak and corrupt leader whose prospects for ultimate success were at best exceedingly dim; massive aid to a doomed regime

7 Steven I. Levine, "A New Look at American Mediation in the Chinese Civil War: The Marshall Mission and Manchuria," *Diplomatic History* 3 (Fall 1979): 349.

8 Paterson, "If Europe, Why Not China?" 26. See also Gary May, *China Scapegoat: The Diplomatic Ordeal of John Carter Vincent* (Washington, 1979); Stueck, *Road to Confrontation*; John H. Feaver, "The China Aid Bill of 1948: Limited Assistance as a Cold War Strategy," *Diplomatic History* 5 (Spring 1981): 107–20; and Russell D. Buhite, *Soviet-American Relations in Asia, 1945–1954* (Norman, 1981).

would be useless in the opinion of most top officials. In sum, most recent accounts of America's China policy are agreed that Truman and his advisers correctly surmised that European-style containment would not work in China and would simply be a wasted effort. Hence, by 1947 the Truman administration was simply awaiting the inevitable: Jiang's demise.[9]

Why did Washington continue to provide aid to a government that it fully expected to crumble? The answers to that question have been far from unanimous. Some historians assert that domestic politics provides a sufficient explanation. Token aid for the Guomindang, in this view, mollified the adminstration's public and congressional critics, especially the so-called China bloc, thus helping to ensure bipartisan support for critical European initiatives.[10] Others discount the influence of the China bloc. Feaver, in his examination of the China aid bill of 1948, suggests that U.S. policymakers judged continued assistance "as a necessary tactical maneuver in the effort to obstruct the expansion of Soviet power and influence." They believed that by helping Jiang to "avoid defeat for the time being, limited American assistance would serve to delay for as long as possible the negative international consequences that they feared would follow a Communist victory in China."[11] Yet other scholars raise the issue of credibility. "A belief that the United States must build credibility abroad," Stueck offers, "discouraged the Truman administration from expanding American commitments to Nationalist China, but it also helped prevent a total abandonment of the Chiang regime."[12] Cohen makes the point more bluntly: "What happened in China

9 Warren I. Cohen, "Acheson, His Advisers, and China, 1949–1950," in *Uncertain Years: Chinese-American Relations, 1947–1950*, ed. Dorothy Borg and Waldo Heinrichs (New York, 1980), 15–52; John Lewis Gaddis, "The Strategic Perspective: The Rise and Fall of the 'Defensive Perimeter' Concept, 1947–1951," in Borg and Heinrichs, eds., *Uncertain Years*, 61–118; Paterson, "If Europe, Why Not China?"; Buhite, *Soviet-American Relations in Asia*; William Stueck, *The Wedemeyer Mission: American Politics and Foreign Policy during the Cold War* (Athens, GA, 1984); idem, *Road to Confrontation.*

10 Michael Schaller, *The United States and China in the Twentieth Century* (New York, 1979), 115–20; Cohen, *America's Response to China*; Stueck, *Road to Confrontation*; idem, *The Wedemeyer Mission*; Buhite, *Soviet-American Relations in Asia*; Robert P. Newman, "The Self-Inflicted Wound: The China White Paper of 1949," *Prologue* 14 (Fall 1982): 140–56.

11 Feaver, "The China Aid Bill of 1948," 112. See also Paterson, "If Europe, Why Not China?"

12 Stueck, *Road to Confrontation*, 225.

was less important than the lessons other nations would draw from American action there."[13]

More fundamental interpretive disputes surface with regard to the controversial "lost chance" thesis. That thesis has been expounded with admirable force and eloquence by Warren I. Cohen and Nancy Bernkopf Tucker. They contend that the Truman administration, following the advice of Dean Acheson, was moving realistically toward accommodation with the People's Republic of China (PRC) prior to the outbreak of war in Korea. Acheson sought to establish the best possible relationship with Beijing, hoping eventually to drive a wedge between China and the Soviet Union and to foster the emergence of Mao Zedong as an "Asian Tito." To that end, he was prepared to end all aid to Jiang's forces and to acquiesce in the fall of Taiwan. Trade, diplomatic recognition, and support for Beijing's representation at the United Nations Security Council were the carrots that Washington planned to offer. The hallmarks of the Acheson policy, then, were realism and flexibility. Absent the fighting in Korea, formal and regularized, if not intimate, relations would have been established between the United States and China.[14]

Although based on extensive research and astute analysis, the Cohen-Tucker thesis has not proved entirely convincing. Some specialists discount the likelihood of China's revolutionary new rulers embracing rapprochement with the United States. Of course, in the absence of hard documentary evidence such speculation must remain highly tentative.[15] More seriously, scholars such as

13 Warren I. Cohen, "The United States and China since 1945," in Cohen, ed., *New Frontiers in American-East Asian Relations*, 135.

14 Cohen, "Acheson, His Advisers, and China"; idem, *America's Response to China*; Nancy Bernkopf Tucker, "Nationalist China's Decline and Its Impact on Sino-American Relations, 1949–1950," in Borg and Heinrichs, eds., *Uncertain Years*, 131–71; idem, *Patterns in the Dust: Chinese-American Relations and the Recognition Controversy, 1949–1950* (New York, 1983); idem, "American Policy toward Sino-Japanese Trade in the Postwar Years: Politics and Prosperity," *Diplomatic History* 8 (Summer 1984): 183–208. See also David Allan Mayers, *Cracking the Monolith: U.S. Policy against the Sino-Soviet Alliance, 1949–1955* (Baton Rouge, 1986).

15 For differing views of Chinese Communist intentions and the prospects for accommodation see especially the essays by Michael H. Hunt and Steven Goldstein in Borg and Heinrichs, eds., *Uncertain Years*; Russell Buhite, "Missed Opportunities? American Policy and the Chinese Rapprochement in 1949: Was There Another 'Lost Chance in China'?" *China Quarterly* 89 (1982): 74–96; and James Reardon-Anderson, *Yenan and the Great Powers: Origins of Chinese Communist Foreign Policy, 1944–1946* (New York, 1980).

John Lewis Gaddis, Waldo H. Heinrichs, Robert M. Blum, and William Stueck point to a dualism in America's China policy overlooked by Cohen and Tucker. While Acheson might have been willing to acquiesce in the fall of Taiwan, the Department of Defense was not. The Pentagon viewed Taiwan as critical to its defensive perimeter strategy for containing Soviet power along the Asian rim. That perspective represented a second, equally important, strand in U.S. policy, one that rejected the "Asian Tito" theory in favor of the assumption that a communized China would be "a satellite of the Soviet Union and a springboard for Soviet expansion."[16] Two competing policy currents may even have existed within Acheson himself. Andrew J. Rotter praises Tucker for describing the realistic, flexible Acheson. "But she has missed Acheson the Cold Warrior," he argues, "whose ideology was formed by social class, molded by public service, then hardened in the fire of anticommunism. Both Achesons made United States China policy during 1949 and 1950."[17]

Starting from a different premise than Cohen and Tucker, David McLean seeks to answer another critical question: "Why did the United States, in its dealings with the Chinese Communist Party (CCP), follow a course so clearly at odds with the preferred policies of most other Western and most Asian states?" Rejecting the arguments that public, media, or bureaucratic pressures, the mistreatment of Americans in China, or the U.S. economic stake there explain Washington's failure to recognize Beijing before June 1950, he emphasizes instead the importance of American ideology and deeply held American myths about China. The Truman administration experienced an enormous amount of difficulty in reconciling itself to China's new rulers; never far beneath the surface "lurked a sense of dismay and even indignation toward the Chinese Communists." Their "most profound transgression," McLean writes, "was that, through allegiance to an

16 Waldo Heinrichs, "American China Policy and the Cold War in Asia: A New Look," in Borg and Heinrichs, eds., *Uncertain Years*, 287. See also Gaddis, "The Strategic Perspective"; Stueck, *Road to Confrontation*; and Robert M. Blum, *Drawing the Line: The Origin of the American Containment Policy in East Asia* (New York, 1982).

17 Andrew J. Rotter, "Blunder Out of China," *Reviews in American History* 12 (June 1984): 272.

ideology that was un-American and to a state that was the major rival to the United States, they had betrayed America's expectations of achieving its world destiny in Asia." True, Acheson did embrace for a time a policy of accommodation, but he did so half-heartedly for it "went against the American grain." McLean's provocative article illuminates the larger truth that America's China policy was significantly more hostile than that of other states even before the outbreak of hostilities in Korea.[18]

Nearly all recent studies see the Korean War as a benchmark event for U.S.-Chinese relations. They conclude that it led to the complete abandonment of the accommodation option, brought direct U.S. intervention in the Chinese civil war, and ultimately led to vicious fighting between American and Chinese forces, all of which helped foreclose the prospects for rapprochement for more than two decades. Still, within that broad consensus lay important interpretive differences. For Cohen and Tucker, it was the Korean conflict that brought the Cold War to East Asia. Cohen calls that conflict "the critical event in the Cold War" since it "shattered Acheson's schemes for separating Chinese communists from Soviet Communists, impaired his judgement, brought the United States into direct conflict with China, and radically changed the nature of the competition with the Soviet Union."[19] But that sharp policy reversal seems almost inexplicable within the framework of pragmatism and flexibility so carefully set forth by Cohen and Tucker. Why had Acheson's judgment

18 David McLean, "American Nationalism, the China Myth, and the Truman Doctrine: The Question of Accommodation with Peking, 1949–50," *Diplomatic History* 10 (Winter 1986): 25–42. The quotations are from pp. 26, 41–42, and 39. On the role of ideology see Kenneth S. Chern, "The Ideology of American China Policy, 1945–60," *Journal of Oriental Studies* 20 (1982): 115–72; and idem, *Dilemma in China: America's Policy Debate, 1945* (Hamden, CT, 1980). For comparative views of British and American policy see David C. Wolf, "'To Secure a Convenience': Britain Recognizes China – 1950," *Journal of Contemporary History* 18 (April 1983): 299–326; Ritchie Ovendale, "Britain, the United States, and the Recognition of Communist China," *Historical Journal* 26 (March 1983): 139–58: idem, "Britain and the Cold War in Asia," in *The Foreign Policy of the British Labour Government, 1945–51*, ed. Ovendale (Leicester, England, 1984), 121–48; and Edward M. Martin, *Divided Counsel: The Anglo-American Response to Communist Victory in China* (Lexington, KY, 1986).

19 Warren I. Cohen, "Cold Wars and Shell Games: The Truman Administration and East Asia," *Reviews in American History* 11 (September 1983): 436. See also Tucker, *Patterns in the Dust*, 195–207.

suddenly become "impaired"? Could Korea by itself have reversed America's China policy so dramatically and so decisively? More convincing is the alternative framework sketched above by McLean and others. Acheson, these skeptics insist, never wholeheartedly accepted the "Asian Tito" option; Howard Schonberger, for example, refers to the "ambivalence and expedience of Acheson's belief in a possible Sino-Soviet split."[20] That option, moreover, was vigorously opposed by other power centers within the Truman administration that urged direct U.S. military support for an independent state on Taiwan. Most important, these scholars contend that the Korean hostilities simply deepened a trend already well under way in policy circles, suggesting that the containment doctrine was being applied to East Asia well before the North Korean invasion and that the chances for U.S. recognition of Mao's regime were virtually nil by the spring of 1950.[21] The current scholarly debate about the "lost chance" thesis thus encapsulates some of the more fundamental issues about the Cold War in Asia that still divide historians.

A brief examination of the recent literature on U.S.-Korean relations during the early postwar years reveals a similar pattern: major interpretive disputes about larger questions hidden within a surprising congruence of views on a number of once hotly contested points. The points of consensus are striking. First, nearly all recent accounts agree that the Truman administration's commitment to defend Korea stemmed almost entirely from its symbolic value and its relationship to U.S. credibility worldwide. Indeed, the military establishment disparaged the peninsula's military significance, and the Joint Chiefs of Staff repeatedly urged the removal of U.S. troops from Korea and the annulment of the American commitment to that troubled land. Truman rejected that advice primarily on account of Korea's symbolic importance to overall U.S. foreign policy objectives. "After the Communist

20 Howard B. Schonberger, "The Cold War and the American Empire in Asia," *Radical History Review* 33 (1985): 148.

21 McLean, "American Nationalism, the China Myth, and the Truman Doctrine"; Stueck, *Road to Confrontation*; Blum, *Drawing the Line*; William M. Leary and William Stueck, "The Chennault Plan to Save China: U.S. Containment in Asia and the Origins of the CIA's Aerial Empire, 1949–1950," *Diplomatic History* 8 (Fall 1984): 349–64.

victory in China," notes Burton I. Kaufman, "Korea became the only symbol left of America's willingness to contain Communist expansion in Asia. Washing its hands of Korea would be a signal to other Asians that the United States had abandoned them as well."[22] Charles M. Dobbs makes the point even more forcefully: "Korea mattered little for its own sake; rather, the perceived requirements of the cold war made it important." Domestic politics and international pressures combined to transform Korea into "a litmus test of the Truman administration's resolve."[23]

Second, most contemporary historians of U.S.-Korean relations, in dramatic contrast to previous interpreters, consider the Korean War essentially civil in its origins. Bruce Cumings, whose influential work has asserted this thesis most fully and most persuasively, says that the war that began in June 1950 represented "a denouement, not a beginning; it was a civil and revolutionary struggle fought over issues that were joined immediately after liberation in 1945."[24] Kaufman, who has penned the most comprehensive recent account of American diplomacy toward the Korean conflict, concurs. "The conflict between North and South Korea was a true civil war," he writes, "and not merely part of the global confrontation between Washington and Moscow. The North apparently attacked the South unilaterally and without the knowledge of either the Soviet Union or the PRC."[25] Even William Stueck, who places much greater emphasis on the international dimensions of the conflict and Kim Il Sung's dependence on external assistance, concedes the point. "Contrary to prevailing opinion in the United States in June 1950," he observes, "the

22 Burton I. Kaufman, *The Korean War: Challenges in Crisis, Credibility, and Command* (New York 1986), 23–24.

23 Charles M. Dobbs, *The Unwanted Symbol: American Foreign Policy, the Cold War, and Korea, 1945–1950* (Kent, OH, 1981), 160–92. For the view that Korea became essential to the administration's credibility see Stueck, *Road to Confrontation*; Buhite, *Soviet-American Relations in Asia*; James I. Matray, "Korea: Test Case of Containment in Asia," in *Child of Conflict: The Korean-American Relationship*, ed. Bruce Cumings (Seattle, 1983), 169–93; and idem, *The Reluctant Crusade: American Foreign Policy in Korea, 1941–1950* (Honolulu, 1985).

24 Bruce Cumings, "Introduction: The Course of Korean-American Relations, 1943–1953," in Cumings, ed., *Child of Conflict*, 41. See also Bruce Cumings, *The Origins of the Korean War*, vol. 1, *Liberation and the Emergence of Separate Regimes, 1945–1947* (Princeton, 1981), esp. xx–xxi.

25 Kaufman, *The Korean War*, 32.

initiative for the North Korean attack came from Pyongyang, not Moscow or Peking."[26] That such unanimity could be reached on an issue once marked by bitter scholarly exchanges would have been unthinkable in the 1960s and 1970s.

Third, recent scholarship concurs that American policymakers grievously misread Soviet and Chinese Communist intentions and capabilities with regard to Korea. Failing to understand the indigenous roots of the North Korean attack, the Truman administration assumed almost immediately that it had been inspired directly by Moscow and Beijing as part of a dangerous and aggressive new worldwide push for extending Communist influence. That fallacious assumption led not only to American military intervention in the Korean peninsula but also brought renewed U.S. intervention in the Chinese civil war, stepped-up support for the Philippines government, and increased aid for the French in Indochina. All those policy decisions stemmed from the misplaced conviction that the Kremlin had embarked on a brazen global challenge to U.S. interests. Similarly, the administration made a monumental miscalculation of Chinese Communist intentions and capabilities in late 1950 as General Douglas MacArthur marched to the Yalu. Nearly all scholars now believe that the devastating Chinese counterattack could have been prevented if only the United States had taken seriously Beijing's numerous warning signals. Stueck blames the administration's misperception on American ethnocentrism. U.S. analysts considered China a backward nation so preoccupied with internal problems and so feeble militarily that it would not dare engage superior American firepower. "Introspection," Stueck points out, "was notably absent from American thought. When communist China counter-attacked in Korea, therefore, Acheson, rather than viewing the action as a response to a threatening U.S. move toward the Manchurian boarder, labeled it aggression against the United States."[27]

Finally, the latest historical literature roundly condemns the war's long-term impact on American foreign policy. James I.

26 William Stueck, "The Korean War as International History," *Diplomatic History* 10 (Fall 1986): 293–94.

27 Stueck, *Road to Confrontation*, 254–55. See also D. Clayton James, *The Years of MacArthur*, vol. 3, *Triumph and Disaster, 1945–1964* (Boston, 1985), 518–64.

Matray speaks for many when he speculates that the war represented "a crucial turning point in postwar American diplomacy" and had "a regrettable impact on the subsequent course of Soviet-American relations." "After June 1950," he argues, "American diplomacy became steadily more rigid as the nation's leaders pursued policies and programs with noticeably greater inflexibility."[28] Blaming Korea for the militarization and globalization of American foreign policy has become a staple theme in much recent Cold War historiography. According to Robert Jervis, it led to a vast increase in the U.S. defense budget, the militarization of NATO, the rapid proliferation of U.S. security commitments around the world, and an altered perception of the Sino-Soviet bloc. "Without Korea," he contends, "U.S. policy would have been very different, and there were no events on the horizon which could have been functional substitutes for the war."[29]

As with recent work on Sino-American relations, the latest accounts of U.S. policy toward Korea reveal discord as well as agreement. While nearly all scholars of U.S. diplomacy agree that the war profoundly influenced subsequent American foreign policy, some date the globalization of American interests and commitments to a much earlier period. Nor is the difference merely one of nuance; indeed, the question of when Washington adopted a globalist outlook underlies most current debates about the origins and course of the Cold War.[30]

Likewise, historians part company on such fundamental questions as the nature of U.S. interests in post-World War II Korea,[31]

28 Matray, *Reluctant Crusade*, 247–58.

29 Robert Jervis, "The Impact of the Korean War on the Cold War," *Journal of Conflict Resolution* 24 (December 1980): 563.

30 See especially Melvyn P. Leffler, "The American Conception of National Security and the Beginnings of the Cold War, 1945–1948," along with the accompanying comments by John Lewis Gaddis and Bruce R. Kuniholm and the reply by Leffler, in *American Historical Review* 89 (April 1984): 346–400. Compare also John Lewis Gaddis, *Strategies of Containment: A Critical Appraisal of Postwar American National Security Policy* (New York, 1982) and Robert A. Pollard, *Economic Security and the Origins of the Cold War, 1945–1950* (New York, 1985) with Melvyn P. Leffler, "Was 1947 a Turning Point in American Foreign Policy?" (Paper delivered at Princeton University, September 1987).

31 Compare, for example, the different approaches pursued by Stueck and Cumings. See Stueck, *Road to Confrontation*; and Cumings, "Introduction," in Cumings, ed., *Child of Conflict*.

when and why containment was applied to Korea,[32] and the reasons for U.S. military intervention in June 1950.[33] At the risk of simplification, the different perspectives might be termed liberal versus radical. In the former camp are Stueck, Matray, and Kaufman. Operating from a pluralist model, they see American officials striving desperately to maintain the nation's credibility in the face of mounting domestic and international pressures. They fault U.S. leaders less for their intentions than for their failure to coordinate means with ends, the classic realist complaint. The latter approach, exemplified best by the provocative work of Bruce Cumings, views the United States as a hegemonic power that sought from the outset to contain both communism and revolutionary impulses within the peninsula. Washington's larger goal always was to help shape a new regional order in Northeast Asia conducive to American security and economic interests. American rule in Korea, he says, "took no heed of Korean needs and demands for a full restructuring of colonial legacies"; rather, it represented "a new imperium" that "worked out the logic of its own interests." Cumings's work, informed by his deep knowledge of Korean culture and sources and his sophisticated application of Immanuel Wallerstein's world-systems theory, challenges diplomatic historians to study Asian developments more closely and to place their subject in a wider world-historical framework.[34]

32 For the view that containment characterized American policy from the very inception of the occupation see Mark Paul, "Diplomacy Delayed: The Atomic Bomb and the Division of Korea, 1945," in Cumings, ed., *Child of Conflict*, 67–91; and Matray, "Captive of the Cold War: The American Decision to Divide Korea at the Thirty-Eighth Parallel," *Pacific Historical Review* 50 (May 1981): 145–68. For the view that the United States also sought to contain leftist forces within Korea during that early period see Cumings, *The Origins of the Korean War*.

33 Compare the relative weight assigned to domestic and international factors in the following: James I. Matray, "America's Reluctant Crusade: Truman's Commitment of Combat Troops in the Korean War," *Historian* 42 (May 1980): 437–55; idem, *Reluctant Crusade*; Stephen Pelz, "U.S. Decisions on Korean Policy, 1943–1950: Some Hypotheses," in Cumings, ed., *Child of Conflict*, 93–132; Charles M. Dobbs, "Limiting Room to Maneuver: The Korea Assistance Act of 1949," *Historian* 48 (August 1986): 525–38; Stueck, *Road to Confrontation*; Cumings, "Introduction," in Cumings, ed., *Child of Conflict*; and Kaufman, *The Korean War*.

34 Cumings, *The Origins of the Korean War*, 444. See also Cumings, "Introduction," in Cumings, ed., *Child of Conflict*; and idem, "The Origins and Development of the Northeast Asian Political Economy: Industrial Sectors, Product Cycles, and Political Consequences," *International Organization* 38 (Winter 1984): 1–40. For world-systems theory see especially Immanuel Wallerstein, *The Modern World System I*,

The availability of new sources in the United States and abroad has enabled scholars in recent years to broaden the debate about the war itself as well as the overall nature of Korean-American relations. The diplomacy of the war, the nature of inter-Allied relations, and the negotiations that brought the hostilities to a close have lately been subjected to penetrating new analyses. In a stimulating book, Rosemary Foot demonstrates conclusively that debates about widening the war continued to rage in Washington long after MacArthur's recall. By the spring of 1953, she says, President Eisenhower stood ready to threaten China, if negotiations stalled once again, with the use of nuclear weapons.[35] Foot, Stueck, Kaufman, Peter N. Farrar, and Ra Jong-Yil have carefully examined the nature of Anglo-American differences over the Korean question. Although their assessments of British influence in the wartime coalition differ, all agree that the story of inter-Allied discord is a critical one that requires far more attention.[36] Barton J. Bernstein, John Kotch, Kaufman, Edward C. Keefer, and Henry W. Brands, Jr., have ably described the daunting dilemmas faced by both Truman and Eisenhower in their efforts to attain a peace settlement while preserving a mutually acceptable postwar relationship with their independent-minded South Korean ally.[37]

Capitalist Agriculture and the Origins of the European World Economy in the Sixteenth Century (New York), 1974; and idem, ed., *The Capitalist World-Economy: Essays* (New York, 1979).

35 Rosemary Foot, *The Wrong War: American Policy and the Dimensions of the Korean Conflict, 1950–1953* (Ithaca, 1985).

36 Rosemary J. Foot, "Anglo-American Relations in the Korean Crisis: The British Effort to Avert an Expanded War, December 1950–January 1951," *Diplomatic History* 10 (Winter 1986): 43–57; William Stueck, "The Limits of Influence: British Policy and American Expansion of the War in Korea," *Pacific Historical Review* 55 (February 1986): 65–95; Kaufman, *The Korean War*; Peter N. Farrar, "Britain's Proposal for a Buffer Zone South of the Yalu in November 1950: Was It a Neglected Opportunity to End the Fighting in Korea?" *Journal of Contemporary History* 18 (April 1983): 327–51; Ra Jong-Yil, "Special Relationship at War: The Anglo-American Relationship during the Korean War," *Journal of Strategic Studies* 7 (September 1984): 301–17.

37 Barton J. Bernstein, "The Struggle over the Korean Armistice: Prisoners of Repatriation?" and John Kotch, "The Origins of the American Security Commitment to Korea," in Cumings, ed., *Child of Conflict*, 261–307, and 239–59, respectively; Edward C. Keefer, "President Dwight D. Eisenhower and the End of the Korean War," *Diplomatic History* 10 (Summer 1986): 267–89; Henry W. Brands, Jr., "The Dwight D. Eisenhower Administration, Syngman Rhee, and the 'Other' Geneva Conference of 1954," *Pacific Historical Review* 61 (February 1987): 59–85.

Although much of the story probably still remains untold, the scholarship of the 1980s has unquestionably moved well beyond the themes that animated a previous generation of scholars.

The rich scholarly harvest of the past decade has also compelled a fundamental rethinking of the postwar relationship between the United States and Japan.[38] Much of that work has focused perforce on the occupation period. Traditionally, historians joined with memoirists in their assessment of the occupation as a glorious chapter in American history, celebrating what they judged a virtually unalloyed success story for the United States – and for Japan. As John W. Dower has noted, those positive evaluations "reflect more than just a sanguine evaluation of developments in postwar Japan. . . . Implicit also is a comparably benign assessment of the nature and motivations of the postwar American state itself."[39] Thus, what Carol Gluck (borrowing from Herbert Butterfield) has dubbed the "heroic narrative" genre largely dominated this field well through the 1960s.[40] Dower and others began to chip away at that complacent interpretation in the 1970s. Yet until the end of that decade the occupation, in the words of Ray A. Moore, "attracted little serious attention from scholars."[41] No longer can historians of Asian-American affairs justly be accused of neglecting Japan. To the contrary, some of the more thoughtful and challenging works to appear in recent years have focused on American policy toward Japan, including Michael Schaller's important reinterpretation of the occupation.[42] Specialists, moreover, eagerly await long-promised books from such authorities as Dower, Roger Dingman, and Howard Schonberger.

38 A superb historiographical review that examines Japanese as well as American contributions is Carol Gluck, "Entangling Illusions – Japanese and American Views of the Occupation," in Cohen, ed., *New Frontiers in American-East Asian Relations*, 169–236. See also Sadao Asada, "Recent Works on the American Occupation of Japan: The State of the Art," *Japanese Journal of American Studies* 1 (1981): 175–91; and Ray A. Moore, "The Occupation of Japan as History: Some Recent Research," *Monumenta Nipponica* 36 (Autumn 1981): 317–28.

39 John W. Dower, "Occupied Japan as History and Occupation History as Politics," *Journal of Asian Studies* 34 (February 1975): 486.

40 Gluck, "Entangling Illusions," 174–75.

41 Ray A. Moore, "Reflections on the Occupation of Japan," *Journal of Asian Studies* 38 (August 1979): 721.

42 Michael Schaller, *The American Occupation of Japan: The Origins of the Cold War in Asia* (New York, 1985).

The broad conclusions of the new literature have demolished the once-dominant image of a benevolent, altruistic occupier. Recent accounts concur that the liberal reform phase of the occupation was not only limited but short-lived, replaced in 1947–48 by a newfound concern with Japan's economic recovery and political stability. They agree as well that the "reverse course" in U.S. occupation policy was spurred by a combination of strategic and economic interests. The Truman administration sought, on the one hand, to enlist Japan's support in its worldwide effort to contain Soviet power; on the other, it endeavored "to make Japan the Asian workshop of a global capitalist order dominated by the United States."[43] By placing Japan policy squarely within the context of America's global Cold War strategy and diplomacy, these studies have moved well beyond the long-popular myth of the occupation as a unique and distinct aspect of postwar history – "an experiment in social engineering isolated from the international arena," in Schonberger's apt phrase.[44]

One impetus for the reverse course, specialists now agree, was the nagging "dollar gap" in U.S.-Japanese trade. That growing trade imbalance, part of a wider international problem occasioned by American economic supremacy and the devastation wrought by World War II, gravely threatened both world economic recovery and continued American prosperity. In a stimulating study of the economic dimensions of U.S.-Japanese relations, William S. Borden directly connects America's reverse course to this international trade crisis. The Truman administration sought "to correct the massive structural disequilibrium in world trade,"

43 Howard Schonberger, "U.S. Policy in Post-War Japan: The Retreat from Liberalism," *Science and Society* 46 (Spring 1982): 58–59.

44 Schonberger, "The Cold War and the American Empire in Asia," 145. See also John W. Dower, *Empire and Aftermath: Yoshida Shigeru and the Japanese Experience, 1878–1954* (Cambridge, MA, 1979); Howard Schonberger, "American Labor's Cold War in Japan," *Diplomatic History* 3 (Summer 1979): 249–72; idem, "U.S. Policy in Post-War Japan"; Michael Schaller, "Securing the Great Crescent: Occupied Japan and the Origins of Containment in Southeast Asia," *Journal of American History* 69 (September 1982): 392–414; idem, "Japan, China, and Southeast Asia: Regional Integration and Containment, 1947–1950," in *The Occupation of Japan: The International Context*, ed. Lawrence H. Redford (Norfolk, 1984), 163–84; Schaller, *The American Occupation of Japan*; William S. Borden, *The Pacific Alliance: United States Foreign Economic Policy and Japanese Trade Recovery, 1947–1955* (Madison, 1984); and James, *The Years of MacArthur*, esp. 3:221–47.

he argues, "by rebuilding the 'workshop' economies of Europe and Japan and restoring their economic ties with primary producing areas in Asia, Africa, and Latin America."[45] American planners consequently viewed the establishment of an interdependent economic relationship between Japan and Southeast Asia as an essential goal of U.S. policy. "By 1948," notes Michael Schaller, "they envisioned Japan as an industrial hub, sustained by trade with less developed states along an Asian economic defense perimeter." Japan would help preserve the political independence and economic security of Southeast Asia while the countries of that region would provide it with secure and affordable raw materials and reliable markets, thus lessening Japan's need to trade with Communist China.[46]

The second major impetus for the reverse course, in the near unanimous verdict of recent scholarship, can be found in America's Cold War national security needs. Roger Dingman notes that by 1949 the Joint Chiefs of Staff considered Japan "*the* key strategic position in East Asia for the United States" and were insisting on the permanent retention of military bases on the Japanese home islands. A continued American military presence there "would force the Soviets to think about a two-front war, stiffening Japanese resistance to communist political pressures and providing 'staging areas' from which American power could be projected onto the East Asian mainland."[47] Adds Schaller: "Besides the widely held concern over trends within Japan, influential Americans saw the collapse of Nationalist China, anticolonial rebellions in Southeast Asia, and the rise of Soviet power as integrally related to Japan's future. Containing both Soviet power and a more amorphous Communist threat as well as building a pro-American alliance in Asia seemed to pivot on the theme of Japanese recovery."[48]

45 Borden, *The Pacific Alliance*, 8.

46 Schaller, "Securing the Great Crescent," 393. See also Yoko Yasuhara, "Japan, Communist China, and Export Controls in Asia, 1948–52," *Diplomatic History* 10 (Winter 1986): 75–89.

47 Roger Dingman, "The U.S. Navy and the Cold War: The Japan Case," in *New Aspects of Naval History*, ed. Craig L. Symonds (Annapolis, 1981), 299. See also Roger Dingman, "Strategic Planning and the Policy Process: America Plans for War in East Asia, 1945–1950," *Naval War College Review* 32 (November–December 1979): 4–21.

48 Schaller, *The American Occupation of Japan*, 51. On the broader strategic context see Leffler, "The American Conception of National Security."

Instead of quibbling over the relative significance of the various economic and strategic motivations underlying America's policy reversal, most specialists now agree that the two sets of interests were inseparably intertwined. The United States abandoned the reform phase of its occupation policy after 1947 because it viewed an economically revitalized Japan as a key to world economic recovery *and* as an indispensable barrier to Soviet and Chinese Communist expansion. American planners encouraged the creation of interdependent economic links between Japan and Southeast Asia because they believed such links would contribute to that recovery *and* help thwart Communist threats to the Asian region as a whole. Indeed, according to recent scholarship, the numerous policy threads were so tightly interwoven as to appear part of a seamless web. Even Borden, whose book presents the most single-minded examination of the economic rationale for the reverse course, admits that "strategic and economic goals were mutually reinforcing."[49]

What proves most striking about recent accounts of U.S. policy toward postwar Japan is the close convergence of views on major interpretive points. Differences in emphasis persist, to be sure. Toshio Nishi's thoughtful account of educational reforms during the occupation, for example, runs counter to the new mainstream in its unabashed enthusiasm for "the massive American attempt to democratize Japan."[50] Additional work is clearly necessary on the extent of those reforms and on the broader question of America's impact on Japan's political, economic, and social structure.[51] Nonetheless, in comparison to the literature on U.S. policy elsewhere in East Asia, the essential agreement among specialists – Japanese as well as American – about the nature of the occupation and the reasons for the reverse course is most remarkable.[52]

49 Borden, *The Pacific Alliance*, 4. Similarly, Schaller says that "strategic concerns mirrored economic considerations." See Schaller, "Securing the Great Crescent," 395.

50 Toshio Nishi, *Unconditional Democracy: Education and Politics in Occupied Japan, 1945–1952* (Stanford, 1982), 297. For a similar interpretation see James C. Thomson, Jr., Peter W. Stanley, and John Curtis Perry, *Sentimental Imperialists: The American Experience in East Asia* (New York, 1981), 203–16.

51 Some of those issues are addressed in Lawrence H. Redford, ed., *The Occupation of Japan: Economic Policy and Reform* (Norfolk, 1980); and Thomas W. Burkman, ed., *The Occupation of Japan: Education and Social Reforms* (Norfolk, 1982).

52 For the convergence of American and Japanese views see Gluck, "Entangling Illusions."

In recent years, scholars have begun to raise some important new issues about U.S.-Japanese relations. Roger Buckley's monograph on Britain's role during the occupation suggests one such fruitful area for investigation.[53] The work of Michael M. Yoshitsu, Ronald Pruessen, Roger Dingman, and Howard Schonberger on the diplomacy of the Japanese peace treaty illuminates another area in need of greater attention.[54] Yoko Yasuhara's careful examination of American efforts to stifle Sino-Japanese trade through an extensive system of export controls may help draw attention to that long-neglected subject.[55] But, surprisingly, the overall nature of the post-settlement relationship between Washington and Tokyo has escaped close scholarly scrutiny. Schonberger's provocative charge that the peace treaty of 1951 brought "a fraudulent independence under U.S. hegemony" demands more systematic analysis.[56] Yet, inexplicably, Eisenhower's policy toward Japan, despite the recent explosion of interest in the diplomacy of his administration, remains almost virgin territory.[57]

The same can hardly be said about American policy toward Southeast Asia. The scholarship of the past decade has greatly enhanced our understanding of the complex roots of U.S. involvement in that region. This work has not, however, yielded a new consensus. To be sure, some broad generalizations enjoy nearly universal acclaim among specialists: that American intervention in Indochina grew out of broader, global concerns and that the United States badly underestimated the strength of revolutionary nationalism within Vietnam are among the most important of those. As George C. Herring argues in his popular survey

53 Roger Buckley, *Occupation Diplomacy: Britain, the United States, and Japan, 1945–1952* (Cambridge, England, 1982). See also the essays in Ian Nish, ed., *Anglo-Japanese Alienation, 1919–1952* (Cambridge, England, 1982).

54 Michael M. Yoshitsu, *Japan and the San Francisco Peace Settlement* (New York, 1983); Ronald W. Pruessen, *John Foster Dulles: The Road to Power* (New York, 1982); Roger Dingman, "The Diplomacy of Dependency," *Journal of Southeast Asian Studies* 17 (September 1986): 307–21; Howard Schonberger, "Peacemaking in Asia: the United States, Great Britain, and the Japanese Decision to Recognize Nationalist China, 1951–52," *Diplomatic History* 10 (Winter 1986): 59–73.

55 Yasuhara, "Japan, Communist China, and Export Controls in Asia, 1948–52."

56 Schonberger, "Peacemaking in Asia," 73.

57 See, however, H. W. Brands, Jr., "The United States and the Reemergence of Independent Japan," *Pacific Affairs* 59 (Fall 1986): 387–401.

of the Vietnam War, Washington's intervention was the logical culmination of its global containment strategy. Like most authorities, Herring is sharply critical of the extension of containment to Southeast Asia. "By wrongly attributing the Vietnamese conflict to external sources," he argues, American leaders "drastically misjudged its internal dynamics" and "elevated into a major international conflict what might have remained a localized struggle."[58] Gaining broad scholarly acceptance of those general propositions has been relatively easy, in large part because they already represented the conventional scholarly wisdom about the war's origins before the fall of Saigon. Untangling the intricate web of political, economic, strategic, and ideological motivations for U.S. policy, however, has proved an infinitely more daunting task.

Recent studies have offered a plethora of theories to explain America's deepening involvement in Southeast Asia in the late 1940s. As noted earlier, Borden and Schaller trace Washington's initial commitment to the reverse course in Japan. "Japan was the key to all Asian policy," contends Borden, and "intervention in Southeast Asia was central to the success of policy in Japan."[59] Robert M. Blum emphasizes the political context, suggesting that the Truman adminstration's decision in 1949 to give military support to the French stemmed from domestic pressures unleashed by the wrenching debate over who "lost" China. That controversy, he writes, "created both a perceived political need on the part of the adminstration to act forcefully somewhere in Asia and a $75-million contingency fund that provided money to embark on an activist policy in the region."[60] Other scholars stress Britain's influence on American policy toward Southeast Asia. According to Andrew Rotter and Ritchie Ovendale, the government of Clement Attlee believed that British economic recovery required substantial outside assistance to stabilize anti-Communist regimes in Malaya, Indochina, Burma, Thailand, and Indonesia. In view of its own limited resources, London pressed for Washington's help,

58 George C. Herring, *America's Longest War: The United States and Vietnam 1950–1975*, 2d rev. ed. (New York, 1986), 279. A similar perspective is offered, although less fully, in Stanley Karnow, *Vietnam: A History* (New York, 1983), esp. 175–80.
59 Borden, *The Pacific Alliance*, 16.
60 Blum, *Drawing the Line*, 5.

a lobbying effort that ultimately succeeded.[61] Offering a more radical perspective, Gabriel Kolko ascribes U.S. intervention to the logic of America's world hegemonic position; given the economic and strategic needs of the American political economy, indigenous revolutions and Communist expansion had to be resisted in Vietnam and elsewhere.[62] Gary R. Hess stresses America's limited leverage in influencing French colonial policy. He argues that U.S. officials by 1949 somewhat reluctantly came to judge the French presence in Vietnam, "whatever its imperfections," as vital to the preservation of interrelated economic and strategic interests, both in Southeast Asia and Western Europe.[63]

Those interpretations are not all mutually exclusive, of course. Hess's recent book, for example, tries with considerable success to explicate the multiple sources of America's Southeast Asian policy. Still, the extent to which dissonance rather than harmony has characterized scholars' efforts to reconstruct the roots of U.S. involvement in Southeast Asia is striking, bearing a much closer resemblance in that regard to recent studies dealing with China and Korea than to those concentrating on Japan.

Equally striking is the relative scholarly neglect of nearly all parts of the region outside Indochina. Some notable work has of course been produced within the past decade. In painstakingly researched books, Hess and Rotter both offer effective treatments of U.S. policy toward the region as a whole.[64] Stephen R. Shalom's monograph presents a solid critique of American neocolonialism in the Philippines.[65] My own book on the decolonization of the Dutch East Indies elucidates the critical relationship between European and Asian priorities that underlay Washington's belated

61 Andrew J. Rotter, "The Triangular Route to Vietnam: The United States, Great Britain, and Southeast Asia, 1945–1950," *International History Review* 6 (August 1984): 404–23; Ritchie Ovendale, "Britain, the United States, and the Cold War in Southeast Asia, 1949–1950," *International Affairs* 63 (Summer 1982): 447–64.

62 Gabriel Kolko, *Anatomy of a War: Vietnam, the United States, and the Modern Historical Experience* (New York, 1985), esp. 72–87.

63 Gary R. Hess, *The United States' Emergence as a Southeast Asian Power, 1940–1950* (New York, 1987), 311–65.

64 Hess, *The United States' Emergence as a Southeast Asian Power*; Andrew J. Rotter, *The Path to Vietnam: Origins of the American Commitment to Southeast Asia* (Ithaca, 1987).

65 Stephen Rosskamm Shalom, *The United States and the Philippines: A Study of Neocolonialism* (Philadelphia, 1981).

support for Indonesian independence.[66] Rotter, Ovendale, Peter M. Dunn, and others have added immeasurably to our understanding of British policy in the region.[67] But significant gaps remain for the Truman period. And when one moves into the Eisenhower era, the available literature concerning developments beyond Indochina becomes meager indeed. Burma, Thailand, Malaya, Indonesia, the Philippines – all are in need of more systematic analysis if we are to understand fully the origins and impact of the Cold War in Asia.[68]

That observation is even more true for South Asia. The region has suffered from grievous scholarly neglect. Few authors have written about America's South Asian policy; fewer still have tried to place it within a larger regional or global context. Yet such an effort is essential if we are to paint a full and accurate picture of the Cold War in Asia. Beyond question, American officials displayed mounting concern about India and Pakistan during the late 1940s and early 1950s. Dennis Merrill's pathbreaking article on Indo-American relations shows that by 1949 some top American planners considered India critical to U.S. interests in Asia.[69] Likewise, my essay on the origins of the American military commitment to Pakistan highlights that country's importance to the global defense strategy of both the Truman and Eisenhower administrations.[70] Integrating India and Pakistan, along with the

66 Robert J. McMahon, *Colonialism and Cold War: The United States and the Struggle for Indonesian Independence, 1945–49* (Ithaca, 1981).

67 Rotter, "Another Root of Vietnam"; Ovendale, "Britain, the United States, and the Cold War in Southeast Asia"; Peter M. Dunn, *The First Vietnam War* (New York, 1985).

68 For the Eisenhower administration's policy toward Indochina see Ronald H. Spector, *Advice and Support: The Early Years of the U.S. Army in Vietnam, 1941–1960* (Washington, 1983); and George C. Herring and Richard H. Immerman, "Eisenhower, Dulles, and Dienbienphu: 'The Day We Didn't Go to War' Revisited," *Journal of American History* 71 (September 1984): 343–63.

69 Dennis Merrill, "Indo-American Relations, 1947–50: A Missed Opportunity in Asia," *Diplomatic History* 11 (Summer 1987): 203–26. For India's importance to the Truman adminstration see also Robert J. McMahon, "Food as a Diplomatic Weapon: The India Wheat Loan of 1951," *Pacific Historical Review* 56 (August 1987): 349–77.

70 Robert J. McMahon, "American Cold War Strategy in South Asia: Making a Military Commitment to Pakistan, 1947–1954," *Journal of American History* 75 (December 1988): 812–40. See also M. S. Venkataramani, *The American Role in Pakistan, 1947–1958* (New Delhi, 1982). An invaluable historiographical essay that analyzes the writings of South Asian as well as Western authors is Gary R. Hess, "Global Expansion and Regional Balances: The Emerging Scholarship on United States Relations with India and Pakistan," *Pacific Historical Review* 56 (May 1987): 259–95.

other "forgotten" nations of South and Southeast Asia, into the broader framework of Asian-American relations should be a major priority for future scholarship.

The frenetic scholarly activity of the past decade has had a profound impact on our understanding of the Cold War in Asia. Clearly, the utilization of innovative methodologies, the incorporation of different perspectives, and the absorption of fresh archival sources have helped invigorate and transform the study of Asian-American relations. Yet, despite a significant shift in the terms of the historiographical debate and despite important points of convergence, the new literature has not yielded a new synthesis. Major interpretive quarrels among specialists remain the norm. In a recent review, Howard Schonberger reflected one prominent orientation when he listed the "three interrelated aims" of U.S. policy in postwar Asia as: "1) integrating the region into the American-dominated world capitalist economy; 2) thwarting the power and influence of the Soviet Union; 3) channeling the revolutions sweeping the European and former Japanese colonial empires away from communism, or alternatively, repressing them."[71] A few years earlier, three distinguished experts on Asian-American affairs captured a competing, and still popular, perspective in a text appropriately entitled *Sentimental Imperialists*. Emphasizing throughout the idealistic components of American policy, they concluded: "If Americans were, as a group, imperialists, their inexhaustible fuel was sentiment."[72] Although they criticized the *results* of U.S. policy as sharply as Schonberger, their conceptualization of the root *causes* of that policy point to a very different synthesis from that implied by his comments. But interpretive differences, however basic, are not the only obstacle to a synthesis because divergent interpretations can sometimes be woven into a new synthesis. Equally important has been the disinclination of most specialists to offer an overreaching framework within which the various strands of U.S. policy can be subsumed and comprehended.

As desirable as a synthesis might be, its absence now should

71 Schonberger, "The Cold War and the American Empire in Asia," 140.
72 Thomson, Stanley, and Perry, *Sentimental Imperialists*, 311.

not be cause for undue alarm. There are good reasons why historians of American-Asian relations have thus far failed to produce one, among them the relative newness of the sources and the lack of essential monographic building blocks for many parts of the region. There can be dangers of grave oversimplification, moreover, if historians rush to produce too early a synthesis, thereby glossing over important gaps in current knowledge.[73]

A successful synthesis of the Cold War in Asia would have to be multifaceted. It would have to integrate the findings of Asian specialists with those of more traditional Washington-centered diplomatic historians. It would have to treat the Asian states as independent actors, not just pawns in a global chess game. It would have to account for the policies of other major actors in the region, especially the Soviet Union and Great Britain. It would have to analyze American policy toward the *whole* continent, demonstrating the relationship between Northeast Asia, Southeast Asia, and South Asia in U.S. planning while also accounting for the region's place in global U.S. strategy and diplomacy. It would have to explicate the various sources for American policy in Asia, carefully assessing the relative weight of and interrelationships among economic, strategic, political, geopolitical, and ideological forces. It would have to evaluate more fully the impact of the United States on the region as a whole and on the political economies and social structures of the various Asian states affected by the United States. Such an undertaking would be formidable, to say the least. But in many respects it remains an essential one, not just to our comprehension of international relations in the modern era but also to our appreciation of the overall American national experience.

Historians of American-Asian relations can make an important contribution to the latter debate. Indeed, much of the work discussed in this essay transcends its specific subject matter; it speaks as well to those who seek a holistic understanding of American history. For it is often in encounters with alien societies and cultures that a nation reveals itself most fully. How has the United

73 On this point see Eric H. Monkkonen, "The Danger of Synthesis," *American Historical Review* 91 (December 1986): 1146–57.

States projected its power and influence abroad? How have American values, attitudes, preconceptions, and prejudices shaped its interactions with other states? The turbulent encounter with Asia over the past half-century – an encounter that has changed both America and Asia – provides a fascinating laboratory in which some of those larger questions can be examined. At a time when it is fashionable for many American historians to ignore the field of diplomatic history, a problem that goes well beyond the oft-discussed tendency toward professional fragmentation, it is well to keep in mind the indispensable perspectives that studies in foreign affairs can furnish to those who seek a new synthesis for American history.

Postscript

Much has happened, and much has been written, since I originally penned those words. When the foregoing appeared in print in the summer of 1988, the Cold War had already entered into its death throes. I, unfortunately, had no more inkling of that impending transformation in international relations than most other interested observers. Yet the sudden end to the four-and-a-half-decade-long confrontation that largely defined world politics in the postwar era has inevitably affected scholarly debates about that confrontation's structure, duration, and meaning. Not only has it led scholars to pose new questions and suggest new perspectives about the origins and course of the Cold War – in Asia and elsewhere – but it has also led to the opening of new archival sources, sources that permit a much closer scrutiny of "the other side" than scarcely anyone could have imagined possible just a few years ago.

The trickle of documentary and first-hand evidence emerging from China, the Soviet Union, even from Vietnam, has made the writing of a truly international history of the Cold War suddenly appear a not-so-impossible prospect. Although the results of the new openness remain distressingly uneven, historians of the Cold War have already benefited enormously from the availability of fresh sources from the former Communist world. Our understanding of the crucial Soviet and Chinese roles in the initiation and continuation of hostilities in Korea, for example, as Rosemary Foot's essay in this volume well demonstrates, has been transformed by the pioneering work of scholars such as Sergei Goncharev, John W. Lewis, and Xue Litai, Kathryn Weathersby, Michael Hunt, and Chen Jian, who have drawn imaginatively upon new Russian and Chinese materials.[74] Similarly, the continuing debate about the "lost chance" in Chinese-American relations during the late 1940s has been reinvigorated over the past several years, though hardly resolved, by scholars utilizing newly opened Chinese records.[75] A handful of recent books and articles demonstrate that Chinese sources can even shed significant new light on many of the well-studied flash points in Cold War history, such as the Taiwan Strait crises of the mid- and late 1950s.[76]

74 Sergei N. Goncharov, John W. Lewis, and Xue Litai, *Uncertain Partners: Stalin, Mao, and the Korean War* (Stanford, 1993); Kathryn Weathersby, "New Findings on the Korean War," *Cold War International History Project Bulletin* 1 (Fall 1993): 14–18; idem, "The Soviet Role in the Early Phase of the Korean War: New Documentary Evidence," *Journal of American-East Asian Relations* 2 (Winter 1993): 425–58; idem, "Soviet Aims in Korea and the Origins of the Korean War, 1945–1950," Working Paper No. 8, Cold War International History Project (CWIHP), Woodrow Wilson International Center for Scholars, November 1993; Michael H. Hunt, "Beijing and the Korean Crisis, June 1950–June 1951," *Political Science Quarterly* 107 (Fall 1992): 453–78; Thomas J. Christensen, "Threats, Assurances, and the Last Chance for Peace: The Lessons of Mao's Korean War Telegrams," *International Security* 17 (Summer 1992): 122–54; Chen Jian, "The Sino-Soviet Alliance and China's Entry into the Korean War," Working Paper No. 1, CWIHP, December 1991; idem, "China's Changing Aims during the Korean War, 1950–1951," *Journal of American-East Asian Relations* 1 (Spring 1992): 8–41; idem, *China's Road to the Korean War: The Making of the Sino-American Confrontation, 1948–1950* (New York, 1994); Hao Yufan and Zhai Zhihai, "China's Decision to Enter the Korean War: History Revisited," *China Quarterly* 121 (March 1990): 94–115.

75 Steven M. Goldstein, "Sino-American Relations, 1948–1950: Lost Chance or No Chance?" in *Sino-American Relations, 1945–1955: A Joint Reassessment of a Critical Decade*, ed. Harry Harding and Yuan Ming (Wilmington, DE, 1989), 119–42; Zhigong Ho, "'Lost Chance' or 'Inevitable Hostility'? Two Contending Interpretations of the Late 1940s Chinese-American Relations," SHAFR *Newsletter* 20 (September 1989): 67–78; Chen Jian, "The Making of a Revolutionary Diplomacy: A Critical Study of Communist China's Policy toward the United States, 1949–50," *Chinese Historians* 3 (January 1990): 27–44; Yang Kuisong, "The Soviet Factor and the CCP's Policy Toward the United States in the 1940s," *Chinese Historians* 5 (Spring 1992): 17–34; Michael Sheng, "The United States, the Chinese Communist Party, and the Soviet Union, 1948–1950: A Reappraisal," *Pacific Historical Review* 63 (November 1994): 521–36; Qiang Zhai, *The Dragon, the Lion, and the Eagle: Chinese-British-American Relations, 1949–1958* (Kent, OH, 1994).

76 Shu Guang Zhang, *Deterrence and Strategic Culture: Chinese-American Confrontations, 1949–1958* (Ithaca, 1992); He Di, "The Evolution of the People's Republic of China's Policy toward the Offshore Islands," in *The Great Powers in East Asia,*

Scholars have thus far gained access to just a smattering of Vietnamese archival sources. The work of Robert K. Brigham and Mark Bradley suggests, nonetheless, how even limited access to long withheld documentation can significantly widen the historian's angle of vision on that most studied of modern conflicts.[77] Indeed, the unexpected opening of a significant body of documentary evidence in countries long vilified as America's enemies stands as probably the most significant – and potentially the most transformative – trend for students of the Cold War in Asia.

Almost as important to scholars exploring U.S.-Asian relations during the postwar era, or any other aspect of Cold War history for that matter, have been the surprisingly vituperative debates about the Cold War's meaning that have erupted anew over the past few years. Has the collapse of the Soviet Union, the near-universal discrediting of Communist ideology, economics, and political culture, and the widespread belief that the United States "won" the Cold War demonstrated the inherent superiority of American values and institutions? Have those developments vindicated U.S. Cold War strategies? Have they, along with revelations about the oppression and cruelty seemingly woven into the very fabric of Communist societies, unveiled a transcendent moral

1953–1961, ed. Warren I. Cohen and Akira Iriye (New York, 1990), 222–45; He Di and Gordon H. Chang, "The Absence of War in the U.S.-China Confrontation over Quemoy-Mastsu in 1954–1955: Contingency, Luck, Deterrence?" *American Historical Review* 98 (December 1993): 1500–24; Qiang, *The Dragon, the Lion, and the Eagle*. See also John W. Lewis and Xue Litai, *China Builds the Bomb* (Stanford, 1988); Qiang Zhai, "China and the First Indo-China War, 1950–1954," *China Quarterly* 133 (March 1993): 85–110; Chen Jian, "China's Involvement with the Vietnam War, 1964–1969," *China Quarterly* (forthcoming). For an early survey and analysis of Chinese archival sources see Steven M. Goldstein and He Di, "New Chinese Sources on the History of the Cold War," *Cold War International History Project Bulletin* 1 (Spring 1992): 4–6. For a comprehensive assessment of the historiography on U.S.-Chinese relations see Nancy Bernkopf Tucker, "Continuing Controversies in the Literature of U.S.-China Relations since 1945," in *Pacific Passages*, ed. Warren I. Cohen (New York, forthcoming).

77 Mark Bradley and Robert Brigham, "Vietnamese Archives and Scholarship on the Cold War Period: Two Reports," Working Paper No. 7, CWIHP, September 1993; Mark Bradley, "An Improbable Opportunity: The Truman Administration and the Democratic Republic of Vietnam's 1947 Initiative," in *The Vietnam War: Vietnamese and American Perspectives*, ed. Jayne Werner and Luu Doan Huynh (New York, 1993). For critical reviews of the extensive literature on the Vietnam War see the essay by Gary Hess in this volume; and Robert J. McMahon, "U.S.-Vietnamese Relations: An Historiographical Survey," in Cohen, ed., *Pacific Passages*.

dimension to the Cold War? And should historians now write about that struggle with such perspectives firmly in mind? A number of academic and nonacademic critics have offered a resounding yes to each of those questions; some, indeed, have taken Cold War historians to task precisely because so many have proven reluctant to reconsider previous views in the light of the epochal events of 1989–1991.[78]

Even within the usually civil fraternity of U.S. diplomatic historians, charges and countercharges have been hurled with an anger and passion unmatched since the superheated traditionalist-revisionist arguments of the late 1960s and early 1970s.[79] Scholars of Asian-American relations cannot insulate themselves from those powerful political currents; their essential subject matter, after all, includes the two bloodiest and most destructive conflicts of the entire Cold War era. In the long run the new intellectual ferment, which has at a minimum forced scholars to question, rethink, defend, and/or sharpen basic moral and political assumptions, may help inspire more probing and imaginative historical treatments. In the short run, however, the intemperate and often mean-spirited nature of the new debates have rendered the achievement of scholarly consensus about so complex and controversial a subject as the Cold War in Asia an increasingly elusive goal.

As crucial as archival openings outside the United States and shifting political currents within the United States have been to the developing scholarly literature on Asian-American relations, a series of less spectacular changes have placed an equally powerful stamp on this field of study. Among the more significant of those have been the new geographical, temporal, and conceptual directions blazed by the recent literature. I complained in my original essay that South Asia and much of Southeast Asia (Indochina excepted) had been ignored by specialists who concentrated their attention on China, Japan, and Korea. That problem now appears

78 See, for example, Jacob Heilbrunn, "The Revision Thing," *New Republic*, 15 August 1994, 31–39.

79 See, for example, John Lewis Gaddis, "The Tragedy of Cold War History," *Diplomatic History* 17 (Winter 1993): 1–16; and Bruce Cumings, "'Revising Postrevisionism,' Or, The Poverty of Theory in Diplomatic History," in this volume. See also the diversity of views represented in Michael J. Hogan, ed., *The End of the Cold War: Its Meaning and Implications* (New York, 1992).

much less acute than it did in 1988. A number of solid monographs and innovative articles have appeared in recent years covering various aspects of American relations with India, Pakistan, the Philippines, Taiwan, and Hong Kong.[80] Although U.S. relations with such important countries as Indonesia, Thailand, and Burma continue to suffer neglect, the geographical scope of the literature on Asian-American relations has widened appreciably within the past half-decade – a most encouraging development for all who seek a more holistic approach to the Cold War in Asia.

Since the late 1980s, scholars of Asian-American relations have also extended significantly the temporal scope of the subfield. When I wrote my original appraisal, the Cold War in Asia appeared synonomous for most scholars with the period of the Truman administration. Plainly, that is no longer the case. Historians have increasingly extended the time frame of their work to include the 1950s and 1960s, drawing on a growing body of documentary evidence found primarily but not exclusively at the National Archives, the presidential libraries, and various private depositories scattered throughout the United States. In a surprisingly brief period of time, they have produced an impressive body of work. That work has ranged from monographic assessments of bilateral and regional relationships over a long period of time, such as the studies by Nancy Tucker, Gordon H. Chang, Roger

80 Dennis Merrill, *Bread and the Ballot: The United States and India's Economic Development, 1947–1963* (Chapel Hill, 1990); H. W. Brands, *India and the United States: The Cold Peace* (Boston, 1990); Dennis Kux, *India and the United States: Estranged Democracies* (Washington, 1993); Robert J. McMahon, *The Cold War on the Periphery: The United States, India, and Pakistan* (New York, 1994); A. P. Rana, ed., *Four Decades of Indo-US Relations: A Commemorative Retrospective* (New Delhi, 1994); Andrew J. Rotter, "Gender Relations, Foreign Relations: The United States and South Asia, 1947–1964," *Journal of American History* 81 (September 1994): 518–42; Stanley Karnow, *In Our Image: America's Empire in the Philippines* (New York, 1989); H. W. Brands, *Bound to Empire: The United States and the Philippines* (New York, 1992); Nick Cullather, *Illusions of Influence: The Political Economy of United States-Philippines Relations, 1942–1960* (Stanford, 1994); Dennis Merrill, "Shaping Third World Development: U.S. Foreign Aid and Supervision in the Philippines, 1948–1953," *Journal of American-East Asian Relations* 2 (Summer 1993): 137–59; Nancy Bernkopf Tucker, *Taiwan, Hong Kong, and the United States, 1945–1992: Uncertain Friendships* (New York, 1994); Nick Cullather, "'Fuel for the Good Dragon': The United States and Industrial Policy in Taiwan, 1950–1965," *Diplomatic History* (forthcoming).

Buckley, Marilyn Blatt Young, Gary Hess, H. W. Brands, Stanley Karnow, Nick Cullather, Dennis Merrill, Dennis Kux, and myself,[81] to several important collections of original essays focusing on U.S. relations with different Asian nations during either the Truman, Eisenhower, Kennedy, or Johnson years.[82]

Different conceptual, methodological, and theoretical concerns have also been reflected in the more recent literature on the Cold War in Asia, much as they have been reflected throughout the discipline of history as a whole. Specialists in Asian-American relations have displayed a growing interest in matters relating to the roles played by culture, ideology, psychology, and political economy in state-to-state interactions and a greater appreciation for theoretical frameworks derived from work in international relations and international political economy.[83] An increasing number of scholars have demonstrated a sensitivity to the political, social, and cultural dynamics within Asian societies. Nick Cullather's pathbreaking analysis of the symbiotic relationship

81 Tucker, *Taiwan, Hong Kong, and the United States*; Gordon H. Chang, *Friends and Enemies: The United States, China, and the Soviet Union, 1948–1972* (Stanford, 1990); Roger Buckley, *US-Japan Alliance Diplomacy, 1945–1990* (Cambridge, England, 1992); Marilyn Blatt Young, *The Vietnam Wars, 1945–1990* (New York, 1991); Gary R. Hess, *Vietnam and the United States: Origins and Legacy of a War* (Boston, 1990); Karnow, *In Our Image*; Brands, *Bound to Empire*; Cullather, *Illusions of Influence*; Merrill, *Bread and the Ballot*; Kux, *India and the United States*; McMahon, *Cold War on the Periphery*.

82 Harding and Yuan, eds., *Sino-American Relations, 1945–1955*; Warren I. Cohen and Akira Iriye, eds., *The United States and Japan in the Postwar World* (Lexington, KY, 1989); Cohen and Iriye, eds., *The Great Powers in East Asia*; Richard H. Immerman, ed., *John Foster Dulles and the Diplomacy of the Cold War* (Princeton, 1990) (esp. the essays by Nancy Bernkopf Tucker, George C. Herring, and Seigen Miyasato); Thomas G. Paterson, *Kennedy's Quest for Victory: American Foreign Policy, 1961–1963* (New York, 1989) (esp. the essays by James Fetzer, Robert J. McMahon, and Lawrence J. Bassett and Stephen E. Pelz); Diane B. Kunz, ed., *The Diplomacy of the Crucial Decade: American Foreign Relations during the 1960s* (New York, 1994) (esp. the essays by Robert D. Schulzinger, Arthur Waldron, and Michael Schaller); Warren I. Cohen and Nancy Bernkopf Tucker, eds. *Lyndon Johnson Confronts the World: American Foreign Policy, 1963–1968* (New York, 1994) (esp. the essays by Walter LaFeber, Richard H. Immerman, Nancy Bernkopf Tucker, and Robert J. McMahon).

83 An invaluable compendium of the various new approaches being utilized by diplomatic historians is Michael J. Hogan and Thomas G. Paterson, eds., *Explaining the History of American Foreign Relations* (New York, 1991). For the influence of these various new approaches, and especially for the growing interest in the cultural dimension of policy, see the historiographical essays on U.S.-Asian relations in Cohen, ed., *Pacific Passages*.

forged between the United States and the Philippines in the early postwar era offers an outstanding example of how a close reading of the social structure and political economy of a seemingly dependent ally can yield a host of fresh insights. In his appropriately titled *Illusions of Influence*, Cullather points out how limited America's ability was to effect the changes it sought in its former colony.[84] Those findings may well have wide applicability to the U.S.-Asian iteraction as a whole.

Over the past eight years, the scholarship on Asian-American relations has been as rich, challenging, and innovative as it has been prodigous. But, to raise again the question that framed my earlier assessment of this field of study: Has all this work brought us closer to a synthetic history of the Cold War in Asia? The answer now, as in 1988, must be negative. The fault lines dividing scholars are as gaping today as they were then, as so many other essays in this volume attest.[85] Much as scholars have continued to voice sharp disagreements about the nature of America's global role during the postwar era, so too have they expressed fundamental differences about the forces driving U.S. policy throughout those years. A convergence of views has occurred, to be sure, on certain discrete issues. In the broadest sense, however, the debate about the Cold War in Asia and elsewhere is – like the debate about the Vietnam War – actually a debate about something much larger: It is about the purpose of U.S. foreign relations, the nature of American society, and the meaning of the American historical experience. Such issues, by their very nature, are no more resolvable through the canons of "objective" historical scholarship than are debates about the American Revolution, the Civil War, or the Progressive movement.

Synthesis is – and should remain – a prime goal for those engaged in the scholarly enterprise, much as the creation of a prosperous, stable, and just world order should be a prime goal

84 Cullather, *Illusions of Influence.*

85 Particularly revealing of how deep those fault lines remain are the sharp interpretive and theoretical differences reflected in what have been the two most important books about the early Cold War to appear in recent years: Melvyn P. Leffler, *A Preponderance of Power: National Security, the Truman Administration, and the Cold War* (Stanford, 1992); and Bruce Cumings, *The Origins of the Korean War*, vol. 2, *The Roaring of the Cataract, 1947–1950* (Princeton, 1990).

for those engaged in the diplomatic arena. That, in actuality, neither objective can be achieved in any meaningful sense should no more dishearten scholars and diplomats than should the recognition by parents of the impossibility of rearing "perfect" children lead to despair and abandonment.

18

The Power of Money: The Historiography of American Economic Diplomacy

DIANE B. KUNZ

I

Books concentrating on economic diplomacy rarely find an audience. Even professional historians, whose business it is to read weighty tomes, often retreat when confronted with a book with the word "economic" in the title or if they see financial facts figuring heavily in the notes. Yet one of the most influential books of the last fifteen years was a work that profoundly affected the way we think about economic diplomacy in general and American economic diplomacy in particular. Even more astoundingly, the book not only became a basic university text but a must-buy for nonspecialist readers and a crucial part of the 1988 presidential election campaign.

The book in question is *The Rise and Fall of the Great Powers* by Paul Kennedy.[1] It represented first of all a return to history on the grand scale. In his book, Kennedy analyzed the trajectory of every imperial state since the end of the Renaissance. He covered the seventeenth- and eighteenth-century Spanish, Dutch, British, and French systems, which ended with the British victory at Waterloo. Kennedy then incorporated an analysis of British strengths and weakness within a discussion of the struggle for mastery of the European Great Powers during the nineteenth century. His twentieth-century survey did not neglect the two world wars but focused on the Cold War superpowers, the United States and the Soviet Union. Kennedy ended his book by projecting the

1 Paul Kennedy, *The Rise and Fall of the Great Powers: Economic Change and Military Conflict from 1500 to 2000* (New York, 1987).

future path of the main powers that existed fifteen years before the end of the twentieth century: the Soviet Union, the European Economic Community, Japan, China, and the United States.

Kennedy concentrated on "the *interaction* between economics and strategy, as each of the leading states in the international system strove to enhance its wealth and its power, to become (or to remain) both rich and strong."[2] In text and notes, he included a wealth of detail that demonstrated an encyclopedic knowledge of his subject. Kennedy was not afraid to generalize from his research: The history of empire reveals a constantly changing balance among the various important nations of the period; shifts in economic power herald changes in military power; "there is a very clear connection *in the long run* between an individual Great Power's economic rise and fall and its growth and decline as an important military power (or world empire)"; in trying times, "the Great Power is likely to find itself spending much *more* on defense than it did two generations earlier and yet still discover that the world is a less secure environment – simply because other Powers have grown faster, and are becoming stronger."[3]

The United States of 1988 was a nervous nation indeed. The high of Reaganomics had disappeared, leaving the country with a hangover in the form of a trillion dollar deficit. Expressly because of its compelling logic, *The Rise and Fall* hit a nerve with pundits, politicians, and the public. The *New York Times Magazine* in April 1988 made the subject of American decline its lead story with a cover featuring a puffed up and dandified American eagle scowling into an old-fashioned looking glass.[4] Kennedy's ideas in simplified and less nuanced form became the coin of the public realm. Few serious discussions during the presidential race did not mention "imperial overstretch." That Kennedy so accurately understood the economic Chernobyl that led to the dissolution of the Soviet Union enhanced the credibility of his observations about the United States. Americans reading Kennedy's description of the economic rise of the Pacific Rim bore witness to its results when the Mitsubishi real estate company (a cognate

2 Ibid., xv (emphasis in original). (All references are to the 1989 Vintage edition.)
3 Ibid., xxii–xxiii (emphasis in original).
4 *New York Times*, 17 April 1988.

[if nothing more] of the company that produced the World War II Zero airplane) purchased Rockefeller Center, one of America's most symbolic real estate parcels.

Whether or not one agreed with all of Kennedy's thesis (and few failed to agree with at least some of it), Kennedy clearly succeeded in giving the economic side of diplomacy far greater attention than it had previously enjoyed. This essay will cover books on the history of American twentieth-century economic diplomacy that have appeared in the last fifteen years. Among other things, these volumes provide information that illuminates the Kennedy thesis.[5]

II

The United States entered World War I as a debtor nation but emerged as the world's leading creditor state. William Becker, together with Samuel Wells, edited the seminal *Economics and World Power: An Assessment of American Diplomacy since 1789*.[6] No collection could better elucidate the relationship between economic and other forms of diplomacy in the formation of American foreign policy. Becker's excellent article "1899–1920: America Adjusts to World Power" presents an ideal starting point for a study of U.S. foreign economic policy during the early twentieth century. Mira Wilkins's book, *The History of Foreign Investment in the United States to 1914* is an encyclopedic work that clearly and carefully explains how the United States operated during its expansionist climb to economic power. The trajectory was simple: from the trough of a debtor state so unreliable that it was shut out of international capital markets ("You may tell your government that you have seen the man who is at the head of the finances of Europe and he has told you that they [the U.S. Treasury] cannot borrow a dollar, not a dollar," said Baron James de Rothschild in 1842), the United States became a favored

5 This article will concentrate mainly on books written within the field of American economic diplomatic history. Political scientists and economists also devote significant attention to subjects covered in this chapter.

6 William H. Becker and Samuel F. Wells, Jr., eds., *Economics and World Power: An Assessment of American Diplomacy since 1789* (New York, 1984).

borrower and then not a borrower at all.[7] In the process, Wilkins provides the details of the American shift in economic circumstances, which, as Kennedy had documented, echoed the path taken by every imperial nation.

Kathleen Burk in *Britain, America, and the Sinews of War, 1914–1918* gives a precise rendering of the movement of wartime economic resources from Britain to the United States.[8] That this process would have happened without the Great War is clear, but just as apparent is the fact that the ghastly conflict greatly accelerated the change. Burk concentrates on the role played by J. P. Morgan & Co. (Morgans) as the purchasing agent and banker for the British and French governments. The unprecedented demands of total war far exceeded the capabilities of British and French factories and rapidly drained Allied treasuries. Clearly the United States held the key to Allied requirements. London, taking the lead on behalf of its co-belligerents, hired Morgans to represent its interests in the United States. In delineating the resulting negotiations, Burk provides an important account of one of the classic instances of the American mode of public/private economic diplomacy. At the beginning of the twentieth century, private bankers performed most of the tasks necessary to maintain the international financial system. The Bank of England and the Banque de France were private companies that looked at their respective governments merely as their largest clients. Morgans was the strongest American investment bank, and until the formation of the Federal Reserve System in 1913, dominated American merchant banking. Indeed, it was J. P. Morgan, Sr., who virtually single-handedly rescued the American financial system during the panic of 1907, in the process swelling the demand for government supervision of the American financial structure.

As the momentum to create the Federal Reserve System had arisen from domestic concerns, it is not altogether surprising that the Fed's enabling legislation had been vague on its international functions. Working in tandem, the Federal Reserve Bank of New York and Morgans filled this breach. The House of Morgan

7 Mira Wilkins, *The History of Foreign Investment in the United States to 1914* (Cambridge, MA, 1989). The quoted passage is from p. 71.

8 Kathleen Burk, *Britain, America, and the Sinews of War, 1914–1918* (Boston, 1985).

(actually three interrelated branches in New York, London, and Paris) is profiled in the masterly *The House of Morgan* by Ron Chernow.[9] As Burk and Chernow show, to the British and French governments, one of Morgans' attractions was its Anglophilia and lack of German connections. Many powerful American banking houses during the early part of the century were German-Jewish in origin. In *The Warburgs*, Chernow supplies an excellent account of a bank that, like Morgans, had related branches in several countries – in this case located in New York, London, and Hamburg.[10] What none of these books supplies is a detailed account of the American government's economic diplomacy once the United States entered the First World War on the side of, but not allied to, Britain, France, and Russia. An excellent book that does shed light on a crucial part of the evolving internationalization of both the federal government and American industry is William H. Becker's *The Dynamics of Business-Government Relations: Industry and Exports, 1893–1921*.[11]

III

Chernow's concentration on the biographical method of economic diplomacy succeeds admirably, making one wish for new studies of particular bankers.[12] This need is especially pressing for the

9 Ron Chernow, *The House of Morgan: An American Banking Dynasty and the Rise of Modern Finance* (New York, 1990). On the early history of the Morgan Bank also see Vincent P. Carosso, *The Morgans: Private International Bankers, 1854–1913* (Cambridge, MA, 1987).

10 Ron Chernow, *The Warburgs: The Twentieth-Century Odyssey of a Remarkable Jewish Family* (New York, 1993).

11 William H. Becker, *The Dynamics of Business-Government Relations: Industry and Exports, 1893–1921* (Chicago, 1982).

12 Edward M. Lamont recently published an account of his grandfather's career in *The Ambassador from Wall Street: The Study of Thomas W. Lamont, J.P. Morgan's Chief Executive* (New York, 1994). The book's information gleaned from private papers makes it useful for any historian but leaves scope for further volumes. Only one biography exists of Morrow, lawyer, banker, diplomat, and politician as well as father-in-law of Charles Lindbergh: Harold Nicholson, *Dwight Morrow* (New York, 1935). Nicolson, a British diplomat and writer, proved a singularly poor choice, for he thought bankers no better than tradesmen. Despising the Morrows as he took their money, the man best known for this works on peacemaking and diplomacy produced a boring book devoid of any significant information on Morrow's banking career. Russell Leffingwell, perhaps the most analytical of the Morgan partners, is lacking the biography that his career, spent in the Treasury Department and on Wall

interwar period. After 1920, the tide of Washington's international economic diplomacy rapidly receded. President Woodrow Wilson took the leading role at Versailles, and American diplomats drafted some of the most important clauses in the treaties that created the postwar regime. Future American secretary of state John Foster Dulles, grandson of Benjamin Harrison's secretary of state, John Foster, and nephew of Wilson's secretary of state, Robert Lansing, drafted the most well known clause, Article 231, the infamous war guilt provision, which made Germany assume responsibility for the First World War. Dulles's phraseology, drawn from his experience at the New York corporate law firm of Sullivan & Cromwell, actually represented an attempt to expand Germany's theoretical responsibility for the war while limiting its actual liability for reparations. This sophisticated lawyer's language did less than satisfy no one. Dulles's activities and rationale are clearly explicated in Ronald Pruessen's excellent *John Foster Dulles: The Road to Power*. Allen Dulles, always the younger brother, known for his charm as Foster was not, also participated in Versailles treaty making and joined Sullivan & Cromwell. His career is chronicled in the fascinating *Gentleman Spy* by Peter Grose.[13] The French and Belgian governments desperately needed reparations in order to rebuild their destroyed lands and reconstruct their shattered economies; because Germany had escaped almost all of the fighting, had it not paid reparations it would have emerged stronger from the conflagration than the countries that had ostensibly won the war. Furthermore, only with reparations could Britain and France repay the multibillion dollar loans they had received from the United States. Reparations had long been an established part of postwar settlements. Most recently, France had paid five million gold francs to

Street, so richly deserves. George Harrison, governor of the Federal Reserve Bank of New York during the Wall Street Crash and the Depression and later a key civilian figure on the Manhattan project, richly deserves a biography. As with Morrow, Lamont, and Leffingwell, Harrison left an extensive set of papers. Morrow's papers are at Amherst College, Lamont's are at the library of the Harvard Business School, Leffingwell's are at Yale University, and Harrison's extensive collection resides at Columbia University.

13 Ronald W. Pruessen, *John Foster Dulles: The Road to Power* (New York, 1982); Peter Grose, *Gentleman Spy* (New York, 1994).

Germany as the penalty for losing the Franco-Prussian War. But Germans did not take this view of the matter: Government officials and their constituents viewed the reparations burden as an unfair and intolerable hardship. In this belief they were confirmed by John Maynard Keynes, whose brilliantly written *The Economic Consequences of the Peace* firmly established reparations as an evil inflicted by small-minded men on Germany in particular and by the world at large.[14] As reparations and the related question of war debts dominated international economic diplomacy during the 1920s, it is not surprising that Keynes's views have held sway over historians as well. A pair of excellent biographies have conveyed Keynes's ideas to new readers in the past decade: historian Robert Skidelsky has completed two of his projected three volumes on the life of Keynes while economist D. E. Moggridge, with a more single-minded concentration on Keynes's career, published a one-volume biography.[15]

Only in the 1970s did American historians challenge this view. Using newly opened documentary sources, they painted a far different picture of interwar financial relations.[16] Leading the way was Stephen A. Schuker's unsurpassed *The End of French Predominance in Europe*.[17] In one book, Schuker accomplished several feats, any one of which would have been impressive. He dissected the French governments of the period, laying bare their financial and political travails. He explicated the relationship between the French government and its Morgan bankers as well as delineating the American government's refusal to take an explicit role in the crisis that followed the French invasion of the Ruhr in 1923. The British government's growing disdain for its former ally did not escape Schuker's microscope, nor did Germany's successful use of its hyperinflation to lower reparations payments.

14 John Maynard Keynes, *The Economic Consequences of the Peace* (New York, 1920).

15 Robert Skidelsky, *John Maynard Keynes: A Biography*, vol. 1, *Hopes Betrayed, 1883–1920* (London, 1983), and vol. 2, *The Economist as Saviour, 1920–1937* (London, 1992); D. E. Moggridge, *Maynard Keynes: An Economist's Biography* (London and New York, 1920).

16 During the Second World War, Etienne Mantoux wrote *The Carthaginian Peace: or, The Economic Consequences of Mr. Keynes* (New York, 1946), a passionate refutation of Keynes's work.

17 Stephen A. Schuker, *The End of French Predominance in Europe: The Financial Crisis of 1924 and the Adoption of the Dawes Plan* (Chapel Hill, 1976).

No one will ever look at the reparations question or the Dawes Conference of 1924 in the same way again.

American financial relations with Europe during the 1920s received further clarification in the following years. Those focusing on the American role built on the superb foundation provided by Joan Hoff-Wilson in *American Business and Foreign Policy, 1920–1933*.[18] Hoff-Wilson laid bare the relationship between American private and public decision making during the period when private actors, assisted by Secretary of Commerce Herbert Hoover, played the leading role and liberated businessmen from their left-wing caricatures.[19] Next came the unparalleled work of Melvyn P. Leffler, *The Elusive Quest: America's Pursuit of European Stability and French Security, 1919–1933*, which further elucidated the triangular relationship among the French government, the American government, and the House of Morgan, as Paris sought to retain military and economic security.[20] Leffler also presented a more general yet richly detailed portrait of American economic diplomacy entitled "1921–1932: Expansionist Impulses and Domestic Constraints" in the Becker/Wells volume. Dan P. Silverman in *Reconstructing Europe after the Great War* provides further information pertaining to Morgans' role during the interwar period in the context of a complex portrait of European post-First World War reconstruction.[21] American relations with Germany received their due in *American Money and the Weimar Republic: Economics and Politics on the Eve of the Great Depression* by William McNeil.[22] McNeil, an excellent scholar whose untimely death in 1993 was a tragedy for the field of diplomatic history, portrayed the ongoing attempt by German politicians and bankers to use American money and American

18 Joan Hoff-Wilson, *American Business & Foreign Policy, 1920–1933* (Lexington, KY, 1971).

19 The most recent biography to discuss Hoover's role in foreign economic policy is Richard Norton Smith's fascinating *An Uncommon Man: The Triumph of Herbert Hoover* (New York, 1984). Because Smith is primarily interested in Hoover's post-presidential career, much remains to be said on this subject.

20 Melvyn P. Leffler, *The Elusive Quest: America's Pursuit of European Stability and French Security, 1919–1933* (Chapel Hill, 1979).

21 Dan P. Silverman, *Reconstructing Europe after the Great War* (Cambridge, MA, 1982).

22 William McNeil, *American Money and the Weimar Republic: Economics and Politics on the Eve of the Great Depression* (New York, 1986).

bankers' influence to lessen Germany's reparations burden. Stephen Schuker's *American "Reparations" to Germany, 1919–33: Implications for the Third-World Debt Crisis* compares the German government's actions during the interwar period with Latin American decisions in the 1970s and 1980s, providing illumination and insight into both crises in the process.[23] While focusing on Germany, Harold James in *The Reichsbank and Public Finance in Germany, 1924–1933* and *The German Slump* gives a brilliant account of American private and public economic decision making as the Great Depression came and conquered interwar governments.[24]

The standard historical account of the world's slide to depression was written by economic historian Charles P. Kindleberger. His work, *The World in Depression*, focused on the need for a lender of last resort if the world's economies were to keep turning. As Britain could no longer fulfill this function and the United States refused to step into the breach, the crash was inevitable.[25] Kindleberger discussed the writing of his seminal work as well as other aspects of his career in his engrossing memoir, *The Life of an Economist*.[26] Recently, economic historian Barry Eichengreen in *Golden Fetters: The Gold Standard and the Great Depression, 1919–1939* presented an account of international financial policy that combined economic analysis with the fruits generated by the recent historical scholarship.[27]

The decision by successive Republican regimes to ignore Washington's responsibility for the reparations/war debts conundrum decreased its influence on 1920s economic diplomacy. Frank Costigliola in *Awkward Dominion: American Political, Economic, and Cultural Relations with Europe, 1919–1933* combined an analysis of economic diplomacy with a first-rate investigation of

23 Stephen A. Schuker, *American "Reparations" to Germany, 1919–33: Implications for the Third-World Debt Crisis*, (Princeton, 1988).

24 Harold James, *The Reichsbank and Public Finance in Germany 1924–1933: A Study of the Politics of Economics during the Great Depression* (Frankfurt, 1985); idem, *The German Slump: Politics and Economics, 1924–1936* (Oxford, 1986).

25 Charles P. Kindleberger, *The World in Depression, 1929–1939* (Berkeley, 1973).

26 Charles P. Kindleberger, *The Life of an Economist: An Autobiography* (Cambridge, MA, 1991).

27 Barry Eichengreen, *Golden Fetters: The Gold Standard and the Great Depression, 1919–1939* (New York, 1992).

growing American interconnections with Europe. Focusing on the links between the "lost generation" and their banker fathers illuminated the decisions of those on both sides of the generational divide.[28] Michael J. Hogan in *Informal Entente: The Private Structure of Cooperation in Anglo-American Economic Diplomacy, 1918–1928* presented a path-breaking use of corporatist theory to explain economic relations between the United States and Britain during the 1920s. This paradigm, now one of the most influential explanations of state action in the twentieth century, holds that governments provide influential private-sector groups with an opportunity to influence decision making. The resulting negotiations among powerful private-sector group representatives and public officials produce the final sovereign decisions.[29]

Hogan's book, which catapulted him into the forefront of this school of analysis, concentrated on Anglo-American relations. Britain, unwilling to accept that it was no longer the world's financial leader, in April 1925 relied on Morgans' help to return the pound to the gold standard at the prewar rate of £ = $4.86. But neither the FRBNY nor the House of Morgan could prevent the British government from giving up the battle and detaching sterling from its fixed rate on 20 September 1931. This struggle is recounted in *The Battle for Britain's Gold Standard in 1931* by Diane B. Kunz.[30] Two years later it was the United States's turn to jettison the gold standard. The course of American external financial relations under Franklin D. Roosevelt received masterly treatment in *From the Morganthau Diaries: Years of Crisis, 1928–1938* by John Morton Blum and *Economic Aspects of New Deal Diplomacy* by Lloyd C. Gardner.[31] Robert M. Hathaway ably

28 Frank Costigliola, *Awkward Dominion: American Political, Economic, and Cultural Relations with Europe, 1919–1933* (Ithaca, 1984).

29 Michael J. Hogan, *Informal Entente; The Private Structure of Cooperation in Anglo-American Economic Diplomacy, 1918–1928* (Columbia, MO, 1977). Charles S. Maier in *Recasting Bourgeois Europe: Stabilization in France, Germany, and Italy in the Decade after World War I* (Princeton, 1975) used the corporatist structure to interpret European interwar economic diplomacy in a work which has become essential to an understanding of the historiography of this period.

30 Diane B. Kunz, *The Battle for Britain's Gold Standard in 1931* (London, 1987).

31 John Morton Blum, *From the Morganthau Diaries*, vol. 1, *Years of Crisis, 1928–1938* (Boston, 1959); Lloyd C. Gardner, *Economic Aspects of New Deal Diplomacy* (Madison, 1964).

described Roosveltian economic diplomacy in "1933–1945: Economic Diplomacy in a Time of Crisis," another article from the Becker/Wells collection. The growing relevance of the history of the 1930s to current problems of international relations should lead to a reexamination of American economic diplomacy during Roosevelt's peacetime presidency.[32] While the post-Cold War crisis in Bosnia has obvious parallels with interwar tragedies, foreign economic policy in the 1990s is beginning to have a 1930s feel about it. By and large, during his first term in office, Roosevelt set his preference for free trade within an isolationist context. As Americans seemingly reject the internationalist impulse that underlay the Cold War, Roosevelt's paradigm may reappear.

IV

Cambridge historian David Reynolds provided a first-rate reexamination of Anglo-American relations during the period before America's entry into World War II flavored by a British point of view in *The Creation of the Anglo-American Alliance, 1937–41: A Study in Competitive Co-operation.*[33] Alan Dobson totes up the dollars and cents of the Anglo-American relationship once the war began in *US Wartime Aid to Britain, 1940–1946.*[34] Excellent treatments of Anglo-American economic relations can be found in Randall Bennett Woods's *A Changing of the Guard: Anglo-American Relations, 1941–1946* and Robert Hathaway's *Ambiguous Partnership: Britain and America, 1944–1947.*[35] The

32 In *Mostly Morganthaus: A Family History* (New York, 1991) Henry Morganthau III gives a warm portrait of his father, Roosevelt's treasury secretary and his grandfather, Wilson's ambassador to the Ottoman Empire. Morganthau's book does little to illuminate American economic diplomacy during Morganthau's tenure.

33 David Reynolds, *The Creation of the Anglo-American Alliance, 1937–41: A Study in Competitive Co-operation* (Chapel Hill, 1981). In *An Ocean Apart: The Relationship between Britain and America in the Twentieth Century* (London, 1988) written with David Dimbleby, Reynolds extends his treatment of Anglo-American relations with particular attention to economic issues. Although the book was originally written in conjunction with a BBC television series, it deserves to be taken seriously on its own account.

34 Alan P. Dobson, *U.S. Wartime Aid to Britain, 1940–1946* (London, 1986).

35 Randall Bennett Woods, *A Changing of the Guard: Anglo-American Relations, 1941–1946* (Chapel Hill, 1990); Robert M. Hathaway, *Ambiguous Partnership: Britain and America, 1944–1947* (New York, 1981).

availability of such a wide range of work on Anglo-American relations attests to the intensity of the "special relationship" during this period but also owes something to the availability of British documents and the charms of London. Not surprisingly, these authors agree that the most Anglophile American expected a quid pro quo for the American aid that flowed in unprecedented amounts beginning in 1941.

The interwar financial autarchy had convinced American officials that after the second global conflagration the United States must take an official and ongoing governmental role in international economic relations. Roosevelt's secretary of state Cordell Hull dedicated his career to ending the economic rivalry and autarchy that he blamed not only for the Depression but also for the coming of the Second World War. During wartime, Hull's views had gained general currency among Washington elites. Robert Pollard and Samuel Wells have provided an excellent introduction to the most dynamic decade in American foreign policy with "1945–1960: The Era of American Economic Hegemony," contained in the Becker/Wells volume. Richard Gardner's *Sterling-Dollar Diplomacy in Current Perspective* remains the classic and irreplaceable account of the American journey toward the Bretton Woods agreements.[36] He explains the agreements that created the International Monetary Fund and the International Bank for Reconstruction and Development (World Bank), sketches out the basic principles of the still-born International Trade Organization, and paints a fascinating picture of the negotiations between the United States and Britain. Picking up where Gardner leaves off is *Economic Security and the Origins of the Cold War, 1945–1950*.[37] In this account, Robert A. Pollard looks at American economic diplomacy at the end of one war and into the height of the next confrontation, analyzing the interaction of economic and security policy. Also important is *A Search for Solvency: Bretton Woods and the International Monetary System, 1941–1975* by Alfred E. Eckes, Jr. Eckes's work, although written

36 Richard N. Gardner, *Sterling-Dollar Diplomacy in Current Perspective: The Origins and the Prospects of our International Economic Order* (New York, 1969).

37 Robert A. Pollard, *Economic Security and the Origins of the Cold War, 1945–1950* (New York, 1985).

in 1975, remains one of the most comprehensive accounts of the first half of the Bretton Woods system.[38]

The Marshall Plan embodied economic diplomacy at its most disinterested and most influential. Washington had initially assumed that the Bretton Woods agreements would be a sufficient American contribution to postwar economic recovery. By 1947, however, events had overtaken this belief. Officials in the Truman administration concluded that further American assistance was necessary were Western Europe to survive economically. Moreover, without economic aid, putative American allies would fall victim to the Communist wave that threatened to drown Europe. The Marshall Plan and the other components of the American system of anti-Communist containment were successful but not cost-free. Indeed, many of the economic problems that grew out of the Cold War were foreseen by Walter Lippmann in his series of articles published in September and October 1947 and later published as *The Cold War.*[39] Lippmann, responding to George Kennan's "X article," predicted a geopolitical system in which the United States would view any Soviet action as requiring a direct or delegated reaction. What Lippmann understood was that adopting this Cold War strategy (Lippmann himself devised the phrase) would require a national security establishment that would exact a heavy economic and political price from the United States, setting off the spiral of expenditure that Kennedy would later chronicle.

The relationship between economic and military containment is definitively explicated in a classic work of Cold War history, *Strategies of Containment* by John Lewis Gaddis.[40] In a magisterial

38 Alfred E. Eckes, Jr., *A Search for Solvency: Bretton Woods and the International Monetary System, 1941–1971* (Austin, 1975). In this connection see also the various official accounts of the IMF: J. Keith Horsefield and others, *The International Monetary Fund, 1945–1965: Twenty Years of International Monetary Cooperation*, 3 vols. (Washington, 1969); Margaret Garritsen de Vries, *The International Monetary Fund, 1966–1971: The System under Stress* (Washington, 1976); and idem, *The International Monetary Fund, 1972–1978: Cooperation on Trial* (Washington, 1985). Harold James is now completing a comprehensive account of the IMF's international financial activities.

39 Walter Lippmann, *The Cold War: A Study in U.S. Foreign Policy* (New York, 1947). An excellent exegesis of Lippmann's work is found in Ronald Steel's masterpiece, *Walter Lippmann and the American Century* (Boston, 1980).

40 John Lewis Gaddis, *Strategies of Containment: A Critical Appraisal of Postwar American National Security Policy* (New York, 1982).

study, *The Marshall Plan: America, Britain, and the Reconstruction of Western Europe, 1947–1952*, Michael Hogan uses the corporatist framework he pioneered to analyze the creation and implementation of the Marshall Plan.[41] No book has ever provided a better analysis of the domestic framework in which American foreign economic policy is made. Hogan's portrait not only explains the enactment of the Marshall Plan but is indispensable for an understanding of the entire history of American postwar economic diplomacy as it illuminates the process and substance of the "free world" economic structure that triumphed during the four decades that followed the Marshall Plan's birth. Hogan's subtitle indicates the importance with which he views the American contribution to the unprecedented European recovery. Alan S. Milward, in *The Reconstruction of Western Europe, 1945–51*, takes a different view.[42] He believes that the crisis of 1947 that paralyzed the economies of Western Europe was a temporary payments crisis of little long-range importance. The national security aspects of the Marshall Plan received their due in the authoritative work on the creation of the postwar American security state: *A Preponderance of Power: National Security, the Truman Administration, and the Cold War* by Melvyn Leffler.[43] A popular account of the Marshall Plan that provides interesting details on the negotiations at home and abroad is *The Marshall Plan* by Charles L. Mee, Jr.[44] Will Clayton, Texas businessman and Truman confidante, played a key role in the Marshall Plan, as his biographer, Gregory Fossedal, explains.[45] Finally, Charles Kindleberger, who participated in the grunt work for the Marshall Plan, recounted and analyzed his experiences in *Marshall Plan Days*.[46]

41 Michael J. Hogan, *The Marshall Plan: America, Britain, and the Reconstruction of Western Europe, 1947–1952* (Cambridge, England, 1987).
42 Alan S. Milward, *The Reconstruction of Western Europe, 1945–51* (London, 1984).
43 Melvyn P. Leffler, *A Preponderance of Power: National Security, the Truman Administration, and the Cold War* (Stanford, 1992).
44 Charles L. Mee, Jr., *The Marshall Plan: The Launching of Pax Americana* (New York, 1984).
45 Gregory A. Fossedal, *Our Finest Hour: Will Clayton, the Marshall Plan, and the Triumph of Democracy* (Stanford, 1993).
46 Charles P. Kindleberger, *Marshall Plan Days* (Boston, 1987).

V

The Republicans had campaigned on a platform of encouraging trade in order to obviate the need for economic aid. In *Trade and Aid: Eisenhower's Foreign Economic Policy, 1953–1961*, Burton I. Kaufman ably portrays the not entirely successful attempt by President Dwight D. Eisenhower, John Foster Dulles (now secretary of state in his own right), and other Republican officials to reconcile party principles with practical realities.[47] Foreign aid could not be renounced completely; the most notable example of an American offer of nonmilitary aid was the 1955 offer made by the United States in conjunction with Britain and the World Bank to fund the Aswan High Dam. A combination of disillusion with Egyptian president Gamal Abdel Nasser and domestic pressure convinced American and British leaders to withdraw this proposal. In response Nasser nationalized the Suez Canal on 26 July 1956, thereby triggering the most serious crisis among the Western allies during the Cold War. An account of the American use of economic pressure against Britain, France, Egypt, and Israel is found in *The Economic Diplomacy of the Suez Crisis* by Diane Kunz.[48] As the denouement of the Suez crisis indicates, economic sanctions only affect a nation's foreign policy in rare instances. Democracies are the most susceptible, particularly if the sanctions are imposed by their allies. In this case, Britain, critically weakened during World War II, had relied on American financial assistance to fund its financial and foreign policy. The Eisenhower administration's decision to withhold economic assistance from Britain after it invaded Egypt (in company with France and Israel) against American wishes forced Washington's closest ally to retreat rapidly.

The Suez crisis occurred precisely because the Cold War–induced stasis in Europe left the two superpowers to battle for the loyalty of what was then called the underdeveloped world. H. W. Brands in *The Specter of Neutralism: The United States and the Emergence of the Third World, 1947–1960* does not shirk economic

47 Burton I. Kaufman, *Trade and Aid: Eisenhower's Foreign Economic Policy, 1953–1961* (Baltimore, 1982).

48 Diane B. Kunz, *The Economic Diplomacy of the Suez Crisis* (Chapel Hill, 1991).

issues in his treatment of American relations with Egypt, India, and Yugoslavia.[49] A more detailed treatment of American economic relations with India is found in Dennis Merrill's important study *Bread and the Ballot: The United States and India's Economic Development*.[50] American officials' enthusiasm for aid to India clearly grew in direct proportion to Communist attention to the subcontinent. By contrast, U.S. interest in the Middle East steadily increased as Washington realized that the bulk of new petroleum resources were located in the region. Aaron David Miller in *Search for Security: Saudi Arabian Oil and American Foreign Policy, 1939–1949* and Michael B. Stoff in *Oil, War, and American Security: The Search for a National Policy on Foreign Oil, 1941–1947* recount the early years of the American government's relationship with the Middle Eastern oil producing states.[51] The question of petroleum policy vividly displays the public/private decision-making nexus that interwar financial relations had demonstrated. David S. Painter explains how this connection produced the formulation of the fifty-fifty oil split that set the scene for the Iranian crisis of 1951–1953 in *Oil and the American Century: The Political Economy of U.S. Foreign Oil Policy, 1941–1954*.[52] Excellent articles on American policy during the nationalization crisis by Irvine Anderson and James Bill are found in *Musaddiq, Iranian Nationalism, and Oil* edited by James A. Bill and Wm. Roger Louis.[53] Louis's monumental work *The British Empire in the Middle East, 1945–1951: Arab Nationalism, the United States, and Postwar Imperialism* explains the preconditions to the Iranian oil crisis while James Bill's *The Eagle and the Lion: The Tragedy of American-Iranian Relations*, explicates the Anglo-American decision to topple Iranian Prime Minister

49 H. W. Brands, *The Specter of Neutralism: The United States and the Emergence of the Third World, 1947–1960* (New York, 1989).

50 Dennis Merrill, *Bread and the Ballot: The United States and India's Economic Development, 1947–1963* (Chapel Hill, 1990).

51 Aaron David Miller, *Search for Security: Saudi Arabian Oil and American Foreign Policy, 1939–1949* (Chapel Hill, 1980); Michael Stoff, *Oil, War, and American Security: The Search for a National Policy on Foreign Oil, 1931–1947* (New Haven, 1980).

52 David S. Painter, *Oil and the American Century: The Political Economy of U.S. Foreign Oil Policy, 1941–1954* (Baltimore, 1986).

53 James Bill and Wm. Roger Louis, eds., *Musaddiq, Iranian Nationalism, and Oil* (London, 1988).

Mohammed Mossadegh after he nationalized the Anglo-Iranian Oil Company and removed the shah of Iran from power.[54]

The exigencies of World War II and the Cold War lured American businessmen and bankers to Washington. Having run their own companies with popular acclaim during the 1920s and to public disdain in the 1930s, these men now moved to the greatest stage of all – Washington at the height of its influence. Financier and diplomat W. Averell Harriman is well served by biographer Rudy Abramson. Former Pentagon official Townsend Hoopes and Douglas Brinkley authored an impressive study of the career of James V. Forrestal. John J. McCloy listed Wall Street lawyer, chief executive officer of the Chase Bank, first president of the World Bank, and high commissioner of Germany among his accomplishments. His career has been chronicled in two excellent studies: Thomas Alan Schwartz's *America's Germany: John J. McCloy and the Federal Republic of Germany* and Kai Bird's more comprehensive *The Chairman: John J. McCloy, the Making of the American Establishment.*[55]

VI

The Kennedy administration had no choice but to concentrate on the Third World – the plethora of newly emergent nations made this orientation obligatory. Indeed, the worst confrontation of the Cold War arose over Cuba – the Communist-led island ninety-one miles from the Florida shore. In *Contesting Castro: The United States and the Triumph of the Cuban Revolution*, Thomas G. Paterson lays bare the economic interrelationship between Cuba and the United States. The existence of these ties intensified the

54 Wm. Roger Louis, *The British Empire in the Middle East, 1945–1951: Arab Nationalism, the United States, and Postwar Imperialism* (Oxford, 1984); James A. Bill, *The Eagle and the Lion: The Tragedy of American-Iranian Relations* (New Haven, 1988).

55 Rudy Abramson, *Spanning the Century: The Life of W. Averell Harriman, 1891–1986* (New York, 1992); Townsend Hoopes and Douglas Brinkley, *Driven Patriot: The Life and Times of James Forrestal* (New York, 1992); Thomas Alan Schwartz, *America's Germany: John J. McCloy and the Federal Republic of Germany* (Cambridge, MA, 1991); Kai Bird, *The Chairman: John J. McCloy, the Making of the American Establishment* (New York, 1992).

pain of the thirty-five years of strife that began after Fidel Castro's seizure of power on 1 January 1959.[56] As the State Department documents for the 1960s are only beginning to become available, few monographs on economic diplomacy after 1960 have yet appeared. Thomas W. Zeiler's *American Trade and Power in the 1960's* marks an outstanding beginning. He discusses American trade policy in the postwar era, painting a nuanced and convincing picture of the domestic and foreign constraints that Kennedy overcame to achieve passage of the Trade Expansion Act.[57] In *Kennedy's Quest for Victory: American Foreign Policy, 1961–1963*, edited by Thomas Paterson, Stephen G. Rabe presents a detailed discussion of the origins and implementation of the Alliance for Progress. One of Kennedy's advisers, Walt W. Rostow, had produced in *The Stages of Economic Growth: A Non-Communist Manifesto* a theory that attempted to counter the Marxist theory of development.[58] Rostow urged that Washington supply foreign aid at the crucial "take-off" point in a developing country's journey toward economic maturity; the Alliance for Progress, now virtually forgotten, was Washington's attempt to implement Rostow's theory in Latin America as well as a bid to counter growing Communist strength in the region.

Paterson's volume also contains two excellent articles on economic diplomacy: William Borden's "Defending Hegemony: American Foreign Economic Policy" and Frank Costigliola's "The Pursuit of Atlantic Community: Nuclear Arms, Dollars and Berlin," which discusses the connection among American nuclear policy, the Berlin crisis and the American bottom line.[59] Robert Divine has edited three volumes entitled *The Johnson Years*. Burton Kaufman contributed an article to the second volume on "Foreign Aid and the Balance of Payments Problem: Vietnam and

56 Thomas G. Paterson, *Contesting Castro: The United States and the Triumph of the Cuban Revolution* (New York, 1994).

57 Thomas W. Zeiler, *American Trade and Power in the 1960's* (New York, 1992).

58 Walt W. Rostow, *The Stages of Economic Growth: A Non-Communist Manifesto* (Cambridge, England, 1960). Rostow elaborated on his ideas and shed light on their implementation in *The Diffusion of Power: An Essay in Recent History* (New York, 1972).

59 Thomas G. Paterson, ed., *Kennedy's Quest for Victory: American Foreign Policy, 1961–1963* (New York, 1989).

Johnson's Foreign Economic Policy."[60] A one-volume study of Kennedy and Johnson foreign policy, *The Diplomacy of the Crucial Decade: American Foreign Relations during the 1960s* edited by Diane Kunz, includes William O. Walker III's impressive skewering of American economic and general foreign policy toward Latin America, "Mixing the Sweet with the Sour: Kennedy, Johnson, and Latin America."[61]

Various articles in these volumes make clear the manifold effects on American foreign economic and security policy of the weakening American economic position vis-à-vis its allies. David P. Calleo has made this subject his own. *The Imperious Economy*, published in 1982, anticipated many of the conclusions that would worry Americans at the end of the 1980s.[62] Five years later, *Beyond American Hegemony* prefigured the virtual collapse of NATO triggered by the Bosnian crisis.[63] Calleo summed up the period as a whole in "Since 1961: American Power in a New World Economy," the final article in the Becker/Wells collection. He understood the significance of Richard M. Nixon's decision, announced on 15 August 1971, to sever the link between gold and the dollar. The American commitment to make gold available to other governments on demand at the price of $35/ounce lay at the heart of the Bretton Woods system and had brought political and economic hegemony to the United States as well as financial stability and prosperity to Western economies. But Nixon was no longer willing to pay the domestic political cost that the discipline of a quasi-gold standard demanded. The president also believed that trade, not currency, would provide the measure of future international strength. For that reason he chose to replace an overvalued American dollar with a devalued one that would

60 Burton I. Kaufman, "Foreign Aid and the Balance of Payments Problem: Vietnam and Johnson's Foreign Economic Policy," in Robert A. Divine, *The Johnson Years*, vol. 2, *Vietnam, the Environment, and Science* (Lawrence, 1987), 79–109.

61 William O. Walker III, "Mixing the Sweet with the Sour: Kennedy, Johnson, and Latin America," in *The Diplomacy of the Crucial Decade: American Foreign Relations during the 1960s*, ed. Diane B. Kunz (New York, 1994), 42–79. This volume also includes Diane Kunz's article on the triangular relationship between American aid, the exchange rate and reserve status of sterling, and the Anglo-American defense commitment to the Federal Republic of Germany, "Cold War Dollar Diplomacy: The Other Side of Containment," 80–114.

62 David P. Calleo, *The Imperious Economy* (Cambridge, MA, 1982).

63 David P. Calleo, *Beyond American Hegemony: The Future of the Western Alliance* (New York, 1987).

increase American exports. Joanne Gowa's *Closing the Gold Window: Domestic Politics and the End of Bretton Woods* gives a fascinating account of the Washington decision-making process during the development of Nixon's New Economic Policy.[64] Two key international financial officials provide their own account of this and other crises in *Changing Fortunes: The World's Money and the Threat to American Leadership*.[65] Paul Volcker was Nixon's undersecretary of the treasury while Toyoo Gyohten was one of Japan's leading economic policymakers. That they write in alternating chapters gives this volume a point-counterpoint aspect that increases its utility and interest.

Nixon's attempt at international financial stabilization combusted in the flames of the first oil shock. Beginning in the late 1960s, the oil-producing states wrested control of their assets from the oil companies, in the process quadrupling the price of oil. Using the international crisis occasioned by the Yom Kippur War, Arab oil-producing states placed an embargo on oil shipments to the United States, the Netherlands, and Portugal as well limiting oil shipments to Western Europe and Japan. Daniel Yergin, in his spellbinding *The Prize*, chronicles this geopolitical turning point within the context of a comprehensive history of the oil industry during the twentieth century.[66] The purpose of the oil boycott was to move Western policy against Israel and in favor of the Palestinian Arabs; while Western Europe and Japan altered their position markedly, the United States, whose stance was more significant, moved less than its allies.

Instrumental in arranging the oil price hike was the shah of Iran, in the 1970s the West's favorite Middle Eastern (although not Arab) ruler. The oil price revolution brought a bonanza to the shah; ironically, the flood of money into Iran accelerated the process of destabilization that brought about the Iranian revolution and the shah's overthrow in January 1978. The resulting turmoil in the Iranian oil fields sparked a second oil shock; Yergin details it as well. The new Iranian regime dominated by the radical

64 Joanne Gowa, *Closing the Gold Window: Domestic Politics and the End of Bretton Woods* (Ithaca, 1983).

65 Paul A. Volcker and Toyoo Gyohten, *Changing Fortunes: The World's Money and the Threat to American Leadership* (New York, 1992).

66 Daniel A. Yergin, *The Prize: The Epic Quest for Oil, Money, and Power* (New York, 1991).

Muslim cleric the Ayatollah Ruhollah Khomenini exchanged a pro-Washington policy for fervent anti-Americanism. The taking of American hostages in November 1979 brought the Carter administration to its political knees. Its military response proved calamitous; economic sanctions proved little more effective. Their use deserves a book in itself. For now the most extensive account is in Gary Sick's *All Fall Down: America's Tragic Encounter with Iran.*[67]

The oil shocks were partly responsible for the ballooning of Third World debt during the 1970s and early 1980s. Of equal importance was the retirement of the generation of bankers whose enthusiasm for loans to developing nations had been tempered by their memories of the myriad of interwar international defaults.[68] Faced with an unprecedented and unexpected transfer of assets from the major industrial states to the oil-producing nations, Western governments reluctant to contribute their own funds to international stability looked again to the private sector to fill the void. Western banks delightedly stepped into the breach, recycling Arab money into loans to oil-poor nations while taking a hefty cut for their services. But as American inflation ran riot, Paul Volcker, now chairman of the Federal Reserve Board, raised American interest rates to unprecedented levels. International loans bore interest rates that fluctuated in relation to American rates; foreign borrowers could not pay loans when prime or LIBOR soared into the high teens. Volcker and Gyohten's eyewitness accounts of the Third World debt crisis that began when Mexico declared itself unable to make interest payments on its loans in August 1982 is invaluable. Also crucial to an understanding of the debt crisis are Benjamin Cohen's *In Whose Interest? International Banking and American Foreign Policy* and Karin Lissakers's *Banks, Borrowers, and the Establishment: A Revisionist Account of the International Debt Crisis.*[69] The banking environment that made this crisis possible is re-created in *Banking on the World:*

67 Gary Sick, *All Fall Down: America's Tragic Encounter with Iran* (New York, 1985).

68 A fascinating portrayal of American private contacts with Latin America during the interval between debt crises is Elizabeth A. Cobbs, *The Rich Neighbor Policy: Rockefeller and Kaiser in Brazil* (New Haven, 1992).

69 Benjamin J. Cohen, *In Whose Interest? International Banking and American Foreign Policy* (New York, 1986); Karin Lissakers, *Banks, Borrowers, and the Establishment: A Revisionist Account of the International Debt Crisis* (New York, 1991).

The Politics of American International Finance by Jeffry Frieden.[70] Memories of the effect of the chain reaction of defaults from 1931 to 1933 greatly influenced policymakers in the early 1980s; Schuker's comparative work drives home the similarities.[71]

Saddam Hussein, Iraq's dictatorial leader, could not pay his debts either. Oil had given Iraq the wherewithal to maintain a brutal war against Iran from 1980 to 1988. Iraq's battle against the Ayatollah partially explained the generous Western aid to Iraq that began in the early 1980s and continued until virtually the eve of Operation Desert Shield. Bruce Jentleson recounts the American attempt to woo Saddam Hussein in *With Friends Like These: Reagan, Bush, and Saddam, 1982–1990*.[72] The collapse of oil prices in the second half of the 1980s supplied part of Hussein's motive for seizing Kuwait in August 1990. The Western response initially ran to sanctions applied through the United Nations. In *The Gulf Conflict, 1990–1991: Diplomacy and War in the New World Order*, Lawrence Freedman and Efraim Karsh provide an excellent account of American aid and American economic pressure against Saddam Hussein's regime.[73] They show that economic sanctions once again proved useless. Also instructive on the economic diplomacy of Desert Shield and Desert Storm is *Triumph without Victory: The History of the Persian Gulf War* by the staff of *U.S. News and World Report*.[74]

The multilateral invasion of Iraq took place in the post-Cold War world. Many pundits believed that the end of communism as a governing system meant that future wars would be economic, not military. Alarmingly, by 1989 the American economy seemed singularly ill-positioned to thrive in the brave new Darwinian economic competition that seemed to have begun.[75] In his prescient work, *Solvency, the Price of Survival*, James Chace,

70 Jeffry A. Frieden, *Banking on the World: The Politics of American International Finance* (New York, 1987).

71 Schuker, *American "Reparations" to Germany*.

72 Bruce W. Jentleson, *With Friends Like These: Reagan, Bush, and Saddam, 1982–1990* (New York, 1994).

73 Lawrence Freedman and Efraim Karsh, *The Gulf Conflict, 1990–1991: Diplomacy and War in the New World Order* (Princeton, 1993).

74 The staff of *U.S. News and World Report*, *Triumph Without Victory: The History of the Persian Gulf War* (New York, 1992).

75 Lester Thurow's *Head to Head: The Coming Economic Battle among Japan, Europe, and America* (New York, 1992) authoritatively explained the strengths and weaknesses of the United States in a putative three way battle with its former allies.

writing in 1980, warned that the American government must bring its commitments into line with its resources or face a devastating economic future.[76] The high American interest rates during the early 1980s had raised the value of the dollar in comparison to other currencies. As a result Americans developed an apparently unquenchable thirst for imports that had already been whetted by Japan's high-quality and low-price exports. Japan, by contrast, fit the Kennedy portrait of a poor country on the way up: lean, hungry, and willing to sacrifice present consumption for future power. The origins of Japan's economic recovery are ably developed in two excellent studies: William S. Borden's *The Pacific Alliance: United States Foreign Economic Policy and Japanese Trade Recovery, 1947–1955* and Michael Schaller's *The American Occupation of Japan: The Origins of the Cold War in Asia.* Schaller takes the story of the Japanese revival through the 1960s in "Altered States: The United States and Japan during the 1960s," an article in the Kunz collection.[77]

In 1985, the United States once more became a debtor nation. The Reagan administration responded by driving down the value of the dollar, particularly against the Japanese yen. Suddenly, American companies and properties became attractive investments. Books such as *Trading Places: How We Allowed Japan to Take the Lead* by Clyde Prestowitz, Jr., *Selling Out: How We Are Letting Japan Buy Our Land, Our Industries, Our Financial Institutions, and Our Future* by Douglas Frantz and Catherine Collins, *Zaibatsu America* by Robert L. Kearns, and *Selling our Security: The Erosion of America's Assets* by Martin and Susan J. Tolchin reflected the concern occasioned when the United States seemed to be the target of other nations' economic diplomacy. These authors worried that allowing Japanese ownership of important American companies and resources would cost the United States jobs and ultimately economic sovereignty. Their words

76 James Chace, *Solvency, the Price of Survival: An Essay on American Foreign Policy* (New York, 1981).

77 William S. Borden, *The Pacific Alliance: United States Foreign Economic Policy and Japanese Trade Recovery, 1947–1955* (Madison, 1984); Michael Schaller, *The American Occupation of Japan: The Origins of the Cold War in Asia* (New York, 1985); idem, "Altered States: The United States and Japan during the 1960s," in Kunz, ed., *Diplomacy of the Crucial Decade*, 251–82.

brought back memories of Jean-Jacques Servan-Schrieber, who thirty years earlier in *Le Defi Americain* [The American challenge], had warned the French nation against just such a penetration by American investors.[78]

The fear that had been tapped by *The Rise and Fall* and nurtured by Japanese and other inroads on American icons now spawned a spate of declinology books that warned that the United States would be ill prepared to face the coming economic conflict. Prominent among these were *Facing Up: How to Rescue the Economy from Crushing Debt and Restore the American Dream* by Peter Peterson, *The Endangered American Dream: How to Stop the United States from Becoming a Third-World Country and How to Win the Geo-Economic Struggle for Industrial Supremacy* by Edward N. Luttwak, and *The Age of Diminished Expectations* by Paul Krugman.[79] The titles say it all. Worthy of special mention is David Calleo's *The Bankrupting of America: How the Federal Deficit is Impoverishing the Nation.*[80] Among its other virtues, this book contains an unequaled explanation of the meaning and effects of the ever-growing federal deficit. Kennedy himself contributed to this debate with *Preparing for the Twenty-First Century.*[81] Now looking toward the future rather than the past, Kennedy presented a pessimistic assessment of current domestic and international demographic, environmental, and political trends. Thomas J. McCormick in *America's Half-*

78 Clyde Prestowitz, Jr., *Trading Places: How We Allowed Japan to Take the Lead* (New York, 1988); Douglas Frantz and Catherine Collins, *Selling Out: How We Are Letting Japan Buy Our Land, Our Industries, Our Financial Institutions, and Our Future* (Chicago, 1989); Robert L. Kearns, *Zaibatsu America: How Japanese Firms are Colonizing Vital U.S. Industries* (New York, 1992); Martin and Susan J. Tolchin, *Selling Our Security: The Erosion of America's Assets* (New York, 1992).

79 Peter G. Peterson, *Facing Up: How to Rescue the Economy from Crushing Debt and Restore the American Dream* (New York, 1993); Edward N. Luttwak, *The Endangered American Dream: How to Stop the United States from Becoming a Third World Country and How to Win the Geo-Economic Struggle for Industrial Supremacy* (New York, 1993); Paul Krugman, *The Age of Diminished Expectations: U.S. Economic Policy in the 1990s* (Cambridge, MA, 1990). In 1994 Krugman published *Peddling Prosperity: Economic Sense and Nonsense in the Age of Diminished Expectations* (New York, 1994) in which he discussed various fashions in economic thought and their influence on policymaking the last two decades.

80 David P. Calleo, *The Bankrupting of America: How the Federal Deficit is Impoverishing the Nation* (New York, 1992).

81 Paul Kennedy, *Preparing for the Twenty-First Century* (New York, 1993).

Century: United States Foreign Policy in the Cold War presented one of the last Cold War analyses of American foreign policy during the preceding forty-five years. He presented a coherent and compelling worldview that knit together American economic and miliary strategy in an attempt to prove that an excessive American commitment to internationalist and anti-Communist policy had cost the United States dearly.[82]

Not surprisingly, the flourishing of the declinology school of history triggered a reaction, in this case books that set out to refute the pessimistic projections current in the late 1980s. *Bound to Lead: The Changing Nature of American Power* by Joseph Nye stressed the still-mighty American economic and military position. While admitting that the position of the United States vis-à-vis its allies had deteriorated over the Cold War decades, Nye maintained that this shift was natural and would not be detrimental to continued American prosperity and security.[83] Henry Nau in *The Myth of America's Decline: Leading the World Economy into the 1990's* took an equally sanguine view of America's capabilities.[84] To Nau, it was America's will not its wherewithal that was in question. The indications concerning American policy at the midpoint of the last decade of the century are mixed. On the one hand, the American commitment generally to an internationalist foreign policy is rapidly deteriorating. On the other, as the successful outcome of the NAFTA and GATT debates proves, the American determination to continue an internationalist foreign economic policy survives but is under siege. The next generation's books on American economic diplomacy will tell us whether the nineties' old-time free trade religion was the wave of the future or the last trumpet blast of the past. In this connection it is worth noting that the 1994 GATT legislation, which provided for a World Trade Organization, is the most sweeping delegation of American economic sovereignty in our history. For the first time the United States has agreed to be bound by the decisions

82 Thomas J. McCormick, *America's Half-Century: United States Foreign Policy in the Cold War* (Baltimore, 1989).

83 Joseph S. Nye, Jr., *Bound to Lead: The Changing Nature of American Power* (New York, 1990).

84 Henry R. Nau, *The Myth of America's Decline: Leading the World Economy into the 1990's* (New York, 1990).

of a multilateral organization with an unadorned one country, one vote governing system. Both the NAFTA and GATT battles will merit serious study. Indeed, the record of American trade policy as a whole during the Cold War needs to be reexamined.

As the titles discussed above make clear, the field of economic diplomacy has been an active one for historians during the last fifteen years. While predictions are a risky business, changes in the world economic order and the American role within it will probably make this field even more active in the next decades. The shifts begun by the end of the Cold War will solidify, leaving historians to explain what happened. All of the books written in light of this changed world order will have to come to terms with the relationship between foreign economic policy and domestic economic design that Kennedy's *The Rise and Fall* exploded into the public consciousness almost a decade ago. As the Cold War retreats into the past, the military and economic framework that spawned the unprecedented post-Second World War prosperity will also become a subject for general nostalgia. Just how much depends on the course of diplomatic and domestic events into the next millennium.

19

Coming in from the Cold War: The Historiography of American Intelligence, 1945–1990

JOHN FERRIS

A new branch of history has arisen: the study of intelligence. Not that the topic has ever been ignored. In most decades of this century, some scholars referred to intelligence, their works augmented by a few semi-official accounts and a good many bad books.[1] Diplomatic and military historians often discussed espionage and used it for purposes of evidence or explanation. In *Russia and the Balkans, 1870–1880* (1937), for example, B. H. Sumner integrated intelligence and diplomacy as well as any subsequent writer.[2] Meanwhile, beginning in the later nineteenth century, the genre of spy fiction began to flourish. Old-hands-turned-hacks like Somerset Maugham, Ian Fleming, and E. Howard

1 The base of writing is so small and, relatively speaking, so many new works are produced each year, that bibliographies or review essays in this field, even good ones, have a short shelf life. At present, the most useful of the critical bibliographies is Neal H. Peterson, *American Intelligence, 1775–1990: A Bibliographical Guide* (Claremont, CA, 1992). Two older critical bibliographies, George C. Constantinides, *Intelligence and Espionage: An Analytical Bibliography* (Boulder, 1983), and Walter Pforzheimer, *Bibliography of Intelligence Literature: A Critical and Annotated Bibliography of Open-Source Literature*, 8th ed. (Washington, 1985), offer intelligent comments on the literature up to the mid-1980s and are particularly useful about memoirs. Neither was in a position to cover the recent academic literature, whether on the period before or after 1945. The most useful review essays on American intelligence since 1945 are Kenneth G. Robertson, "The Study of Intelligence in the United States," in *Comparing Foreign Intelligence: The U.S., the USSR, the U.K. & the Third World*, ed. Roy Godson (Washington, 1988), 7–42; and Rhodri Jeffreys-Jones, "Introduction: The Stirrings of a New Revisionism?" in *North American Spies: New Revisionist Essays*, ed. Rhodri Jeffreys-Jones and Andrew Lownie (Lawrence, 1991), 1–30.

2 B. H. Sumner, *Russia and the Balkans, 1870–1880* (London, 1937).

Hunt shaped that genre and general views about espionage: They publicized the secret services.[3]

The number of works, scholarly and popular, that referred to intelligence began to rise around 1960; in the early 1970s began a flood. The decision of Her Majesty's Government to release some – not all – of its records about "Ultra" during the Second World War transformed public attitudes as "Magic" never had. So, too, did the era of angst in the United States that culminated in the Watergate scandal. The secret world suddenly seemed central to the real world. It also became accessible to the public. Much material about contemporary American intelligence was released through congressional committees, while the number of journalists interested in the field and old hands willing to speak about their careers increased. Facts sensational (that the Western Allies had read German codes during the Second World War), sinister (that the Central Intelligence Agency [CIA] had attempted to assassinate Fidel Castro), and silly (the ways in which it had tried to do so) made secret intelligence a public obsession. Spying came to rival money, sex, and war as a topic in the popular market for history. All of this has produced a large literature, and an odd one.

There can be no conventional review of the writings on American intelligence since 1945 because there are no conventional writings to review. They begin in a literature of leaks, move toward works of fantasy and studies in paranoia, and culminate in articles as unreadable as the most demanding scholar could wish. On one side, a body of critical writers, many of them diplomats, has attacked American intelligence. As a retired junior member of the State Department wrote in 1971,

> In something akin to Masonic ritual, top policy makers passively participate in the daily intelligence briefing, delivered with an aura of mystery

3 This area has received much attention from scholars. A good introduction is Wesley K. Wark, ed., "Spy Fiction, Spy Films and Real Intelligence," special issue of *Intelligence and National Security* 5 (October 1990). Perhaps the best account to date is Keith Neilson, "Tsars and Commissars: W. Somerset Maugham, 'Ashenden' and Images of Russia in British Adventure Fiction, 1890–1930," *Canadian Journal of History* 27 (December 1992): 475–500.

and importance by little men with locked black bags or in more relaxed fashion by horn-rimmed senior officers with impressive maps, charts and photos. The romance of secrecy has a seductive intellectual appeal, perhaps even a narcotic effect, on the minds of many otherwise level-headed statesmen.

Reginald Hibbert, a more senior British diplomat, held that readers of intelligence ran the danger of "becoming absorbed into a culture of secrecy, a culture where secrecy comes to be confused with truth."[4] Other writers have demonized American intelligence, assisted by a marvelously paranoid strain in popular entertainment.[5] On the opposite wing, more conservative writers and advocacy groups, often linked to retired intelligence officers, have counterattacked with seminars, specialist periodicals, and summer schools. The center of the field is held primarily by journalists, some of whom have been little more than mouthpieces or have produced works that marry fistfuls of fact to shiploads of speculation. Others – especially, but not exclusively, John Barron, Duncan Campbell, Seymour Hersh, Thomas Powers, Tom Mangold, and David Wise – have published excellent accounts.[6] This change of attitudes was reflected in the mirror of academe. By 1990, courses on intelligence were taught at hundreds of universities throughout North America while a few dozen scholars had become serious specialists in the topic. An academic literature also emerged – a multidisciplinary literature, not merely the product of historians. The many political scientists who entered the field through concern with issues like the Cold War,

4 John Franklin Campbell, *The Foreign Affairs Fudge Factory* (New York, 1971), 157; Reginald Hibbert, "Intelligence and Policy," *Intelligence and National Security* 5 (January 1990): 120, 125.

5 Representative examples of the critical literature, which often are also good works in themselves, include Morton H. Halperin, Jerry J. Berman, Robert L. Borosage, and Christine M. Marwick, *The Lawless State: The Crimes of the U.S. Intelligence Agencies* (New York, 1976); Leslie Cockburn, *Out of Control: The Story of the Reagan Administration's Secret War in Nicaragua, the Illegal Arms Pipeline, and the Contra Drug Connection* (New York, 1987); Jonathan Marshall, Peter Dale Scott, and Jane Hunter, *The Iran-Contra Connection: Secret Teams and Covert Operations in the Reagan Era* (Boston, 1987); and William Blum, *The CIA: A Forgotten History: US Global Interventions since World War 2* (London, 1986).

6 John Barron, *KGB: The Secret Work of Soviet Secret Agents* (New York, 1974); idem, *KGB Today: The Hidden Hand* (New York, 1983); idem, *Breaking the Ring* (Boston, 1987); Duncan Campbell, *The Unsinkable Aircraft Carrier: American Military Power in Britain* (London, 1984). Other works will be cited in the text below.

strategic surprise, and deterrence theory have added no less than historians to our understanding of the effect of intelligence on American policy since 1945. The brief account that best defines the place of intelligence in the structure of American strategic decision making between 1945 and 1975 remains Richard Betts's *Soldiers, Statesmen, and Cold War Crises*.[7] The academic study of intelligence is marked by an unusually high integration of the topics and techniques of two disciplines, political science and history (more specifically, strategic studies and military history): The largest groups in the field are American-trained political scientists and British-trained historians. Although many academic periodicals have offered space for articles in the field over the past fifteen years, since 1986 *Intelligence and National Security* has dominated the area, augmented by such other specialist serials as *Cryptologia* and *The International Journal of Intelligence and Counter-Intelligence*. Several publishers currently are producing works or monograph series in the field, most notably Frank Cass but also the Cornell University Press, Edinburgh University Press, the University Press of Kansas, and the Pennsylvania State University Press.

This academic work has been limited in breadth and depth, and professional subgroups have incorporated it in entirely different ways. Michael Fry and Miles Hochstein have recently complained of the "remarkable and regrettable . . . failure to integrate intelligence studies, even in a primitive way, into the mainstreams of research in international relations."[8] Nor is the situation notably better with international history. In particular, as eminent scholars like John Lewis Gaddis and D. Cameron Watt have emphasized, intelligence has not been integrated into the study of the Cold War.[9] But before scholars rush to fill this gap, they might note one fact. It has not proven easy to incorporate intelligence

7 Richard K. Betts, *Soldiers, Statesmen, and Cold War Crises* (Cambridge, MA, 1977).

8 Michael G. Fry and Miles Hochstein, "Epistemic Communities: Intelligence Studies and International Relations," in "Espionage: Past, Present, Future?" ed. Wesley K. Wark, special issue of *Intelligence and National Security* 8 (July 1993): 14–15.

9 John Lewis Gaddis, "Intelligence, Espionage, and Cold War Origins," *Diplomatic History* 13 (Spring 1989): 191–212; D. Cameron Watt, "Intelligence and the Historian: A Comment on John Gaddis's 'Intelligence, Espionage, and Cold War Origins,'" ibid. 14 (Spring 1990): 199–204.

into any field of history. Consider the most mature part of the discipline. The study of military intelligence during the Second World War rests on a large and fairly complete documentary base in the public domain and on a long and lively debate between specialists. The lessons it teaches are balance, patience, and precision. In hindsight, even the best of the first-generation works in the field – equivalent in quality to all but the very best of the literature about American intelligence since 1945 – seriously overestimated the significance of their topic. The more enthusiastic the account, the most misleading. Contrary to a well-known statement by Michael Howard, the history of the Second World War as a whole has not had to be rewritten. Nonspecialist academics routinely exaggerate the effect of intelligence on the war and its literature. Some specialists do the same. Nor does the mere act of incorporating intelligence into an analysis automatically improve its quality. Marc Milner, the leading authority on the antisubmarine campaign of the Second World War, has argued persuasively that studies of Ultra did not improve our understanding of submarine conflict. On the contrary, they reinforced the greatest weaknesses in the literature: the overwhelming tendency to focus on operational issues and to ignore the strategic, economic, and administrative issues that really won the submarine battle.[10] Almost fifteen years after scholars first began to study Ultra, they have only just begun to assess with precision its function and effect.[11] The best studies, however, have fundamentally reshaped our understanding of key aspects of the Second World War. Scholars such as Ralph Bennett and Edward Drea have demonstrated in specific terms – instead of simply asserting in a general fashion – how Ultra shaped certain events and why. Just as important, they have demonstrated how irrelevant Ultra, one of the best sources of intelligence in history, was to other events.[12]

10 Marc Milner, "The Battle of the Atlantic," in *Decisive Campaigns of the Second World War*, ed. John Gooch (London, 1990), 45–64.

11 John Ferris, "Ralph Bennett and the Study of Ultra," *Intelligence and National Security* 6 (April 1991): 473–86.

12 Ralph Francis Bennett, *Ultra in the West: The Normandy Campaign, 1944–45* (London, 1979); idem, *Ultra and Mediterranean Strategy, 1941–1945* (New York, 1989); Edward J. Drea, *MacArthur's ULTRA: Codebreaking and the War against Japan, 1942–1945* (Lawrence, 1992).

Intelligence cannot easily be taken from the Cold War and placed in its history. This task will be doubly difficult until scholars come to terms with the accepted views and unspoken assumptions about the topic that arose during the Cold War. Many facts about American intelligence since 1945 are already in the public domain, more so than with any other contemporary secret service except, perhaps, the Stasi, but this has produced problems of its own. Writers write from their record. When this body of evidence is large, one can easily assume that the issues it illuminates are the only issues to be illuminated. That is far from true in this case. Some aspects of contemporary American intelligence are notorious, others neglected; much that we know is trivial, much that we do not is fundamental. We know all of what we know because it fits one of several institutionalized means by which material about intelligence reaches the public domain, because it surfaced in scandal, was central to crises, or was assimilated in estimates.

The government has been far more willing to declassify assessments than raw intelligence – say, National Intelligence Estimates (NIE) as opposed to the solutions produced by the National Security Agency (NSA). In 1989, William Slany, the historian of the State Department, complained how "increasingly stringent requirements for safeguarding US government national security information" had hampered the postwar volumes in the series *Foreign Relations of the United States* (*FRUS*). "Compartmentilization of information and hierarchies of security clearance," he asserted, had "made the identification and assembly of a comprehensive historical documentary record increasingly formidable." These problems were multiplied by dissension regarding the criteria used to determine what could or could not be published, the authorities who would define these criteria, and the means used to notify readers that *FRUS* could not even mention the fact that some material relevant to a decision had been left out.[13] Although

13 William Z. Slany, "Preparing the Official Historical Diplomatic Record of the United States: Problems and Possibilities," in *FCO Historical Branch Occasional Papers* 2 (November 1989): 48–50. While Slany was speaking specifically of material from other governmental departments, his comments certainly apply to intelligence material as well.

the National Security Archive (NSA) and the CIA have begun to release more material and the cryptological history section of the NSA is well disposed to scholarship, years will pass before this situation changes. Fortunately, the government's extraordinary ability to define the public record has often been subverted by its need to shape public opinion. Given Washington's rule of politics by publicity, the more widely a document is circulated, the more likely it is to be disclosed. Indeed, reflecting on his experience with the selective release of intelligence through official channels under Richard Nixon and Henry Kissinger, Admiral Elmo Zumwalt concurred that "intelligence leaks better than it disseminates."[14] Thus, much material originating from the intelligence services becomes public property almost immediately; but the most carefully guarded of secrets, and ipso facto the most important of them, are also those most likely to remain secret. Material from these highest branches of the decision-making tree may still be shaken loose by scandal, as with the Watergate or Iran-contra affairs, or be deliberately released by the government to affect public attitudes, as with the Cuban missile crisis or the KAL 007 incident. Otherwise, the richest fruit rarely reaches our hands. Subsequently, whenever intelligence officers or government officials publish memoirs or speak to journalists, they are far more likely to discuss matters that have already reached the public domain than those that have not. Nor can journalists, senators, or academics ask about matters of which they are ignorant – a rather larger category of things than they would care to think.

We know less about American intelligence since 1945 than we think we do, and this missing context ensures that much of what we do know does not mean what we think it does. It is characteristic of attitudes on this issue that Stephen Ambrose, one of the first historians to assimilate intelligence into the history of American policy during the 1950s, assumed that it consisted essentially of coups and U-2s.[15] Far more is clear about the CIA's scandals

14 Zumwalt quoted in Roy Godson, ed., *Intelligence Requirements for the 1980's*, no. 2, *Analysis and Estimates* (Washington, 1980), 212.

15 Stephen E. Ambrose, *Eisenhower*, vol. 2, *The President* (New York, 1984); idem, *Ike's Spies: Eisenhower and the Intelligence Community* (New York, 1981). On the other hand, an indication of how far our knowledge has progressed can be provided by examining an account that was ground breaking in its time, Harry H. Ransom, *The Intelligence Establishment* (Cambridge, MA, 1970).

than its successes, about covert operations than analysis, about how intelligence briefly affected American policy toward a few small states – Albania, Guatemala, and Cuba – than toward any major power throughout the entire course of the Cold War. We know more about the CIA than the NSA, even though the latter probably had more influence on American diplomacy and strategy. Much is clear about the institutional structure of the intelligence services and the personalities and personal rivalries within them, relatively little about how and why these issues affected decisions. There is a small but excellent literature on how intelligence affected military and strategic matters, the technical background to signals intelligence and satellite reconnaissance, and the sociocultural background to the intelligence services. Beyond this narrow range of topics, the records are weak. So are the writings.

The existing body of work is politicized, written to shape a private and/or public debate about the intelligence community. There is nothing wrong with that fact – so long as it is recognized. But this has not always been the case. The literature is dominated (and thus distorted) by works of opposition or apology. Nor is that the only problem at hand. Students of intelligence are unusually open to manipulation; many of them have been. Defectors, memorialists, or authors working largely from "unattributed" or "unattributable" sources and privileged access to documents have written most of the books extant on intelligence during the Cold War. The methodology of such authors varies considerably. Where Seymour Hersh uses source references as if to the academy born, Bob Woodward's interviews for *Veil* were conducted on "background," and the sources for his statements can be determined only by reading between the lines.[16] Even then they are often unclear. In such cases, one has no choice but to accept or reject the honor of authors. Although many of them merit respect, this situation is filled with obvious dangers. The "war of the defectors" between various factions within the CIA, for example, distorted public views for a fifteen-year period of American intelligence and of issues such as the ability of the

16 See the methodological statements and general practice in Seymour M. Hersh, *The Price of Power: Kissinger in the Nixon White House* (New York, 1983), 9; and Bob Woodward, *Veil: The Secret Wars of the CIA, 1981–1987* (New York, 1987), 13–14.

United States to verify an arms limitation agreement in the face of deception from the USSR.[17] A senior CIA veteran of that battle has referred to its literature – a relatively good one – with these words:

> With few exceptions, the information contained in these books is derived from interviews from retired CIA and FBI officials so that much of it is hearsay covering events which occurred decades ago. Thus it reflects the inevitable distortions caused by memory lapses, often colored by personal attitudes. In many cases, the statements on individuals and events contained in these books are simply not true.[18]

Any and every source with an axe to grind has had the chance to do so on paper, to become an established but anonymous authority. The intelligence services have been able to palm disinformation off as fact, to write their own history or to determine who will do so; the losers in official turf battles have had nothing to lose from hitting below the beltway. The literature on intelligence since 1945 is largely demi-official or inspired in nature. A similar tendency is emerging in the new writing about the old KGB, with the added disadvantage that its successor is deliberately shaping its disclosures so as to milk the market for popular intelligence history.[19]

Nor has the ivory tower provided a better view. Academic works about intelligence during the Cold War are small in number and often low in quality. Some are marked by the fashionable emphasis on machinery as an end rather than a means – on decision making rather than decisions, on process rather than

17 The best known exponent of this view was Edward Jay Epstein, "Disinformation: Or, Why the CIA Cannot Verify an Arms-Control Agreement," *Commentary* 74 (July 1982): 21–28; and idem, *Deception: The Invisible War between the KGB and the CIA* (New York, 1989). Godson, *Analysis and Estimates*, 123–62, includes an interesting discussion of such views.

18 David E. Murphy, "Sasha Who?" *Intelligence and National Security* 8 (January 1993): 102–7.

19 For an illuminating account of relations between the ex-Soviet intelligence services and Western popular historians of intelligence see Philip Knightley's commentary in *The London Review of Books*, 7 August 1993, 11–12. This background should be borne in mind by any reader of sensationalist works, such as Pavel Sudaplatov and Anatoli Sudaplatov, with Jerrold and Leona Schecter, *Special Tasks, The Memoirs of an Unwanted Witness – A Soviet Spymaster* (Boston, 1994).

product. Academics outside the field criticize those within for having a bizarre fixation on spy fiction and nuts and bolts, for distorting the significance of their topics, and for using slack methods. Unfortunately, there is truth to these accusations. Many works by academics certainly do violate the first rule for rabbit stew, "first, catch your rabbit," and its corollary, "if you haven't caught a bunny, you can't bake it." In this field, each step from the path of documented fact leads immediately to a wilderness of quicksand. During the 1980s, failure to recognize this danger swallowed up two dons who built elaborate conspiracy theories on the basis of more speculation than fact.[20]

Not merely a path but a map is needed to cross this wilderness. During the Cold War, specialists painfully acquired such a method, which rests on two sources. The first is a didactic literature about how intelligence should be assessed and used, best exemplified by Sherman Kent's classic study, *Strategic Intelligence for American World Policy*.[21] This work of social science had some influence on history because, as head of the CIA's Board of National Estimates, its author put his principles into practice for thirty years and framed the method of professional analysts throughout the Western world. The second source, often called the "no-fault" school, arose in reaction to the theory and practice of the first. This academic literature – part empirical, part theoretical – about how intelligence actually is assessed and used, includes such influential works as Robert Jervis's assessments of the links among information, perception, and action and the studies of surprise, deception, interpretation, and intelligence failure of Richard Betts and Michael Handel. Its classic work is Roberta Wohlstetter's

20 Anthony Glees, *The Secrets of the Service: British Intelligence and Communist Subversion, 1939–51* (London, 1987); R. W. Johnson, *Shootdown: Flight 007 and the American Connection* (New York, 1986).

21 Sherman Kent, *Strategic Intelligence for American World Policy* (Princeton, 1949). A work by a member of Kent's staff and later deputy director for intelligence in his own right, Ray S. Cline, *Secrets, Spies, and Scholars: Blueprint of the Essential CIA* (Washington, 1976), and *Strategic Intelligence and National Decisions* (Glencoe, IL, 1956), by Roger Hilsman, a director of the State Department's Bureau of Intelligence and Research, offer intelligent refinements of Kent's arguments, which in some respects bring them close to the views of the "no-fault" school. This is also true of the most recent study in this vein, and a good one, Bruce D. Berkowitz and Allan E. Goodman, *Strategic Intelligence for American National Security* (Princeton, 1989).

study of the intelligence failure at Pearl Harbor.[22] The didactic literature assumed that so long as a specific approach was followed, one that married rigorous social science method to proper institutional structures, such as the creation of Chinese walls between analysts and actors, intelligence could be assessed with a high and almost guaranteed level of accuracy and could produce material of an almost guaranteed level of value. Any failure to achieve these standards was a failure of intelligence. The "no-fault" school, conversely, assumes that some kind of error, whether of omission or commission, is unavoidable in intelligence, that no method can always lead to truth and that the truth is often useless. Failures of intelligence, therefore, are common – in fact, unavoidable. The question is their nature and significance.

Most academic students of intelligence would probably accept a view like the following. In isolation, any single piece of information is useless and meaningless. Its effect depends upon its interpretation in the context of a set of conditions that govern expectation and usability. Statesmen, of course, can understand the world, and they do affect it. They are not mere prisoners of perception, unable to learn from error or to change their minds. The study of intelligence is a study of practical epistemology. It illuminates not merely why statesmen act but how they think. But decision makers are reluctant to change their minds, and they do tend to interpret bits of information on the basis of preconception.

22 Robert Jervis, "What's Wrong with the Intelligence Process," *International Journal of Intelligence and Counterintelligence* 1 (Spring 1986): 28–41; idem, *Perception and Misperception in International Politics* (Princeton, 1976); Richard K. Betts, "Analysis, War and Decision: Why Intelligence Failures are Inevitable," in *Power, Strategy and Security: A World Politics Readers*, ed. Klaus Knorr (Princeton, 1983), 37–46; idem, "Policymakers and Intelligence Analysts: Love, Hate or Indifference?" *Intelligence and National Security* 3 (January 1988): 184–89; Michael I. Handel, *War, Strategy and Intelligence* (London, 1989); idem, "Intelligence and Military Operations," in *Intelligence and Military Operations*, ed. Michael I. Handel (London, 1990), 1–98; Roberta Wohlstetter, *Pearl Harbor: Warning and Decision* (Stanford, 1962). See also Mark M. Lowenthal, "The Burdensome Concept of Failure," in *Intelligence: Policy and Process*, ed. Alfred C. Maurer, Marion D. Tunstall, and James K. Keagle (Boulder, 1985), 43–56; and Thomas Lowe Hughes, *The Fate of Facts in a World of Men: Foreign Policy and Intelligence-Making* (New York, 1976). A useful social science account of how statesmen learn, George W. Breslauer and Philip E. Tetlock, *Learning in U.S. and Soviet Foreign Policy* (Boulder, 1991), virtually ignores the role of secret intelligence and of intelligence organizations in that process.

Nor is it ever easy to assess intelligence. A given event may well have an unambiguous meaning. Information about it rarely has an unambiguous interpretation. The meaning of some pieces of intelligence, as when a statesman outlines his imminent intentions, is intuitively self-evident against the framework of common sense. This sort of material is easy to understand, trust, and use, but hard to find. The typical piece of intelligence is not absolutely certain proof acquired two days after the fact that Adolf Hitler said on 5 November 1937, "This is my reading of the balance of power, my aims are X, Y, Z, and unless they are achieved I will start World War II on 3 September 1939." Even the Hossbach memorandum did not reach that standard of precision and accuracy. Had Western intelligence services received an accurate account of Hitler's statements at the meeting in question, they would have been correctly informed about his general attitudes but misled about specific issues, such as the earliest date that he thought war could occur.[23] Intelligence is more typically news provided five months after the event to His Majesty's Government by British code breakers of a report from the French ambassador in Bucharest, which he received through the intermediary of a Greek journalist, of the views of Hitler's aims offered by a drunken Japanese chargé d'affaires in Sofia. Intelligence services usually provide masses of material, often utterly irrelevant, of unknown accuracy, or on a tangent of relevance, drawn from the hearsay of third-hand sources.

The content of such material, by itself, is ambiguous. Its meaning can be determined only through two distinct, if simultaneous, processes, what Raymond Garthoff, a member of the Office of National Estimates in the 1950s and subsequently a historian of that topic, called "the interrelationships between personalized intuitive and formalized analytical assessments,"[24] between the intuition of statesmen and the elaborate, and seemingly arbitrary and arcane, estimations of professional analysts. The second

23 *Documents on German Foreign Policy, 1918–1945: Series D (1937–1945)*, vol. 1, *From Neurath to Ribbentrop (September 1937–September 1938)* (Washington, 1949), 29–37.

24 Raymond L. Garthoff, *Assessing the Adversary: Estimates by the Eisenhower Administration of Soviet Intentions and Capabilities* (Washington, 1991), 48.

process is clearly described by an Australian analyst, R. H. Mathams:

The analyst must guide his reader as far into the future as the available facts permit; the business of intelligence begins, rather than ends, with an accurate description of the current situation. In some matters, particularly in political affairs where volatile human behaviour is often at the root of the matter, prediction can be a chancey and rather intuitive business. . . . In the main, judgements as to the future activities of a particular nation will result from consideration of its industrial, military and economic capabilities, which can be estimated with reasonable accuracy, combined with a review of its historical pattern of behaviour, which, in most instances, has been shaped by persistent influences rather than fleeting circumstances. The analyst appraises these factors in the light of his appreciation of the gain-versus-loss consequences of probable national policies; it is generally assumed that a nation will not risk a particular course of action unless it perceives some gain commensurate with the risk involved in that action. In those cases (and there are many) where intelligence assessments have successfully defined the future, it is because nations have acted in a sensible, if not an accustomed, manner to achieve reasonable objectives. Where intelligence analysis has failed, it has usually been as a result of a poor appreciation of the perceptions of the nation being studied or, more likely, because the nation's action was unprecedented or did not make for a sensible gain-versus-risk equation.[25]

Similarly, a former deputy director for intelligence at the CIA, Ray S. Cline, emphasized that assessment was

an analytical task, that is, an evidence-based description of the real world around us, with as much objectivity and accuracy as possible, taking a crack at commenting on the implications of the evidence available to us for the long stretch of future behaviour of the Soviet Union and other countries. At the same time we recognised that there are very clear limitations on the clarity and certainty with which one can make these predictions.

It does not surprise me that many of the predictions were wrong. . . . Certainly my experience in intelligence estimates is that intelligence estimators are always wrong, and there are always plenty of people

25 R. H. Mathams, *Sub Rosa: Memoirs of an Australian Intelligence Analyst* (Sydney, 1982), 14–15.

around to tell them so. The questions that are brought up for public scrutiny and even scrutiny in the high levels of the government are never the simple questions on which intelligence can give clear and precise answers. They are the questions on which usually there are no clear answers and your judgement is all that you have to go on.

. . . In a sense these NIEs are the dry bones, almost the archeological remains, of a big debate with real intellectual conflicts and attempts by many hundreds of people to express themselves in ways which were circulating in Washington at that time. And in the last analysis, a formal estimate is just a racetrack bettor's book on what he thinks is going to happen, "It's six-to-five this way." If it is six-to-five this way . . . it is five-to-six the other way. So it is not always an egregious error not to be able to predict which side of a close bet is going to pay off.[26]

A preexisting body of ideas and expectations shapes both personalized and formalized assessment. These range from broad matters like social, political, or religious schools of thought to official doctrines about specific topics and the eccentricities of individuals. This whole process is dogged by problems, such as ethnocentrism and the tendency to project one's own way of thinking onto others, that produce such well-known errors as mirror-imaging and best-and-worst-case logic. Intelligence services, moreover, are often asked to explain not only how other states will behave at a given moment but to guess how they will do so years in the future: to predict decisions that have not yet been made. Above all, they have to determine not what another state should do but what it will do. If you know better than the party you are analyzing what line of policy it should follow, then if it makes a mistake so will you. Thus, after grossly misunderstanding Soviet intentions before the Cuban missile crisis, Sherman Kent said that he had not made a mistake, Khrushchev had.[27] Similar problems emerge with the use of intelligence. Bad intelligence can lead to good decisions. Good intelligence may not affect policy. It may be unusable or it may be used counterproductively or it may invalidate itself. If one accurately determines another side's intentions and forestalls them, one may force it

26 Cline recorded in Godson, ed., *Analysis and Estimates*, 76–78.
27 See ibid., 76–81; and Raymond L. Garthoff, *Reflections on the Cuban Missile Crisis* (Washington, 1987), 110.

toward a new and unexpected policy. Intelligence can fail by succeeding.

In any case, intelligence does affect the thoughts and actions of statesmen. The question is how. In theory, states need information in order to formulate and follow a grand strategy and a foreign policy: to determine which aims they can or must achieve, the means by which they can best do so, the options that are open to them, and the optimum way to allocate their resources and to elucidate the power and the policies, the intentions and the capabilities, of every player in the game. In practice, intelligence rarely affects the determination of policy – although this does happen. Frequently, however, it does affect the execution of policy. Intelligence shapes tactics more than strategy. It is difficult enough to understand the capabilities of other powers: The answer to the question "what can X do," for example, varies with the questions "why?" "against whom?" and "where?" and with calculations about the outcome of the interaction among luck, types of tactics, styles of diplomacy, and untested pieces of technology. To uncover intentions is an even more ambitious undertaking. Governments often reach their decisions in literally unpredictable fashions – or, alternately, in ways that can be predicted only if one knows the aims and means of each element in their bureaucratic political processes. Statesmen frequently do not know what they will wish to do in the future; even should they think that they do, they may change their minds or have their minds changed for them. Nor are all of their actions taken in order to achieve these intentions: Necessity may force leaders to march one step forward, two steps back; opportunity may alter one's calculus of aims and means. Intelligence officers are neither mind readers nor seers. It is rare for any state continually and certainly to know the central elements of another's policy, those that shape each of its specific actions. States usually understand the intentions and capabilities of their peers only in particular instances, and in a fragmentary way. This information can illuminate some aspects of a problem but cannot reconstruct the whole. These partial successes in intelligence are sometimes entirely counterproductive. Correct knowledge of capabilities but not intentions can easily lead to best- or worst-case assumptions;

knowledge of the intentions but not the capabilities of a hostile but impotent power may produce hysteria or smugness. On the other hand, sometimes one really needs just partial successes: One need not know why an action is being taken so long as one knows that it is, or understands capabilities that are never used.

When incorporating intelligence into the study of the Cold War, certain fallacies of evidence and argument should be avoided. The most common is the Bloomsbury syndrome, the focus on anecdote instead of analysis, as if the most important thing to know about the CIA was the average number of drinks consumed each day by James Jesus Angleton. The most dangerous of these errors is the assumption (as opposed to the proof) of influence, the idea that because secret intelligence was available to a statesman, it must have affected his decisions, and significantly so. Such arguments are not necessarily wrong, simply unproven, and therefore useless in themselves even if accurate. What really matters about intelligence is not what it is but what it does. Discussions about how intelligence affected decisions must rest on the strongest and most precise argument that the evidence will allow. Often this may be no more than a case by coincidence resting on circumstantial evidence, but that fact must at least be recognized and tested in the most rigorous fashion possible. Ideally, in order to determine the function of intelligence within the evolution of any event, one should define its causal status relative to all other relevant factors in the framework of cause and effect. This ideal, of course, is difficult to achieve, because of the peculiar and paradoxical effect of intelligence on decisions. Intelligence often leads statesmen not to take specific actions that are carried into effect – thus letting one judge how information affected actions – but, instead, leads them to favor conflicting policies that stalemate decision, or to favor actions that ultimately were never carried into effect, or not to take certain actions at all. It is difficult to trace the causal significance of intelligence in such cases, which are characteristic of diplomacy.[28]

Many commentators on American intelligence since 1945 have

28 For a discussion of the methodological problems involved in the field, and the use of counterfactual logic by historians, see John Ferris, "The Intelligence-Deception Complex: An Anatomy," *Intelligence and National Security* 4 (October 1989): 719–34.

fallen victim to myths about the background to the matter. One is exceptionalism. Its victims assume that their topics are new or unique and ignore the historical and historiographical context. Covert action, for example, has been practiced for centuries. Although historians rarely look before American and British experiences in the Second World War, the topic is illuminated by works like Lamar de Jensen's study of Don Diego de Mendoza, a man who combined the modern roles of ambassador and CIA station chief for Philip II, and the amusing and accurate memoirs of Compton MacKenzie, chief of British counterintelligence in Athens between 1915 and 1917.[29] Similarly, the subsidy of political parties did not begin with the United States and Italy in 1948; during the eighteenth and nineteenth centuries, Britain, France, and Russia eagerly financed newspapers and bribed statesmen abroad.[30] Few techniques of intelligence have been newly minted since 1945, but the size and structure of intelligence services have changed in revolutionary ways since that time. Other commentators have failed to recognize the latter fact. They have adopted a view, stemming from the cover story British intelligence officers gave their American colleagues during the Second World War, about a permanent and subterranean struggle between organized intelligence services that dates back to the days of the Virgin Queen. In particular, it is often assumed that for centuries before 1939, British intelligence had the same place and power in the world that the CIA and the KGB had after 1945. Such views are nonsensical and easily correctible. Many studies, especially accounts of the administration of European diplomacy, refer to the organization and effect of intelligence services over the past three hundred years. Even today, the best studied period of diplomatic intelligence is that between 1570 and 1630.[31] This literature is

29 Lamar de Jensen, *Diplomacy and Dogmatism: Bernardino de Mendoza and the French Catholic League* (Cambridge, MA, 1964); Compton Mackenzie, *First Athenian Memories* (London, 1931); idem, *Greek Memories* (London, 1939); idem, *Aegean Memories* (London, 1940).

30 J. F. Chance, ed., *British Diplomatic Instructions, 1689–1789*, vol. 1, *Sweden, 1689–1727* (London, 1922) and vol. 5, *Sweden, 1727–1789* (London, 1928), illustrate this issue regarding Sweden in the eighteenth century.

31 Excellent studies of diplomatic intelligence between 1570 and 1630 include John Bossy, *Giordano Bruno and the Embassy Affair* (New Haven, 1991); Charles Howard Carter, *The Secret Diplomacy of the Habsburgs, 1598–1625* (New York, 1964); Jensen, *Diplomacy and Dogmatism*; idem, "The Spanish Armada: The Worst-Kept

riddled with as many gaps as that on the contemporary American case, but the gaps are different. Comparison between the two illuminates American intelligence from the perspective not of the evidence that has been released but of the evidence that has been withheld. In particular, it reveals the glaring absence of evidence on and works about diplomatic intelligence and the overemphasis of military and paramilitary topics.

Walter Laqueur's *A World of Secrets* is the best general account of intelligence on the market. Its chapters about intelligence sources, organization, and assessment are excellent; unfortunately, its discussion of historical events is brief, superficial, and sometimes inaccurate. Although the specialist literature on American intelligence between 1776 and 1945 matches that of any other country in that period, there is no standard textbook on the topic. Works by Charles Ameringer and Nathan Miller come closest to the ideal, combining a reasonably thorough coverage of events with relatively few errors of fact. Two weaker works by G. J. A. O'Toole and Ernest Volkman and Blaine Baggett contain some useful observations but also some factual errors

Secret in Europe," *Sixteenth Century Journal* 19 (Winter 1988): 621–41; Garrett Mattingly, *Renaissance Diplomacy* (New York, 1955); and Geoffrey Parker, "The Worst-Kept Secret in Europe? The European Intelligence Community and the Spanish Armada of 1588," in *Go Spy the Land: Military Intelligence in History*, ed. Keith Neilson and B. J. C. McKercher (Westport, 1992), 49–71. While the literature on diplomatic intelligence between 1659 and 1945 is more scattered, some useful works deal with the topic: see Lucien Bely, *Espions et ambassadeurs au temps de Louis XIV* [Spies and ambassadors in the time of Louis XIV] (Paris, 1990); Alfred Cobban, *Ambassadors and Secret Agents* (London, 1954); D. B. Horn, *The British Diplomatic Service, 1689–1789* (Oxford, 1961); Charles Ronald Middleton, *The Administration of British Foreign Policy, 1782–1846* (Durham, 1977); John Ferris, "Lord Salisbury, Secret Intelligence, and British Policy toward Russia and Central Asia, 1874–1878," in Neilson and McKercher, eds., *Go Spy the Land*, 115–53; James Westfall Thompson and Saul K. Padover, *Secret Diplomacy: Espionage and Cryptography, 1500–1815* (New York, 1965); Edward A. Whitcomb, *Napoleon's Diplomatic Service* (Durham, 1979); and John C. Rule, "Gathering Intelligence in the Age of Louis XIV," *International History Review* 14 (November 1992): 732–53. Derek J. Waller, *The Pundits: British Exploration of Tibet and Central Asia* (Lexington, KY, 1990), is a useful introduction to the relationship between intelligence and exploration. The literature on diplomatic intelligence between 1900 and 1939 is particularly strong. Two useful introductions are Christopher M. Andrew and David Dilks, eds., *The Missing Dimension: Governments and Intelligence Communities in the Twentieth Century* (London, 1984); and Christopher M. Andrew and Jeremy Noakes, eds., *Intelligence and International Relations, 1900–1945* (Exeter, England, 1987). Bernard Porter, *Plots and Paranoia: A History of Political Espionage in Britain, 1790–1988*, 2d ed. (London, 1992), 1–24, raises important questions regarding the nature of intelligence services before the modern period.

and ignore many important issues.[32] Two books offer the best general introductions to American intelligence since 1945. Scott D. Breckinridge provides a broadbrush account of the structure of American intelligence, particularly its bureaucratic organization, and its place in decision making. Jeffrey T. Richelson's *American Espionage and the Soviet Target* includes as systematic a discussion as the evidence allows of how the disparate sources of intelligence and services of assessment affected American policy in the key area of the Cold War.[33]

The general literature on American intelligence since 1945 suffers from a fundamental imbalance. In 1968, Richard Bissell, a retired but senior veteran of the CIA, argued that the most important intelligence sources for the United States at that time were satellite reconnaissance, with signals intelligence ranking "slightly below" and human intelligence "considerably below" them both.[34] Bissell was notoriously indifferent to agents and attracted by high technology. Nonetheless, his statement is probably correct as a generalization about the Cold War as a whole. This immediately points to a major problem. We know far more about the organization that Bissell ranked least in importance than about his most significant one. We know very little about the bureau in the middle. The fact that the CIA is taking the lead among the intelligence services in declassifying some of its material from the Cold War era is increasing the scale of this problem.

Fundamental aspects of American strategic policy hinged on accurate knowledge of Soviet conventional and nuclear capabilities. For a decade after 1945, intelligence of this standard was lacking and strategy rested on ignorance. To make matters even more complex, American strategists knew that they were ignorant. Their thoughts and actions were marked by conscious uncertainty

32 Walter Laqueur, *A World of Secrets: The Uses and Limits of Intelligence* (New York, 1985); Charles D. Ameringer, *U.S. Foreign Intelligence: The Secret Side of American History* (Lexington, MA, 1990); Nathan Miller, *Spying for America: The Hidden History of U.S. Intelligence* (New York, 1989); G. J. A. O'Toole, *Honorable Treachery: A History of U.S. Intelligence, Espionage, and Covert Action from the American Revolution to the CIA* (New York, 1991); Ernest Volkman and Blaine Baggett, *Secret Intelligence* (New York, 1989).

33 Scott D. Breckinridge, *The CIA and the U.S. Intelligence System* (Boulder, 1986); Jeffrey T. Richelson, *American Espionage and the Soviet Target* (New York, 1987).

34 Bissell cited in Victor Marchetti and John D. Marks, *The CIA and the Cult of Intelligence*, rev. ed. (New York, 1980), 330.

and a vulnerability to worst-case assessments and recurrent bouts of hysteria. Between 1956 and 1959, however, U-2s and from the early 1960s satellite reconnaissance monitored current Soviet strategic forces with extraordinary accuracy, ending fears of the missile gap and of a surprise and sudden Soviet ability to acquire strategic superiority. These sources provided a host of accurate and detailed strategic intelligence – more than the bureaucracy could handle. In some ways, they offer a classic example of the uselessness of good intelligence. Backlogs of unscanned photographs clogged channels and embarrassed intelligence officers. Photographic analysts often were six to twelve months behind in their examination of this material. The Soviet invasion of Czechoslovakia in 1968 surprised the United States; satellite photographs that were available but unscrutinized until after the event, however, did show the buildup of Soviet strength. The same problem emerged again with the Syrian-Jordanian war of 1970 and the Yom Kippur War of 1973 and subsequently in areas of tertiary concern, as is shown by the affair of the "Soviet brigade" in Cuba of 1979. Nonetheless, aerial photography greatly reduced the conditions of ignorance and conscious uncertainty in American strategic policy and moderated but did not eliminate hysteria. It gave the United States far more precise and current strategic intelligence than any other country in peacetime has ever had, including its main adversary of the Cold War. Satellite photography helped American diplomacy and conventional strategy in other ways. Without it, for example, the United States could not have known (and acted against) the deployment of Soviet nuclear missiles to Cuba in 1962 or conducted its diplomacy against possible Soviet intervention in Poland during 1979. The best studies of these topics are by William E. Burrows and Jeffrey T. Richelson, augmented by the accounts in works by Thomas Powers and John Ranelagh. Michael R. Beschloss has also provided a useful study of the U-2 affair of 1960.[35] This literature is extraordinarily

35 William E. Burrows, *Deep Black: Space Espionage and National Security* (New York, 1986); Jeffrey T. Richelson, *America's Secret Eyes in Space: The U.S. Keyhole Spy Satellite Program* (New York, 1990); idem, *American Espionage and the Soviet Target*; Thomas Powers, *The Man Who Kept the Secrets: Richard Helms & the CIA* (New York, 1979); John Ranelagh, *The Agency: The Rise and Decline of the CIA* (New York, 1986); Michael R. Beschloss, *MAYDAY: Eisenhower, Khrushchev, and the U-2 Affair* (New York, 1986).

good about technical details and program histories but weaker about interpetation and use. That gap will vanish with the normal process of declassification. Scholars are unlikely to want to see original photographs but simply to determine their influence. This should be possible. Cases where satellite photographs affected decisions probably will be clear in the documentary record, because no particular attempt will, or probably can, be made to hide it.

None of this is true of Bissell's second-ranking source. We know very little about American signals intelligence. Because its product was not circulated widely or referred to explicitly in intelligence summaries, its significance will be unusually hard to trace. The government may well be able to keep most of the evidence from the public record if it wishes to do so. The best work on the topic – virtually the only long one – is by James Bamford. *The Puzzle Palace* has received the finest review possible – in 1987, General William Odom, head of the NSA, rated it a major security risk. Works by Richelson, Burrows, and Desmond Ball illuminate the technical background to the topic, while Jeffrey Richelson and Desmond Ball, *The Ties That Bind*, illuminate the web of international agreements that links the NSA to other Western services. Seymour Hersh's *"The Target is Destroyed"* incidentally offers much important material about military signals intelligence. *The CIA and the Cult of Intelligence* by Victor Marchetti and John D. Marks and memoirs by Peter Wright and Philip Agee discuss techniques used in support of cryptanalysis, such as the bugging of embassy code rooms.[36]

For the United States, forms of signals intelligence provided much information on Soviet and other military forces and shaped

36 James Bamford, *The Puzzle Palace: A Report on America's Most Secret Agency* (Boston, 1982); for Odom's statement see Peter Grier, "Chief of the US's top-secret listening post says leaks have harmed security," *Christian Science Monitor*, 9 March 1987. See also Jeffrey Richelson and Desmond Ball, *The Ties That Bind: Intelligence Cooperation between the UKUSA Countries – The United Kingdom, the United States of America, Canada, Australia, and New Zealand*, 2d ed. (Boston, 1990); Seymour M. Hersh, *"The Target is Destroyed": What Really Happened to Flight 007 and What America Knew about It* (New York, 1986); Marchetti and Marks, *The CIA and the Cult of Intelligence*, 161–65; Peter Wright with Paul Greengrass, *Spycatcher: The Candid Autobiography of a Senior Intelligence Officer* (Melbourne, 1987), 78–109, passim; and Philip Agee, *Inside the Company: CIA Diary* (New York, 1975), 351, 370, 475–76, 480, 489.

diplomacy. A conservative assessment of American success can be derived from an analysis of the known facts. Communications intelligence was assisted by common practices like bugging offices of states and by the interception of traffic sent in plain language or in simple cryptographic systems on land or submarine cables thought to be secure. Her Majesty's Government systematically bugged Lancaster House, the scene of many of its negotiations on decolonization, from 1957 until 1980.[37] Between the 1960s and the 1980s, the CIA did the same with such disparate locations as the main hotel in Quito, the offices of the presidents of South Vietnam and Egypt, the homes of Soviet diplomats throughout the world, and the code rooms of every embassy they could reach.[38] When properly used and not physically compromised, the most advanced cryptological systems of any year after 1945 were highly difficult (or impossible) to break through cryptanalysis. But all such systems were vulnerable through common means like surreptitiously copying cryptographic hardware and software, especially because many foreign offices, notably those in the Third World, used inferior systems that could be broken through purely cryptanalytical techniques.

It is not unreasonable to assume that at any time during the Cold War, the NSA read some of the important systems of half the countries on earth. Defectors from the NSA publicly claimed in 1960 that the United States was reading some of the systems of forty countries, including Italy, France, Yugoslavia, Indonesia, and Uruguay, and that the NSA's Near East Section read some of the diplomatic traffic of every country it handled (Egypt, Syria, Iraq, Jordan, Saudi Arabia, Yemen, Libya, Morocco, Tunisia, Turkey, Iran, Greece, Ethiopia, and Lebanon).[39] Either Stansfield Turner or William Casey or both were sources for Bob Woodward's statement about the NSA's success in January 1980: "Of the twenty principal target countries, well, in summary it was possible to break some of the codes some of the time, but not all

37 Wright, *Spycatcher*, 73.

38 Agee, *Inside the Company*, 162; Powers, *The Man Who Kept the Secrets*, 212; Frank Snepp, *Decent Interval: An Insider's Account of Saigon's Indecent End Told by the CIA's Chief Strategy Analyst in Vietnam* (New York, 1977), 15, 294; Woodward, *Veil*, 87, 416.

39 Bamford, *The Puzzle Palace*, 189–90, 201.

of them all of the time. . . . There were dozens of other countries that were not primary targets and the NSA could break their codes."[40] Other references in the open literature indicate that the United States read the diplomatic traffic of Egypt, France, Greece, and Indonesia in the 1950s and 1960s, South Vietnam throughout the 1960s and 1970s, Japan in 1969, South Korea in the late 1970s, and Algeria, Iran, Libya, and Japan in the 1980s.[41]

The NSA had rather less success against its main adversaries. Small and incomplete amounts of current Soviet intelligence and trade department traffic were read between 1945 and 1948.[42] During the 1950s and 1970s, the United States tapped Soviet cables carrying military traffic in lower cryptographic systems in Europe and at sea.[43] It always broke low-grade Soviet military traffic and acquired useful material through other forms of signals intelligence. Moreover, according to Seymour Hersh, between 1970 and 1973, "a series of NSA intercepts emanating from the Soviet Embassy" of an unspecified nature gave Henry Kissinger and Richard Nixon "what they believed to be reliable intelligence on the attitude and activities of Ambassador Dobrynin and others in the embassy."[44] Beyond that, the NSA decoded some Czech diplomatic traffic for several months in the late 1950s, various Chinese, North Vietnamese, and Viet Cong cryptographic systems in the 1950s, and Cuban intelligence messages in the 1960s.[45] Meanwhile, Soviet signals intelligence was formidable in quality and probably at least the match of its Western rivals.

It is difficult to determine the significance of this material. Several sources report that solutions of the reports by foreign ambassadors of cocktail conversations in Washington were regularly

40 Woodward, *Veil*, 88.

41 Joseph Burkholder Smith, *Portrait of a Cold Warrior* (New York, 1976), 389–90; Hersh, *The Price of Power*, 74, 101, 183; David C. Martin and John Walcott, *Best Laid Plans: The Inside Story of America's War against Terrorism* (New York, 1988), 284–86; Woodward, *Veil*, 84, 165–66, 245–46; 387–88, 409; Powers, *The Man Who Kept the Secrets*, 227.

42 The best account is in Robert J. Lamphere and Tom Shactman, *The FBI-KGB War: A Special Agent's Story* (New York, 1986), augmented by Wright, *Spycatcher*, 179–88, passim.

43 Powers, *The Man Who Kept the Secrets*, 155, 190–91; Richelson, *American Espionage*, 164.

44 Hersh, *The Price of Power*, 256–57.

45 Ibid., 74; Mathams, *Sub Rosa*, 19.

received by American officials the following morning. The consequences of this information remain unclear.[46] Informed contemporaries certainly regarded much communications intelligence as useless. Joseph Smith, a CIA officer who received solutions of Indonesian police traffic for use in covert action during 1957, never "read any NSA intercepts . . . that were of much use to me. This may have been bad luck, but there was a growing suspicion by the time I left CIA (1973) that most of NSA's material was of little value."[47] Similarly, according to Peter Wright, a well-informed officer, when British intelligence bugged Nikita Khrushchev's room at Claridge's in 1956,

> Khrushchev was far too canny a bird to discuss anything of value in a hotel room. . . . We listened to Khrushchev for hours at a time, hoping for pearls to drop. But there were no clues to the last days of Stalin, or to the fate of the KGB henchman Beria. Instead, there were long monologues from Khrushchev addressed to his valet on the subject of his attire. He was an extraordinarily vain man. He stood in front of the mirror preening himself for hours at a time, and fussing with his hair parting.[48]

The usual unnamed sources say the same of the NSA's interception of the radio-telephone traffic of Soviet leaders while driving in Moscow streets during the later 1960s: "We didn't find out about, say, the invasion of Czechoslovakia. It was very gossipy – Brezhnev's health and perhaps Podgorny's sex life."[49]

Nonetheless, communications intelligence often provided precisely the material that decision makers wanted to know and could use. Breaks into NKVD traffic in the late 1940s cracked open the great Soviet mole networks of that era. Communications intelligence let American authorities monitor President Thieu's policy between 1968 and 1975[50] and follow the internal debate in Tehran and read the diplomatic traffic between Iran and the

46 Hersh, *The Price of Power*, 207–9; Woodward, *Veil*, 387–88; Marchetti and Marks, *The CIA and the Cult of Intelligence*, 171–72.
47 Smith, *Portrait of a Cold Warrior*, 389–90
48 Wright, *Spycatcher*, 73.
49 Bamford, *The Puzzle Palace*, 360.
50 Hersh, *The Price of Power*, 83; Powers, *The Man Who Kept the Secrets*, 212; Snepp, *Decent Interval*, 15, 394.

intermediary state of Algeria during the hostage negotiations of January 1980.[51] In the 1980s, communications intelligence showed President Qaddafi's hostility toward Washington and his links with terrorist groups and sparked the bombings of Libya.[52] Signals intelligence, then, was continually significant to American foreign policy. It was most successful against Third World countries. This was also true of American human intelligence.

Since 1980, American intelligence has been routinely criticized for emphasizing technical sources at the expense of agents. This may have been true in relative terms, but not in absolute ones. During the Cold War, the United States controlled more agents than any previous government in history. Soviet security, combined with the paralysis that internal factionalism wreaked on the CIA's recruitment of agents in the USSR, meant that the United States had few of them there. The figure usually given, in words attributed to a well-informed senator, Barry Goldwater, was that in the 1970s the United States "had only five sets of eyeballs there working for us."[53] Although France and Britain each had roughly as much success as the United States in this sphere, the Soviet bloc won the human intelligence struggle with the West. The real American successes and its best human sources lay in the Third World. They were sometimes in high places – Moraji Desai, King Hussein of Jordan, Manuel Noriega, and Bashir Gemayel. Sources so eminent were often an embarrassment, because of the need to tolerate their foibles and the risk that they might manipulate their paymaster. Thus, during the Indo-Pakistani war, Moraji Desai's information on Indira Gandhi's intentions was wrong and contributed to some ill-advised American actions.[54] Less exalted contacts often provided more useful information. Relatively insignificant agents like Jonathon Pollard, David Walker, and Aleksandr Ogorodnik sold foreign governments between fifteen hundred and two thousand top-secret documents on relatively narrow topics. The most important

51 Woodward, *Veil*, 84.
52 Martin and Walcott, *Best Laid Plans*, 284–86; Woodward, *Veil*, 165–66, 409, 444.
53 Goldwater quoted in Woodward, *Veil*, 209.
54 Powers, *The Man Who Kept the Secrets*, 236; Hersh, *The Price of Power*, 450, 459–60.

Western agent in place, Colonel Oleg Penkovsky, gave Britain and the United States ten thousand microfilmed pages of documents about Soviet strategic intentions and capabilities at the highest levels. The Walker spy ring as a whole – which ranks with the atomic bomb spies as the most successful agent network of the twentieth century – gave the USSR the means to read millions of radio messages and perhaps solve every cryptographic system used by the U.S. Navy between 1968 and 1985.[55] The two volumes of selections from the documents provided by Oleg Gordievsky during his thirteen years as a British mole in the KGB illustrate the volume, scale, and significance of the material provided by an effective agent in place.[56] And this material was often used for important purposes – for example, Penkovsky's papers guided the improvement of NIEs on Soviet strategic forces and provided important background information during the Cuban missile crisis.[57]

The body of writing on the CIA is remarkably good. It is far and away the strongest part of the literature on American intelligence since 1945 and one of the brightest jewels in the crown of intelligence studies. The best general accounts are John Ranelagh's *The Agency*, despite the somewhat simplistic and traditional theme of the slow decline of the CIA from inspired origins into just another bureaucracy, and Rhodri Jeffreys-Jones's *The CIA and American Democracy*, despite the limits of its research and its overemphasis of the causal significance of the CIA's political and public relations standing in Washington and throughout the country. Three earlier studies, by Ray S. Cline, Thomas Powers, and Marchetti and Marks, retain much value. Although none of these works completely handles the topic, collectively they provide a broad and deep coverage of the history, techniques, structure, politics, and effect of the CIA, and with few

55 Wolf Blitzer, *Territory of Lies: The Exclusive Story of Jonathan Jay Pollard: The American Who Spied on His Country for Israel and How He Was Betrayed* (New York, 1989), 228; Barron, *Breaking the Ring*, 148, 219.

56 Christopher M. Andrew and Oleg Gordievsky, eds., *Instructions from the Centre: Top Secret Files on KGB Foreign Operations, 1975–1985* (London, 1991); idem, *Comrade Kryuchkov's Instructions: Top Secret Files on KGB Foreign Operations, 1975–1985* (Stanford, 1993).

57 Raymond L. Garthoff, *Intelligence Assessment and Policymaking: A Decision Point in the Kennedy Administration* (Washington, 1984), 8.

factual errors.[58] Scott D. Breckinridge and Loch Johnson offer broad and accurate introductions to the topic, although neither of these works is particularly deep. Anna Karalekas's *History of the Central Intelligence Agency*, for over a decade the best book on the topic, is now showing its age, as is another work that had some value in its time, despite its often superficial analysis, Stephen E. Ambrose's *Ike's Spies*. Thomas Troy's *Donovan and the CIA* must now be read very critically.[59] Not surprisingly, the literature becomes weaker for the period after 1976, and every work on offer has serious drawbacks. Of use are Stansfield Turner's *Secrecy and Democracy*, the apologia of an officer who is widely viewed as being one of the least successful directors of central intelligence (DCI), and Bob Woodward's *Veil*, the accuracy of which is debatable. Joseph Persico's biography of William Casey is uncritical and unsatisfactory, while the hostile literature about American intelligence in the Reagan era must be taken with a grain of salt. Certainly, if mud is to be thrown, it must be thrown at specific men and institutions rather than indiscriminately. A quite good work, if somewhat tangential from the perspective of the CIA, by Theodore Draper, deals with a matter documented by Congress, the Iran-contra affair. David B. Newsom's *The Soviet Brigade in Cuba* is a reasonably well documented and analyzed account of one instance of the relationship between intelligence and politics.[60]

This body of writing, in turn, is strongest about the period between 1940 to 1960. Here, alone in the literature under review, one can meaningfully use terms like revisionism and first or

58 Ranelagh, *The Agency*; Rhodri Jeffreys-Jones, *The CIA and American Democracy* (New Haven, 1989); Cline, *Secrets, Spies and Scholars*; Powers, *The Man Who Kept the Secrets*; Marchetti and Marks, *The CIA and the Cult of Intelligence.*

59 Breckinridge, *The CIA and the U.S. Intelligence System*; Loch K. Johnson, *A Season of Inquiry: The Senate Intelligence Investigation* (Lexington, KY, 1985); idem, *America's Secret Power: The CIA in a Democratic Society* (Oxford, 1989); Anne Karalekas, *History of the Central Intelligence Agency* (Laguna Hills, CA, 1977); Ambrose, *Ike's Spies*; Thomas F. Troy, *Donovan and the CIA: A History of the Establishment of the Central Intelligence Agency* (Frederick, MD, 1981).

60 Admiral Stansfield Turner, *Secrecy and Democracy: The CIA in Transition* (Boston, 1985); Woodward, *Veil*; Joseph E. Persico, *Casey: From the OSS to the CIA* (New York, 1990); Theodore Draper, *A Very Thin Line: The Iran-Contra Affairs* (New York, 1991); David D. Newsom, *The Soviet Brigade in Cuba: A Study in Political Diplomacy* (Bloomington, 1987).

second generations of scholarship. This period saw the creation of the CIA and its founding myth. The myth emphasized heroism and charisma, the high quality of the Office of Strategic Services (OSS), the passing of the mantle of legitimacy from General Donovan to Allen Dulles – bypassing the chiefs in between – the necessity for a large, permanent, and specialist intelligence service after 1945, and the fashion in which this was foolishly misunderstood by the Truman administration.[61] The second generation of scholars has entirely challenged this view, and with effect. It has, for example, become clear that the break in the continuity of American intelligence between 1945 and 1951 was far less radical than the CIA myth had suggested, while the reputation of Allen Dulles and of the tradition of bureaucratic and operational buccaneering that he embodied have been badly shaken. The pendulum of scholarship is swinging so far that it threatens to replace new myths for old, substituting bureaucracy for charisma and incompetence for brilliance. That trend certainly is indicated by Burton Hersh's *The Old Boys*, the most revisionist work yet attempted on the topic, and an ambitious one. Its reach, unfortunately, exceeds its grasp. Its great advantage is irreverence. Its great disadvantage is sensationalism. While useful reading to the serious student, it is far inferior to other more balanced works and also less devastating.[62]

In particular, Bradley F. Smith has demonstrated that after 1945 there was no break in the continuity of what, at that time, was the central element in American intelligence, signals intelligence; that the OSS's success was limited (but, within those limits, genuine); and that Truman shut down the OSS because of accurate reports of these limits and fears about its penetration by British intelligence.[63] Subsequent research suggests that no intelligence service on earth was penetrated so thoroughly by the

61 For a good example of such views see the declassified work of an official CIA historian, Troy, *Donovan and the CIA*.

62 Burton Hersh, *The Old Boys: The American Elite and the Origins of the CIA* (New York, 1992).

63 Bradley F. Smith, *The Shadow Warriors: O.S.S. and the Origins of the C.I.A.* (New York, 1983); idem, "An Idiosyncratic View of Where We Stand on the History of American Intelligence in the Early Post-1945 Era," *Intelligence and National Security* 3 (October 1988): 11–23.

NKVD as the OSS.[64] Smith, along with Danny D. Jansen and Rhodri Jeffreys-Jones, has also shown that the Truman administration recognized the need for effective human intelligence and assessment services and created them.[65] Smith, Sallie Pisani, and Robin Winks have illuminated the social, cultural, and political background to American intelligence and its odd relationships to academe. Their works are of particular significance to readers of *Diplomatic History*: They integrate intelligence with Cold War culture and thereby illuminate subterranean aspects of American policy after 1945. Another recent work in this vein by Barry M. Katz has a similar merit, though of a lesser sort: It is far more useful to students of American academe and the German intellectual diaspora than to historians of intelligence or the Cold War.[66] Sallie Pisani has revolutionized our understanding of the intelligence services as a source of information and a tool of policy between 1945 and 1949.[67]

All this has been assisted by the first fruits of the CIA's moves toward reclassification of documents, the release of two internal official histories by Arthur B. Darling and Ludwell Lee Montague.[68] These works are of narrow value – they say virtually nothing about the collection of intelligence, for example. Neither will ever be read for pleasure, and only the most dour of students will embrace all of Darling. There is reason to think that Darling never understood the subject he should have been dealing with – intelligence – as opposed to the one with which he did deal – bureaucracy, while both of these writers contribute to the personality cults that seem to surround DCIs. Nonetheless, these works do illuminate the politics and organization within American

64 Christopher M. Andrew and Oleg Gordievsky, *KGB: The Inside Story of its Foreign Operations from Lenin to Gorbachev* (London, 1990), 302, 309.

65 In addition to the sources cited in footnote 63 see Danny D. Jansen and Rhodri Jeffreys-Jones, "The Missouri Gang and the CIA," in Jeffreys-Jones and Lownie, eds., *North American Spies*, 123–42.

66 See the sources cited in footnote 63, along with Sallie Pisani, *The CIA and the Marshall Plan* (Lawrence, 1991); Robin W. Winks, *Cloak & Gown: Scholars in the Secret War, 1939–1961* (New York, 1987); and Barry M. Katz, *Foreign Intelligence: Research and Analysis in the Office of Strategic Services, 1942–1945* (Cambridge, MA, 1989).

67 Pisani, *The CIA and the Marshall Plan.*

68 Arthur B. Darling, *The Central Intelligence Agency: An Instrument of Government, to 1950* (University Park, PA, 1990); Ludwell Lee Montague, *General Walter Bedell Smith as Director of Central Intelligence, October 1950–February 1953* (University Park, PA, 1992).

intelligence between 1946 and 1953 and throw much incidental light on details.

A number of specialist works on the CIA discuss, accurately enough, specialist topics. For the "war of the defectors," one of the most illuminating events in the history of the CIA, the pioneering work is David Martin's *Wilderness of Mirrors*. Tom Mangold and, to a lesser extent, David Wise, have also offered excellent accounts of this topic, although not necessarily accurate in every aspect; Edward Jay Epstein's *Legend* rests on inaccurate assumptions, but much of the detail about the techniques of counterintelligence is good.[69] Alfred McCoy and Peter Dale Scott and Jonathan Marshall have provided useful introductions to the topic of the relationship between postwar American intelligence and the international drug trade. This literature is controversial: Much rubbish has been printed on this topic, and even more shown on the screen. Although McCoy and Scott and Marshall try to avoid sensationalism, their political views are clear, and details of their arguments may well be wrong. Moreover, of course, the CIA and even the Church Committee rejected such claims.[70] Nonetheless, it seems clear that on occasion the CIA has tolerated the drug trade conducted by its local allies, and for the reason identified by McCoy – "radical pragmatism." William M. Leary, *Perilous Missions: Civil Air Transport and CIA Covert Operations in Asia*, and Peter Coleman, *The Liberal Conspiracy: The Congress for Cultural Freedom and the Struggle for the Mind of Postwar Europe*, address well-known aspects of the CIA's work: the infrastructure for covert action and its work in the cultural Cold War.[71] Above all, the body of writing on covert

69 David Martin, *Wilderness of Mirrors* (New York, 1980); Tom Mangold, *Cold Warrior: James Jesus Angleton: The CIA's Master Spy Hunter* (New York, 1991); David Wise, *Molehunt: The Secret Search for Traitors that Shattered the CIA* (New York, 1992); Edward Jay Epstein, *Legend: The Secret World of Lee Harvey Oswald* (New York, 1978).

70 Alfred W. McCoy with Cathleen B. Read and Leonard P. Adams II, *The Politics of Heroin in Southeast Asia* (New York, 1972); Peter Dale Scott and Jonathan Marshall, *Cocaine Politics: Drugs, Armies, and the CIA in Central America* (Berkeley, 1991).

71 William M. Leary, *Perilous Missions: Civil Air Transport and CIA Covert Operations in Asia* (University, AL, 1984); Peter Coleman, *The Liberal Conspiracy: The Congress for Cultural Freedom and the Struggle for the Mind of Postwar Europe* (New York, 1989). Coleman's account should be augmented by the memoir of the CIA officer most involved in this campaign, Cord Meyer, *Facing Reality: From World Federalism to the CIA* (New York, 1980).

action is particularly substantial. This is far and away the topic most frequently referred to in the academic and popular literature on the CIA – so much so as to grossly imbalance our understanding of the nature and significance of American intelligence since 1945.[72] Any reader of this literature should always ask two questions: Why did this matter? and to whom?

There is also a voluminous memoir literature by members of the CIA, more than with any other espionage service in history or with veterans of American technical sources of intelligence during the Cold War. One can easily illustrate the various genres of this literature with good works. Joseph B. Smith and Frank Snepp represent the disillusioned and tell-all spirit of the 1970s. William Colby offers a strain of pride and apology. Philip Agee

72 John Prados, *Presidents' Secret Wars: CIA and Pentagon Covert Operations since World War II* (New York, 1986), is the best specialist monograph. Gregory F. Treverton, *Covert Action: The Limits of Intervention in the Postwar World* (New York, 1987), is also useful, if written from the "liberal" perspective. Valuable and accurate accounts of American covert action in Europe during the decade following 1945 are Trevor Barnes, "The Secret Cold War: The C.I.A. and American Foreign Policy in Europe, 1946–1956. Parts I and II," *Historical Journal* 24 (June 1981): 399–415 and 25 (September 1982): 649–70; James E. Miller, "Taking Off the Gloves: The United States and the Italian Elections of 1948," *Diplomatic History* 7 (Winter 1983): 35–55; David Smiley, *Albanian Assignment* (London, 1984); Michael W. Dravis, "Storming Fortress Albania: American Covert Operations in Microcosm, 1949–54," *Intelligence and National Security* 7 (October 1992): 425–42. Especially useful is Pisani, *The CIA and the Marshall Plan.* Specialist studies of covert action in the Third World are found in Douglas Little, "Cold War and Covert Action: The United States and Syria, 1945–1958," *Middle East Studies* 44 (Winter 1990): 51–75; David W. Lesch, *Syria and the United States: Eisenhower's Cold War in the Middle East* (Boulder, 1992); H. W. Brands, Jr., *Cold Warriors: Eisenhower's Generation and American Foreign Policy* (New York, 1988), 48–68; and idem, "The Limits of Manipulation: How the United States Didn't Topple Sukarno," *Journal of American History* 76 (December 1989): 785–808. There is a truly extraordinary volume of material on two cases. For Guatemala in 1954 see Richard H. Immerman, *The CIA in Guatemala: The Foreign Policy of Intervention* (Austin, 1982); and Stephen Schlesinger and Stephen Kinzer, *Bitter Fruit: The Untold Story of the American Coup in Guatemala* (Garden City, 1982). The argument currently rests with Frederick W. Marks III, "The CIA and Castillo Armas in Guatemala, 1954: New Clues to an Old Puzzle," and Stephen G. Rabe, "The Clues Didn't Check Out: Commentary on 'The CIA and Castillo Armas,'" *Diplomatic History* 14 (Winter 1990): 67–95. Good introductions to the literature on the Bay of Pigs are Trumbull Higgins, *The Perfect Failure: Kennedy, Eisenhower, and the CIA at the Bay of Pigs* (New York, 1987); *Operation Zapata: The "Ultrasensitive" Report and Testimony of the Board of Inquiry on the Bay of Pigs*, intro. Luis Aguilar, (Frederick, MD, 1981); Lucien S. Vandenbroucke, "The 'Confessions' of Allen Dulles: New Evidence on the Bay of Pigs," *Diplomatic History* 8 (Fall 1984): 365–75; and Peter Wyden, *Bay of Pigs: The Untold Story* (New York, 1979), augmented by E. Howard Hunt, *Give Us This Day* (New Rochelle, NY, 1973).

represents the extreme of revisionism – not surprising, from the CIA's only ideological defector to communism.[73] This literature covers all aspects of the CIA's history, especially the more sensational elements. It must be examined by any serious student of American intelligence during the Cold War.

For intelligence, the proof of the pudding is interpretation and use. Fundamental to that test is the need not to mistake the size of surviving documentation for significance. If and when all of the documents reach the public domain, historians will be swamped by daily and weekly, regular and special summaries produced by dozens of bureaus on thousands of topics. Many of these estimates were waste paper, highest common denominator manuscripts written simply for the sake of form. In themselves, the writings of analysts indicate precisely nothing about the true motivations behind the actions of real decision makers. One has to prove the influence of these writings by thoroughly investigating the relations between staffs and statesmen. Professional analysts are well informed, but not necessarily important. And this fact produces a fundamental danger: that the significance of individuals and intelligence, and thus the nature of a whole decision-making process, will be distorted simply because we take some surviving historical artifacts to be the whole of historical decisions. This problem dogs even good and well-regarded studies of assessment.

Influence was a function not just of the accuracy of analysts but also of the politics of analysis. Competition between bureaus was continual, whether evinced in recurrent differences over analyses or in behavior during high-profile issues when, as Stansfield Turner put it, "the name of the game was getting credit for the scoop," when an air force chief of intelligence could pursue "a best-seller."[74] Although DCIs like Walter Bedell Smith, Allen Dulles, and William Casey found a steady market, others were less effective salesmen for their wares. Even Dwight Eisenhower,

73 Smith, *Portrait of a Cold Warrior*; Snepp, *Decent Interval*; William Colby and Peter Forbath, *Honorable Men: My Life in the CIA* (New York, 1978); Agee, *Inside the Company*.

74 Turner quoted in Newsom, *The Soviet Brigade in Cuba*; Hersh, *"The Target is Destroyed"*, 86.

a president who respected professional assessments, reached his conclusions about the missile gap, in the words of one senior analyst, through "his reading of the available evidence (from U-2 photography and other sources) and feel for the Soviet Union."[75] In cases where NIEs or less formal estimates are already available, as is often true of *FRUS* or the documents published by the National Security Archive, one can trace the effect of intelligence and assessments on strategic decisions. During the Cuban missile crisis, for example, the documents appear to indicate that intelligence was used in the classic fashion. It offered objective data that high-level decision makers queried to their own satisfaction, and once decision makers had defined their views, largely following expert opinion, intelligence fell silent.[76] None of this, however, was necessarily a general rule. Many presidents and their senior advisers loved to serve as their own analysts of raw material, especially communications intelligence. This stemmed in part from a mistrust after 1968 of the accuracy and value of the CIA's analysts. Richard Nixon held that the CIA was crippled by a "muscle-bound bureaucracy which has completely paralyzed its brain" and by personnel drawn primarily from the "Ivy League and the Georgetown set."[77] Stansfield Turner offered similar criticisms and, along with Zbigniew Brzezinski and two Ivy League academics who received privileged access to the files of CIA analysts, Robert Jervis and Richard Pipes, damned them for complacency and mediocrity.[78] Less damning but still damaging criticisms were made by analysts. Two retired senior veterans, Raymond Garthoff and Michael Herman, have attacked Western analyses during the Cold War era for focusing too narrowly on military matters, for making sweeping and crude assumptions

75 Garthoff, *Assessing the Adversary*, 42.

76 Laurence Chang and Peter Kornbluh, eds., *The Cuban Missile Crisis, 1962: A National Security Archive Documents Reader* (New York, 1992), 86–87, 97–99, 123; Scott A. Koch, ed., *CIA Cold War Records, Selected Estimates on the Soviet Union, 1950–1959* (Washington, 1993); Michael Warner, ed., *CIA Cold War Records, The CIA under Harry Truman* (Washington, 1994).

77 Bruce Oudes, ed., *FROM: The President: Richard Nixon's Secret Files* (New York, 1989), 448.

78 Jervis cited in Woodward, *Veil*, 28, 108–11; Pipes cited in Godson, *Analysis and Estimates*, 175; Turner, *Secrecy and Democracy*, 194–204; Zbigniew Brzezinski, *Power and Principle: Memoirs of the National Security Advisor, 1977–1981* (New York, 1983), 367.

about Soviet behavior, for ignoring diplomatic possibilities and Western strength, and for adopting a "consistently worst-case view of intentions." Others, like David Sullivan, have seen the opposite phenomenon.[79] The estimates in question are now being released in increasing numbers. Anyone using these artifacts as evidence should remember the comments of those who produced and used them.

Raymond Garthoff has argued that scholars have paid "too little attention . . . to the subject of assessing the adversary."[80] This claim is not entirely accurate. There is a useful literature on international assessments of strategic capabilities and intentions between 1900 and 1941.[81] Although much work remains to be done on the period after 1945, the body of writing is large and good. The most promising sign of its maturity is, perhaps, the way in which the topic has been incorporated into a mainstream work. Melvyn P. Leffler's recent and magisterial study, *A Preponderance of Power*, pays close attention to intelligence as a source of evidence and influence; his index includes entries for the CIA and for such concepts as "Threat Perception." By comparing the record of assessment with that of decisions, he shows the relationship between the two in a thorough and sophisticated fashion – which, in the end, is the only way to determine the relationship between evidence and interpretation, perception and policy in the Cold War. Leffler's study, a model for future work, integrates the literature on and evidence about intelligence into the Truman administration's formulation and execution of American strategic policy.[82] Several able studies, if by necessity resting on a weaker

79 Garthoff, *Assessing the Adversary*, 43–52; Michael Herman, "Intelligence and the Assessment of Military Capabilities: Reasonable Sufficiency or the Worst Case?" *Intelligence and National Security* 4 (October 1989): 765–99; David S. Sullivan, "Evaluating U.S. Intelligence Estimates" and "Discussion" in *Analysis and Estimates*, 49–83. These works also offer useful comments on the method of Western analysts, as do Michael Herman, "Intelligence and Policy: A Comment," *Intelligence and National Security* 6 (January 1991): 229–39; Reginald Hibbert, "Intelligence and Policy," ibid. 5 (January 1990): 125–39; Garthoff, *Intelligence Assessment and Policymaking*, 5; and Berkowitz and Goodman, *Strategic Intelligence*.

80 Garthoff, *Assessing the Adversary*, 52.

81 The best introduction is Ernest R. May, ed., *Knowing One's Enemies: Intelligence Assessment before the Two World Wars* (Princeton, 1984).

82 Melvyn P. Leffler, *A Preponderance of Power: National Security, the Truman Administration, and the Cold War* (Stanford, 1992).

documentary base than Leffler's, have examined how such assessments affected general American policy toward nuclear weapons and the Soviet Union during large swathes of the Cold War. Specialist studies by Raymond Garthoff and Barry Steiner have augmented the classic works by Lawrence Freedman and John Prados.[83] This material is of fundamental importance to scholars of American policy after 1945. It illuminates American knowledge, information, and preconceptions and thus the entire perceptual root of the Cold War. Garthoff has concluded, for example, that during the 1950s and 1960s, the U.S. government never understood the intentions behind Soviet nuclear policy.[84] That probably was true throughout the whole Cold War. American understanding of Soviet capabilities is a more complex matter, because this included not merely current deployed strength and characteristics of weapon systems but also current growth and technical developments of Soviet forces and thus their power at some point in the future. Between 1953 and 1961, the United States grossly exaggerated the existing size and current increments in Russian strategic forces. From the mid-1960s, it understood current deployed strength with tolerable accuracy but could not be sure of future strength or issues such as the throw-weight of weaponry more than a few years ahead. Thus, during the middle 1960s, the United States was grossly overoptimistic about growth rates in Soviet nuclear forces. Conversely, from the early 1970s the known unknowns about many highly technical issues remained a major source of controversy in American strategic policy.

The literature on American assessments of Soviet nuclear forces is quite good. The weakness in studies of intelligence estimates lies everywhere else. The few useful studies of the effect of assessments on American diplomacy since 1945 have focused on intelligence failures of a classic sort, such as with Tito's break with

83 Garthoff, *Intelligence Assessment and Policymaking*; idem, *Assessing the Adversary*; Barry H. Steiner, "American Intelligence and the Soviet ICBM Build-up: Another Look," *Intelligence and National Security* 8 (April 1993): 172–98; Lawrence Freedman, *U.S. Intelligence and the Soviet Strategic Threat*, 2d ed. (Boulder, 1986); John Prados, *The Soviet Estimate: U.S. Intelligence Analysis and Russian Military Strength* (New York, 1982).

84 See the sources cited in footnote 79.

Stalin or the Iranian Revolution, rather than on successes, let alone the ambiguous realm in between where most cases of diplomatic intelligence fall and in which it has a subtle and odd influence.[85] There is ample room for further work in this area. Knowledge of the intelligence dimension will be necessary for any student of American foreign policy as a whole, especially in the Third World. The same, of course, will be true for the military and strategic dimensions of American foreign policy, and here the literature is more advanced. The literature on American assessments of Soviet military spending is polemical in nature and rests on a fragmentary base of evidence.[86] There is virtually no academic literature on military intelligence services after 1945: The main exception is Patrick Mescall, "The Birth of the Defense Intelligence Agency."[87] Conversely, a small but good literature is beginning to emerge about American military assessments of conventional and guerrilla opponents, whether in Korea, Laos, or Western Europe. These works rest on a solid empirical basis and on a commendable attempt to explain clearly and precisely how such assessments affected decisions. In particular, though much remains to be said about American espionage during the second Indochina war, James Wirtz and Ronald Ford have offered powerful and revisionist examinations of American intelligence before the Tet Offensive. Their works combine an analytical framework derived from the strategic science and historical study of intelligence and a good base of primary research. They have demolished the idea that a corruption of intelligence led the American army to misunderstand the coming storm in late 1967. They have also addressed the causes and nature of the intelligence failure

85 For well researched and analyzed instances see Robert M. Blum, "Surprised by Tito: The Anatomy of an Intelligence Failure," *Diplomatic History* 12 (Winter 1988): 39–57; Zachary Karabell, "'Inside the US Espionage Den': The U.S. Embassy and the Fall of the Shah," *Intelligence and National Security* 8 (January 1993): 44–59; and Amir Taheri, *Nest of Spies: America's Journey to Disaster in Iran* (London, 1988).

86 Useful introductions to this issue are Steven Rosefielde, *False Science: Underestimating the Soviet Arms Buildup: An Appraisal of the CIA's Direct Costing Effort, 1960–80* (New Brunswick, NJ, 1982); Franklyn D. Holzman, "Politics and Guesswork: CIA and DIA Estimates of Soviet Military Spending," *International Security* 14 (Fall 1989): 101–31; and idem, "Correspondence," ibid. (Spring 1990): 185–98.

87 Patrick Mescall, "The Birth of the Defence Intelligence Agency," in Jeffreys-Jones and Lownie, eds., *North American Spies*, 158–202.

before the Tet Offensive, although they reach different conclusions on the topic.[88]

Whatever its gaps, the literature on American intelligence during the Cold War is excellent by the standards of the study. It provides a surprisingly good picture of the structure, size, work, techniques, and internal politics of the intelligence services and of their relationship with decision makers. It also offers some hints as to how this material affected decisions, but not enough, and this territory for the first time is falling open to exploration. It is clear that much of the material provided by the intelligence services to their masters will fall into the public domain, at a time when scholars can still question some of the participants. This record may well be incomplete, especially regarding communications intelligence and its effect on diplomacy, but it probably will be a good record. There was an intelligence dimension to every aspect of American policy during the Cold War; historians have scarcely even begun to come to terms with it. This, the realm of assessment and use, is the area that merits most attention from scholars of American intelligence during the Cold War. It will concern all students of American policy.

88 James J. Wirtz, *The Tet Offensive: Intelligence Failure in War* (Ithaca, 1991); Ronald Ford, "Tet Revisited: The Strategy of the Communist Vietnamese," *Intelligence and National Security* 9 (April 1994): 242–86; idem, "Intelligence and the Significance of Khe Sanh," ibid. (forthcoming). See also Eliot A. Cohen, "'Only Half the Battle': American Intelligence and the Chinese Intervention in Korea, 1950," *Intelligence and National Security* 5 (January 1990): 129–49; Peter S. Usowski, "Intelligence Estimates and US Policy toward Laos, 1960–63," ibid. 6 (April 1991): 367–94; John S. Duffield, "The Soviet Military Threat to Western Europe: US Estimates in the 1950s and 1960s," *Journal of Strategic Studies* 15 (June 1992): 208–27; Rosemary Foot, "The Sino-American Conflict in Korea: The United States Assessment of China's Ability to Intervene in the War," *Asian Affairs* 14:2 (1983): 160–66; and Timothy N. Castle, *At War in the Shadow of Vietnam: U.S. Military Aid to the Royal Lao Government, 1955–1975* (New York, 1993).

Index

Abel, Lionel, 188–9
ABM treaty, 399
About Face (Hackworth), 363
Abrahamian, Ervand, 471
Abramson, Rudy, 552
Acheson, Dean, 27–8, 56–7, 86, 131
  China policy, 509–12
  Korean War policy, 276
  "Press Club speech" of 1950, 30
Act of Chapultepec, 436
Acting President, The (Schieffer and Gates), 419–20
Adler, Les, 197
Advice and Support (Spector), 372
African policy, Kennedy, 354
After Tet (Spector), 385–6
Agee, Philip, 582, 592–3
Agency, The (Ranelagh), 587
Air Power and the Ground War in Vietnam (Mrozek), 384–5
Alamogordo, 228–9
Algerian National Liberation Front, 321
All Fall Down (Sick), 415, 556
Allende, Salvador, 454–5
Alliance for Progress, 322, 333, 335, 353*n*69, 451–2, 553
Allies of a Kind (Thorne), 181
Allison, Graham, 346
Alperovitz, Gar, 173–4, 179, 185, 208–14, 216–17, 224, 227–8
Alteras, Isaac, 476
Ambiguous Partnership (Hathaway), 546
Ambrose, Stephen, 294, 407, 481, 493
  and Eisenhower revisionism, 304–5, 309–10, 323*n*81
  intelligence writings, 568, 588
America in Vietnam (Lewy), 360–1
American Diplomacy during World War II (Smith), 184–5
American Diplomatic History (Combs), 30
American Espionage and the Soviet Target (Richelson), 580
American Israel Public Affairs Committee, 475–6
American Leadership in World Affairs (Holsti and Rosenau), 406
American Money and the Weimar Republic (McNeil), 543
American Occupation of Japan, The (Schaller), 558
American Ordeal, An (DeBenedetti and Chatfield), 381, 406
American "Reparations" to Germany, 1919–33 (Schuker), 544
American Style of Foreign Policy, The (Dallek), 398
Americanization of Brazil, The (Haines), 440–1
America's Germany (Schwartz), 552
America's Half-Century (McCormick), 164, 398, 559–60
America's Longest War (Herring), 368, 405, 408
Ameringer, Charles, 579
Analogies at War (Khong), 374–5
Anatomy of a War (Kolko), 391
Anderson, David L., 312–13, 371–2
Anderson, Irvine H., 195, 196*n*65, 250, 251*n*26, 466, 551
Anderson, Robert, 481
Anderson, Sheldon, 241
Andrade, Dale, 389
Anglo-American relations
  economic policies, 545–7

Anglo-American relations (*cont.*)
  and Egypt, 478–86
  gold standard struggle, 545
  Korean conflict, 283–5
  and Southeast Asia, 523–4
  and World War II, 177–8
Anglo-Iranian Oil Company, 471
anthropology, 109–10
anticommunism and Eisenhower, 319–25
Appleby, Joyce, 63, 64*n*2, 72
Approaching Vietnam (Gardner), 370–1
ARAMCO, 465–8, 482–3
Architects of Illusion (Gardner), 33–4
archival research, 113–14, 146–7, 261
  contributions of, 142
  and Harvard group, 113–14
  limitations, 100–2, 125–6
area studies, 50, 262
  and Harvard group, 114
Arbenz Guzmán, Jacobo, 306, 444
Argentina, 433, 443
arms control
  Carter's policies, 414
  Eisenhower's policies, 317–19
Armstrong, Anne, 171
Army and Vietnam, The (Krepinevich), 364
Arnold, James, 370
Aronson, Geoffrey, 479
Arrighi, Giovanni, 50
Ashby, Timothy, 457
Ashes to Ashes (Andrade), 389
"Asia-firsters," 283
Asian-American relations, 501–35
assassination plots
  and Eisenhower, 323, 323*n*81
  and Kennedy, 338
Aswan Dam, 480–1, 550
At the Highest Levels (Beschloss and Talbott), 421
atheory, 133
atomic bomb decision (*see also* nuclear weapons), 206–33
  alternatives to, 221–3
  and American view of Japanese, 220
  bureaucratic imperatives, 225–6
  Cold War role, 209
  diplomatic considerations, 207–17, 225
  military necessity factor, 217, 227
  moral considerations, 220–2
  and Russian bomb project, 231–2
  saving American lives factor, 217–19
  scientists' role, 230–1
  and Soviet–American relations, 232–3
  Truman's ambivalence, 219–20
  Truman's diary notes, 214–15
  Truman's motivation, 173–4, 207–22
  and unconditional surrender modification, 221–2
  warning shot alternative, 222
Atomic Diplomacy (Alperovitz), 185, 208–13, 216–17
atomic scientists, 230–1
Atoms for Peace speech, 317–19
Attlee, Clement, 523
Australia and Korean conflict, 283
Awkward Dominion (Costigliola), 544–5

Backfire (Baritz), 369
Badeau, John, 492
Baggett, Blaine, 579–80
Baghdad Pact, 482, 488
Bailey, Sydney, 288
Baily, Samuel L., 438
Bain, Kenneth, 474
Baldwin, Hanson, 168
Balfour Declaration, 465
Balfour-Paul, Glen, 493
Ball, Desmond, 349, 582
Ball, Douglas, 476
Ball, George, 355, 379, 476, 495
Bamford, James, 582
Banking on the World (Frieden), 556–7
banking practices, 556–7
Bankrupting of America, The (Calleo), 559
Baram, Philip J., 195, 196*n*65, 465
Bard, Ralph, 217
Baritz, Loren, 369
Barnes, Harry Elmer, 60, 104
Bassett, Lawrence J., 352*n*68
Batista, Fulgencio, 322
Batista dictatorship, 448
Baum, Kim Chull, 272*n*10
Bay of Pigs, 444, 451
  and Eisenhower, 322
  Kennedy's decisions, 335–7
Beard, Charles Austin, 60, 104, 138
Becker, William H., 540
Before the Fall (Safire), 403
Beirut, 488–90
Bemis, Samuel Flagg, 4–9, 133, 140–1, 426–7, 429
Bender, Thomas, 63–4, 502
Benjamin, Jules R., 449–50
Bennett, Edward, 191
Bennett, Ralph Francis, 566
Bergerud, Eric, 387

Berkowitz, Bruce D., *571n21*
Berlin Crisis, The (Slusser), 339
Berlin Crisis, 1958–1962, The (Schick), 340
Berlin crisis of 1948–49, 246, 259
Berlin crisis of 1961, 338–42
Berlin Wall, 338, 340–1
Berman, Larry, 373, 376–7
Berman, William C., 382
Bernstein, Barton J., 179, 211–12, 218–19, 223–4, 286, 288, 343, 517
Beschloss, Michael R., 339–40, 421, 581
Best and the Brightest, The (Halberstam), 329–30, 359
Bethell, Leslie, 437–8
Betts, Richard K., 291, 360–1, 565, 571
Bevin, Ernest, 243, 468
Beyond American Hegemony (Calleo), 554
Bick, Etta Zablocki, 495
Bill, James A., 406, 415–16, 471–2, 494, 551–2
Billings-Yun, Melanie, 311, 370
biological weapons, Korea, 290
Bird, Kai, 28, *224n24*, 552
Bishku, Michael, 493
Bissell, Richard, 580, 582
Blackett, P. M. S., 207
Blair, Clay, 289
Blasier, Cole, 457
Bloom, Allan David, 40
Bloomsbury syndrome, 577
Blum, John Morton, 545
Blum, Robert M., 510, 523
Bohlen, Charles E., 251–2
Boll, Michael M., 241
Bonner, Raymond, 413
Borden, William S., 29–30, 355–6, 519–21, 523, 553, 558
Borg, Dorothy, 115
Borowski, Harry R., 259
Bound to Lead (Nye), 422, 560
Braden, Spruille, 443
Bradley, Mark, *368n17*, 530
Brands, Henry W., Jr., 241–2, 252, 313, 319, 475, 486, 491, 496, 517, 533, 550–1
Brazil, 432–3, 435, 440–1, 453
Brazil and the Great Powers, 1930–1939 (Hilton), 432
Brazilian-American Alliance, 1937–1945, The (McGann), 432
Bread and the Ballot (Merrill), 551
Breckinridge, Scott D., 580, 588
Bretton Woods, 239, 547–8, 554–5
Brezhnev summit, 399–401
Bricker Amendment, 307
Brigham, Robert K., 530
Bright Shining Lie, A (Sheehan), 379–80
Brinkley, Alan, 302
Brinkley, Douglas, 552
British Empire in the Middle East, 1945–1951, The (Louis), 551
Brophy, William J., 347
Brown, L. Carl, 498
Brown, Walter, 213
Brzezinski, Zbigniew, 594
Buckingham, William, 385
Buckley, Roger, 522, 532–3
bugging practices, 582–5
Buhite, Russell D., 186, 255, 507
Bullen, Roger, 285
Bulletin of the Atomic Scientists special issue, 214
Bullitt, William C., 168, 187, 200–1
Bullock, Alan, 243
Bundy, McGeorge, 222–3, 232, 319, 342, 345
Bungert, Heike, *247n20*
Buraimi oasis, 483
Bureaucracy at Work, The (Commer), *389n57*
bureaucratic politics
  and atomic bomb decision, 196–7, 225–6
  in Cuban missile crisis, 346
  and Eisenhower, 308
  influence on Roosevelt, 195–6
  lack of appeal to historians, 428
  and Latin America, 427–8
Burgess, Guy, 256
Burk, Kathleen, 539–40
Burk, Robert, 302
Burke, John P., 310–11, 373–4
Burns, E. Bradford, 458
Burns, James M., 172
Burns, William, 480, 490–1, 495
Burrows, William E., 581–2
Bush administration, 421
Byrnes, James F., 212, 217, 254–5

Cable, Larry, 363–4
Cairo summit conference, 185
Calingaert, Daniel, 291, *292n52*
Calleo, David P., 421, 554, 559
Callison, Charles, 390
Camp David (Quandt), 415

capitalism
  postrevisionist view, 35–8
  World War II policy influence, 173–4
capitalist intentionality, 137
Caridi, Ronald, 283
Carrol, Peter, 409
Carter, Jimmy, 409
Carter administration, 410–16
  Central America policy, 412–13, 455
  human rights policies, 411–12
  Middle East diplomacy, 414–16
  Soviet policy, 413–14
Casey, William, 588
Castañeda, Jorge G., 459–60
Castillo Armas, Carlos, 444
Castro, Fidel, 447–52
  Eisenhower's policy, 322–3
  Kennedy's fixation, 337–8, 345, 348–9, 451–2
Cate, Curtis, 341
Catudal, Honore, 341–2
Caveat (Haig), 417
Central America (*see also* Latin America)
  Carter administration policies, 412–13
  Reagan administration policies, 456–8
Central America and the United States (Coatsworth), 458
Central Intelligence Agency, *see* CIA
Certain Trumpet, The (Kinnard), 378
Césari, Laurent, 311
Chace, James, 557–8
Chafe, William H., 325
Chairman, The (McCloy), 552
Chamoun, Camille, 317, 488–90
Chandler, Robert, 388–9
Chang, Gordon H., 297, 313–14, 349, 532
Changing of the Guard, A (Woods), 546
Chanoff, David, 390
Chatfield, Charles, 381
Chen Jian, 275, 280, 290, 293, 529
Chernow, Ron, 540
Chiang Kai-shek (Jiang Jieshi), 179, 314–15, 507–9
Chile, 433, 440, 454–5
China, 506–12
  attitude to atomic threat, Korea, 292
  and Eisenhower, 314–15
  foreign policy mindset, 79–80
  Korean conflict role, 278–81, 292, 511–12
  "lost chance thesis," 509–12
  reinterpretations of relations with, 179
  Truman's policy, 506–12
Chomsky, Noam, 32–3
Churchill, Winston S.
  comment on Syngman Rhee, 296
  correspondence with Stalin, 175*n*21
  1960s reassessment of, 172–3
  and post–World War II diplomacy, 168–9
  reinterpretation of policies, 181
Churchill-Roosevelt correspondence, 188–9
CIA, 587–96
  bugging practices, 582–5
  criticism of, 594–5
  Eisenhower's use of, 322–3, 487
  founding myth, 589
  influence of, 593–6
  information about, weaknesses, 568–70
  literature on, 587–96
  memoir literature, 592–3
  postwar Iran role, 471–2
  and Syria, 487
CIA and American Democracy, The (Jeffreys-Jones), 409, 587
CIA and the Cult of Intelligence, The (Marchetti and Marks), 582
CIA in Guatamala, The (Immerman), 306
Clark, Mark, 293
Clarke, Jeffrey, 386
Clausewitzian revisionists, 361–2, 364, 393–4
Clayton, Will, 549
Clemens, Diane Shaver, 173
Clements, Kendrick A., 254, 256
Clifford, Clark, 81–2, 473
Clifford, J. Garry, 195, 196*n*65
Cline, Ray S., 571*n*21, 574–5
Clodfelter, Mark, 384
Close Neighbors, Distant Friends (Findling), 457
Closing the Gold Window (Gowa), 555
Coatsworth, John H., 458
Cobbs, Elizabeth A., 441
Cohen, Benjamin, 556
Cohen, Michael, 474–5
Cohen, Warren I., 96, 377, 422, 495, 503, 506, 508–11
Cohn, Carol, 76
Colby, William, 389, 592
Cold Dawn (Newhouse), 399–400
Cold War, 151–2, 154–5, 238
  and American foreign service, 251–2
  and Asia, synthesis, 526–8, 530–5
  atomic diplomacy role, 209

economics, 548
end of, 420–1
European origins, 234–69
and gender issues, 69
and intelligence, 580
Korean conflict significance, 296–7
national security theme, 234–69
Near Eastern origins, 234–69
1960s interpretations, 171–3
1990s themes, 199–201
post–World War II interpretations, 167–70
race relations influence, 69
schools of thought, 236–7
and Stalin's expansionist tendencies, 243–5
three-realm appraisal, 123–4, 149–52
Truman administration role, 254–8
and Vietnam War, 368*n*17
Cold War, The (Lippmann), 548
Cold War and Counter-Revolution (Walton), 329
Cold War as Rhetoric, The (Hinds and Windt), 77
Cold War International History Project, 80*n*53
Cold War revisionists, *see* revisionism
Cold Warrior, 330–1, 340–1, 353
Cold Warriors and Coups D'Etat (Weis), 441
Coleman, Peter, 591
collaboration-resistance model, 111
Collins, J. Lawton, 312, 372
Colville, John, 187–8
Combined Action Platoons, The (Peterson), 388
Combs, Jerald A., 30–4, 122, 236*n*3
Commentary series, 187–9
Commer, Robert, 389
Communist Road to Power in Vietnam, The (Duiker), 391
Conant, James B., 219
Condemned to Repetition (Pastor), 412–13
Conflict of Myths (Cable), 364
Congo, Eisenhower's policy, 323
conspiracy theory, 134–5, 571
containment doctrine, 34, 53, 59–60, 143–5, 180
economic considerations, 239, 548–9
Kennan's view, 253–4
Roosevelt's strategy, 180
and Stalin's regime, 143
and Vietnam, 522–4
Containment of Latin America, The (Green), 435–6
Contesting Castro (Paterson), 448, 552
Cook, Blanche Wiesen, 444
Coolidge, Archibald Cary, 113–14
corporatism, 40, 58, 84–5, 107–8, 204, 545
limitations, 264
and Marshall Plan, 263–5, 549
and progressivism, 107–9
roots of, 107
Costigliola, Frank, 89, 355, 544–5, 553
Cottam, Richard, 471–3
Cousins, Norman, 207
covert action (*see also* intelligence, 1945–1990), 578, 591–2
Cragg, Dan, 390
Craig, Gordon A., 93, 269
Cripps, Stafford, 192
Cronkite, Walter, 352
Cross and the Flag, The, 75
cryptology, 568, 582–4, 587
Cuba
Castro's revolution, 321–2, 447–52
and economics, 552–3
Eisenhower's policy, 321–2
intelligence on, 581, 594
Cuban missile crisis, 342–9, 452, 594
Cullather, Nick, 533–4
cultural approach, 72–4, 77–8, 80
benefits of, 109–10
and international policy, 112
Vietnam War interpretation, 369–70
World War II interpretation, 181–2
Cumings, Bruce, 9–12, 18, 69–70, 85, 270*n*1
Korean War writings, 272–8, 281, 513, 516
Melvyn Leffler's commentary on, 145–7
Michael Hunt's commentary on, 152–3
Cumings-Schlesinger debate, 9, 9*n*10
Currey, Cecil B., 367
Cutler, Robert, 310
Czechoslovakia, 356
Czechoslovakian invasion, 581

Dallek, Robert, 180, 185, 398
Darling, Arthur B., 590
Dau Tranh strategy, 391–2
Davidson, Phillip B., 362
Davies, Joseph, 213
Davis, Lynn, 198
Dawes Conference of 1924, 543

Day of the Bomb (Kurzman), 216
Day One (Wyden), 216
de Folin, Jacques, 311
Deadly Gambits (Talbott), 418
Deadly Paradigms (Shafer), 372
Deane, John R., 168
Death in November, A (Hammer), 366
Debate over Vietnam, The (Levy), 381
DeBenedetti, Charles, 381, 406
Decision against War (Billings-Yun), 370
Decisions at Yalta (Buhite), 186
DeConde, Alexander, 176
defoliation campaign, Vietnam, 385
Degler, Carl, 64, 65*n*6
Delzell, Charles F., 170
dependency theory, 42, 111–12, 438–40
Der Derian, James, 132
Desai, Maraji, 586
DeSantis, Hugh, 252
détente, 398–400
Détente and Confrontation (Garthoff), 395–6, 399–401, 407–8, 413–14
Diamond, Sigmund, 50*n*60
Diem, Ngo Dinh, 312, 351–2, 365–7, 371–2
  overthrow of, 365–6
Dienbienphu crisis, 310–11
Dietz, Terry, 383*n*44
diffusionist model, 438–40
DiLeo, David L., 379
Dingman, Roger, 270, 282, 290–2, 294, 309, 504, 520, 522
Diplomatic History, 94, 116, 590
discourse theory, 73
Dismantling of the Good Neighbor Policy, The (Wood), 443
Divine, Robert A., 96, 172, 553
  and Eisenhower revisionism, 303–4, 309–10, 315, 324
Dobbs, Charles M., 272, 513
Dobson, Alan, 546
Dominican Republic, 453–4
domino theory, 79
Donovan, Robert J., 212
Donovan and the CIA (Troy), 588
Double-talk (Smith), 399, 401
Dowd, Gregory E., 150
Dower, John W., 78, 163, 181, 220, 518
Dowty, Alan, 489
Draper, Theodore, 188–90, 194, 588
Drea, Edward J., 218*n*14, 566
Dubofsky, Melvyn, 64, 65*n*6
Duiker, William, 391
Dulles, Allen, 336, 541, 589
Dulles, Eleanor Lansing, 340–1
Dulles, John Foster, 188, 300, 305
  anticommunism, 324–5
  Lebanon intervention role, 489
  relationship with Eisenhower, 305–7
  Suez crisis role, 315–16, 481–2, 484, 486
  and Vietnam, 312, 370–2
  World War I treaty participation, 541
Dumbarton Oaks Conference, 257–8
Dunn, Peter M., 525
Dutch East Indies, 524
Dynamics of Defeat (Bergerud), 387

Eagle and the Lion, The (Bill), 406, 415–16, 551–2
Eagleton, Terry, 46–7
Eastern Europe
  Kennedy administration policy, 356
  Truman administration policy, 241
Eckes, Alfred E., Jr., 547–8
Economic Aspects of New Deal Diplomacy (Gardner), 545
Economic Consequences of the Peace, The (Keynes), 542
economic determinism (*see also* corporatism), 36, 104–10
economic diplomacy, 536–61
Economic Diplomacy of the Suez Crisis, The (Kunz), 550
Economics and World Power (Becker and Wells), 538
Eden, Anthony, 480–2, 484–5
Edmonds, Robin, 201
Edward Lansdale: The Unquiet American (Currey), 367
Egypt, 477–86
  Eisenhower's policy, 316–17
  postwar period, 477–86
  Truman's policy, 257
Egyptian-Israeli treaty, 414–15
Ehrlichman, John, 403
Eichengreen, Barry, 544
Eisenhower, Dwight D., 300–25
  anticommunism, 319–25
  and arms control, 317–19
  and atomic bomb decision, 217
  comment on Syngman Rhee, 286
  comparison to Lyndon B. Johnson, 310–11
  crisis management, 309–17
  Latin America policies, 321–2, 443–8
  leadership style, 303–8
  Lebanon intervention, 488–91

Middle East policy, 316–17, 479–87
nuclear diplomacy in Korea, 290–3, 309–10
popularity resurgence, 301–2
presidential style in Korean conflict, 294
relationship with Dulles, 305–7
revisionism, 300–25
Sputnik launch response, 303
Third World policies, 446–7
Vietnam policy influence, 310–13, 370
Eisenhower, Milton, 445
Eisenhower and Latin America (Rabe), 446–7
Eisenhower Doctrine, 316–17, 485, 487, 490
Eisenhower Library, 300–1
Eisenhower revisionism, 300–25, 445–7
El Salvador
Carter administration policies, 413
Reagan administration policies, 456
Ellsberg, Daniel, 360
Elusive Quest, The (Leffler), 543
"empire by invitation," 84
End of French Predominance in Europe, The (Schuker), 542
End of the Cold War, The (Hogan), 420–1
Enders, Thomas O., 456
Endgame (Talbott), 414
Endless War, The (Harrison), 386–7
Ends of Power, The (Haldeman), 403
Enola Gay exhibit, 206
Epstein, Edward Jay, 591
Erikson, Kai, 222
Essence of Decision, The (Allison), 346
Eubank, Keith, 185
European Recovery Program, 265
Evangelista, Matthew, 319–20
Evensen, Bruce, 474
"exceptionalism," 60–1, 111, 138–9
ExCom, 346–7
Exporting Democracy (Lowenthal), 460

Fairbank, John K., 113–15
Fairlie, Henry, 329, 331–3
Falcoff, Mark, 454, 457
Farrar, Peter, 284–5, 517
FDR & Stalin (Perlmutter), 203
Feaver, John H., 507–8
federal deficit, 559
Federal Reserve System, 539–40
Feinberg, Abe, 495
Feis, Herbert, 23–4, 170, 179
atomic bomb decision evaluation, 208
as orthodox historian, 23–4, 39
Feldman, Shai, 477
Ferguson, Thomas, 85
Ferrell, Robert H., 96, 218*n*14
Fighting for Peace (Weinberger), 417
Fighting to a Finish (Sigal), 196, 225–6
Findling, John E., 457
Finland, 262*n*40
Finletter, Thomas K., 207
Fire in the Lake (FitzGerald), 359
First Domino, The (Arnold), 370
Fischer, Fritz, 105
FitzGerald, Frances, 359–60
Fitzsimons, Louise, 329–31
Fleming, D. F., 173, 207
Foot, Rosemary, 310, 517, 529
Ford, Gerald, 408
Ford, Ronald, 597
Ford administration, 407–8
foreign aid, 550
Foreign Policy by Congress (Franck and Wiesband), 406, 408
Foreign Relations of the United States (*FRUS*), 175, 271, 567, 594
Førland, Tor Egil, 308–9, 324
Forrestal, James V., 552
Fortas, Abe, 495
Fossedal, Gregory, 549
Foucault, Michel, 26, 73, 131–2
Francis, Michael L., 430
Franck, Edward, 406, 408
Frank, Gary, 430
Frazier, Robert, 248*n*23
Freedman, Lawrence, 421, 557, 596
Freeman, Robert, 104
Freiberger, Steven, 483
Frieden, Jeffry, 557
From the Morganthau Diaries (Blum), 545
Fry, Michael, 565
Fulbright, J. William, 347, 382

Gaddis, John Lewis, 4–11, 18, 69–70, 83*n*62, 127–8, 130, 164, 180, 237–8, 253–4, 260, 565
as anti-revisionist, 44
and atomic bomb decision, 212
and China, 510
and containment, 143–5, 180, 548
corporatism view, 264
Melvyn Leffler's commentary on, 142–5

Gaddis, John Lewis (*cont.*)
  Michael H. Hunt's commentary on, 151–2
  Nixon administration view, 398
  postrevisionist views, 34–44, 238
  as realist, 97
  on Stalin, 244
Galloway, Joseph, 383–4
Gallucci, Robert L., 376*n*31
game theory, 59
Ganin, Zvi, 474
Gardner, Lloyd C., 33–4, 104, 173, 198, 311, 370–1, 427, 429–30, 545
Gardner, Richard, 547
Garthoff, Raymond, 320, 342–3, 395–6, 399–401, 407–8, 413–14, 420, 573, 594–6
Gasiorowski, Mark, 472
Gates, Gary Paul, 419–20
GATT legislation, 560–1
Gazit, Mordechai, 491–2
Geertz, Clifford, 46–7, 73
Gelb, Leslie, 360–1
gender studies, 72–6, 80, 89, 197
Gendzier, Irene, 485, 490
Geneva Accords, 371
Gentleman Spy (Grose), 541
Gerber, Larry, 256*n*32
germ warfare, Korea, 290
German progressives, 105–6
German Slump, The (James), 544
Giancana, Sam, 338*n*30
Gibson, James William, 369–70
Giglio, James N., 332–4
Gilbert, Martin, 180, 191–2
Glad, Betty, 409
Gleijeses, Piero, 150, 444, 454
Gluck, Carol, 518
gold standard, 545, 554–5
Gold Standard and the Great Depression, 1919–1939, The (Eichengreen), 544
Goldwater, Barry, 586
Goncharov, Sergei N., 78, 143, 275, 278, 529
Good Neighbor Policy, 429–32, 443–4
"Good Neighbors?" (Salisbury), 424
Goode, James F., 470–1, 494
Goodman, Allan E., 380*n*39, 381*n*39, 571*n*21
Goodpaster, Andrew J., 301
Gorbachev, Mikhail, 420
Gordievsky, Oleg, 587
Gordon, Joel, 478
Gormly, James L., 239, 247*n*21, 256*n*32
Gorodetsky, Gabriel, 192–3
Goulart, João, 453
Goulden, Joseph, 270
Gowa, Joanne, 555
Graebner, Norman A., 97
Grand Alliance, 199–201, 258
"grand design," 355
Great Britain, *see* Anglo-American relations
"great crescent" allusion, 146
Great Transition, The (Garthoff), 420
Greece, 248–50
Green, David, 435–6
Green, Stephen, 475, 495
Green Berets, 333
Greenstein, Fred I., 303–4, 310–11, 373–4
Gromyko's *Memoirs*, 277
Grose, Peter, 473, 541
groupthink, 336
Groves, Leslie R., 226
Grow, Michael, 430–1
Guatemala
  and Eisenhower, 306, 321, 443–4, 446, 451
  as model for Cuba, 451
Gulf Conflict, 1990–1991, The (Freidman and Karsh), 421, 557
gunboat diplomacy, 316
"guns-and-butter" thinking, 373
Gustainis, Justin, 333
Gyohten, Toyoo, 555–6

Hackworth, David, 363
Hahn, Peter L., 257, 316, 477, 484
Hahn, Werner G., 247
Haig, Al, 417
Haines, Gerald K., 434, 440–1
Halberstam, David, 329–30, 359–60
Haldeman, H. R., 403
Haldeman Diaries, The, 401, 403, 413
Haley, P. Edward, 381, 408–9
Halliday, Jon, 270*n*1, 290
Hallin, Daniel, 383
Hamel, William Christopher, 255
Hammer, Ellen J., 352*n*68, 366
Hammond, Thomas T., 209–10
Hammond, William, 383
Handel, Michael, 571
Hao Yufan, 279–80
Harbut, Fraser J., 243
Harriman, W. Averell, 552
Harrington, Fred Harvey, 105
Harrison, James, 386–7

Hartlyn, Jonathan, 460
Hartz, Louis, 44, 47–8, 61
Harvard group, 112–16
Harvey, David, 128–9
Hatcher, Patrick, 366
Hathaway, Robert M., 545–6
Hau Nghia province, 387
hearts-and-minds revisionists, 361, 363–4, 388, 394
Heidegger, Martin, 21–2, 33
Heinrichs, Waldo H., 510
Heiss, Mary Ann, 471
Henderson, Loy, 251–2, 475
Henrikson, Alan, 197
Henry Kissinger (Schulzinger), 455
Herken, Gregg, 212, 245*n*17, 259
Herman, Michael, 594–5
Herring, George C., 311, 368, 405, 408, 522–3
Herrington, Stuart, 389
Hersh, Burton, 589
Hersh, Seymour, 454–5, 476–7, 569, 582, 584
Hershberg, James G., 218–20, 343
Hess, Gary R., 311, 524, 533
Heuser, Beatrice, 298
Hexter, J. H., 260
Hibbert, Reginald, 564
hidden-hand presidency, 303, 307–8, 310
Higgins, Trumbull, 336–7, 451
Higham, John, 64, 68
Hilderbrand, Robert C., 257–8
Hilsman, Roger, 327, 329, 571*n*21
Hilton, Stanley E., 432
Hinds, Lynn Boyd, 77
Hinsley, F. H., 113
Hiroshima, 210–11, 219, 221
History of the Central Intelligence Agency (Karalekas), 588
Hixson, Walter L., 253
Ho Chi Minh, 391
Hochstein, Miles, 565
Hoff, Joan, 238, 407
Hoffmann, Stanley, 294–5
Hoff-Wilson, Joan, 543
Hogan, Michael J., 57–8, 71, 85, 412, 421
  corporatist theory, 545, 549
  Marshall Plan study, 263–5
  Melvyn Leffler's commentary on, 147–8
Holden, Robert H., 458
Holloway, David, 231–2
Holocaust policies, 181
Holsti, Ole, 406
homophobia, 69
Hong Kong, 532
Hoopes, Townsend, 305, 481, 552
Hopkins, Harry, 183
Hossbach memorandum, 573
House of Morgan, The (Chernow), 540
How Presidents Test Reality (Burke and Greenstein), 373–4
Howard, Michael, 566
Hull, Cordell, 194, 202, 433, 547
human rights policy, 411–12
Humboldt, Wilhelm, 113
Humphreys, R. A., 434–5
Hung, Nguyen Tien, 405
Hunt, Lynn, 63, 64*n*2, 72
Hunt, Michael H., 10–11, 15–18, 45–52, 164, 235*n*2, 236*n*2, 499, 529
  internationalism of, 260–1
  and Korean conflict, 294
  and postrevisionism, 45–52
Huntington, Samuel, 136–7
Hussein (King), 486–7
Hussein, Saddam, 567
Hyland, William G., 408

Ia Drang Valley campaign, 383–4
Iatrides, John O., 248–50
idealism, 138
Ideology and U.S. Foreign Policy (Hunt), 164
ideology and World War II, 197
Ides of August, The (Cate), 341
Ike's Spies (Ambrose), 588
Illusion of Peace, The (Szulc), 403–4
Illusions of Influence (Cullather), 534
Immerman, Richard H., 263, 264*n*44, 306–7, 310–11, 317, 423, 444
Imperial State and Resolution (Morley), 450
Imperialism at Bay (Louis), 177–8
Imperious Economy, The (Calleo), 554
In the Arena (Nixon), 402–3
In Whose Interest (Cohen), 556
Inchon landing, 282
India, 525–6
  economic relations, 551
  Korean conflict role, 287
  U.S. policy, 525–6, 532
Indochina, 522–4
Indonesia, 524–5
Informal Entente (Hogan), 545

Inside the National Security Council (Menges), 417–18
Inside the VC and the NVA (Lanning and Cragg), 390
intelligence, 1945–1990 (*see also* CIA), 562–98
  bugging practices, 582–6
  didactic literature, 571–2
  history, 578–9
  interpretation, 572–6, 593–6
  limitations of writings on, 569–71
  "no fault" school, 571–2
  and nuclear weapons policy, 596–7
  policy influences of, 576–7, 593–6
intentionality, 135–6
International History of the Vietnam War, An (Smith), 350, 365
International Monetary Fund, 547
internationalism, 110–21
  Cold War appraisal, 123–4, 154–5
  contributions, 117, 142
  crossover research need, 124–6
  Harvard group's influence, 112–16
  impact of, 120–1
  implications of, 118–19
  research agenda diversity, 111–12
Intervention (Kahin), 375
Into the Quagmire (Van de Mark), 374
Iran
  Eisenhower's policy, 322–3
  postwar relations, 469–73
Iran-contra affair, 417, 419–20
Iranian crisis of 1945–1946, 237
Iranian crisis of 1951–1953, 551
Iranian hostage crisis, 414–16, 556
Iraq, 488–9, 491, 497
Ireland, Timothy P., 247*n*20
Iriye, Akira, 77–8, 163, 181, 223, 261, 501
Irony of Vietnam, The (Gelb and Betts), 360–1
Isaacs, Arnold R., 380
Isaacson, Walter, 252*n*28, 404, 407
isolationism, 74–5, 78
Israel, 473–7, 494–7
Issue of War, The (Thorne), 181–2
It Seemed Like Nothing Happened (Carrol), 409
Italy, 261–2, 268

Jackson, Henry, 399–401
Jacob, Margaret, 63, 64*n*2, 72
James, Harold, 544
James, Robert Rhodes, 481
Janis, Irving L., 336
Jansen, Danny D., 590
Japan, Korean conflict role, 287–8
Japanese-American relations
  economic factors, 519–22, 558–9
  malleability of, 78
  occupation period, 518–22
Jeffords, Susan, 74
Jeffreys-Jones, Rhodri, 409, 587, 590
Jentleson, Bruce, 557
Jervis, Robert, 296–8, 515, 571, 594
Jewish state issue, 473–7
J.F.K. (Parmet), 332
JFK and Vietnam (Newman), 350–1, 373*n*25
Jiang Jieshi (Chiang Kai-shek), 179, 314–15, 507–9
Jimmy Carter (Glad), 409
John Foster Dulles (Pruessen), 541
Johnson, Loch, 588
Johnson, Lyndon B.
  economic policy, 553–4
  Eisenhower comparison, 310–11, 373–4
  and Latin America, 453–4
  Middle East policy, 493–6
  secret arrangement with Diem, 351
  Vietnam decisions, 367, 373–7
Johnson, Nixon, and the Doves (Small), 382
Johnson Plan, 491–2
Johnson Years, The (Divine), 553
Jones, Howard, 242, 248–50
Jordan, 486–7
journalists, foreign affairs writings, 396–8
Joy, C. Turner, 289
J. P. Morgan and Co., 539–40, 545
Juggler, The (Kimball), 190

Kahin, George, 375
Kaiser, Henry J., 441
Kaldor, Mary, 25, 53
Kaplan, Lawrence S., 265, 296
Karalekas, Anna, 588
Karnow, Stanley, 533
Karsh, Efraim, 421, 557
Kattenburg, Paul, 368
Katyn Forest massacre, 199
Katz, Barry M., 590
Kaufman, Burton I., 273–4, 282–3, 288, 291, 294, 308, 445–6, 513, 516–17, 550, 553–4
Keefer, Edward C., 286, 291, 294, 309, 517

Kehr, Eckart, 106
Kelly, J. B., 493
Kenen, I. L., 476
Kennan, George F., 56–7, 86, 137
  and Cold War origins, 251–4
  and Latin America, 442
  realist views, 96
Kennedy, John F., 326–57
  Bay of Pigs decision, 335–7
  Berlin crisis management, 338–42
  Castro fixation, 337–8, 345, 348–9, 451–2
  as Cold Warrior, 330–1
  as crisis manager, 342, 348
  and Cuban missile crisis, 342–9
  early assessments of, 327–9
  economic policy, 355–6, 552–3
  and Eisenhower's legacy, 335–7
  Khrushchev relationship, 338–40
  Middle East policies, 353–4, 491–3
  and nuclear weapons, 348–9
  public opinion manipulation, 332–5
  public perceptions of, 326
  revisionism, 329–32
  and Third World countries, 352–4
  Vietnam legacy, 349–52
Kennedy, Paul, 160, 421–2, 536–8, 558–9
Kennedy, Robert, 347
Kennedy Crises, The (Kern, Levering, and Levering), 334
"Kennedy Doctrine," 330–1
Kennedy Doctrine, The (Fitzsimons), 329
Kennedy Promise, The (Fairlie), 329, 331
Kennedy's Quest for Victory (Paterson), 332, 451, 553
Kent, Sherman, 571, 575
Kern, Montague, 334
Kerr, Malcolm, 492
Keynes, John Maynard, 542
KGB, 570
Khomeni (Ayatollah), 555
Khong, Yuen Foong, 374–5
Khrushchev, Nikita
  bugging of, 585
  Kennedy relationship, 338–49
  memoirs, 277
Kim Gye-Dong, 277
Kim Il Sung, 276–8, 513
Kimball, Warren F., 10, 12, 188, 190, 205
Kindleberger, Charles P., 544, 549
Kinnard, Douglas, 378
Kinzer, Stephen, 444
Kiraly, Bela, 298
Kirkpatrick, Jeane, 188, 411
Kissinger, Henry, 568
  and Chile, 454–5
  détente role, 399–400
  evaluation of, 404, 407–8
  memoirs of, 401–2
  standing with the press, 402
  and Vietnam, 380–1
Kissinger: A Biography (Isaacson), 404, 407
Kofas, Jon V., 248–9
Kolko, Gabriel, 31–3, 35–6, 41, 105, 483, 524
  and atomic bomb decision, 209
  bureaucratic model opinion, 428
  post–World War II diplomacy criticism, 173
  Vietnam analysis, 391
Komer, Robert W., 389, 507
Korean conflict, 270–99
  Asian allies' role, 287–8
  biological weapon accusation, 290
  Britain's role, 283–5
  China's role, 278–81, 510–11, 514
  civil aspects, 274, 513
  Cold War significance of, 296–7
  Eisenhower's handling of, 309–10
  impact on Koreans, 299
  international background, 275
  long-term impact on U.S. diplomacy, 514–15
  nuclear weapons threat, 290–3, 309–10
  POW issues, 289–92
  Soviet role, 276–7
  stabilizing influence of, 298–9
  and Syngman Rhee, 286–7
  38th parallel crossing decision, 281–2, 285
  Truman administration policies, 281–2, 512–14
  United Nations decisions, 277–8
  World War II role, 182
Korean-U.S. relations, 512–18
Kotch, John, 286, 517
Krepinevich, Andrew, 363–4
Krim, Arthur, 495
Kristol, Irving, 188
Kubricht, A. Paul, 356
Kuklick, Bruce, 247*n*21
Kuniholm, Bruce R., 242, 248–50, 467, 470
Kunz, Diane B., 484, 545, 550, 554

Kupchan, Charles, 496
Kurzman, Dan, 216
Kux, Dennis, 533
Kyle, Keith, 480, 484
Kyushu invasion plan, 223–4

LaFeber, Walter, 104, 263, 297, 412, 427, 457–8
Lake, Anthony, 403, 413
Lamont, Edward M., 540*n*12
Land-to-the-Tiller program, 390
Landslide (Mayer and McManus), 419–20
Lane, Patricia, 368*n*17
Langer, William L., 113
language studies, 73, 76–7, 80
Lanning, Michael, 390
Lanouette, William, 230
Lansdale, Edward, 367, 372
Lansing, John, 541
Laos and Kennedy, 338
Laqueur, Walter, 579
Larson, Deborah Welch, 247, 248*n*22, 294, 306–7
Last Years of the Monroe Doctrine, 1945–1993, The (Smith), 442–3
Latin America, 424–61
  bureaucratic perspective, 427–9, 433
  Carter administration policies, 455
  and Cuban revolution, 447–52
  dependency model, 438–40
  diffusionist model, 438–40
  economic policies, 554
  Eisenhower's policies, 321–2, 443–8
  end of Cold War effect, 460
  and Good Neighbor policy, 429–32
  Johnson administration policies, 453–4
  Kennedy administration policies, 353, 451–2
  liberal perspective, 426–7, 429–31
  radical perspective, 427, 429–31, 435–6
  Reagan administration policies, 456–8
  Truman years, 435–41
  in World War II period, 432–4
Latin America and the Second World War, 1938–1945 (Humphreys), 434
Lauren, Paul Gordon, 499
Lawson, Fred, 474
Leacock, Ruth, 453
Leahy, William D., 217
Leary, William M., 591
Lebanon, 488–91
Lebow, Richard Ned, 347–8
Lees, Lorraine M., 242
Lefebvre, Jeffrey, 490
Leffingwell, Russell, 28
Leffler, Melvyn P., 10–15, 18, 52–9, 130–1, 198, 297, 468, 543
  and atomic bomb decision, 225
  Michael Hunt's commentary on, 153–4
  and national security concept, 265–7
  U.S. intelligence assessment, 595–6
Legend (Epstein), 591
"legitimacist" revisionists, 361, 364–5, 394
Lensen, George A., 170
Leonard, Thomas E., 457
Lesch, David, 487
Leuchtenburg, William, 64
Levering, Patricia W., 334
Levering, Ralph B., 197, 334
Levin, N. Gordon, 105
Levine, Steven I., 506–7
Levy, David, 381–2
Lewis, John W., 78, 143, 529
Lewy, Gunther, 360–1
Liberal Conspiracy, The (Coleman), 591
Life of an Economist, The (Kindleberger), 544
limited nuclear war concept, 319
limited war concept, 309
Limits of Air Power, The (Clodfelter), 384
Limits of Hegemony, The (Francis), 430
Limits to Friendship (Pastor and Castañeda), 459
Linebacker campaign, 384
linguistic approach, 73, 76–7, 80
Link, Arthur S., 97
Linz, Susan J., 245*n*17
Lippmann, Walter, 421, 548
Lissaker, Karin, 556
Little, Douglas, 354
Litwak, Robert, 399*n*5
Lockhart, Greg, 392
Lomperis, Timothy J., 367–8, 392
Long, David, 493–4
Long An province, 387
"lost chance" thesis, 509–12, 529
Lost Victory (Colby), 389*n*57
Louis, Wm. Roger, 177–8, 195, 196*n*65, 315–16, 468, 471, 474, 551
Lowe, Peter, 275
Lowenthal, Abraham F., 425–8, 460
Lucas, Scott, 484
Lukas, Richard C., 241

Lumumba, Patrice, 323
Lundestad, Geir, 198, 235, 242, 261–2, 265
Lyndon Johnson's Dual War (Turner), 376
Lyndon Johnson's War (Berman), 376–7
Lytle, Mark Hamilton, 237, 470

MacArthur, Douglas A., 282, 514
McCagg, William O., Jr., 245
McCarthy, Joseph R., 169
McCloy, John J., 28, 224*n*24, 552
McCormick, Thomas J., 11, 58–9, 104, 146, 164, 268, 398, 431, 441, 461, 559–60
McCoy, Alfred, 591
McCullough, David, 228, 475
MacDonald, Callum A., 275, 285, 288, 291–3
McDougall, Walter A., 232–3
McEnaney, Laura, 74–5
McFarland, Stephen L., 237, 470
McGann, Frank D., 432
McGerr, Michael, 61
McGlothlen, Ronald, 276
MacIntyre, Alasdaire, 25, 27
MacKenzie, Compton, 578
McLean, David, 510–12
Maclean, Donald, 256
McMahon, Robert J., 261, 320–1, 423, 447, 524–5
McManus, Doyle, 419–20
Macmillan, Harold, 484–5
McMullen, Christopher, 493
McNamara, Robert, 345, 367, 378
  and Vietnam, 378
McNeil, William C., 543–4
McNeill, William H., 170
Maddox, Robert James, 210
Mahoney, Richard, 354
Maier, Charles S., 115–16, 140
Making of the Atomic Bomb, The (Rhodes), 215–16
Mangold, Tom, 591
Manhattan Project, 210, 213, 216, 226, 229
Manuel, Frank, 473
Mao Tse-tung
  Dean Acheson's policy toward, 509, 512
  and domino theory, 79
  Korean conflict decisions, 278–81
Marchetti, Victor, 582
Mark, Edward, 197–8
Marks, Frederick W., III, 186, 307, 311, 321*n*74, 444
Marks, John D., 582
Marshall, George C., 194, 238–9, 473, 506–8
Marshall, Jonathan, 591
Marshall Plan, 57–8, 254, 263–5
  British role, 243
  and corporatist model, 263–4
  economics, 548–9
Marshall Plan, The (Hogan), 549
Marshall Plan, The (Mee), 549
Marshall Plan Days (Kindleberger), 549
Martel, Leon, 195, 196*n*65
Martin, David, 591
Marty, John D., 447
Marxist theory, 45–8
Marzani, Carl, 207
Mastny, Vojtech, 191, 243–4
Mathams, R. H., 574
Matray, James I., 272, 276, 514–16
Max, Stanley M., 241
May, Elaine Tyler, 69
May, Ernest R., 97, 98*n*7, 113, 115
May, Gary, 507
Mayr, Jane, 419–20
Meaning of Yalta, The (Snell, Pogue, and Delzell), 170
media influences
  overseas impact, 112
  and Vietnam War, 383
media manipulation and Kennedy, 332–5
Mee, Charles L., Jr., 549
Melanson, Richard A., 410*n*34
memory, 22–3, 33
Menges, Constantine, 417–18
Merrill, Dennis, 525, 533, 551
Merrill, John, 274, 277
Mescall, Patrick, 597
Messer, Robert L., 212, 214–15, 220, 224, 254–5
Meyer, Eugene, 34
Meyer, Gail, 479
Middle East, 463–500
  Carter's diplomacy, 414–16
  economic policies, 551
  and Egypt, 477–86
  Eisenhower's policy, 316–17, 476, 479–86, 489–91
  Johnson administration policy, 493–6
  Kennedy administration policy, 353–4, 491–3

Middle East (*cont.*)
Nixon administration policy, 496–7
oil policy, 28–9, 464–73
Palestine issue, 473–7
postwar Iranian relations, 469–73
"three pillars" approach, 496
Truman's diplomacy, 465–9, 473–8
Middle East Defense Organization, 469
Middlebrook, Kevin J., 459
Mikoyan, Sergo, 344
Miles, Rufus E., Jr., 217–18
Military and the Media, The (Hammond), 383
military-industrial complex, 318
military intelligence (*see also* intelligence, 1945–1990), 597
Miller, Aaron David, 250, 251*n*26, 466, 551
Miller, James Edward, 261–2
Miller, Nathan, 579
Miller, Nicola, 457
Milward, Alan S., 265, 549
Miner, Steven Merritt, 192–3
Miroff, Bruce, 332
Miscamble, Wilson S., 251–2
"missile gaps," 318, 349, 594
"moderate revisionists," 31
Moffett, George, III, 412
Moggridge, D. E., 542
Mommsen, Wolfgang J., 50, 50*n*61
Monroe Doctrine, 442–3
Montague, Ludwell Lee, 590
Moore, Harold, 383–4
Moore, Ray A., 518
moral considerations
atomic bomb decision, 207, 220–2
atomic scientists, 231
and U.S. position on Stalin, 81–2
Morality, Reason, and Power (Smith), 410–11
Morgan, J. P., 539–40
Morley, Morris H., 450, 458
Mortal Rivals (Hyland), 408
Mossadegh, Mohammed, 322, 470–2, 551–2
Mowrer, A. Glenn, 412
Mrozek, Donald J., 384–5
Mueller, John, 298
multiarchival method, 113–14, 126, 261–2
Muravchik, Joshua, 411
Mutual Security Program, 308
Myth of America's Decline, The (Nau), 560
Nadeau, Remi, 200
NAFTA legislation, 560–1
Nagasaki, 210–11, 221
Nasser, Gamal Abdel, 316, 354, 477–86, 488, 491–3, 495
Nation in Arms (Lockhart), 392
National Intelligence Estimates, 567, 594
National Security Agency, 567, 569, 582–5
National Security Archive, 568, 594
national security concept, 234–69
dominant theme, 234–5
Stalin's emphasis, 245–6
and trade policies, 239
National Security Council, 306
national security information, 567
NATO, 243
European nations' motive, 247
Korean conflict effects on, 296–7
as threat to Russia, 258
Nau, Henry, 560
Necessary War, The (Stueck), 298
Neff, Donald, 479–80, 494–5
Nelson, Anna Kasten, 306
neo-Marxist theory, 109
nerve gas, Korean conflict, 290
New Frontiersmen, 353
"New Left," 37, 173–4, 236–7
"New Look" policy, 317
New York Review of Books 1986 issue, 188
Newhouse, John, 400
Newman, John M., 351, 373*n*25
Newsom, David B., 588
Nicaragua
Carter administration policies, 412–13
Reagan administration policies, 456–8
Nietzsche, Friedrich, 21–3, 25–7, 62, 129–32, 136, 146
Ninkovich, Frank A., 182
Nisbet, Robert, 186, 188–9, 194
Nishi, Toshio, 521
Nitze, Paul, 414
Nixon, Richard M., 568
détente role, 398–401
memoirs of, 402–3
opinion of CIA, 594
South American visit, 446
and Vietnam, 380–1
Nixon administration, 403–7
and Chile, 454–5
détente policy, 398–400
economic policy, 554–5
journalistic accounts, 403–6

memoir accounts, 401–3
Middle East policy, 496–7
Nixon Papers, 400
Nixon Reconsidered (Hoff), 407
"non-rational actor" model, 196–7
North, Oliver, 417
NSC-48, 281
NSC-68, 57, 60
NSC-152/2, 308
NSC-162/2, 317
nuclear arms race, 318
nuclear family, 74–5
nuclear weapons (*see also* atomic bomb decision)
Eisenhower's policies, 317–19
intelligence information, 580–1, 596–7
Kennedy's policies, 342, 348–9
and Korean conflict diplomacy, 290–3, 309–10
and Taiwan Straits crisis, 314–15
nuclear weapons testing, 317–19, 348–9
Nuri Said, 488
Nye, Joseph, Jr., 422, 560

Oberdorfer, Don, 418
objectivity standard, 22–3
Odom, William, 582
O'Donnell, Kenneth, 349–50
Office of Strategic Services, 589–90
Ogorodnik, Aleksandr, 586
Oil and the American Century (Painter), 551
oil policy, 28–9, 464–73
economics, 551, 555–6
Truman administration, 250–1, 465–8
oil shocks, 555–6
Oil, War, and American Security (Stoff), 551
Old Boys, The (Hersh), 589
On Diplomacy (Der Derian), 132
On Strategy (Summers), 361
O'Neill, Robert, 272, 288
Open Door thesis, 173, 427
"Open Skies" proposal, 318–20
Operation Ajax, 471–2
Operation Mongoose, 338, 343
Operation Musketeer, 484
Operation Omega, 481
Operation Ranch Hand, 385
Operation Ranch Hand (Buckingham), 385
Operation Rolling Thunder, 364, 384
Oren, Michael, 490
Organization of American States, 436–7
Origins of the Vietnam War, The (Short), 371
orthodox school, 30–4
and Asia, 503
meaning of, 23–5, 236–7
and postrevisionist hermeneutics, 38–9
Other Arab-Israeli Conflict, The (Spiegel), 406
O'Toole, G. J. A., 579–80
Ovendale, Ritchie, 523, 525

Pach, Chester J., Jr., 268, 314, 324, 438
Pacific Alliance, The (Borden), 558
Packenham, Robert A., 440
Painter, David S., 250–1, 466–7, 551
Pakistan, 525–6, 532
Palace File, The (Hung and Schechter), 405
Palestine, Truman's policies, 473–7
Palestine Liberation Organization, 487
Palestinian refugees, 474, 491
Palmer, Bruce, Jr., 362, 453
Palmer, David Richard, 360–1
Palmer, Michael, 490, 496–7
Panama Canal treaty, 412
Panikkar, K. M., 280
Pape, Robert A., 224*n*24
Paraguay, 430
Parker, Phyllis R., 453
Parmet, Herbert S., 332, 407, 491
Partners in Conflict (Lowenthal), 460
Pastor, Robert A., 412, 459
Paterson, Thomas G., 71, 105, 197, 205, 236*n*5, 321, 322*n*75, 332, 337, 343, 345, 347–9, 397, 448, 451–2, 486, 493, 507, 552–3
Patterson, David S., 236*n*3
Peace Corps, 354–5
Pearl Harbor, 572
Pelz, Stephen E., 276, 352*n*68
Pemberton, Gregory, 311
Penkovsky, Oleg, 587
Pentagon Papers, 360
Perfect Failure, The (Higgins), 451
Perfect War, The (Gibson), 370
Perilous Missions (Leary), 591
Perkins, Bradford, 114
Perkins, Dexter, 113
Perlmutter, Amos, 203*n*78
Perón, Juan Domingo, 443
Persian Gulf War, 421, 557
Persico, Joseph, 588
Petersen, Tore Tingvold, 483
Peterson, Michael E., 388

Pfau, Richard, 470
Philippines, 524–5, 532
Phoenix program, 389
Pieck, Wilhelm, 81
Pieragostini, Karl, 493
Pike, Douglas, 391–2
Pike, Frederick B., 442
Pinochet, Augustín, 454
Pipes, Richard, 594
Pisani, Sallie, 590
Planning a Tragedy (Berman), 373
Podhoretz, Norman, 365
Pogue, Forrest C., 170, 238
Poland and Truman, 241
Politics in Brazil, 1930–1964 (Skidmore), 441
Politics of War, The (Kolko), 36
Pollack, Jonathan, 279–80
Pollard, Jonathon, 586
Pollard, Robert A., 239, 547
Porter, Gareth, 380*n*39
Portrait of the Enemy (Chanoff and Van Toai), 390
Portuguese Angola, 354
Post, Ken, 392–3
postmodernism, 128–9, 131
postrevisionism, 20–62, 145–8, 152–3, 238, 295–6
Potsdam Conference, 210, 212, 214
power
  Foucoult's view, 131–2
  international behavior role, 266–7
Power and Culture (Iriye), 181
Powers, Thomas, 581
Prados, John, 311, 596
Pragmatic Illusions (Miroff), 332
Preponderance of Power, A (Leffler), 52–9, 154, 549, 595–6
Presidency of John F. Kennedy, The (Giglio), 332
Presidential Materials Project, 407
Price, Raymond, 403
Price of Power, The (Hersh), 454–5
Prize, The (Yergin), 555
"progressivism," 49, 141
  Cold War interpretation, 123–4, 152–3
  corporatism relationship, 107–8
  crossover research need, 124–6
  and internationalism, 116–17
  revival of, 104–5
  roots of, 104
  Third World views, 108
Project Alpha, 481
Promise and Power (Shapley), 378
Pruessen, Ronald, 522
public opinion
  influence on Roosevelt, 197–8
  Kennedy's manipulation of, 332–5
Puzzle Palace, The (Bamford), 582

Qiang Zhai, 285
Quandt, William, 406–7, 415, 490, 495
Quemoy-Matsu crisis, 313–14
quiet diplomacy, 342, 344
Quwatly, Shukri, 317

Rabe, Stephen G., 322, 353, 438, 446–7, 451–2, 553
Race, Jeffrey, 387
racism, 88–9
Radford, William, 314
"radical" revisionists, 31
Randall, Stephen J., 250, 251*n*26
Ranelagh, John, 581, 587
Rankean method, 22
Rankin, Karl L., 314
Reagan administration, 416–21
  Central America policies, 456–8
  and Cold War interpretations, 187
  foreign policy, 416–21
realism, 96–102
  archival research emphasis, 100–2
  Cold War interpretation, 123–4, 170
  crossover research need, 124–6
  language of, 97–8
  limitations, 99–102
  meaning of, 97–9, 141
  and Roosevelt, 193
realpolitik doctrine, 59
Reconstruction of Western Europe, 1945–51, The (Milward), 549
"reductionism," 41
Rees, David, 271
Reeves, Thomas, 327, 348
Reichard, Gary W., 283, 325
reparations burden, Germany, 541–2, 544
revisionism *(see also* Eisenhower revisionism), 30–44, 295
  and Asia, 504
  and atomic bomb decision, 209
  and Eisenhower, 294
  Korean War view, 271
  and Latin America, 429
  meaning of, 23–4, 236–7
  Pentagon Papers effect, 360
Reynolds, David, 181, 546

Rhee, Syngman, 277, 288–9
rhetoric, 77
Rhodes, Richard, 215–16, 231
Rich Neighbor Policy, The (Cobbs), 441
Richelson, Jeffrey T., 580–1
Rico, Carlos, 459
Ricoeur, Paul, 77
"Riga" axiom, 193–4
Rio Pact, 436–7
Rise and Fall of the Great Powers, The (Kennedy), 160, 421–2, 536–8, 559
Robinson, Ronald, 111
Rockefeller, Nelson A., 441
Rodney King question, 7
"roll-back" coalition, 281
Rolling Thunder, 364, 384
Rolling Thunder (Thompson), 384
Roosevelt, Franklin D.
  atomic bomb policy, 211
  atomic diplomacy of, 179
  correspondence with Stalin, 175*n*21
  criticism of policies, 168–70
  economic policy, 545–6
  Good Neighbor policy, 429–31
  influence of bureaucracy on, 195–6
  Jewish state issue, 473
  neoconservative criticisms of, 185–90, 193
  pragmatism toward Soviet relations, 191
  as realist, 193, 201
  reinterpretation of policies, 171–3, 180, 184–94
  secrecy and deviousness of, 194
  and Stalin, 194, 200–1
Roosevelt and Stalin (Nisbet), 186
Roosevelt–Churchill correspondence, 188–9
Rosati, Jerel, 411
Rose, Lisle A., 210, 216
Rosenau, James, 406
Rosenberg, David Alan, 259, 319
Rosenberg, Emily S., 42, 72, 89, 262–3
Rostow, Walt W., 335, 553
Rotblat, Joseph, 231
Rotter, Andrew J., 297, 510, 523–5
Roxborough, Ian, 437
Rubenberg, Cheryl, 475, 495
Rubin, Barry, 470, 478–9, 494
Ruddy, T. Michael, 252
Rusk, Dean, 327, 328*n*3, 345, 350, 377
Russell, Richard, 282, 347
Russian World War II archives, 199–200, 202–3
Russians and Reagan, The (Talbott), 419
Rust, William J., 350–2, 372*n*25
Rystad, Göran, 256

Safire, William, 403
Safran, Nadav, 476, 493–4
Said, Edward, 498
Saikal, Amin, 470
Sainsbury, Keith, 185
Salinger, Pierre, 350
Salisbury, Richard V., 424
SALT I, 399–400
SALT II, 414
Sandinistas, 413, 457–8
Sandman, Joshua H., 336–7
satellite reconnaissance, 580–2
Saudi Arabia, 493–4, 497
Scandinavian relations, 262
Schaffer, Ronald, 221
Schaller, Michael, 179, 282, 518, 520, 523, 558
Schechter, Jerrold, 405
Schick, Jack M., 340
Schieffer, Bob, 419–20
Schlesinger, Arthur M., Jr.
  Alliance for Progress opinion, 353*n*69
  assessment of Kennedy, 327–8, 331
  Bay of Pigs opinion, 336
  and Cuban missile crisis, 345
  opinion of Eisenhower, 305
  as orthodox historian, 23–4, 38–9
  and Vietnam, 350
Schlesinger, Stephen, 444
Schlesinger-Cumings debate, 9, 9*n*10
Schlight, John, 384–5
Schoenbam, Thomas, 377
Schoenbaum, David, 477, 496
Schonberger, Howard, 512, 518–19, 522, 526
Schoultz, Lars, 411–12, 460
Schuker, Stephen A., 542–4, 557
Schulzinger, Robert D., 407, 455
Schwartz, Thomas Alan, 243, 552
Scott, Peter Dale, 591
Seabury, Paul, 189
Seale, Patrick, 487
search-and-destroy strategy, 363
Search for Security (Miller), 551
Search for Solvency, A (Eckes), 547–8
Secrecy and Democracy (Turner), 588
Sentimental Imperialists, 526
sexism, 69, 88–9
Shafer, D. Michael, 372
Shalom, Stephen R., 524

Shapley, Deborah, 378
Sharp, U. S. Grant, 360–1
Shawcross, William, 405
Sheehan, Neil, 379–80
Sherry, Michael S., 163, 182, 221–2
Sherwin, Martin J., 179, 210–12
Shlaim, Avi, 246–7, 259
Short, Anthony, 371
Shuckburgh, Evelyn, 481
Shultz, George, 417
Sick, Gary, 415, 556
Sideshow (Shawcross), 405
Sigal, Leon V., 196, 225–6
Silence Was a Weapon (Herrington), 389
Silverman, Dan P., 543
Sino-American relations, *see* China
Six Day War, 494–5
Skates, John Ray, 218
Skidelsky, Robert, 542
Skidmore, Thomas E., 441, 453
Skocpol, Theda, 64, 65*n*6
Slany, William, 567
Slusser, Robert, 339, 342
Small, Melvin, 197, 382, 406
Smith, Bradley F., 589–90
Smith, E. Timothy, 268
Smith, Gaddis, 97, 171, 184–5, 410–12, 419, 442–3, 455
Smith, Geoffrey S., 69, 150
Smith, Gerard, 399, 401
Smith, Joseph B., 585, 592
Smith, R. B., 350, 365–7, 392
Smith, Robert Freeman, 438
Snell, John L., 170–2
Snepp, Frank, 592
Snetsinger, John, 473
Socialism and Nationalism in Vietnam (Post), 392–3
Society for Historians of American Foreign Relations, 94
Soldiers, Statesmen, and Cold War Crises (Betts), 565
Solvency, the Price of Survival (Chace), 557–8
Somoza Falling (Lake), 413
Sorensen, Theodore, 327–9, 336, 345, 347
South America, *see* Latin America
South Asia, 525–6
Southeast Asia, 522–4
Soviet archives, 199–200, 202–3, 260
Soviet bomb project, 231–2
Soviet Brigade in Cuba, The (Newsom), 588
Specter of Neutralism, The (Brands), 550–1
Spector, Ronald, 372, 385–6
Spiegel, Steven L., 406, 476, 491–2, 496
Sputnik launch, 303
Stages of Economic Growth, The (Rostow), 553
Stalin, Churchill, and Roosevelt Divide Europe (Nadeau), 200
Stalin, Josef, 81–3, 142–3, 151–2, 184
  barbarity of, 81–3, 142–3, 199–200
  correspondence with Churchill and Roosevelt, 175*n*21
  expansionist tendencies, 243–5
  Korean War decisions, 277–8, 293
  national security emphasis, 245–6
  personality of, 244–5
  recent trends in interpretation, 202–3
  Soviet archives revelations, 199–200, 202–3
  U.S. moral stance toward, 81–3
Stalin and the Bomb (Halloway), 231–2
Stanton, Shelby, 362
Stavrakis, Peter J., 244, 248–50
Stearns, Peter, 64
Steel, Ronald, 346
Steiner, Barry, 596
Steinitz, Mark S., 241
Stephanson, Anders, 74, 253
Sterling Siver-Dollar Diplomacy in Current Perspective (Gardner), 547
Stevens, Richard L., 385
Stimson, Henry L., 195, 212–13, 219, 222, 228–9
Stivers, William, 485, 496
Stoff, Michael B., 250, 251*n*26, 551
Stoler, Mark A., 239
Stookey, Robert, 492
Strategic Intelligence for American World Policy (Kent), 571
Strategies of Containment (Gaddis), 164, 180, 548–9
Strategy for Defeat (Sharp), 360–1
Struggle for Hegemony in South America (Frank), 430
Stueck, William W., 272, 275, 281, 288, 296, 298–9, 507–8, 510, 513–14, 516–17
Suez Canal crisis, 315–17, 478–86, 550
Suicide of an Elite, The (Hatcher), 366
Sullivan, David, 595
Sulzberger, C. L., 404

Summers, Harry, 361
Summit at Teheran (Eubank), 185
Summons of the Trumpet (Palmer), 360–1
Sumner, B. H., 562
Susman, Warren, 61
Syrian relations, 487–8
Szilard, Leo, 230
Szulc, Tad, 403–4

Taiwan, 510, 532
Taiwan Strait confrontation, 313–15, 529
Talbott, Strobe, 414, 418–19, 421
Tananbaum, Duane A., 307
Tar Baby Option, The (Lake), 403
Taubman, William, 191, 243–4
Taylor, Maxwell, 378–9
Taylor-Rostow report, 378
"Technowar" logic, 370
Tehran summit conference, 185–6
Tet Offensive, 367, 377, 597–8
Third World
  debt crisis, 556–7
  Eisenhower's policies, 320–3, 446
  Kennedy's policies, 352–4
  progressive movement view toward, 108
Thomas, Evan, 252*n*28
Thompson, James Clay, 384
Thorne, Christopher, 84*n*63, 180–2, 260
"Three pillars" approach, 496–7
Ties That Bind, The (Richelson and Ball), 582
Tilly, Louise, 64
Time to Heal, A (Ford), 408
Tito, Josip Broz, 242
Tivan, Edward, 475–6, 495
Tonnesson, Stein, 368*n*17
totalitarianism theory, 59
Tower Commission, 419
Trachtenberg, Marc, 255
Trade and Aid (Kaufman), 550
trade policies
  Kennedy administration, 355–6
  and national security, 239
traditionalist school, *see* orthodox school
Tragedy of American Diplomacy (Williams), 45–6, 104
Trail, The (Stevens), 385
Trapped by Success (Anderson), 371–2
Trask, Roger R., 436–7
Trinity shot, 228–9
Tripartite Declaration, 469
Triumph without Victory, 557
Troy, Thomas, 588
Trullinger, James, 387–8
Truman, Harry S.
  ambivalence on atomic bomb use, 219–20
  atomic bomb decision, 179, 208–29; bureaucratic influences, 225–6; diary notes, 214–15
  and James F. Byrnes, 254–5
  Korean policy, 276
  post–World War II decisions, 173–4
  presidential style in Korean conflict, 294
Truman administration
  Cold War origins role, 254–9, 266–7
  globalism, 266–7
  Jewish state policies, 473–7
  Korean conflict decisions, 281–2, 289–90, 512–14
  Latin American policies, 435–41
  Middle East policy, 465–9, 473–8
  and nuclear weapons use, Russia, 259
  oil policy, 250–1
  strategic priorities, 268
Truman Doctrine, 247–50, 254
Tsou, Tang, 171
Tuchman, Barbara, 179
Tucker, Nancy B., 296, 315, 509–11, 532
Tucker, Robert C., 244–5, 267
Turkey, 248, 487–8
Turmoil and Triumph (Shultz), 417
Turn, The (Oberdorfer), 418
Turner, Kathleen J., 376
Turner, Stansfield, 588, 593–4
Turning Point, The (Sainsbury), 185
"two Chinas policy," 315
Tyrrel, Ian, 61

U-2 incident, 318, 320, 581
Ultra, 176, 566
Uncertain Crusade, The (Muravchik), 411
Unholy Grail (Cable), 364
United Arab Republic, 488
United Fruit Company, 444
United Nations, 345
United States and Latin America, The (Pike), 442
United States and the Origins of the Cold War, The (Gaddis), 34–6
Utley, Jonathan, 195, 196*n*65
Utopia Unarmed (Castañeda), 460

Van de Mark, Brian, 374
Van Toai, Joan, 390
Vann, John Paul, 379–80
Varas, Augusto, 460
Veil (Woodward), 569, 588
Versailles treaty, 541
Vietnam Trauma in American Foreign Policy, The (Kattenburg), 368
Vietnam War, 358–94
  air power in, 384–5
  and containment strategy, 522–4
  cultural interpretations, 369–70
  determination of Communists, 390–3
  domestic influences, 381–3
  early Cold War origins of, 368*n*17, 370–1
  and Eisenhower's policy, 310–13, 370–2
  Johnson's policy, 373–7
  Kennedy's legacy, 349–51
  media role, 383
  neo-orthodox criticism, 368–9
  Nixon administration's policy, 380–1
  propaganda campaign in, 388–9
  revisionist views, 360–8, 393
  and Vietnamization, 386–9
Vietnamization, 372, 386–9
Village at War (Trullinger), 387–8
Volcker, Paul, 555–6
Volkman, Ernest, 579–80
von Ranke, Leopold, 113

Walker, David, 586–7
Walker, J. Samuel, 259–60
Walker, Martin, 91–2
Walker, William O., III, 554
Wall, Irwin M., 320–1
Wallerstein, Immanuel, 11–12, 59, 516
Walton, Richard J., 329–32
War Comes to Long An (Race), 387
war debts, 541–2, 544
War Everyone Lost – And Won, The (Lomperis), 367
War of Ideas (Chandler), 388–9
War without Mercy (Dower), 181, 220
Warburgs, The (Chernow), 540
Ward, Patricia Dawson, 255
Warner, Geoffrey, 311, 484
Warriors at Suez (Neff), 479
Watt, Donald Cameron, 169, 565
We Were Soldiers Once . . . and Young (Moore and Galloway), 383
Weakness and Deceit (Bonner), 413
Weathersby, Katherine, 278, 529
Webster, Charles, 113
Weeks, Sinclair, 308
Wehler, Hans-Ulrich, 105
Weinberger, Casper, 417
Weis, W. Michael, 441, 453
Welch, Richard E., Jr., 449
Welles, Sumner, 202
Wells, Samuel, 538, 547
Wells, Tom, 406
Westmoreland, William, 363
Whirlpool (Pastor), 459
Whitaker, Arthur P., 426
White House Years (Kissinger), 400, 402
"White Revolution," 494
Whitman, Ann, 300–1
Why We Were in Vietnam (Podhoretz), 365
Wiarda, Howard J., 457, 459
Wiebe, Robert, 14
Wiesband, Thomas, 406, 408
Wilderness of Mirrors (Martin), 591
Wilkins, Mira, 538–9
Williams, William Appleman, 4–6, 9*n*10, 23–4, 41–6, 90–1, 104–5, 132–3, 138–9, 151–3, 173, 207, 427
Wilmot, Chester, 168
Wilson, Charles E., 308
Wilson, Evan, 474
Wilson, Theodore A., 195, 196*n*65
Wilsonian influences, 184, 410*n*34
Wind over Sand (Marks), 186
Windt, Theodore Otto, 77
Winks, Robin, 590
Wirtz, James, 597
"Wisconsin School," 65*n*8, 105
Wise, David, 591
With Friends Like These (Jentleson), 557
With Nixon (Price), 403
Without Honor (Isaacs), 380
Witness to Power (Ehrlichman), 403
Wittner, Lawrence S., 248–9
Wohlstetter, Roberta, 571–2
Wood, Bryce, 443
Woods, Randall Bennett, 195, 196*n*65, 239, 257–8, 264, 433, 546
Woodward, Bob, 569, 583–4, 588
World and Richard Nixon, The (Sulzberger), 404
World Bank, 547
World Destroyed, A (Sherwin), 210, 222
World in Depression, The (Kindleberger), 544
World of Secrets, A (Laqueur), 579

world systems theory, 70–1, 130–1, 146, 153, 268, 398, 461, 516
World War II, 166–205
Wright, Peter, 582, 585
Wyden, Peter, 216, 231, 337
Wyman, David S., 180–1

"X" article, 253, 548
Xue Litai, 78, 143, 529

"Yalta" axiom, 193–4
Yalta Conference, 169, 174, 185–8, 225
Yasuhara, Yoko, 522
Years of the Offensive (Schlight), 384
Years of Upheaval (Kissinger), 400, 402
Yemeni conflict, 492–3
Yergin, Daniel, 193, 212, 483, 555–6
Yoshitsu, Michael M., 522
Young, Marilyn Blatt, 533
Yugoslavia, 241–2

Zeiler, Thomas W., 553
Zhai Zhihai, 279–80
Zhang Shuguang, 292
Zhou Enlai, 280
Zionist lobby, 474
Zoumaras, Thomas, 446
Zumwalt, Elmo, 568